Memoirs

Jean Monnet

MEMOIRS

Introduction by George W. Ball

Translated from the French by
Richard Mayne

DOUBLEDAY & COMPANY, INC.
Garden City, New York
1978

ISBN: 0-385-12505-4
Library of Congress Catalog Card Number 76-56322
Copyright © 1978 by Doubleday & Company, Inc.
Printed in the United States of America
First Edition (in the United States of America)

CONTENTS

The author would like to thank François Fontaine for his assistance and for contributing that clear-headed understanding and long perseverance without which no achievement is possible.

'We are not forming coalitions between States,
but union among people.'

INTRODUCTION

On Thanksgiving Day last year, I dined with Jean and Sylvia Monnet in their thatched-roof house at Houjarray, a few kilometers from Paris. In the course of our dinner – which, as a gesture to an old friend and to America, included a turkey complete with cranberries and chestnut dressing – Monnet told me, with that quiet conviction which gives exceptional force to whatever he says: 'George, you should stop diffusing your energies. You should select a single, great objective and concentrate on it until it is accomplished. You may have to make short-term tactical detours, but you must never lose sight of your central goal, even when the road ahead seems hopelessly blocked.'

That sage counsel had formed the *leitmotiv* of many conversations during the years that I worked closely with Monnet, yet even more persuasive than his words was the testimony of his own career. Men of genius sometimes validate clichés that have lost their credence, and Monnet's life graphically illustrates the old saying that a deeply committed man can move mountains. Yet to do so he must, like Monnet, possess indefatigable energy, an uncommon measure of both resilience and resourcefulness and the willingness to forego all personal gain or glory in the single-minded pursuit of a transcendent purpose.

Jean Monnet's transcendent purpose was to transform Europe and he has quite literally succeeded. Not only has he been the architect of the European Economic Community but also its master builder. Yet what gives him the greatest satisfaction is that Europeans now regard that Community as an uncompleted structure, that they take for granted what has already been accomplished – substantial economic integration and practices of co-operation that twenty years ago would have seemed visionary. Today most Europeans would find it difficult to imagine Europe without the Community. Only very rarely do transient conflicts of will or policy recall even faintly the chaotic, divided Europe of quarreling nations that marred the period between the wars and led to ultimate catastrophe. To Monnet all that is proof of the soundness of one of his more controversial hypotheses that, while men and women cannot change human nature, they can, by establishing new rules and institutions to which human beings must adjust, create new habits of thought and action that can profoundly affect economic and political attitudes and behavior.

But, though Monnet's career for the first thirty years was in a sense prelude to the building of a new Europe, even had he disappeared before either the Treaties of Paris or Rome, he would still have left a formidable record of achievement. Over more than a half-century he quietly influenced major decisions of his country and its allies by the persuasive power of his logic and insights, invariably in support of certain principles. The major theme of this book is the evolution and realization of those principles.

Monnet's central conviction is that men and women of different nations can achieve almost any objective if they combine their resources and energies and avoid frustrating one another's efforts by pursuing narrow national ends. Though the idea is too obvious for philosophical challenge, Monnet has found by his years of experience that its application is by no means easy or simple.

Related to that idea – perhaps flowing from it – is the belief that the nation-state survives in the Twentieth Century as an anachronism quite inadequate to define the boundaries of modern political and economic action. Although, within limits, Governments can develop common policies and approaches through co-operation, if they are fully to meet the expanding requirements of the present day, the smaller nations must create more comprehensive units. Within a federal or confederal structure common action need no longer depend on the caprice of Governments, each subject to its own domestic pressures and national ambitions; rather people will be able to work and act together for a common purpose, to speak with a single voice and act with a single will. European problems are incapable of solution within the present structure of competing sovereignties, so they must change the conditions that create the problems – or, in other words, change the structure – and, thus, transform the problems themselves.

However sound these substantive convictions may be, they would have had little impact on the course of history had Monnet not been the master of highly individualistic techniques for translating ideas into institutions. In Monnet's view, there is never a lack of opportunity for action. But to seize those opportunities, one must be equipped with a strong conviction derived from careful reflection; then, when the critical moment arrives, one can act without hesitation. It was because of his well-formed convictions that, even though he had neither taste nor flair for the conventional procedures of politics and little talent for oratory or public presentation, Monnet could brilliantly utilize a wide repertory of persuasive devices, all based on the optimistic conviction that most men will respond to logic if it is patiently and forcefully brought to their attention. In his subtle but effective operations he was well served by an almost infallible instinct for detecting the *loci* of real, as contrasted with apparent, power. Thus, in dealing with Governments, he never confined his operations to official channels, recognizing that often the most effective way to induce official action was to persuade key individuals outside of government to carry the burden of persuading the political leaders empowered to take that action. That this required him to reiterate the same arguments again and again did not deter him, nor did he even hesitate, as he points out in this book, to use the same terminology repeatedly to get his points across, since that terminology had been carefully devised and could not be bettered by improvisation. One technique of analysis and persuasion he regularly employed was to prepare a *bilan*, a balance sheet of needs and resources; only in that way could he compel less imaginative men to view a problem as a whole.

Monnet understood instinctively the supreme importance of timing, recognizing that, at moments of crisis, political leaders could be induced to make far braver decisions than they would ever consider in conditions of less stress. As a negotiator, he was without equal, in part because he applied to even the most marginal exchange excruciating efforts to achieve the right phrase, the precise nuance, so that, as I came to expect in working with him, even the simplest letter might have to be redrafted fourteen or fifteen times. Beyond that, he held to the fixed principle that, in every effective negotiation there had to be a crisis.

Many intellectuals have failed to grasp Monnet's instinctive talent for penetrating to the heart of problems while leaving technical elaboration and philosophical shadings to specialists. But, though some were put off by his apparent simplicity and that single-mindedness which led him to ignore those philosophical rabbits he so frequently flushed, the most perceptive felt his elemental strength and were willing to work interminable hours with an almost *kamikaze* loyalty.

If I were to try to reduce the essence of Jean Monnet to a single phrase, I would say that he is preeminently a modern man who has perceived a major dilemma of our complex times – the discord between our technology, on the one hand, with its rapid pace of advance and its requirements of scale and scope, and, on the other, our institutional arrangements which are so slow to change and so often parochial in character. Yet to call Monnet a modern man does not mean that he is unaware or disdainful of the past. Though admittedly no scholar, his insight has told him that history is not static, not the constant replaying of old themes, but a flow of events which, if man is to survive, must be so channeled as to meet the needs of an evolving age. He has, therefore, never been tempted into the unhappy error – induced by an atavistic longing for a world that never was – of seeking to recapture the past. Instead he has pursued the more relevant purpose of bending men's efforts toward a nobler future.

It is because Jean Monnet so clearly perceives the nature of the great tidal forces now at work that he is sturdily immune to disappointments. I was with him on more than one occasion when the progress of a new design seemed irrevocably halted by the abrupt intrusion of obsolete – yet fiercely held – ideas that echoed a distant and earlier age. Invariably – and sometimes almost alone – Jean Monnet remained undismayed. 'What has happened, has happened,' he would say with a Gallic shrug, 'but it does not affect anything fundamental. The important point is for us not to be deflected, not to lose momentum. We must find a way to go forward.'

It is because of this apparent imperturbability that Monnet is known – to the admiration of his friends and the exasperation of his opponents – as an incorrigible optimist. Yet his optimism does not stem from any Panglossian idea that all is for the best in the best of all possible worlds, but rather from a belief in the logic of events and the essential rationality of man – a dauntless faith in the ineluctable direction of deeply moving forces. Optimism to Jean Monnet is the only serviceable hypothesis for a practical man or woman with a passionate desire to get things done.

Since the beginning of time many men have tried to alter the structure of world power. When their ambitions have been selfish and hegemonic, they have usually failed. When they have sought to realize their dreams by force, whatever success they have achieved has been transient and illusory. But there have also been those rare men whose visions were ample and generous, whose goal was no less than the good of mankind, and who have relied not on force but persuasion – the energy latent in an indomitable idea – to accomplish their objectives. Sometimes those men have wrought miracles.

This book is a chronicle of the miracles of Jean Monnet.

George W. Ball

Part One

THE FAILURE OF FORCE

Chapter 1

1940 – UNITY IN PERIL

I

The limits of co-operation

The morning of May 10, 1940, was fine all over Europe. The heat and sunshine had taken us by surprise. We had feared this moment for which the Germans had been waiting: for several weeks, armies and peoples had been watching anxiously for the bright skies that would favour attacks by the Luftwaffe and the Panzer divisions. In London, where I was then living, I was called at dawn by Alexandre Parodi*: the Germans had invaded Belgium and the Netherlands. I went to my office in Richmond Terrace, walking as usual across St James's Park. On the way I met General Sir Hastings Ismay†, some of whose people worked in the same building. 'What do you say to that?', I asked him. 'It's exactly what we were hoping for,' he replied.

It was then that I remembered a strange conversation with Edouard Daladier a few weeks before. I had told the French Premier that in my view, if the Germans took the offensive, they would attack where the Maginot Line stopped, just on the Belgian frontier. 'That's what the generals tell me,' he said thoughtfully: 'It's what they're counting on.' I found this strategy incomprehensible at the time, and no one since then has been able to explain to me why our reserves were stationed hundreds of miles away from the point where the Germans were likely to break through. As it turned out, Belgium proved no trap for the German army: within a few days, the Germans broke the line at Sedan.

Leaving General Ismay to his illusions, I went up to my office, the headquarters of the 'Anglo-French Co-ordinating Committee'. There

* A former member of the *Conseil d'Etat*, Permanent Under-Secretary at the French Ministry of Labour, and later Minister of Labour himself.
† Secretary to the Imperial Defence Council.

we had collected economic data to measure the strength and weakness of the Allies against the German Reich. It gave us a first glimpse of what lay ahead: a long and uncertain total war in which organization and willpower, helped by time and space, would determine the final military outcome.

The Committee had been at work since November 1939. I had been made Chairman by a joint decision of the French and British Governments. The methods of work and the objectives which I had proposed to the two Premiers, Daladier and Neville Chamberlain, and which they had accepted, were not very different from those of the Allied Executive Committees to which I had devoted my efforts in the 1914–18 war. Seeing the same needs now, I had once again followed the same course – with, incidentally, some of the same people, who had remained my friends. What was needed was to bring together and unite all the strength of the free world, to resist and crush the onslaught of totalitarianism. No one disagreed; but this common-sense idea was simply not being applied.

It is astonishing how little the word 'alliance', which people find so reassuring, really means in practice if all it implies is the traditional machinery of co-operation. I had learned this by long experience in World War I, whose military outcome had hung in the balance so long as the Allies had fought side by side instead of forming a single organized force. It had taken two years of persistent effort, and the deadly threat of unlimited submarine warfare, before we could combine our resources and pool our shipping. The decision to do so, which ensured the Allies' economic superiority and the security of their supplies, in the end proved as decisive as men's heroism in battle. It was simply less widely known. This time, our Governments were easier to convince, because the concept of 'total war' imposed by the enemy had become familiar. But it was still a national concept. Total war at the level of the Alliance seemed to have no meaning, and certainly little hope of being achieved. In each of our countries the civil and military war machine was preparing, as best it could, to wage its own war. The two Governments were acting separately, and public opinion in Britain and France was reacting in two different ways to the same threat. Now, that threat was very great and very close.

I had long been convinced that the only way to win this war, like the first war, was to pool the two countries' material resources and productive potential. But it was growing more and more obvious that unity must be on a different scale from the start. On March 28, 1940, France and Britain had both undertaken not to negotiate for a separate armistice, and to act together in postwar reconstruction. But what underlying basis could there be for such solidarity? What tangible form could be given to a unity of purpose strong enough to resist the ordeals to come? The more limited machinery for co-ordination and co-operation that we were setting up was proving too slow. It had taken no less than four months to get from our national administrations a simple balance-sheet of our potential air-power – which was the only way of persuading the United States to increase their output of aero-engines. I was all the more anxious, that morning of May 10, 1940, as I watched the mists dispersing from the London sky. At that very moment, I learned later, the air-raid sirens were sounding over Paris.

The patient work of co-ordination that we were doing in our Committees would bear fruit when the Allies had recovered the initiative. Today, the enemy was calling the tune and seeking immediate victory. Against the psychological advantage of surprise, coupled with superior armed might, had we enough strength and willpower to resist? In those spring days of 1940, history was advancing with the speed of the Panzer divisions: we could stem it only by a bold stroke that would seize the imagination and sweep aside the material and psychological obstacles that were delaying joint action by the Allies.

My friends on the Anglo-French Committee were very well placed to realize the impasse. Chief among them was Sir Arthur Salter, who had worked with me on the Allied Combined Boards between 1916 and 1918, and who had seen their achievements dissipated at the end of the war. He was anxious that our present work should lead to institutions that would give it both legitimacy and permanence. In political circles, some voices were calling for closer unity, and editorials in the London *Times* lent their weight to some ambitious proposals whose equivalent it would have been difficult to find at that time in France, no doubt because the danger was less clearly seen and less willingly acknowledged. I discussed these ideas with the then Prime Minister, Neville Chamberlain. In general terms he was receptive to them. There was broad agreement on the principle of a union which might go as far as uniting our two peoples. But how to proceed – when to act: that remained vague; and I have to confess that I myself had no ready-made answers.

Events spurred our minds and opened the way to action. The first big battles, in the second half of May, showed how vulnerable the French army was. At the same time, they forced even the greatest optimists to recognize the inadequacy of the British land forces. No less dangerous, we then realized, was the weakness of Allied morale. Evidently, the Alliance lacked roots. The need to make clear our war aims had been forgotten – whereas a common effort depends on common aims. Against the Nazi attempt at domination, free men had to know what they were fighting for. They were not yet fully alive to the mortal danger with which Hitler's will to hegemony threatened the world. Both nations, and even their individual citizens, still believed in their heart of hearts that they could escape and survive alone, by their own separate efforts.

At the beginning of June, the British withdrawal from Dunkirk put the Alliance to the test. It looked as if Hitler's plan to divide the Allies, militarily and psychologically, might be in the process of succeeding. I wrote to Winston Churchill, who had become Prime Minister on the fateful day of May 10:

> If British strategists start thinking of ways in which Britain and the British Empire could defend themselves if France were knocked out of the fight; or if French statesmen start wondering whether they might be able to negotiate less onerous peace terms before the French armies are driven from their new lines of defence, and perhaps destroyed – then the Nazis will have attained their goal.

Nevertheless, the situation as we saw it still left us in hopes of an organized resistance. In a further personal letter to Churchill, on June 6, I proposed a merger of the two air forces, whose strength I had managed, not without difficulty, to have assessed in a continuing inventory.

> 'The present balance-sheet,' I wrote to the Prime Minister, 'shows clearly that if the forces of our two countries are not treated as one, we shall see the Nazis gain mastery of the air in France, overpowering her, and then concentrating all their strength against the United Kingdom. The Allied aircraft now operating in France are outnumbered by several to one. But if we combine the two countries' air forces, the ratio becomes about one to one-and-a-half; and with our proven superiority when evenly matched we should then have a chance of winning. In a word, victory or defeat may be determined by an immediate decision to use our respective aircraft and pilots in the present battle as a single force. If that in turn requires a unified command for our two air forces, then this problem should in my opinion be studied, and studied now.'

II

One parliament, one army

A single force. . . . But when Churchill read my letter it was already too late – too late to save the aircraft or the entire army corps which, one by one, we were losing trace of, day after day, hour after hour. Paradoxically, as we lost the opportunity to take the most logical decisions and co-operate in the simplest ways, we were led to raise our sights and try to recover on the political level the control of events that was escaping us in the field. When there was no longer any hope of achieving a unified command, a merger of sovereignty became conceivable. With the Germans threatening Paris, we had to think of saving London, still untouched as a centre of the Alliance. France might be invaded, but not the French Empire. Yet in whose name could unity on this basis be maintained? And would men go on fighting when it looked as if they had lost the war? Arthur Salter and I decided to use every means in our power to put into effect the bold plan that events had made both reasonable and essential.

On June 13 we put the finishing touches to a paper five pages long exploring all the possibilities then open to us: each one pointed to the conclusion that only total union between France and Britain could safeguard the hope of final victory. On the English text of the note, which was headed 'Anglo-French Unity', I had to make a correction that night. 'Paris may fall at once' became 'Paris has fallen'. From one moment to the next, part of the history of France had to be written in the past tense. It was urgently necessary to build a different future. 'Even if the French forces are thrown back further and further,' said the note, 'even if no front can be held, even if the struggle has to be continued in pockets of desperate resistance, France can, with Britain, continue the war. Even if the worst happens and the Germans conquer the whole of France, at least her fleet and her air force will be able to go on fighting alongside Britain, and a large part of the French army and its equipment will be able to embark and join forces with the British troops. In this case the two countries will be able to continue the battle until at last the infinitely superior resources of the Allied Empire and the United States bring them victory.'

'The two countries will be able to continue the battle . . .' – we knew how frail this hope would be if it were limited to the military sphere. Even the best strategists would be unable to regroup and amalgamate forces that had lost faith in the future. It was necessary to give them the prospect of a common destiny. 'The plan', we wrote, 'would be impossible to apply if in the present battle, as afterwards, the two countries did not act and fight as a single people and if the two nations were not completely and profoundly aware of their unity.' It therefore seemed essential, first, that France should continue the war; secondly, that French resources should be husbanded to carry on the struggle elsewhere; thirdly, that the United States should join in as a belligerent; and fourthly, that the Nazis should be prevented from invading the British Isles. In conclusion, the note outlined some suggestions.

'There should be a dramatic declaration by the two Governments on the solidarity of the two countries' interests, and on their mutual commitment to restore the devastated areas, making clear also that the two Governments are to merge and form a single Cabinet and to unite the two Parliaments.'

On June 13 we did not think that it was necessary to draw up too precise a proposal. The document was not intended to go before the British Cabinet in that form. It was aimed at persuading statesmen, and its final wording had been left to circumstances. But events left us no time for niceties: the worsening military situation convinced us that we must take the paper to the highest political level at once. Already, I had had some difficulty in interesting Churchill in our ideas. 'I am fighting the war,' he had answered during one recent conversation, 'and you come to talk about the future.' He was preoccupied by immediate action and he still hoped to redress the military situation, if not in France then at least over the Channel. But after the Allied Conference in Tours, where for the first time there was talk of the possibility of a separate armistice, and after the fall of Paris, the British authorities began to think about what guarantees they could obtain from France, and in the eyes of certain people our plan became very relevant.

It was then that I had a visit from a friend, Desmond Morton, who was a close adviser of Churchill's. 'I've come to give you some advice,' he said. 'I hear that you're trying to persuade Mr Churchill to put this Anglo-French Unity plan to Cabinet. I don't think you'll succeed yourself – simply because you're not the Prime Minister of France. That's the way Churchill is. If you were the French Premier, he'd listen to you. But he will listen to a man who has a senior position in the British Government. For example, he has a high regard for Mr Chamberlain, and he'd listen to him. If Mr Chamberlain said to him: "Prime Minister, I'd like this question discussed in Cabinet," he would answer: "Very well, Lord Chancellor," and it would at least be discussed.'

I realized how wise Morton's advice was, and I at once went to see Mr Chamberlain's private secretary, Horace Wilson, whom I already knew. 'You've heard,' I said, 'that I've been trying to convince Churchill of the need for union between France and Britain?' He said he had. 'Well, I believe that the time has come to conclude this union, because we are entering a new phase. The French are in great trouble, and before long the British in their turn will face disaster. We cannot live through these things separately, and we cannot tell our peoples that they must go on fighting for fighting's sake. The British and the French must be convinced that they share the same duty, which is to defend freedom against totalitarianism. Only then will they understand why the struggle must be pursued in Africa or in Britain, and why there will be no defeat so long as both peoples together are not conquered. That's the aim of this unity plan.'

'What do you want me to do?' asked Wilson.

'You could ask Mr Chamberlain to try to convince Churchill.'

'I will. You really mean unity – complete unity? That would mean one Parliament, one army?'

'Exactly.'

'Very well, I'll do my best. Let's meet again this evening.'

It was Friday, June 14, 1940.

At midnight, I met Horace Wilson and David Margesson, the Conservative Chief Whip, who himself had vainly tried to recruit support for our plan from Lord Halifax, the Foreign Secretary. But Wilson had persuaded Chamberlain to talk to Churchill, who had agreed to put the subject on the agenda for next day's Cabinet. I also learned that Sir Robert Vansittart, Permanent Under-Secretary at the Foreign Office, had been asked to draw up the final document.

Next morning, I went in search of Vansittart. The weekend had begun, and we had a lot of difficulty finding him in the country. Finally, with him, Morton, Salter, and René Pleven, who was my assistant in London, we drew up the draft declaration of indissoluble union. Every Frenchman and every Englishman would have the full rights of citizenship in both countries. There would be a customs union and a common currency. The war damage suffered by each country would be jointly repaired. The text was submitted to Churchill.

Churchill, who had come to power to defend the very existence of the British Empire, was startled when he read our words. They called upon Britain to embark on a new course, turning her back on the past and on her island history. He raised objections: he refused to be convinced. But his sense of duty was more powerful, and because he saw in our plan a chance to change the course of events he put the text to the War Cabinet that afternoon. There, to his great surprise, statesmen whom he respected, from all parties, welcomed the project warmly, and quickly turned to studying its practical consequences. Apparently, the romantic in Churchill was troubled by this enthusiasm – but won over by its generosity. He decided to support the proposal, which was to be put formally to a further meeting of Cabinet next day.

Meanwhile, however, events in France were gathering speed. The most impressive evidence of this we had that same night from the mouth of General Charles de Gaulle, Secretary of State for War in Paul Reynaud's Government. Arriving on an official mission in London, he telephoned me at once from the apartment that had been put at his disposal by Jean Laurent, his *chef de cabinet**. 'I am here officially to negotiate for the transportation of French units to North Africa and to Britain,' he said. 'But that is not the only reason I have come. For your own information, I have decided to stay here. There is nothing more to be done in France just now. It is here that we must operate.' Thereupon we agreed to meet without delay and to have dinner together at my apartment, together with de Gaulle's aide-de-camp Lieutenant Geoffroy de Courcel and my assistant René Pleven.

De Gaulle was welcomed by my wife; but then he plunged into an embarrassing silence. To break the ice while awaiting my return, Silvia asked him how long his mission here would last.

'I am not here on a mission, Madame,' de Gaulle replied: 'I am here to save the honour of France.'

For him, so recently escaped from the defeatist atmosphere then reigning in Bordeaux, there was no longer any hope of stemming the tide in France. He was therefore rather sceptical when I announced the plan we had been preparing. But I set out to persuade him that so extraordinary a gesture, a solemn proposal from the British Government to the French, would halt the drift and give Paul Reynaud both the courage and the opportunity to take his Government from Bordeaux† to North Africa. De Gaulle admitted that although the chances

---

* Head of private office or chief executive assistant.
† Where it had withdrawn from Paris in mid-June.

of success were slim, the attempt had to be made, because everything was ready. He agreed to lend the plan his full support.

De Gaulle's support, we knew, could have a great effect on Churchill. The two men had met for the first time in London the week before, and they had made a great impression on each other. The date of their meeting was Monday June 9: it had been arranged through a telephone call to me from Jean Laurent in Paris. 'De Gaulle wants to go to London,' he had said: 'he's worried about our lack of contact with the British. We need to show them that, despite everything, there's still some strength and action on our side. De Gaulle can do it better than anyone. Can you arrange for him to see Churchill?' I made the arrangements straight away, because I was distressed to see our two countries, which had not had the time to forge solid links, starting to drift apart as soon as the storm began. Our plan for Franco-British unity would give the French courage and a reason to continue the struggle whatever happened. But the British needed to be sure that their proposal would be heard, and that somewhere in the State of France the spirit of resistance was still unquenched. De Gaulle was a new man with a reputation as a fighter, newly brought into the Government by Paul Reynaud to try to counter its defeatist elements. It was urgent for a man of this stamp to come and bear witness to France's willpower, which in London was now seriously in doubt.

I can see de Gaulle now as he came into my office at the Anglo-French Committee. Pleven was with me. I felt at once that the two men would understand each other. They could look one another in the eye, and they got on at once. De Gaulle gave us a very gloomy account of the French Government's morale, and especially that of its military leaders. What had struck him on his arrival in London had been the calm of the British people, and their apparent unawareness of the danger that was so close. But he quickly realized that in official circles at least, and in general behind the outward show, there were few illusions left. Churchill saw him after he left us, and gave him little hope that the British would be prepared to risk much military aid in a continental débâcle. But he did confirm that Britain would never surrender. De Gaulle was stung by such selfishness but impressed by such determination. Would he have come back to London now, a week later, when all seemed lost in France, if he had not realized that everything could be won back again by the indomitable people of whom Churchill was the incarnation? The two men's mutual judgement is eloquent. 'He is made for grandiose tasks,' said de Gaulle of Churchill. 'He is a man of my stature,' said Churchill of de Gaulle.

They had seen each other again briefly at Tours on the following Thursday, at the last meeting of the Inter-Allied Council, when the French Government was authorized to sound out possible conditions for a unilateral armistice. Now, they were due to meet again at lunch on the following day, Sunday. If it was still necessary to persuade Churchill to speed up the proclamation of unity, de Gaulle was the man to do it. We had good reason to believe that both men would appreciate the grandeur of the gesture as well as its immediate practical usefulness. But it was also clear that both, by their upbringing and their mystical belief in national sovereignty, were deeply opposed to aspects of the plan which they regarded as inconceivable and impracticable. Our view was just the opposite. For us, the plan was not simply an opportunist appeal or a merely formal text: it was an act which, with luck, could have changed the course of events for the good of Europe. That is still my opinion today.

Sunday June 16, 1940, was a day of lost opportunities. In London, it began well enough. After de Gaulle had dealt with his official business at the Foreign Office, he came to see us. As he entered my office, the telephone rang: it was Vansittart, asking us all to go round and put together the final version of text, which the British Cabinet had approved in principle the day before. De Gaulle then asked me to telephone Bordeaux so that he could talk to Paul Reynaud. 'Something very important is being prepared on the British side to help France,' he told him. 'I can't be more specific now, but I would urge you not to take any serious decisions before you know the content of the British Government's message.' 'Every moment counts now,' said Reynaud. 'We're holding a decisive Cabinet meeting this afternoon. I can delay it a little, but certainly not later than five p.m. Act quickly and act firmly. The gesture you speak of will have to be a very big one if it's to withstand the pressure for an immediate negotiation with the Germans.' 'It is,' said de Gaulle.

We spent the rest of the morning, de Gaulle, Pleven, Vansittart and I, putting our text in the form of a proclamation, rather different from the earlier versions and more appropriate to the dramatic atmosphere in which it would be read in Bordeaux. Then Vansittart gave a copy to Lord Halifax, who asked him to add the necessary formal touches for its presentation to Cabinet that afternoon. This was not the least of our difficulties that day. For a document to be discussed in Cabinet, it had properly to have 'red binding'; but the Foreign Office was closed on Sundays and the officials concerned were away. After a long hunt, we found a 'red binding' that served well enough, although it was white.

De Gaulle went off with the French Ambassador, Charles Corbin, to lunch with Churchill at the Carlton Club. The rest of us − Vansittart, Morton, Pleven and myself − went back to lunch with my wife in our apartment in Mount Street. We felt optimistic: but I was suddenly perturbed to hear Morton ask Vansittart: 'Have you any news of the telegram that went off this morning?' Although it seemed none of my business, I asked: 'What telegram?'

'Oh, it's in answer to a message sent last night by the French Government. They were asking for immediate written confirmation of the permission to negotiate that Churchill agreed to orally in Tours last Thursday.'

'So what did you do?'

'The War Cabinet met a short while ago. It reminded the French Government of their inalienable commitments, but obviously we couldn't refuse to let Reynaud ask the Germans what their terms might be, with the express reservation that the French fleet be kept out of reach of the enemy.'

'What?' I exclaimed. 'This morning you send a telegram authorizing the French Government to sound out terms for a separate armistice, and this afternoon you plan to propose indissoluble union? It's crazy. I don't understand.'

My guests were appalled. Even British empiricism has its limits, and it certainly could not explain such inconsistency, symptomatic no doubt of the confusion then reigning.

'You're right,' said Morton. 'We must stop the telegram, otherwise our offer of union won't even be listened to.'

Using the direct line between my apartment and the Cabinet Office, we got in touch with the British Ambassador in Bordeaux, Sir Ronald Campbell. He had already taken the telegram to Paul Reynaud − who now had in his hand two contradictory British cards: that afternoon, he could play one or other, as he chose. One was the authorization to split the Alliance, under rigorous conditions it was true, but certain to be exploited immediately by the defeatist group in the French Cabinet. The other was the offer of total solidarity − but would it be formally made in time? The risk was too great.

It was decided that Campbell should go back to Reynaud to suspend the telegram − or rather, the telegrams, since we learned meanwhile that a second message confirming the first, but strengthening its reservations, was on its way. We had to act quickly, because within a few hours the die would be cast. At that moment, Morton's office told us that de Gaulle and Corbin were already there and that the Cabinet meeting was beginning. We went at once to No. 10 Downing Street. Morton's office was next to the Cabinet Room, and various Ministers came and went, proposing changes in the text. These did not affect its content, and although they made it less precise it remained none-theless imposing. Churchill had behaved very fairly. Although he did not conceal his own objections, he encouraged his colleagues to make the gesture that could have so profound an effect.

'At a time as grave as this,' he said to me, 'it shall not be said that we lack imagination.' I can see him now as he came out of the Cabinet Room to talk to us, in a grey suit with pink stripes, a cigar in his mouth, treating it all with a careless air. It was his way of rising above events.

Meanwhile, Pleven translated the text back into French. At 4.30 p.m., de Gaulle spoke to Reynaud by telephone and told him that the declaration was coming. Reynaud could not wait for the telegram: he had the text dictated to him, in the presence of Campbell and Spears*, who afterwards described how his face lit up as he took down the words:

> At this most fateful moment in the history of the modern world the Governments of the United Kingdom and the French Republic make this declaration of indissoluble union and unyielding resolution in their common defence of justice and freedom against subjection to a system which reduces mankind to a life of robots and slaves.
>
> The two Governments declare that France and Great Britain shall no longer be two nations, but one Franco-British Union.
>
> The constitution of the Union will provide for joint organs of defence, foreign, financial and economic policies.
>
> Every citizen of France will enjoy immediately citizenship of Great Britain; every British subject will become a citizen of France.
>
> Both countries will share responsibility for the repair of the devasta-tion of war, wherever it occurs in their territories, and the resources of both shall be equally, and as one, applied to that purpose.
>
> During the war there shall be a single War Cabinet, and all the forces of Britain and France, whether on land, sea, or in the air, will be placed under its direction. It will govern from wherever best it can. The two Parliaments will be formally associated. The nations of the British Em-pire are already forming new armies. France will keep her available

* Churchill's personal representative to Paul Reynaud in May 1940. From July 1940 to December 1941 he headed the British mission to de Gaulle's Free French.

forces in the field, on the sea, and in the air. The Union appeals to the United States to fortify the economic resources of the Allies, and to bring her powerful material aid to the common cause.

The Union will concentrate its whole energy against the power of the enemy, no matter where the battle may be.

And thus we shall conquer.

When de Gaulle had finished dictating, Reynaud was seized by an understandable doubt. Had the text been approved by Churchill himself? De Gaulle gave his word of honour that it had. Then Churchill, who was listening, picked up the telephone and said to Reynaud: 'Hold on! De Gaulle's leaving now: he'll bring you the text. . . . And now, we must meet quickly. Tomorrow morning at Concarneau. I'll come with Attlee*, the First Lord of the Admiralty, the Chief of Staff, and our best experts. And bring some good generals! *Au revoir!'*

I went with de Gaulle to his plane. The rest of us were to take a train at nine o'clock that evening to go aboard a destroyer with members of the British Government. Just as we were setting out, the Cabinet told us that the trip was off. A message had come from Bordeaux: Reynaud had resigned. When the news came, Churchill was already on the train. He climbed out, he wrote later, 'with a heavy heart'. That was how we all felt on the evening of so hard a day.

At about ten o'clock that night, I managed to reach de Gaulle by telephone. On arriving at Bordeaux airport, he had learned that Albert Lebrun, the President of France, had appointed Marshal Pétain as Prime Minister. It was all over, said de Gaulle: further effort was useless: he was coming back.

Myself, I was less pessimistic – or rather, I saw the problem in a different light. The French Government was still free. We must attempt the impossible and persuade it to move to Africa and continue the war in the spirit of the Declaration of Union. The circumstances in which that Declaration had been received in Bordeaux did not discourage me – far from it. That the defeatists had done everything to block it in the French Cabinet, that General Maxime Weygand, the Minister for War, who had intercepted all de Gaulle's telephone calls that day, had hastened to launch his attack on the plan – this made it all the more necessary for those who wanted to go on fighting alongside the British to get out of France and into her overseas territories.

* Clement Attlee, Labour Party leader who acted as Churchill's deputy in many aspects of the War Cabinet's work, and succeeded him as Prime Minister in 1945. (T.N.)

First among them should be Government Ministers and the Speakers*
of the two Houses of Parliament, who could act legitimately in the
name of France.

III

Bordeaux: the last attempt

It may seem today that I was too optimistic; yet I am not an optimist. I
am simply persistent. If action is necessary, how can one say that it is
impossible, so long as one has not tried it? That is what I said to
Churchill that night, when I went to see him with Lord Beaverbrook†.
'It may be,' I argued, 'that Pétain is now in power. But nothing is
ever lost until one's dead. You never know.... I still believe that
something can be done in Bordeaux, and I propose to go there if you
can let me have transport. If it were possible, I should like to go with
a member of your Government. And could I ask you to approach
Roosevelt personally to see if he could put urgent pressure on the
French Government?' On this point Churchill answered: 'I will.'
But he did not wish to make contact with the French Government
himself before receiving official notification that it had changed.

That announcement never came, at least through normal channels,
and it was from Pétain's statement on the radio, at midday on Monday
June 17, that Churchill learned of the course that the Bordeaux
Government had taken. The British reacted with bitterness, but above
all with anxiety. For Churchill, it was an argument against making a
gesture towards the new Government. For us, it was a reason for
offering an alternative to capitulation; and Vansittart, Pleven and I
drafted a telegram to Pétain proposing that the French Government
should leave for North Africa, accompanied by a massive evacuation
of troops under the double protection of the French and British fleets.
But Churchill stood on his dignity and refused to send the telegram.

Even so, the idea began to appeal to him, and on the morning of
Tuesday June 18 he wrote a very brief message offering the French
Government all the ships necessary to evacuate men and equipment. I
suggested that a member of the War Cabinet should carry the message to Bordeaux, and that I should go with him to back him up,

* Presidents. (T.N.)
† Minister of Aircraft Production.

together with Pleven, Emmanuel Monick (financial attaché at the French Embassy) and Robert Marjolin, his assistant. Churchill decided to send two separate parties, one headed by Lord Lloyd, the Colonial Secretary, the other consisting of myself and my friends. Early that afternoon we met de Gaulle, who had returned the day before in the British aircraft that Churchill had placed at his disposal, in company with Major-General Sir Edward Spears and the faithful Courcel.

De Gaulle believed that our mission would fail. Technically, it had become very difficult to evacuate French troops. Psychologically, anglophobia reigned in the corridors of power and even in the entourage of Paul Reynaud, whose military adviser accused me of 'treason'. Reynaud was a strange character. Previously he had welcomed our plan for Anglo-French unity with enthusiasm; now, released from his responsibilities as Prime Minister, he became facile and shifty. The evening before, he had remarked to de Gaulle: 'After all, the Germans are disappointed suitors.' Perhaps he still believed that the depth of their disappointment would make them impose humiliating armistice terms, whereupon there would be a reaction and he would return to power. De Gaulle did not think so. But I wanted to explore this confused situation, knowing that very often firm determination and a simple idea have their best chance of success when indecision is rife.

We asked de Gaulle to come with us. He said he would if we thought it essential, but he himself did not. What he saw was the firm choice he had already made; what he heard was his own voice, to be broadcast that night by the BBC, speaking the famous and perceptive words: 'France is not alone! She has a vast Empire behind her. She can make common cause with the British Empire, which commands the sea and is continuing the struggle. She can, like Britain, use to the full the immense industries of the United States . . . This war is not confined to the unhappy land of France. . .'. But very few people heard the appeal on June 18; and before we even knew whether it would be broadcast we took off for France, to try to bring to the heart of what was still the Republic that same will to resist.

Churchill had lent us a seaplane, the *Claire*, with room for thirty passengers and a long range. It was too big for our small party, but it was large enough to bring away the men we hoped to convince, such champions of freedom as Lebrun, Reynaud, Edouard Herriot*,

* President of the Chamber.

31

Jules Jeanneney*, Léon Blum†, and Georges Mandel‡, men who represented the greater part of France. We reached Bordeaux at noon on Wednesday June 19. Our first call was on Paul Baudouin, the Foreign Minister, whom Pleven and I had known for a long time, and who had a receptive mind. Above all, we knew that he enjoyed great influence over Pétain.

I told Baudouin that we knew what he had said on the radio on June 17: 'There can be no question of accepting terms that would deny our honour or our national independence. If the enemy sought to impose such terms, France would prefer to go on fighting.' This, in our view, was likely to be the case; and to prepare for it, the men in authority in France must be withdrawn out of reach of the enemy. We pointed out that the British Government had offered to facilitate and protect the French Government's evacuation. Baudouin said that he had already taken this into account, and that the Cabinet that morning had decided that the President of the Republic, the Presidents of the Chamber and the Senate, together with members of the Government, should withdraw to North Africa. Marshal Pétain and he himself would stay in France. I expressed my astonishment that he, the Foreign Minister, should conceive of doing his job under foreign domination. But he said it was a question of duty and of fellow-feeling.

Fundamentally, he no longer believed that France was capable of resistance. I asked him if he had read Hitler's *Mein Kampf*. 'Of course,' he replied. 'Well, then,' I said, 'haven't you noticed that it treats France and Britain differently? Hitler wants to annihilate France. Yet he has no designs on the British Empire so long as the Empire turns its back on Europe. German policy is to divide France from Britain. And it's very important for the future of France that her cause should not be separate from that of Great Britain. That is the purpose of the offer of unity you have received.'

'The offer has not been rejected,' replied Baudouin. 'It's simply the pressure of events that has prevented us from responding.'

'The offer is still valid,' I said, 'and the message that Lord Lloyd is bringing you will confirm that.'

'We shall study it with care,' said Baudouin. 'I have asked the newspapers to publish it.'

For an hour and a half, I used all the powers of persuasion I could muster. Baudouin seemed divided, hesitating. But something deep-rooted held him back, and we were unable to budge this pawn blocking

* President of the Senate.   † Former Prime Minister.
‡ Minister of the Interior.

the chessboard. We decided to go and see Herriot. Emmanuel Monick, who went with us, has vividly described the scene:

> The house where the President of the Chamber was staying was an astonishing sight. A large stone staircase led to the first floor. On it, as on the grand staircase at Versailles in the time of Louis XIV, there was a crowd of courtiers – in this case, Members of Parliament waiting for news. Not knowing what to do, they spent the whole day there standing or sitting on the steps. Asking each other questions, they passed on the most unlikely rumours, and smoked countless cigarettes. Everywhere one trod on cigarette ends.
>
> After fighting one's way through this smoke-filled throng, one reached the large first-floor antechamber. There, more important people were admitted – senior Members of Parliament, former Ministers. It was like the Salon de l'Œil-de-Boeuf, reserved for the King's favourites. They speculated among themselves, sad and weary. Finally, we were ushered into the dining-room. It was lunchtime. Alone at a huge table, his napkin tucked into his waistcoat, Herriot, like the King, was eating in public. It was a *carré d'agneau à l'oseille*. Seated on chairs around the room, but not around the table, were the dignitaries of the realm: the President of the Senate, former Prime Ministers, former Ministers. They were watching the old lion at feeding time.*

Herriot greeted us most warmly. I put to him our reasons for urging him to leave France, with the Government, and the ways in which we could help. He answered: 'You don't need to convince me: I persuaded the Cabinet to take the decision this morning. But we shall leave under the flag of France. It cannot be otherwise. The *Massilia* is ready to sail.'

'And what if it doesn't sail?' asked Monick.

'Then,' thundered Herriot, 'there will be a Parliament again, and my voice will be heard there protesting against an unjust peace.'

The theatrical atmosphere was painful. On the way out I met Léon Blum, who fell into my arms, and reminded me of the 'delightful evening' he had spent with us a few years before. 'What a catastrophe!' he exclaimed, his eyes filling with tears. 'The only catastrophe,' I said, 'is giving in to oneself.'

I next met Lord Lloyd, who was due to see, first, Lebrun, then Pétain, Baudouin and Herriot. I told him of the talks we had had. Then, with Pleven and Monick, I went in search of a restaurant. But in Bordeaux, the improvised capital of a country in chaos, everywhere was full. The local people were carrying on their lives as usual, and

---

* Emmanuel Monick, *Pour mémoire*, p. 64.

33

looking bemusedly at the hubbub of politicians, soldiers, and refugees. On a bench in the Allées de Tourny, we sat and ate sandwiches. Then we went back to see Herriot. He was worried because the previous orders had been countermanded: the embarkation promised by Admiral Darlan* for that evening had been postponed, with no reasons given. The Cabinet was to meet next morning. It was obvious that the defeatists had got the upper hand. Monick, who had talked with a number of Government officials, confirmed our impression: there was no more to be done and nobody left to persuade.

All that we could do was to embark on our seaplane those people who wanted to leave that small world bereft of willpower or hope. Pleven had had the great good fortune to meet his wife and children in the street, and took them back with him. Henri Bonnet† and his wife also came with us. Early in the morning we flew off from Biscarosse. As we followed the Charente coastline, I thought of the big house in Cognac where my old mother was living, looked after by my sisters. It was four years before I saw them again.

That day, even so, I still believed that so vital a project could not be totally abandoned, and I did not think it far-fetched, as has since been alleged. It was simply the appropriate response to unprecedented circumstances. What was unprecedented was that the enemy was at the gates. At that moment he might be entering Cognac. There was nothing romantic in the idea of a union of two countries, and of joint citizenship for their inhabitants, in the face of the danger they shared. Nor was it doctrinaire: for me, the plan had no federalist overtones. True, it contained the germ of lasting institutions; but I was not thinking in such abstract terms – there was no time. My only thought was of the need to tackle a serious practical plight. At the most, I might just have foreseen that one day similar new situations might call for similar solutions going beyond mere co-operation. But it was not my job to be concerned continually with affairs of state, and the normal course of my life had not conditioned me to look at international problems in terms of national sovereignty. But one thing is certain. I had already encountered these problems on several dramatic occasions; and it was obvious that they were an obstacle to understanding between men, to common action, and to human progress.

While I was on the way to London to try to persuade Churchill that

* Later Vichy Foreign Minister. Assassinated, possibly at Gaullist instigation, in Algiers in 1942.
† Later a member of the Committee of National Liberation.

Anglo-French union was still possible because the French Empire seemed likely to hold firm, the spirit of defeatism in Bordeaux finally succeeded in blocking our plan. So our generation shirked a bold decision that could have changed the course of the war and, what is more, the course of men's minds. 'One Parliament, one Cabinet, one flag' – that stirring vision, put into words by Horace Wilson, was to remain for many years an impossible hope. That is why, looking back, I believe that those days of June 1940 had a profound effect on my idea of international action. All too often I have come up against the limits of mere co-ordination: it makes for discussion, but not decision. In circumstances where union is necessary, it fails to change relations between men and between countries. It is the expression of national power, not a means of transforming it: that way, unity will never be achieved. At the same time, I had come to realize that the quest for unity, even if it were limited to material problems such as production, armaments, and transport, had effects far beyond administrative matters and involved the whole political authority of the countries engaged in a common struggle. When peoples are threatened by the same danger, it is no good dealing separately with the various interests that determine their future.

I had not fully learned this lesson during the First World War, nor at the League of Nations. There had been no time to apply it in resisting the first assault of Nazi power. But I was firmly determined to remember it as soon as a fresh opportunity for joint action arose. Opportunities for action have never been lacking in my life. The essential thing is to be prepared. For that, I need a firm belief, based on long reflection. When the moment comes, everything is simple, because necessity leaves no room for hesitation. That, at least, is the way I am made – or rather, was made by that family into which I was born, at Cognac, on November 9, 1888.

Chapter 2

CHILDHOOD AT COGNAC

I

Small town, wide world

At Cognac, that brandy town, Society was divided into two mutually exclusive categories. One was 'the businessmen', and the other 'the suppliers' – practically everyone else. There was the case of Boucher, the local glass manufacturer who had invented a process for moulding bottles, doing away with the difficult business of glass-blowing. Although he had literally revolutionized glass-making, in Cognac society he never ceased to be one of 'the suppliers'.

It was in my family's time that the Monnet family changed categories and joined the ranks of 'the businessmen'. But we were still close to our roots on the land, and my grandparents exemplified for me its finest virtues. If in later life I have not been inclined to be respectful, this is no doubt because I have been seeking, and seldom found, people with their simple nobility. My paternal grandfather was a small landowner at Cherves, some miles away from Cognac. Widowed early, he died at over a hundred, still in his modest small-holding, which we could never persuade him to leave. Where could he have found better places to shoot or fish? At the age of ninety-four, he fell in the stream, went home to change, drank some hot wine punch, and went out fishing again. All his life he had been popular, and enjoyed company: he was invited to all the local functions because he could play the violin. Towards the end of his life, he taught his seventy-year-old servant to read. He liked Cherves, but he realized that his two sons would be better off at Cognac. There, my father was one of the first pupils at the local College, and did well. He learned German, and found good market outlets beyond the Rhine. It was there that he discovered how trade could be conducted without any written contracts. Very soon, he lost the traditionally suspicious attitude of the

Charente. His view of mankind was optimistic, but I have not inherited it completely. Quite early in life, events taught me that human nature is weak and unpredictable without rules and institutions.

My father was thirty-two when he married the daughter of a former cooper* for the Hennesy family, who had become a vintner. Grandfather Demelle had a goatee beard. He was a man with a sense of the done thing: he put on his Sunday best to go and pay his taxes. Like all of us, he had great respect for his wife, who was intelligent and wise. They lived in the heart of the old town at Cognac, in a little house that for us held all the delights of childhood. Until the end of their lives, which were happily very long, theirs was the first place I visited whenever I went back.

My mother had inherited the moral qualities of these exemplary beings: a sense of duty, and a sense of proportion. She had to transpose them into the world created and often shaken by my father's imagination and his impatient, somewhat excitable nature. It was in comparison with him that she seemed strict and rather authoritarian; but who can say whether her imagination was greater or less than his? Her role was not to express her own real nature, but to strike the balance of this family group which my father launched totally, as a team, into ceaseless activity. When I was born, in 1888, she was nineteen. Then came my brother Gaston and my sisters Henriette and Marie-Louise. In retrospect, I seem to have been surrounded by women; at Cognac, the men were often away. My father travelled in Germany, Sweden, and Russia. As soon as he left, aunts and girl cousins would come to keep my mother company. By the time he came back, everyone had quietly left.

My mother got up early to do the housework: all the shutters were open by seven o'clock. But when night fell and the lamps were lit, they all had to be shut again: 'Someone might see us,' she would say. Her fear of being seen, exposed, was very much a Charente characteristic. Unlike my father, who could daydream, or lose his temper, or if necessary escape on some journey, my mother was tied to reality, and she always brought the family gently back to it. I may have my father's imagination. But my mother taught me that nothing can be achieved unless it is built on reality. She distrusted ideas as such. She wanted to know what was to be done with them.

She was religious and very tolerant. A Catholic, she had great respect for a friend of ours, M. Barrault, who every Sunday abandoned his plough to officiate at the Segonzac synagogue. 'He is a man of the Bible,' she would say. My father spent his Sundays in charitable work:

* Barrel-maker.

37

he went to look after the Mutual Aid Societies which in those days were a first answer to the growing demand for some form of social security. For my father, they were a way of doing something for the public good, which was always his ambition. To satisfy it through politics never entered his head.

This was the world in which I grew up. One did one thing, slowly and with concentration. But through it one had an immense area to observe and a very active exchange of ideas. Through it, or from it, I learned more about men, and about international affairs, than I could have learned from a specialized education. I had only to listen and watch. That, incidentally, is why there was no problem when I asked my father, after my first *baccalauréat**, if I could go straight into the family business.

I had never liked school. I would not, or could not for some reason, learn bookish knowledge by heart. When it was proposed that I should become a boarder at Pons, fourteen miles away, I fell ill. And yet, looking back, I was a serious and disciplined child. Very early on, my instinct told me that thought cannot be divorced from action. It has been a rule with me ever since. I was surrounded by action. My father and mother, whom I admired, were always busy, making plans or carrying them out. I saw very well where I could use my energy and my brains right away: why then take the roundabout route of studying law, living in a room in Poitiers, when I could go to the school of life and see the world?

'See the world' is an expression that Cognac did not use. One spoke of 'visiting clients'. That it might take us to Singapore or New York was scarcely seen as a privilege of the trade: it was an elementary necessity. Pride in belonging to the brandy business, if it was one of the features of local society, was based more on the quality of the product than on the demand for it throughout the world. The demand reflected the quality; and that was the result of a happy marriage between natural advantages and steady care, maintained for two centuries by growers and distillers alike. From there on, selling was no more than a necessity, even if it took us, prosaically enough, to the ends of the earth. The first step in our education was to know the language of our clientèle. So I had to learn English – the sooner the better. As well as leaving school, I had to leave home, and forget the insouciance of childhood. At the age of sixteen I bought a bowler hat and assumed my responsibilities.

* Two-part qualifying examination for entrance to university.

Those responsibilities were real, and my father thought it none too soon to introduce me to all the problems of the firm. In fact, it was not my apprenticeship in the distillery or even in the cooper's department that taught me the most. My experience was acquired at the family table.

Saturday was the day when we were visited by the men from the country, the distillers who supplied us with *eau de vie**. They were rich men, full of wisdom, still close to the soil, like M. Barrault. There was more than a business relationship between them and my father: there was friendship and mutual confidence. This dated from the origins of the firm, and was embodied in it: our title was 'The Society of Cognac Vine-growers', and the men who stayed to lunch with us on Saturdays were our biggest shareholders.

My father was not the founder of the firm. It dated back to 1838, when a certain Antoine de Salignac had brought together several hundred small vine-growers who wanted to escape the purchasing monopoly of the big firms. At that time, brandy was still sold to the British in cask. When the shareholders asked my father to take over the running of the firm in 1897, his experience at Cognac had already earned him a reputation. They were anxious to have an innovating spirit to look after their interests at a time when the trade was having to make big changes, including bottling on the spot. My father contributed his share of experience, and printed the brand name 'J. G. Monnet' on the bottle labels, which already bore a salamander. He had already proved his worth on his travels in Europe – travels which had borne fruit. Out of the profit from his commission, he had just built a house in town.

In my mother's eyes, the house was a sign that the family had arrived, and she was anxious for my father not to get involved in over-ambitious ventures. But when she realized how much the imaginative man she loved needed the stimulus of activity that the new circumstances gave him, she agreed to leave our own house and move into the stately mansion of the Vine-growers' Society. It was there that she began to practise that form of hospitality which is the most characteristic custom of Cognac society. If on Saturdays we kept open house for the vine-growers, who were our friends and suppliers, on every other day our guests included strangers who had come on business. They came from Britain, Germany, Scandinavia, America. Since every firm had its own visitors, and since there were virtually no hotels in Cognac, it was the custom for strangers to be received like

* Raw spirit.

family friends. In any case, most of the great families of the town were of foreign origin, or had foreign connections, as witness their names – Hennesy, Martel, Hine. There was a continual to-ing and fro-ing of people and ideas, and a network of personal acquaintance-ship that made the business a very human affair.

Before I came to know local Cognac society, with which we in fact had little contact, I was already familiar with our visitors' tales of their distant lands and voyages, and I got into the habit of thinking about their problems and ours together. My father, whose curiosity seemed insatiable, asked them endless questions; and at table we habitually talked about world affairs as others talk about local problems. But there was no affectation in it, no feeling of transcending the parochial: we knew that our existence depended on the prosperity and the tastes of people all over the world. Our concerns took us a long way from Cognac, but never far from the cognac it produced.

If we had time to keep ourselves informed, we had no time to day-dream. The gentle Charente river, which flowed by the Vine-growers' Society warehouses where the casks were shipped by the lighter-men, had nothing in common with the atmosphere of the house. J. G. Monnet brandy matured slowly, but the brand was new, and effort was needed to sell it. Life was not easy. The old, big, famous firms had no trouble disposing of their produce, which was in demand all over the world. But the small firms had to stimulate demand and interest distant customers. What was more, from 1907 onwards, competition from whisky began to be felt on the foreign markets, and even in France itself.

There was no joint sales organization. It is only recently that the brandy trade has felt the need to act together. When I was young, I knew of only one kind of agreement, a tacit agreement on prices; and that was a personal matter between M. Hennesy and M. Martel. But they took care to leave room for dozens of other smaller firms, some of them on a tiny scale, all of which were quite independent. Independence was the rule of the trade. For my parents, it was also a rule of life.

My father, enterprising as he was, never thought of turning his Vine-growers' Society into a militant organization leading the pro-fession. Like most of the businessmen, he thought in terms of running the business, not changing it. Why are the big brands successful? Because they have taken care not to change once they have got a reputation. Hennesy has never changed. Others have thought they should, and have not succeeded. My father used to say: 'Every new idea is a bad idea.' As far as brandy is concerned, he was right: not otherwise. I did not agree with him, but I am not sure that I would have done better than he did.

Nor did I want to. When I was a child, I used to play in the firm's vast warehouses. I had a wealth of space. Why should I worry about what to do when I grew up? My natural vocation was to continue my father's business. That in itself was no sinecure. In the big brandy firms, all that need be done is to husband the inheritance. I very soon learned that I had more to do. Day after day, I should have to work at winning the family brand-name its place on the international market.

I had been brought up to run and develop the business, and I should have been astonished to be told that one day I should leave Cognac. My young brother and myself were to help our father, then take over from him. We had no choice. Sometimes I wonder now whether I have ever had any choice but to do what I have done, unquestioningly. To earn my living by selling brandy was for me the first form that necessity took. So much so that I had to make a long effort to adapt to public affairs, which meant getting used to dealing with other people's problems.

When I did, much later, I discovered a different world, and one which lacked the simple, implacable criterion of success – a balance-sheet at the end of the year. It was circumstances – necessity again – which led me to leave private business quite early on, and then to come back for a considerable time: it was not restlessness or ambition. I am not even sure that alternating between private and public affairs, of which America affords striking examples, is always a good idea. If there is any rule of thumb, it is a simpler one: just ask yourself where you can best do what you have to do.

Without the 1914 War and the need to serve in it as best I could, I might never perhaps have left the family business. I certainly never thought I was destined to deal with the affairs of my country, or of people in general. Later, my father often said: 'You think you're doing great things, but you'll see: you'll be glad to come back to the firm.' I think I could have made a success of it; and when the chance came, some years after the First World War, I did. But that was due to circumstances, and in any case the methods were different from those that I had used in public affairs. In Cognac, probably, I should never have thought of organizing the profession or merging firms. That was not my problem.

I was properly prepared for only one thing: to apply myself to doing what I had to do; and what finer example was there than my father? He lived only for the firm he had built up; he allowed himself no distractions; but he needed none, since all his satisfaction was there. If I had wanted to do something else, he would not have tried to stop me; but we knew very well that the firm was still in its infancy, and that it needed the continuing strength that only a family could give it. That is why I do not remember ever having dreamed of vast ambitions. At the age when people discover their vocations, I realized that it was vain to say: 'I want to do this, or that.' Things happen otherwise: at least they have for me. Events that strike me and occupy my thoughts lead me to general conclusions about what has to be done. Then circumstances, which determine day-to-day events, suggest or supply the means of action. I can wait a long time for the right moment. In Cognac they are good at waiting. It is the only way to make good brandy.

Patience is certainly something I learned from where I grew up. People were reflective and serious, tinged perhaps with Anglo-Saxon Puritanism. I learned to listen and to weigh my words. And I also was given a window on the world, such as most young Frenchmen of my generation totally lacked. I had no time to experience the youthful need for escape. At sixteen I was already a traveller. With us, there was nothing unusual in that. Besides, why be unusual?

The people of Cognac were not nationalist, at a time when France was. I cannot say whether that had an influence on the work I have done to try to build Europe. I thought nothing of it at the time. Nor did it give me the idea, then, that I ought to concern myself with international affairs. But no doubt it was that which made it seem natural to me, later, to do what was necessary to bring together as a team men who had previously been divided by artificial barriers. I have never regarded these barriers as real. I have never had problems about the surroundings in which I am to work. So my upbringing may have given me some aptitude for what I have done. But that does not mean it has been easy: I have always found everything very difficult.

II
Distant travels

The rule of the house was that there could be no argument about what
had to be done. So my mother agreed that at sixteen I should go off to
spend two years in England. I was to learn not only the language of
our most important clients, but also their habits and their ways of
doing business. I was going to live with a family of wine merchants,
our agents in London. There, I was able to observe the traditions of
British business circles – or rather, since I was too young to play an
active part – to soak up a certain atmosphere.

Every day I went with Mr Chaplin, my host, to his office in the City.
At that time, the City was a world in itself, dignified and honoured –
as indeed it still is. It is not only an area of business offices and banks:
it is also a circle, socially very exclusive, but professionally open to the
wide world. Its daily concerns are the affairs of Shanghai, Tokyo, New
Delhi, New York. This is the subject of conversation in offices, clubs,
and public-houses. Everyone gets to know everyone, by playing golf
together, or dominoes, or travelling on the train, as everyone does,
whatever his job. It is a close-knit community, within which business
rivalry is smoothed by personal relations. Everyone does his own
business, but at the same time it is the business of the City. Incidentally,
an Englishman will not say: 'I'm sending my son into such-and-such
a firm or bank'. Instead: 'I'm sending him into the City'.

My parents had certainly not sent me into the City; but there I was,
and I could not help being impressed by its organized strength. It was
there that I learned what collective action was. Nowhere in Cognac
or in France had I seen it so seriously at work. Certainly, individual
action went on alongside it; but individual action was not automatically preferred, as it was in my country. Nor would it have been
tolerated if it took a personal, flashy turn. Individual action could
succeed only if it deserved and secured the support of the City as a
whole. One other thing I learned there, and that was to make up my
mind about people. In the City, one makes up one's mind about a
client, and one sticks to one's judgement whether business is good or
bad. One does not withdraw one's credit. I have never seen that anywhere else. On Wall Street, where I found many of the City's charac-

teristics – the same organization, the same sense of collective action – if business gets bad, people want their money back.

At that time, the power of Great Britain was universally respected, and very impressive to a young Frenchman who was ready to regard that country and its Empire as the natural place for him to work. Between Cognac and London, there were direct links that by-passed Paris: they were personal, often family ties, and they owed nothing to the vicissitudes of politics. Whether the *Entente* was *cordiale** or not, we had to be on good terms with the Anglo-Saxon world. The product we sold was of a quality that encouraged the seller and the purchaser to establish relations based on mutual respect – or, more exactly, on common respect for the product. There was something noble about cognac brandy. Incidentally, it owed its success to the enterprise of a few Scottish or Irish emigrants in the seventeenth century.

So, from the days of my childhood, while French society stagnated in its own parochialism, I was taught to realize that we lived in a world of vast distances, and it was natural for me to expect to meet people who spoke other languages and had different customs. To observe and take account of these customs was our daily necessity. But it did not make us feel different, or dependent. At Cognac, one was on equal terms with the British: in Paris, one was somewhat under their influence. So we avoided the proud or defensive nationalistic reactions that were beginning to permeate French politics. In later years, in my relations with other peoples, I have never had to fight against reflexes that I have never acquired.

When I set out on my first long voyage, at the age of eighteen, my father said to me: 'Don't take any books. No one can do your thinking for you. Look out of the window, talk with people. Pay attention to your neighbour.' I went to Winnipeg to visit our clients, tough men in a tough climate, up against forces of nature that were rewarding but pitiless to the weak. These men were sensitive to the fine quality of cognac. They demanded the best. But if we talked about cognac, they asked me little about Cognac. What was going on in Europe had no interest for these Europeans making for the West, turning their backs on the Old World. Their efforts, their vision of a broader, richer future, that was what we talked about nearly all the time. I soaked myself in these new impressions.

* The original *Entente cordiale*, or 'friendly understanding', reached between Britain and France in 1904. (T.N.)

When I returned to Cognac, I had a different type of man to deal with – the people who supplied us with the raw *eau de vie*. These vine-growers had cultivated the same vineyards for generations. A few acres, catalogued and registered with care, sufficed to make them rich. They had no need to conquer new territory: on the contrary, it was to their interest to limit the quality area, that of the *grande champagne*, that of the *fins bois*, that of the *borderies*. Their problem was to win the widest market for the output of one of the most concentrated areas of production in the world. It was our task, as distillers and salesmen, to provide worldwide outlets for this local product.

I remember going to Segonzac, a village close to Cognac, to see M. Barrault. His vines covered gently undulating territory. I do not know whether it is these faint undulations, planted in perfect lines, or the sea air, or the slowness of the river, that has made travellers speak for so long of 'the soft Charente'. M. Barrault was in the vineyard, and I found him driving his own cart, dressed in an old tail-coat. Canada, its forests, its snows and its trappers, seemed to belong to another world. But it was this other world that M. Barrault wanted to know about. Even before I could ask him about the harvest, he said: 'Well, what's the news from Winnipeg?'

After I had returned from England, my father had sent me to America to visit our old clients and develop our retail network. For us, who had to work all the time to make ourselves known, the idea of development was natural. But what I discovered in America was something more, which had a different name: expansion.

In 1906, much of the North American continent was still virgin territory, and the conquest of the Canadian West was still the big thing. At Winnipeg, from the Station Hotel of the Canadian Pacific Railway where I was staying, I saw trainloads of Scandinavian immigrants pulling in. They were not refugees: they were not starving. They had come to hard, rewarding work – the conquest of new lands. The most common type there was not the speculator, but the entrepreneur. For the first time I met a people whose job was not to manage what already existed, but to develop it without stint. No one thought about limits; no one knew where the frontier was.

In this new world always on the move, I learned to get rid of the old atavistic suspicions which are so much a pointless worry and a waste of time. In Charente, people are wary of their neighbours, and distrust newcomers even more. Here, I encountered a new way of looking at things: individual initiative could be accepted as a contribution to the general good. Small examples of this confident attitude, adopted as a principle and now become natural to immigrants from Europe, struck me immensely. One day, at Calgary in Alberta, I wanted to visit some Scandinavian farmers to whom I had an introduction. I asked a blacksmith who was working in front of his forge what means of transport there were. Without stopping work, he answered that there were none. 'But,' he added, pointing to his horse, 'you can always take this animal. When you come back, just hitch him up in the same place.' His confidence was perfectly natural: and if I had shown him how surprised I was, he would certainly have been hurt.

I was already a long way from Cognac, and from countries with written laws. No doubt there were other forms of sanction against wrongdoing. But it was the very notion of law and order that was different here. In contrast to the static balance of the old Europe, this was the dynamism of a world on the move. Each had its merits; each could be explained. But American expansion needed no explanation: it was spontaneous, like necessity itself. To my European eyes, this spontaneity looked like confusion; but I very soon ceased to think in those terms. I became convinced that there could be no progress without a certain disorder, or at least without disorder on the surface.

Still only eighteen, I did extensive business with the Hudson Bay Company, whose Chairman, Mr Chipman, invited me to stay with him at Fort Selkirk. We needed furs: the trappers liked cognac. Some years later, during the First World War, I was able to use my friendly relations with these enterprising men to promote the interests of Allied supplies. I also went to the United States, from New York to California. Everywhere I had the same impression: that where physical space was unlimited, confidence was unlimited too. Where change was accepted, expansion was assured. The United States had retained the dynamism of the Western pioneers, like those I had seen in action at Winnipeg. But to that they had added organization. To organize change – that, I saw, was necessary, and it could be done.

I returned to Cognac after long months of visiting all our agents, and many of our customers, in the most faraway places. I had explained a thousand times, often successfully, that my father's cognac was as reputable as the best-known brands, and that it was cheaper. This took a lot of patience and hard work. I did no sight-seeing, although I could not help being impressed by the magnificence of Nature. It was in the Rockies that I acquired a taste for long walks – a need I have felt ever since. I can hardly call it a form of recreation: on the contrary, it seems to be the time, or the agent, for the concentration of mind that precedes action. But did my work then, selling brandy, really demand so much effort? Had I, like so many adolescents, some dream of transforming the world? No: I was wholly absorbed in my job. I thought I could never have too much time, too much energy, too much experience of men, if I wished to do it well.

As far back as I can remember, I seem to have been busy at some unquestioned task. I have no imagination for anything that does not seem necessary. At eighteen, I had to help my father build up the reputation and the prosperity of the family brandy. That was as far as I could see. I should probably not have been able to say, either, whether I had great plans for Monnet cognac, or what results I hoped to gain from my success. I did not ask such questions. I was simply concerned to maximize my chances, and that was why I tried to keep informed about anything that could help us to sell our product. This involved a great deal, since we were at the mercy of a political crisis in central Europe, a recession in America, or a rise in freight rates in London. I besieged travellers with questions. I needed to judge people and what they were capable of, just as if I were in charge of important affairs. Besides, what is the distinction in one's own life between important affairs and others? There are simply the affairs one is engaged in: that's all.

I broadened my experience as a businessman – as a man – with further travels during these years. I went to England again, to Sweden, to Russia. I went to Egypt, where I learnt new forms of persuasion. I went from village to village with our firm's agent in Greece. We called on the wholesalers, who made us sit down and drink coffee, and chatted about their own affairs. We knew we had to wait a reasonable time. Then Chamah, the Greek, decided that the time had come to do a deal. He wrote in a notebook the quantity that he could expect our client to take. It was never disputed. He had respected the ritual. Later, in the Far East, I encountered this same emphasis on time, which makes one wonder sometimes whether Cognac is closer to New York or to Shanghai. In China, you have to know how to wait. In the United States, you have to know how to come back. Two forms of patience to which cognac, itself the fruit of time, is a good preparation.

III

1914: Viviani says 'Try'

It was in the train at Poitiers station that I heard the news that France was mobilizing for war. I was on my way back from England to Cognac. Among my compatriots, there seemed to be a spirit of ardour and excitement very different from the determination I had found in England during the weeks of tension that had led from one misunderstanding to another and finally to this disastrous confrontation. I knew what vast resources and what tenacious resistance would be mustered and deployed by the British Empire if it felt itself irreparably provoked. It was, after all, the greatest empire in the world. In France, everyone's hopes were placed solely in the ability of their leaders and the heroism of the army. When I reached Cognac, my brother was leaving to join his hussar regiment. People were already saying that it would be a short war; their sole concern was to hurry to the front, as if everything was going to be settled in one decisive battle. I myself had been found medically unfit for military service, so there were no call-up papers waiting for me at home. But I could not stand idly by. I had to serve the war effort as best I could, wherever I should be most useful.

I quickly realized what I had to do. It was clear that the Allies were going to face a formidable problem for which there had been no preparation: the co-ordination of their war efforts. If this was obvious to me, it was *because* I was so young, not *in spite of* the fact. It was a new problem, a twentieth-century problem, which someone without prejudices, without memories of the past, could see more easily than experts brought up on nineteenth-century experience. For them, it was harder to realize that the basis of power had changed, that the war machine would now have to mobilize a nation's whole resources, and that quite new forms of organization would have to be invented. Germany, with a powerful army backed by immense industrial might, seemed to me better prepared for this new kind of warfare than the Allies, whose combined strength was weakened because they were preparing to fight separately instead of as one.

I knew the British, and I had no difficulty in working with them. Nothing seemed to me more obvious than the need to concert the economic war effort: I was convinced that we must do so sooner or later, probably after wasting a lot of time and resources. I wanted to do something to make people see the need to act quickly; but I did not know whom to approach. I tried out my ideas among the people I knew, and I realized how difficult it would be to get anyone to admit that in so grave a situation the authorities had not taken all the necessary steps to prevent waste. My father, for example, hated waste: but he thought it quite normal that France and Great Britain should each run its own war effort according to its individual ideas. Like all Frenchmen, he regarded the Alliance as something sacred, essential to our survival. But he saw it as the juxtaposition of two sovereign powers, two separate armies which both aimed at victory, but which had divided the task between them and were each engaged in their separate pursuits.

It was natural for my father to see things that way. The *'entente cordiale'* was a recent affair, and mutual understanding had its limits. What was more, the two countries' economic systems were not the same: London's free-trading outlook jarred on the protectionism of Paris. To try to link them too closely might hamper one or the other in this time of danger. Even to try listing and consolidating all national resources might constitute a threat to the liberal, free-enterprise principle, which was still sacrosanct even in wartime.

But what seemed natural to my father was far from obvious to me. On my travels I had learned that economic forces were not blind and abstract, but could be measured and steered. Above all, I had come to realize that where there was organization there was real strength. This could already be seen in the growth of industry before World War I. During that war it was to become overwhelmingly clear. That so few people saw the point made me anxious and more eager than ever to get it understood.

But time was slipping by. The first German offensive damaged us economically as much as militarily. We suddenly lost two-thirds of our iron and steel, as well as half our coal. The interest on our overseas investments began to dry up. Our balance of payments was seriously threatened, and at home prices began to rise as a result of panic buying. It was then that we realized how much we had always depended on foreign shipping. Yet we only requisitioned a small part of our merchant fleet, as much as was necessary for military needs.

The British economy was better off, since the country had not been invaded, and the Home Fleet commanded the seas. International trade continued, at the cost of some gaps in the blockade of Germany,

49

which took time to organize, at least as regards the neutrals. But in Britain too only part of the merchant fleet was requisitioned, and a great deal of tonnage was wasted.

So numerous were the signs of this rapid deterioration in our position that I had plenty of practical examples to strengthen my case. I was determined to put it to those who were in a position to act, wherever they might be. My father began to be swayed by my arguments, although he repeated: 'Even if you were absolutely right, at your age, and in Cognac, you won't have any effect on what the big chiefs decide in Paris.' But then I had no intention of staying in Cognac, waiting to be called up into some auxiliary service. The delay gave me a chance to make myself useful, and I looked around for a way of reaching the men in Paris who could at last set about organizing joint action by the Allies.

One of our friends at Cognac was a lawyer, Maître Fernand Benon, who happened to know René Viviani, the Prime Minister, quite well: he had appeared with him in several court cases. He was open to new ideas. He asked me questions about my travels, and I in turn asked him about affairs in France. It was from him that I discovered most of what I knew about French politics, about the workings of the civil service and about its limitations. I had no difficulty in persuading him to share my anxiety about how the war effort was being run on anachronistic lines; and he agreed to introduce me to Viviani. We were on the point of leaving for Paris when the Government withdrew to Bordeaux. The centre of power was now only a few miles away.

My family still thought that these few miles were an impossible distance socially. They thought I was big-headed to want to by-pass everyone and go straight to the top. I had no such scruples: it was not in my nature to respect established authority for its own sake. What counted for me was its usefulness. In something as important as strengthening co-operation between the Allies, the right level to aim at was the Government. I had an idea which only the Prime Minister had the power to put into practice: so why not go knocking on his door? It was not some conceited need to make myself important, but a simple idea of what would be most effective. I have never acted in any other way. First have an idea, then look for the man who can put it to work. Sometimes there have to be intermediaries, who may well be little-known, although they are very much aware of the responsibilities they are taking on. Fernand Benon was the first of many. Without him, I might never have come to deal with what my father called 'other people's business' – that is, public affairs.

We went to Bordeaux in the second week of September. The Battle of the Marne had begun, and there was fresh hope in the Allied camp. But the lessons of the past weeks had been painful; and everyone knew that traditional military and economic ideas had been proved out-of-date. The Allies' initial reverses had gravely strained relations between France and Britain. It was vital to devise a form of organization that would stand up to the long effort needed to win the war.

Viviani received me in his office at the Faculty of Letters. He had built his career on his skill, his charm, and his great talent for public speaking; but in France's time of trial he had shown himself to be firm. By withdrawing to Bordeaux, the Government had not given in to panic: on the contrary, it had made clear that invasion did not imply defeat. Viviani said to me: 'Sir, I gather that you have some interesting proposals. Tell me.'

I had no proposals, properly speaking, but a conviction to express, which must, if accepted, result in action. I explained to Viviani what I knew of Britain's power and determination.

'Despite our present disappointment,' I said, 'Britain is going to commit more and more of her troops to the continent. She needs longer to become a nation in arms, but when she does she will have a formidable army, as she already has an invincible navy. There is no question about that. The problem lies in using to the full the decisive contribution of Britain's economic power. At the moment, we don't know how to do it. And so long as we fail to allocate responsibilities according to the ability of each side, the Alliance will remain a mere juxtaposition of two separate powers. At present, despite all the good intentions of those responsible, there are absurd instances of waste and unnecessary duplication.'

Viviani interrupted. 'Can you give me some examples?'

'The merchant fleets have not been fully requisitioned. There are good reasons for that, I know. But is there any reason why they should compete with each other, why they shouldn't charge the same freight rates, and why their cargoes shouldn't be co-ordinated so that at least priority supplies get through quickly? You're worried at the moment because the price of oats has gone up. But it's not the price that's gone up – it's the cost of shipping them.'

'What do you propose?'

'We need to set up joint bodies to estimate the combined resources of the Allies, share them out, and share out the costs.'

'But we already have machinery for inter-Allied co-operation, and

I'm told that it works well.'

'That's nothing more than a communications system. It doesn't take decisions or make choices. We're beginning to suffer from shortages, and we must devote our resources to the most rational ends – all our resources – all our joint resources. It's this, I believe, that's still not understood. Allied solidarity must be total. In other words, neither side must be free to use its men, its supplies, or its shipping in ways that haven't been agreed by both.'

'I see what you mean: but you must realize that we are talking about two Governments and two sovereign Parliaments. Can you imagine these joint decisions being taken simultaneously?'

'I know the British well enough to be sure that we can reach a real agreement with them if we appeal to their loyalty and if we play fair. They know what a terrible burden the French armies are bearing for the common cause. They will agree to make the biggest contribution in the fields where they are supreme – in production and shipping.'

'I think so too, but it's hard to broach the subject at a time when we're asking them to send more troops. You seem to have some idea of how to go about it. Try. I'll tell Millerand* to expect you. Explain to him what you've just told me.'

Leaving Viviani's office, I found Fernand Benon waiting in the hall of the Faculty of Letters. He told me that Viviani had just that morning heard of the death of his two sons in the Battle of the Marne. We were standing by the tomb of Montaigne. He, I thought, would have respected the stoicism of a Prime Minister falsely reputed to be facile.

* Alexandre Millerand, Minister of War.

Chapter 3

1914-1918: WORKING TOGETHER

I

The inter-Allied executives

I was sent to London in November 1914 in the Civil Supplies Service headed by Comptroller-General Mauclair. Ironically, this French liaison mission had its headquarters in Trafalgar House, Waterloo Place. In Britain, chance itself has a sense of humour.

It was then that I realized the full extent of the anarchy prevailing in the economic organization of the war effort – not only in relations between the Allies, but on both sides separately. This can only have been due to the blind confidence that both placed in the machinery of international trade, which was thought capable of meeting any situation that might arise. People were reluctant to interfere with free trade, for fear of disrupting a system that in any case would have to be resumed once the war was over. Even when it became obvious that the war was going to be a long one, no overt steps were taken to introduce rational planning. It was necessity which here and there led to intervention, control, or takeovers by the State. Myself, I was determined to use such opportunities whenever they arose in the areas for which I was responsible. It was a case of demonstrating empirically, in a few practical instances, that purely private interests could no longer act as the driving-force and the regulator of an economy at war, and that purely national interests could no longer meet the needs of a military Alliance.

There existed in London, when I arrived, an 'International Supply Committee'. Its title was ambitious, its reality meagre. The Committee's responsibilities were limited to supplies for the troops, and did not include wheat, flour, meat, or sugar. Each Government was free to make whatever purchases it thought fit: all it had to do was inform the other of what it was doing or planning. The aim was to avoid competing on foreign markets and thereby forcing up the price.

Imperfect as it was, the International Supply Committee seemed to me full of potential – and in any case I had no choice but to work there. It comprised representatives of the Allied powers who were to come to know each other and to learn to work as a team. In practice, we found ourselves in direct contact with a British-run organization for making purchases paid for with British credit. But what might have been a sterile affair became by the force of circumstances the first step towards closer co-operation. The French and British supply services, which had begun by competing with each other on the Australian and Argentinian markets, soon decided to act together. They also chartered neutral refrigerator ships on identical terms. This was not the result of deliberate overall planning. It would not have happened without the pressure of very great financial need.

Similar necessity led to the Allied organization for wheat purchasing, which itself was the beginning of co-operation on a much larger scale. Wheat was not only essential to feed the services and the civilian population; it was also the key to the purchase and shipment of other foodstuffs. If France and Britain were to bid against each other for wheat, all prices and freight-rates were bound to go up.

This was precisely what happened, and it became obvious in 1915; but the organization designed to deal with the situation proved inadequate. A 'Joint Committee', composed of the French and Italian supply services and the British firm of Ross Smith, had the job of buying wheat for the forces; at the same time, the French Government continued to buy and ship wheat independently for civilian use. The latter was one of my tasks, and it was made easier by the friendly relations I already enjoyed with the heads of the Hudson Bay Company. But while I spent my first months in London doing the best I could, I was still very dissatisfied. I shared the anxiety of my counterparts in the Board of Trade as they watched the various purchasing bodies vying with each other for supplies – to the greater profit of Canadian and Argentinian wheat-growers; and I made urgent representations about it to the French Minister of Commerce, for whom I was working. The result was a first inter-Allied agreement, reached in November 1915. A second result, minor in itself but important for me, was to draw the Minister's attention to this young delegate in London who was always asking for instructions to negotiate tighter agreements.

Etienne Clémentel, the Minister in question, was one of those men who, knowing their own abilities, find their vocation in politics, and are so capable that no one knows if this is the reason for their staying in power, or the result of it. Throughout the war Clémentel had the same job, although its title changed with Cabinet reshuffles: he was in charge of foreign trade and supplies. He had no ambition to enlarge his empire, in a political sense, but he gradually took over industrial affairs, sea transport and, for a while, agriculture. This gave him no feelings of personal aggrandisement; but his civil servants, who encouraged it, found their work greatly simplified when a whole sector of the economy was handled in one piece.

Clémentel was a pleasant, cultivated man, clear-headed and extremely articulate. His greatest virtue in my eyes, obviously, was to be able to listen to advice and make up his mind when he judged that he had learned enough. He was a man who would agree to my suggestions if they were convincing, and give them official backing. He found me a loyal, demanding adviser. I asked for, and obtained, a direct telephone line between my office and his. In this way an uninterrupted dialogue was gradually established between London and Paris.

I passed on British protests against the spectacle of French firms chartering at fifty shillings a ton per month, whereas the British were bound under an agreement with France not to charter at more than forty. The need for a better arrangement was becoming obvious. We were at the mercy of a threat by British shippers to withdraw their services at a time when they were carrying 48% of our supplies. And in April 1916 British expert forecasts were extremely pessimistic: they envisaged a deficit of more than 3 million tons, which would mean cutting British imports by 15%.

The British Government's first reaction was to warn its allies that it could not increase the tonnage at their disposal. But soon Lord Curzon, Lord President of the Council and a member of the War Cabinet, told us that he would have to make large cuts in the amount already allotted. At a time when we were planning to ask for more, the decision to give us less was unacceptable, and I was given the job of trying to have it rescinded. It was a stern test of the personal contacts that I had built up in London. The most reliable of them was Arthur Salter, a young civil servant in the Transport Department. Circumstances were to give him a role that matched his outstanding worth.

Salter was the same age as myself, and he had the same attitude towards what we both regarded as common problems. At that time, the problems were those of organizing the Allied war effort; later, those of organizing the peace at Geneva; and later still those of war again, in 1940. It was through Salter's conception of public service, which he made the subject of his memoirs after having held high political office, that I came to understand the quality of the British civil service*. It had not been trained to deal with economic questions by means of Government intervention, nor trade questions by means of international co-operation. In peacetime, that was not its concern. What nation on earth was more convinced of the superiority of liberalism, or more jealous of its own independence? But, on the other hand, what nation was better able to face adversity and adapt to new needs? It was the British who most quickly recognized the danger that threatened the Allied war economy if trade was not voluntarily reorganized to take account of the blockade.

The ban on trade with the enemy had upset the old patterns of supply and made it necessary to seek new sources. Germany, herself blockaded, was trying to blockade Britain and, indirectly, France. Submarine warfare was a deadly threat to the whole Alliance, whose civil and strategic resources depended to a great extent on supplies brought in by the British fleet. The disruption of trade patterns and the fear of being torpedoed encouraged speculation and higher prices. Rationing by the purse would quickly have led to social unrest. So the authorities had to assume responsibility for buying essential commodities. Overcoming their natural reluctance, the British led the way by setting up the 'Royal Sugar Commission', which bought up all available sugar from America, Cuba, and Java.

In this case, as soon afterwards in that of Australian and Argentinian meat, the leading role was played by officials from the Transport Department. Arthur Salter was at the centre of the machinery for freight allocation, and his method of working out priorities was much more than merely empirical: it had become a way of posing and solving problems of common interest. I had no difficulty in convincing him that for Britain to withdraw ships already on charter to France would be a blow to Allied solidarity. Quite apart from the immediate damage it would do to French supplies, it would put at risk the further co-operation that we both agreed was vital. Salter set about rescinding the order, and I was able to tell Paris that the panic was over, but that it was now urgent for the Allies to look at their common problems together.

Clémentel agreed that there should be a Conference of Ministers of Commerce. He wrote to Aristide Briand, the French Prime Minister, that he thought it 'particularly desirable to establish among the Allies

* Lord Salter: *Memoirs of a Public Servant*, 1961.

a common outlook whose aim would be to bring the *Entente*, in the interests of its member countries, all the commercial and industrial advantages that it can obtain, now and in the future.'

This reference to the future, while the war was still at its height, reflected the anxieties of certain businessmen, who feared that Britain might seek to exploit her present near-monopoly of transport, which was unavoidable, to establish permanent economic supremacy over her allies. Failing overall agreement on burden-sharing among the Allies, there was indeed a risk of permanent inequality, with dependence in peacetime replacing solidarity in war. So there was perhaps a touch of self-interest in the French desire to set up a joint organization. But we were determined to support anything that served the common interest, either immediately or in the longer term. I encouraged Clémentel to negotiate for a fairer distribution of present burdens and for continued solidarity in the future.

Not everyone, of course, looked at the problem in this light. In France, a concern for national independence dominated the Armaments Department where the Under-Secretary Louis Loucheur, who was later to be made Minister, represented the views of industry. His attitude was that 'the British should put at our disposal an agreed number of ships, and that we should do what we like with them'. It would obviously have been impossible for me to get anything from our most important ally if I had negotiated in this spirit; but I too believed that we must safeguard the future. Ever since then I have been convinced that it is never a good thing to let the British have a special position. On the contrary, they must be persuaded to join in and deal with matters in a framework that balances everyone's interests. To form an Allied shipping pool, and participate in running it, would be better from our point of view than obtaining exclusive but temporary rights to part of the British fleet. Joint administration of shipping as a whole would make possible a continuing exchange of information and explanation about all the problems of transport and supplies. This method of co-operation in wartime would be no less useful in the postwar reconstruction period: it would avoid the sudden cuts or threats of cuts that were feared by those responsible for the French economy.

Two years after the outbreak of war, however, the question of an Allied transport pool could still not be tackled head on. It was too big a problem: it threatened to raise questions of sovereignty that no one was ready to answer. Salter and I thought that the first test case for Allied co-operation should be wheat, where there had already been a very unsatisfactory attempt at joint organization, the 'Joint Committee' already mentioned. For a whole year this divided purchasing system had been operating in a spirit of competition that encouraged international speculation. To put an end to this situation had become vital. To use the opportunity to try out a new method of co-operation had become possible. I persuaded Clémentel that with so good an opportunity he should play for high stakes. The British wanted rapid results: we wanted a lasting organization.

By this time, the draft of an agreement was already prepared, and the name of the new system had been chosen. In my mind, the 'Wheat Executive' was to be the prototype of a series of inter-Allied institutions for the joint handling of essential commodities. We had kept it simple – one representative from Great Britain, one from France, and one from Italy, which had entered the war in May 1915. The draft agreement laid down that the Executive should operate 'as much as possible like a commercial firm'. Within the limits of the financial resources available, it was to have 'full authority to meet Allied needs regarding the purchase and sharing of those grains subject to inventory, and to arrange for their shipment'. It was stated that the absence of a unanimous decision should not prevent the Executive's taking action. In the case of a serious difference of opinion, the point at issue was to be submitted to the respective Governments.

This was the maximum degree of co-operation that could then realistically be hoped for between allies who faced a formidable foe but who had not even set up a unified military command. The three men who sat on the Wheat Executive – Vilgrain for France, Bernardo Attolico for Italy, and Sir John Beale for Great Britain – were officials representing their own countries: they were not a collegiate body with its own powers of decision. Yet already there was a foretaste of something more, because in practice the three men behaved as if they were a single entity acting for the common good. For me, therefore, November 29, 1916, is an important date, for it was then that M. Clémentel and Lord Runciman, President of the Board of Trade, signed the agreement – the first step on the long road that led me gradually to discover the immense possibilities of collective action.

The Wheat Executive, in fact, showed me the first concrete proof that when men are put in a certain situation they see that they have common interests, and they are led towards agreement. For that, it is essential that they should be talking about the same problem, with the desire and even the duty to reach a solution acceptable to all. Vilgrain, Attolico, and Beale saw each other every day, and exchanged all the information they had about their countries' needs and stocks. In this way, none of the Allies could have *arrière-pensées*, or suspect one of its partners of concealing some part of the problem. A single purchasing programme was drawn up; a central body put it into effect. For the first time, equality of access to the world's resources of a basic commodity had been organized among several countries. The price was the same for all, and if there had to be restrictions they were equitably shared.

The great novelty of the November 1916 agreement was not only its provisions themselves, important as they were: as much, or perhaps even more, it was the spirit in which it was conceived and then applied by those responsible for it. Suddenly, in a diplomatic document, the notion of national interests took second place to that of the common interest. 'The Wheat Executive,' the agreement declared, 'must always bear in mind the advantage of centralizing all purchases of wheat on behalf of the Allies and all tonnage earmarked for the transport of wheat on behalf of the Allies.' The Allies were three sovereign nations: the Executive consisted of three national delegates. New methods of work had to be found if they were to respect the spirit of the agreement and act as one at the point of decision. It is easy to see that the men who thus lived through one of the first experiments in joint action by different countries began to cherish high hopes, and to grow impatient to apply their experience on a broader front.

II

The submarine blockade

Salter and I believed that the Wheat Executive was a first step towards solving the Allied transport problem as a whole. But we realized that this was something on a very different scale. To persuade a maritime Empire to join a transport organization based on the principle of equality is only possible when faced with a peril that calls for historic decisions. In 1916, Governments and public opinion still seemed unprepared for total war. The fate of the Allies was to be decided on the fields of battle; the balance of forces depended on the generals. But the battle remained inconclusive, and the stalemate at the front led the enemy to attack elsewhere and try to strangle the Allies' vital supply lines. The submarine blockade announced by the Germans on January 31, 1917 at last made the nations that were threatened by it aware of how deeply their economies were linked.

In 1917 the Allied position grew seriously worse. General Nivelle's offensive on the Aisne, launched in April, ended in tragedy: between April 16 and April 30, the French army lost 147,000 men to win a few meagre tactical victories. The survivors were exhausted and discouraged; in May, some of them mutinied. On the home front, workers' strikes in Paris and Saint-Etienne showed how weak morale had become. On this subject, on Pétain's efforts to reform the army, and on Foch's strategy in 1918, much has been written by eye-witnesses and historians. For the most part, however, their accounts are limited to a national viewpoint or to the purely military aspects of the war. What was also involved was the economic might of the world's greatest powers; and it was here that the enemy was now concentrating his attack.

The Germans announced that their submarines would fire without warning on any ship, naval or otherwise, Allied or neutral alike. They knew that this submarine blockade would bring the United States into the war, but this did not worry them. They were gaining no advantage from American neutrality, owing to Britain's command of the seas; and they counted on destroying the power of the *Entente* before the Americans could send an expeditionary force from across the Atlantic. German naval experts calculated that if their U-boats could sink 600,000 tons of shipping a month for six months, then Britain would have to acknowledge defeat, and the Central Powers would have won the war.

They almost did. In February, and again in March, some 550,000 tons of shipping were torpedoed; in April, Allied and neutral losses reached 900,000 tons, Britain losing 34,000 tons in a single day. In May, total losses dropped to 574,000 tons, but they rose again in June to 665,000. In July they dropped sharply, and in August still more so. Between August 1914 and December 1916, Allied and neutral losses had amounted to about 4 million tons; but in the single year 1917 they totalled 6 million. The effect on supplies was dramatic, and was becoming intolerable.

With part of her territory in enemy hands, and much of her labour force lost to the army, France grew more and more dependent on overseas supplies as the war went on. Her production of wheat had fallen by 60%. North America, Argentine, and distant Australia could make up the deficit, but where were the ships to come from? The Government cut back consumption and introduced bread rationing –

300 grammes per person per day. The manufacture of cakes and biscuits was banned. The production of *pasta* was reduced by 90%. Sweet corn disappeared from the market. All types of grain were requisitioned.

France's other needs were enormous. She needed pig-iron and steel for guns, shells, and ships; she needed minerals, coal, and wood. She also needed sugar. In December 1917, she put in an urgent request to the United States for several tens of thousands of tons of gasoline – fuel for the French army's counter-offensive in the following year. From 1917 onwards, and especially after the German attack that began on March 21, 1918, our military leaders were counting on a massive influx of American troops to strengthen the morale of our own men, which had been sapped by the Italian defeat at Caporetto, the Bolshevik revolution, and the stalemate on the Western Front. In March 1918, Foch insisted on asking: 'How soon can American reinforcements be embarked? Do your best. It's essential that I should be able to say now that they are coming.'

The key to the war was now shipping. That was the Allied authorities' major preoccupation, as is shown by contemporary accounts and by their published correspondence. But, even so, they were not yet prepared to accept our plan for a shipping pool. Resistance is proportional to the scale of the change one seeks to bring about. It is even the surest sign that change is on the way. By proposing to carry Allied solidarity into the matter of maritime transport, we were touching the deep feelings of the British nation, the ruler of the waves, and at the same time coming up against the naturally selfish reflexes of peoples anxious about their vital supplies. Each country felt the pressure of its own needs. In March 1917 Britain had only eight weeks' supply of grain left for herself. Freight rates were rising as fast as the shipping losses increased. In the press, France and Britain blamed each other for the shortages. The British described how French ports were blocked by ships waiting to be unloaded. The French retorted that the delays were due to the number of railroad trucks that had gone to the British army.

Our small team was called upon to do miracles of improvisation, from day to day – whereas I never stopped insisting that only a joint overall organization could enable the German challenge to be met. But, as so often in my life, this simple idea had to go through a maze of complications – long and arduous discussions which seemed out of all proportion to what was at stake, and which might seem discouraging if I described them now. And yet to abandon a project because it meets too many obstacles is often a grave mistake: the obstacles themselves provide the friction to make movement possible. The more we went into the difficulties, the more it became clear that we must take decisions together; and I myself never doubted that all our patient pressure and all our daily progress would come to fruition at the moment of maximum danger, probably in the last stages of the war, when there was no other choice than to be bold.

My relations with Clémentel grew closer every day; and I found in him the man to undertake the great negotiations that were now needed. He had faith in the British, and refused to dramatize the difficulties that naturally arose from the different situations and different characters of the two nations. He was not prepared to concede them privileges that would have made dialogue difficult, but he showed understanding when in 1917 the British Government decided to save shipping capacity by reducing imports into France. Since the cuts mainly affected luxury items, they seemed to him just. In reality, purchases of hats, ribbons, and jewels raised moral and financial issues rather than transport problems; but the French Government feared the effects of unemployment, and explained that 'a strike in the fashion industry could lead to a strike of munition workers'. Clémentel spent long months debating which items were inessential. Meanwhile, the shipping problem grew worse. Neutral ship-owners demanded danger money, which the French paid. 'I'd rather be robbed than killed,' said Herriot, the Minister of Supplies, who had to come to London himself to answer British objections. But the heart of the problem was elsewhere: it lay in the different ideas of the economic effort that Britain and France still held after three years of war.

True, not much remained of traditional British Liberal economics now that David Lloyd George's Government had appealed to the nation's sense of discipline and imposed stringent rationing. But while the British authorities were strengthening their system of control over foreign and domestic trade, in France there was a strong reaction against taxes and State control, which were thought to be responsible for the shortages. The French merchant fleet was still not fully requisitioned: private trading interests, and in particular those involved in trade with Indochina, had successfully opposed it. Not until July 1917 was the fleet requisitioned, and then reluctantly, by Anatole de Monzie, Under-Secretary of State for Merchant Marine.

In other words, both Britain and France wanted to continue in their own separate ways. As so often, their solidarity weakened as their military plight grew worse. The failure of Nivelle's offensive had buried for a time any hope of forming a unified command. And although the idea of an Allied shipping pool was making headway among the experts who were my friends and colleagues, the general climate in Britain was still unfavourable for a negotiation as far-reaching as that envisaged by the French Government, which was anxious not only to talk about immediate problems, but also to prepare for the peace. So the first job was to try to re-establish an atmosphere of confidence.

With the British, confidence needs solid backing; and our plans for pooling resources and ensuring fair shares seemed to them theoretical, concerned more with justice than with efficiency. It was my duty to ask for ships, but I was in no position to specify precisely what imports they would carry. I told my colleagues in Paris that, unless they could produce detailed programmes and clear, accurate statistics, the French Ministers would be in no better position when they came back in October in the hope of completing negotiations. For that to be possible, a number of ministries would have to work together and draw up a complete inventory of France's import needs. But relations with de Monzie and the people from Maritime Transport were not good, and I was anxious that my Minister, Clémentel, should have direct charge of both supplies and shipping. I pressed him on the point, as witness this letter, which I wrote to him from London on September 10, 1917:

> The confidence you inspire here, and the position our country has secured in these recent negotiations, could be used to bring about an Allied economic directorate, from which France would gain considerable advantage. But, if you will forgive my repeating it, to achieve this result it is essential for all France's external economic affairs to be in your hands, including not only trade and raw materials, but also supplies and maritime transport.

This hope was to be fulfilled a few months later, in Clemenceau's Cabinet. Meanwhile, I could only act unofficially in the essential matter of shipping, which was always approached obliquely in negotiations about urgent needs like wheat or coal, but which I wanted to turn into the nerve-centre of the Allies' economic organization, and the main feature of a lasting settlement. Arthur Salter has recalled the efforts we made:

> The way for the new advance was prepared mainly by Jean Monnet, then Chef de Cabinet of Monsieur Clémentel the French Economic Minister,

John Beale the Chairman of the Wheat Executive, and myself, at the centre of the main shipping pool as Director of Ship Requisitioning. The first, then a young man in his twenties, had the flair to discern when the moment of possible action had come; Beale brought his experience on his Executive; I worked on the dominating shipping aspect of the question and on the administrative detail of the proposed new structure. It was, I believe, at a small dinner discussion in October 1917 between Monnet, John Anderson (then Secretary of the Ministry of Shipping) and myself that the three of us determined that the thing could be done, and that we would do it.*

III

Pooling transport

It seemed to me that 'the moment of possible action' had come. On October 12, 1917 a large French delegation arrived in London. It was led by Paul Painlevé, the then Prime Minister; but it was Clémentel, assisted by the team we had assembled in London, who for three weeks conducted the crucial negotiations. For me, it was a deep and telling experience. I had drawn up a brief memorandum to try to put the problem in a way that would ensure the agreement of our friends in the British Department of Shipping:

The Allied supply situation, and that of France in particular, is at present so critical that it risks jeopardizing the outcome of the war.

For the past three months, France has been living from hand to mouth, daily and almost hourly dependent on what the next ship will bring. Paris and other main centres have only one day's stocks, the army from one to three days'. Many places have already run out of flour, and public order is increasingly under threat.

It is impossible for the Allies to continue fighting the war in conditions like this, and they must reach an overall solution of the problem without delay.

This solution can only be based on the following principles:

(1) A programme must be drawn up setting out what supplies are strictly indispensable to the survival of the Allies. These would be imported as an absolute priority.

(2) The necessary tonnage must be put at the disposal of the body in

* Lord Salter, *Memoirs of a Public Servant*, London, 1961, p. 113.

charge of ensuring imports, with France and Britain both participating, according to their means, in the establishment of the fleet.

(3) Equality in austerity.

The rigour of this programme, and the burden that it would place on Britain, in view of the shortages in France, made the British War Cabinet anxious. In Albert Stanley, President of the Board of Trade, we faced a negotiator as tough as many others we had met. He tried to evade the problem we were putting to Britain by raising, as it were, an American precondition. Should the United States be asked, as the French Government proposed, to make every effort to help its two oldest allies reach this agreement, or should the agreement, in the words of the British counter-proposal, be dependent on 'the scope and nature of any support given by the United States?'

To understand the British position, it has to be realized that a comparison of import needs with available shipping had revealed that the programmes planned were unworkable. Before readjusting them in formal agreement with France, the British were anxious to know how much American aid could be obtained. Such is their logic. But our aim was total solidarity between France and Britain; and, for us, the prospect of American aid was an opportunity to begin by achieving the maximum economic unity among ourselves, so as to act as a single partner in negotiating with the United States. This point of view, in fact, was shared by many of our British friends. We decided to stick to it.

On October 29, 1917, at Clémentel's request, I drafted a new memorandum to the British Government:

> We have reached a decisive turning-point in the war. The Allies must unite all their forces, and concentrate all their means of action so as to make the greatest impact. This need is especially pressing for Britain and France, who have been fighting side-by-side for three years, as if they were one nation.
>
> At the present moment maritime transport has the key role in the conduct of the war. To use it, the Allies are in duty bound to arrive at the unity of views and of actions which is indispensable if they are to meet their most urgent needs by deploying all their tonnage.
>
> To continue along present lines, with everyone working for the same ends, but each in a watertight compartment, would force the Allies to run very serious risks.

There, set down for the first time, were the essentials of the action that circumstances have led me to repeat on a number of occasions in my life. To tell the truth, I have never really believed that history repeats itself, and when I have found myself facing a crisis that calls for urgent efforts to achieve unity I have had neither the time nor the need to refer back to what I have done in the past. But, at different times, similar situations have produced in me similar reactions, which are naturally expressed in similar ways: 'Unity of views and of actions', 'overall plan', the 'pooling of resources'. In my eyes, Britain and France had been facing adversity 'as if they were one nation'. This image came back to me, just as vividly, twenty-five years later, when the same two countries faced the same enemy, and I drew up with Salter the Declaration of Union reproduced in Chapter I. In 1940, the collapse of the Allied front forced us to skip intermediate steps and to head straight for the highest political goal – that in war and peace France and Britain become one nation with a common citizenship, *de jure* as well as *de facto*. Certainly in 1917 I did not foresee that our plight was to repeat itself or that we should need to confront it with such bold remedies as this. I did not believe that full political union was the only way for the Allies to live together – or for former enemies; and I had no idea that the latter rather than the former would one day have to begin the attempt, as France and Germany did in 1950. I was not trying to peer into the future; but I certainly set no *a priori* limits to the form that 'indispensable unity of views and of actions' in Europe might gradually assume.

There was in any case one form of unity that was well suited to the problem of the time. This was the one we had put to the test in the Wheat Executive, that small but significant embryo of things to come. The memorandum to the British Government referred to it: 'The same method – collaboration under the pressure of circumstances – should be applied to all imports that are essential to the Allies' survival and their war effort, priorities being established in the light of events.'

The British War Cabinet would have preferred the negotiations not to be couched in such general terms. Through the Wheat Executive, it proposed immediate aid in the form of wheat. The French delegation, now reinforced by Paul Painlevé, the Prime Minister, and Henry Franklin-Bouillon, a Minister of State, was inclined to accept this arrangement. But it was then that Clémentel showed his strength of purpose: he stood by us in our struggle to achieve an overall organization. 'Allied policy,' he declared, 'avoids one catastrophe only to head for another. We need a logical programme whose regular execution will prevent accidents of this sort.' The word 'accident' was heavy with meaning in 1917. We were still living under the shadow of defeat at Caporetto. If our supplies were cut off, the fate of our armies might be sealed within a few weeks.

Negotiations opened on November 3, 1917, at the Foreign Office. Clémentel began by expounding his plan to pool both needs and resources. He showed that agreement on a shipping pool was at the heart of all our problems. A. J. Balfour, the British Foreign Secretary, who was in the chair, declared himself convinced. Lord Robert Cecil, Minister of Blockade, also seemed to back the French position: he used an argument whose force has struck me in quite different circumstances. 'The United States,' he pointed out, 'are insisting that if we can only agree among ourselves what we need, then they will do all in their power to help us. So let us work out a joint programme. Otherwise, the United States will tend to take all the decisions themselves.'

But Sir Albert Stanley, who was still opposed to our plans, produced the contrary argument. 'If we go to the Americans with a programme already drawn up,' he said, 'they will be tempted to believe that all is well.' This view reflected a desire to engage in multiple negotiations with the United States, in the hope of getting more out of them if each country applied separate and powerful pressure. What was more, it began to be obvious that the British wanted to limit any programme to the sole category of foodstuffs. Quite suddenly, I realized that three weeks of negotiations were going to fail if we insisted on the British making too general a commitment. On hearing a sentence of Clémentel's translated, they believed that he was insisting on this as a precondition to agreement. Lord Robert Cecil proposed that the talks be broken off.

It was then that on both sides of the table, statesmen took the place of negotiators. In a flash, Clémentel switched from quibbling to expressing his feelings with characteristic fluency and sincerity.

'I don't understand,' he said. 'I believe we are asking no more than is fair. We have sacrificed everything; our country is a martyr, yet doesn't complain. All we are asking is to be treated as equals with our Allies.'

The French interpreter was Paul Mantoux, the historian who was later to play an important role in the League of Nations. He was getting to his feet when Balfour gestured to him to stop.

'I cannot conceive,' said Balfour, 'how the French Government can imagine for one moment that Britain could abandon France and not give her the aid to which she is entitled. I cannot understand how

Monsieur Clémentel can make such allegations when on the contrary I have assured him that Britain will guarantee the security of France's food supplies.'

There was nothing for it then but to find an honourable solution. We drew up the following declaration:

'The Governments of Great Britain, France and Italy find that owing to the failure of the French and Italian harvests, the submarine warfare, and other causes, there is not sufficient tonnage for all their wants. They consider that, of these wants, food is the most important, and can be treated separately; the amount of food that has to be imported is known; and they think that the burden of providing the tonnage for carrying it should be a common charge on all the Allies including the United States; but inasmuch as the need for an immediate agreement is pressing, the three Governments are prepared to accept the responsibility of providing the tonnage that may be required proportionally to their respective means of transport with or without the help of the United States.'

With that, the machine was set in motion. Action that had begun on a specific but decisive point would not stop there. Inevitably, a body would have to be set up to share out the tonnage required for food; and similar steps would have to be taken for other freight as the system was extended to the rest of our needs. We were now within sight of the general 'pool' we wanted: but there was not a moment to lose. Now, and only now, we must turn to the Americans and ask them to reinforce the joint effort that had already begun.

As we left the conference, Clémentel seemed to me slightly disappointed. Young as I was, and impatient as I was said to be, I set about reassuring him. 'Today – November 3, 1917,' I said, 'marks a turning-point in the Allies' economic policy. They have started the ball rolling. Now it's up to us to accelerate and institutionalize this new willingness for permanent co-operation.' 'You're right,' he said. 'Today's agreement is a beginning. Go and see Salter, and work out proposals for a first Allied body to deal with transport. Then we'll gradually enlarge its scope.'

On paper, such a body already existed. We had planned it at our dinner with Salter and John Anderson a few weeks earlier. We had called it 'the Allied Maritime Transport Committee (AMTC)' with its own 'Executive', the 'AMTE'. Seven such 'executives' were already at work, on wheat, oils, grain, fats, sugar, meat, and nitrate. But a transport executive would be something altogether more ambitious: it would supervise all Allied and neutral ships, their specifications, their movements, and their cargoes. A continuing inventory of this sort was only imaginable by means of the extensive information net-work that was at Salter's command, and which he would bring to the AMTE if we could succeed in getting him appointed Secretary-General. More than that, the new Executive should be able gradually to bring about the centralization of all supply programmes, and their adjustment in the light of what shipping was available. For the first time, machinery for large-scale economic information and action would be at the disposal of several countries; and it would oblige them to exchange data that had hitherto been kept secret. It might well be – and for us this was no drawback – that such a system would still be needed for postwar reconstruction and, having proved its worth, could afterwards be a force for greater stability in international life.

It was March 1918 before the AMTE was finally set up. Its members were Salter, Attolico, the American representative George Rublee, and myself. Salter, in his book *Allied Shipping Control**, has very fully portrayed the intense activity of Executive, whose powers were so limited but whose power was so great. No sooner had it been set up than a worsening of the general situation deluged us with dramatic appeals. The German offensive that began on March 21, 1918, deprived France of coal from the Pas-de-Calais and of the cargoes that were due to come in through the northern ports. How could they be replaced when there was already an eight-million-ton shortage of shipping? We were forced to propose cuts in civil and even military supplies – a necessary but ungrateful role. Some people thought we were exceeding our authority.

From then on, the top priority was the transport of American troops. The United States had declared war on Germany on April 6, 1917; but by the end of March 1918 they still had only 350,000 men in Europe. By the time of the Armistice, they were to have two million in France alone. To reach this figure, transport had to perform miracles. Between May and October, 1918, an average of 260,000 American troops crossed the Atlantic every month, with a record figure of 311,000 in July. Not until the summer did the American shipbuilding programme add to the available tonnage: instead, it was increased by requisitioning and repairing German ships immobilized in American ports, and by negotiating with neutrals like Denmark, Sweden, Norway, Holland, and Brazil. On occasion, even cargo boats intended to carry wheat were transformed into troopships. This happened, for example, in March and April with Dutch and American boats.

* J. A. Salter, *Allied Shipping Control* (London, 1921).

All this could not be accomplished without occasional friction. Human relations are never entirely free from ambivalence or ambiguity. People agree in principle, but they remain open to confusion or misunderstanding: they only act decisively when driven by necessity. In 1918, the Germans could probably still have won the war. But one thing is certain: from the moment when we had a single military command and an effective shipping pool, our cause could no longer be defeated. We could not tell exactly when we should win, because we still needed American reinforcements; but we no longer doubted that this was the final effort, the one that would bring us victory. When you go up a mountain, you only know at the last minute when the top is in sight: to reach it, you must make one last effort, otherwise you slip back.

Our actual responsibilities were great; but our administrative position was still precarious. At the end of 1917, I had been officially appointed Head of the London Mission of the Ministry of Commerce and Maritime Transport, and Delegate of the Ministry of Supply. I was France's representative on all the Executives. But our small and very active team disturbed many people's working habits and harassed French officialdom with detailed and urgent requests. Because there were so few of us, we needed a lot of help from all the departments of state, and we ignored hierarchical channels. Naturally, I made a number of enemies, both known and undeclared.

The most powerful was undoubtedly Louis Loucheur, the Minister of Armaments, a man who was very sensitive to pressure from French business circles, and who took every opportunity of expressing his opposition to the methods of co-operation that I was trying to achieve with the British. He manoeuvred to get me transferred from the civil administration to the military supply staff. The French Ambassador in London, Paul Cambon, acting without my knowledge, pointed out to the authorities in Paris that since I had been found unfit for military service I had better be left where I was. That was in December 1917. Shortly afterwards, Loucheur tried again, this time tackling Clemenceau – who was now Prime Minister – direct. 'It's doubly inconceivable,' he said, 'that this young man should not be in the army *and* that he should have so powerful a position in our civil service.'

The Prime Minister summoned me to Paris, to his office in the rue Saint-Dominique. His first words were: 'You – tell me what you're doing in London.' Expecting no further words of welcome, I quietly described my job. He listened, asked me a few questions, then got up and walked with me to the door. Without a word, he helped me on with my overcoat. I advised Clémentel to choose someone to take my place. He was very unhappy about it, but unlike Loucheur he boasted no influence over 'Tiger' Clemenceau. A week later, the Prime Minister called me back. He handed me a piece of paper. On it I read: 'Lieutenant Monnet is to return at once to his post in London.' It was a decree that he had just had approved by the Cabinet. Among the signatures was that of Loucheur. Once more, Clemenceau helped me on with my coat. When I tried to save him the trouble, he said: 'No, let me. There are no valets in my family.'

There were further alarms later, whether due to the persistence of my enemies or to the workings of the bureaucratic machine. The last was the most serious. I was under orders to rejoin the colours when Clémentel cabled me not to leave my post. It was November 11, 1918 – Armistice Day. Our next battle was to win the peace.

IV

Organized peace

Under the predictable pressure of events, the transport pool had become the nerve-centre of the whole war economy. It could be equally vital in the task of postwar reconstruction. For this reason, we thought it very significant when the United States Government formally joined all the bodies we had set up. The decision was announced on October 1, 1918, during the fourth session of the Allied Maritime Transport Council at Lancaster House, by Newton D. Baker, the US Minister of War. That day, Clémentel said to me: 'The Americans have now definitely joined the economic alliance. Baruch* has given his full backing to our plans for pooling Allied resources. It's time we got in touch again with President Wilson. After all, he gave a positive answer to my letter of October 6 last year.'

A year earlier, in fact, Clémentel had written to Woodrow Wilson with the agreement of Clemenceau. Deeply impressed by the success of the Wheat Executive as a means of exercising world control over one product, he regarded it as a weapon convincing enough to be used in a bid for peace:

If we publicly and solemnly declare to Germany that we shall release all

* Bernard Baruch, President of the American War Industries Office.

71

the raw materials that have fallen into our hands as soon as she liberates all the territory that she holds by force, it will demonstrate to her that we possess the most formidable power.

The letter ended as follows:

A peace treaty involving economic sanctions against any State that violates the pact – that must be the very basis of the League of Nations.

These ideas had made headway, and Allied control of the world's raw materials had become a reality through the Executives and the Programme Committees that we had set up in London. The threat against the Central Powers was not expressed as we had originally proposed, with a raw materials blockade starting from the time of the Allied call for peace and lasting for a number of years proportional to the number of months that the Central Powers prolonged the war. Even so, it had its effect on the enemy leaders' morale.

Despite this, however, we were well aware of the danger that the United States, and to some extent Britain, might put an end to economic controls as soon as peace and security were re-established in the world. The immense resources of America and the financial strength of the British Empire would enable them rapidly to return to free trade, and might tempt them to profit from the weakness of worse-hit enemies – or allies. For four years, necessity had taught us the value of sticking together. Many of us were anxious not to forget the lesson, and we therefore suggested the idea of an international raw materials conference. In April 1918, Clémentel asked me to write to the British Government in the following terms:

To consolidate Allied co-operation with a view to the future, and to adapt it to the needs of a period of transition and economic reconstruction, it seems to us essential to study our problems jointly. To this end, we would ask you to make the necessary approaches to the American Government, with a view to securing its acceptance of the plan for an inter-Allied conference to be held as soon as possible.

This proposal was not given serious study, and on the eve of the Armistice the victorious Allies still had no immediate plans. France was already concentrating her attention on the economic terms of the negotiations for peace; and on September 19, 1918, Clémentel wrote to Clemenceau and Wilson proposing, as will be seen later, some extremely ambitious principles for future international co-operation. But my own concern was above all not to jettison the machinery and the habits of working together that we had built up during the war.

With Salter, I had just visited some of the liberated areas in Northern France; and what I had seen showed me how great the tasks of postwar reconstruction would be. On November 2, 1918, I sent a note to the French Government:

> The Armistice will find France and Belgium greatly weakened economically. It would be a negation of our whole war effort and of the ideals for which we fought if during the period of postwar reconstruction we did not continue to put into practice the principles that have enabled the Allies to bring the struggle against the common enemy to a successful conclusion – mutual aid, and the sharing-out of raw materials in proportion to the most urgent needs.

Later my note continued:

> Our present system is artificial. It is based on Draconian measures applied by Governments, substituting State arbitration for the natural interplay of supply and demand. This system has led to *de facto* unity among the countries concerned.
>
> Arbitration and unity are two essential elements in the present economic order, in which goods and means of transport are deployed, not in accordance with legal ownership, but under agreements ensuring that recognized needs are met as of right.

At the same time, I recognized the value and the powerful appeal of Woodrow Wilson's principles: very sensibly, he was already attacking the maintenance of economic frontiers. But I was convinced that the lengthy transition from a war economy to a peacetime economy could not be accomplished without the machinery that had enabled the Allies to apportion fairly their common burdens and common resources.

I was instructed to expound these ideas to Herbert Hoover when he arrived in London two weeks after the Armistice. He did not dispute them, but he would make no commitments. I realized that the time had passed for the Americans to take part in our Allied Committees, share our views of the common struggle, and become accustomed to our methods. In their eyes, the Executives were machinery for strengthening London's influence on the world's raw materials. They preferred to negotiate special arrangements for difficult situations, whose existence they in no way denied. Thus on December 1, 1918, speaking in the name of President Wilson, Colonel House proposed the establishment of a Directorate-General of Supplies for liberated, neutral, or enemy peoples, to be headed by an American. The aim was to prevent the enemy's fleet being included for this purpose in the Allied AMTC shipping pool.

The debate on this point took on very great importance, because it was our last opportunity of getting our views accepted, if only in part. We thought we had the chance to rebuild our partnership with the British. On December 31, 1918, Lord Reading, the Lord Chief Justice, sent us a note from the British Cabinet which contained the following remarkable proposal:

> Economic equilibrium should be established by means of a number of controls sufficient to guarantee, as far as possible at the same price, the availability of raw materials to industrialists in the various Allied countries, taking account of the differences created by their geographical situations and their particular circumstances.

The international economy and peace itself would undoubtedly have made many years' progress if these principles had been accepted by all concerned, and put into practice. We thought we were in sight of our goal when on January 1, 1919, the US presidential adviser Colonel House announced that President Wilson was coming round to our point of view and was appointing the relief organizer Herbert Hoover as the American member of the Council. But no sooner had this happened than all was lost. Intrigues by American exporters induced the United States Government to rob all these agreements of their substance: lists of exceptions made the whole organization useless. Nor did even the Wheat Executive escape. I had left the London end of the organization in the hands of Raymond Fillioux, a school-friend from Cognac. He was horrified to see crumbling away what we had built with such enthusiasm. On February 18, 1919, a telegram from him told me that the American representative had withdrawn, declaring that the Executive was 'contrary to the views of his Government, which intended that prewar methods of trade should be restored as soon as possible'.

At the last meeting of the Supreme Economic Council, on April 4, 1919, Anglo-Saxon and French ideas met head on in a dramatic debate between Baruch and the British representative Lord Robert Cecil on the one side and Clémentel on the other. Baruch declared that his country could not envisage general controls over raw materials in peacetime. Cecil asked that the plan to hold Germany in trusteeship should be dropped. Economic freedom, he said, would be a better guarantee of Germany's ability to pay reparations. Thereupon Clémentel made the following statement:

It is a complete illusion to hope to restore world equilibrium merely by means of the law of supply and demand. The United States have made a grave mistake in immediately throwing off the harness of war as soon as the Armistice is signed. According to the principles advocated by President Wilson himself, should we not be seeking organized peace?

Even now, the situation in maritime transport is a forewarning of the difficulties to come. A free market has been suddenly restored: now, we are short of tonnage, and freight rates are going up. Tension has developed on raw materials markets. The newly emergent states need a financial regime.

Experience will prove the necessity for an international organization which in principle and in practice will take the form of a League of Nations.

As we left the meeting, Clémentel said to me: 'That's the end of the solidarity we worked so hard for. Without it, and without the altruistic, disinterested co-operation that we tried to achieve among the Allies and should have extended to our former enemies, one day we'll have to begin all over again.' They were the words of a generous man who has been under-rated by historians. But what part could he play in the peace, in a world where nations were once more sovereign, each of them preoccupied with recovering its former influence? No one now could argue that collective action was necessary for sheer survival; no politician could realistically propose, even for the common good, limiting the sovereignty that each of our nations had won back at such a price. There is no point in trying to apportion blame for this return to past habits: it was simply that Nature had returned to its normal course. It was to take many years, and much suffering, before Europeans began to realize that they must choose either unity or gradual decline.

One by one, the Executives were dismantled. I myself had returned to Paris, where the Peace Conference was being held. Sir Joseph Maclay*, Salter, and I promised ourselves that we would work together again when the time was ripe: we had no doubt that our experience would soon be put to fresh use. Salter has described that experience in a passage from his book *Allied Shipping Control* that is well worth quoting. I have often been asked to explain the method that I have followed in so many international enterprises. I think that my friend Salter has described it better than anyone:

The work could never have been successfully achieved if daily association had not developed mutual confidence. The position of members of

* British Controller of Shipping.

an international committee with a dual personal capacity, international in relation to their own country, national in relation to other countries, is one of great delicacy. They necessarily receive information from their departments (they are useless if they do not) with regard to policy while still in the process of formation. It is a problem of the utmost difficulty to know how much of this can properly be communicated to their Allied colleagues. So far as the Allies are regarded as competitors with divergent interests any such communication weakens the bargaining position of one's own country. But so far as they are regarded as partners whose common interests are more important than any conflict of claims, such communications may often be essential. . . . If each one of our separate countries considers a problem with international reactions from its own point of view, develops a national policy, begins to give it expression in administrative arrangements, fortifies it with Ministerial decisions and Cabinet authority, adjustment will prove almost impossible. Four rigid and developed policies will confront each other. . . . But if the national points of view can be explained while they are still developing, if policies can be brought into contact while they are still plastic and still unformed, agreement will be easier and probably better. Given the proper personal relations, many things can be explained which would never be put on paper or stated in a formal meeting; the limits of concession can be explored and the several national policies formed and fixed in the first instance within them instead of beyond them. But the delicacy of such work, and the difficulty of the questions of loyalty and good faith involved, are obvious. It is only possible at all under conditions of personal confidence and long personal association. Fortunately the members of the Transport Executive all felt this confidence in each other, and the relations of colleagues in work developed in time into those of personal friendship.*

Salter is right: personal friendships have played a very great role in all the enterprises on which I have worked. But they do not explain everything – or rather, they themselves need to be explained. Working together and battling for the same objective both presuppose and consolidate mutual confidence. I have never lacked friends; but friendship, to me, is the result of joint action rather than the reason for it. The reason is first and foremost mutual confidence. This grows up naturally between men who take a common view of the problem to be solved. When the problem becomes the same for everyone, and they all have the same concern to solve it, then differences and suspicions disappear, and friendship very often takes their place. But how can people be persuaded to approach the problem in the same way, and to see that their interests are the same, when men and nations are divided? That

* J. A. Salter, *op cit*, pp. 179–80.

was what I still had to find out. The teams that we had built up during the war and were trying to keep together in peace – for peace – might be dispersed from one day to the next. Danger had brought them together: victory threatened to dissolve them. They had been formed to fight the enemy: would they be able to help him in defeat? Friendship would not be enough, and danger was no longer there to force us together. What kind of institutions, what international laws, could be established to take the place of necessity?

Chapter 4

THE LEAGUE OF NATIONS

I

Hopes take shape

At the time of the Armistice I was just thirty years old. I had a little knowledge of private business and some experience of public affairs, or rather of the working of the French, British, and American administrations. But I was still a stranger to the rituals of politics. Admittedly, ideological differences and personal rivalry had not been completely eclipsed by the overriding priority of defence during four years of war. But in wartime none of them had seemed insurmountable: a common struggle for survival makes it much easier for men to agree. Nor had I been much concerned by power struggles within Governments: I was in the habit of thinking in terms of economic organization and international co-operation. But no sooner was I demobilized than I saw each of our countries returning to its old political system. Once the interlude of war was over, they all went back to the rules and customs of traditional parliamentary democracies. I felt out of my depth. I found it hard to believe that the conflicting ideologies and interests which had led Europe into war would now fully recover the position that the common danger had made them abandon in favour of organized co-operation. Despite the difficulties that we had faced when we worked for Clémentel – and because we had finally overcome them – we imagined that similar methods could be used to meet similar needs in the years of postwar reconstruction. The war had left a trail of devastation. Raw materials were so scarce and trade was so much disrupted that the methods which had made it possible to run the war economy could surely not be abandoned so soon. In 1917, when victory still hung in the balance, this had already been obvious. It became even more so as the war drew to a close. In September 1918, together with Clémentel, we had written a letter to Clemenceau and

Woodrow Wilson setting out 'the economic conditions for negotiating the peace'. Let me quote a key paragraph from it:

> It is urgently necessary that the Allied democracies establish an economic union that will form the nucleus of the Economic Union of Free Peoples. Already, hints of the structure of this future alliance can be seen in the wartime inter-Allied economic Councils which are drawing up joint programmes of raw material imports, making joint purchases from some of their number, sharing out credit facilities in a number of producing countries, and finally pooling the Allies' total tonnage and deploying it on a basis of equality and shared sacrifice according to the most urgent needs.

For our allies, I now realized, the end of the war meant the end of special controls and the return to the laws of the market. It was on these principles, paradoxically, that the most idealistic statesmen at that time were preparing to found an international system which they wanted to be orderly and strong. When Clémentel had finally asked Robert Cecil and Bernard Baruch, 'According to the principles advocated by President Wilson himself, should we not be seeking organized peace?', he had been alluding to the famous Fourteen Points in which, in January 1918, Wilson had summarized the United States' war aims. The last of the Fourteen Points had raised one of the great hopes of our time. It ran as follows:

> A general association of nations must be formed for the purpose of affording mutual guarantees of political independence and territorial integrity to great and small states alike.

The other points included the freedom of the seas, the removal of trade barriers, and the reduction of armaments. The ideals were noble, but Wilson's doctrinal liberalism and the pressure of British and American business circles were in flat contradiction to our plans, as Clémentel was well aware. 'The same Mr Baruch,' he remarked to me, 'whose name in America throughout the war stood for the control of industry, has now with the Armistice quite naturally become once again the apostle of free trade and competition.' 'Organized peace', it was clear, was not going to mean what we had hoped for – the continuation of our efforts, through a system of 'Executives' enlarged to include the vanquished and the neutrals alongside the victors, to ensure fair shares in the resources available, and above all to share the sacrifices imposed by the overall shortages that threatened the world. We had imagined a political 'grand design', a new international order, based on what already existed; and my friends and I were determined to contribute to it as much as possible of our experience and our ideas.

It was on January 25 that the Supreme Council, which had met in Paris to prepare the peace treaty, set up a committee to draft the Covenant of the League of Nations. Wilson, whose life work it was, took this in hand, seconded by the famous Colonel House. The friendship between these two men – the austere and idealistic professor who was President of the United States and his faithful adviser, the enterprising and imaginative Texan – seemed to be a case of genuine osmosis. Not till twenty years later, in the case of Roosevelt and Harry Hopkins, did I see anything to match it: a different President and a different secret adviser, but the same intimate relationship between two complementary minds, one of them conceiving mighty visions, the other putting them into effect. In each case, constant interaction between the two men made for an extraordinary partnership, profoundly united in planning and carrying out their designs. Wilson, the first US President to stay in Europe, cheered by the Allied crowds, moved into the Hotel Crillon in Paris. From there, for many months, he wielded his immense power, indifferent to the intrigues that were mounted in Washington against his European policy. The Committee drafting the League Covenant had its permanent headquarters in Apartment 315 at the Crillon. There, with Robert Cecil, Léon Bourgeois, the Greek Prime Minister Eleftherios Venizelos, and Field-Marshal Smuts, he produced the draft Covenant of the League in a matter of eleven days.

During this time I was busy between London and Paris, winding up the units of which I had been in charge, and I had no hand in the drafting of the League Covenant. Those who did draft it were careful to avoid setting up a genuine authority independent of the member States, or even a first nucleus of autonomous international power. The whole of the League depended on the Council, which alone was empowered to take decisions, and even then by unanimous vote. The Assembly could issue only opinions, resolutions, and recommendations. The role of the Secretariat was to assist the Council in its work. Quite obviously, such an organization was incapable of expressing and imposing a common will. That, at least, is the conclusion I came to later. But at the time I did not see the pooling of sovereignty as a way of solving international problems. Nobody did, even if their words seemed to imply an appeal to some authority that would be above nations.

In fact, the authority with which it seemed at the time that the League of Nations should be invested was that of reason and co-operative goodwill. People thought that it was bound to prevail, by sheer moral strength, by the appeal to public opinion, and by the force of habit. The order that the League was to maintain was that which the Peace Treaty would recognize or institute. The basis of the Covenant was respect for the integrity and independence of existing or newly established nations. Far from seeking peace as we do today, by gradually abolishing frontiers, the League was concerned to revive old historical demarcation-lines, or to draw new ones, and to guarantee them against any change. On a strict interpretation of the League Covenant, these guarantees lacked any real force: they had no means of coercion and they were hampered by the veto. It was the job of the League Secretariat to make them real and effective – if it could. The success of this great venture, in other words, depended on the organization to be set up. We had no precedents to rely on; all we had was our experience in the inter-Allied committees.

It was undoubtedly on account of this experience that Clemenceau and Balfour asked me to take on the job of Deputy to the League's Secretary-General, Sir Eric Drummond. Drummond was a British diplomat aged forty-three, whose skill, courtesy, and discreet efficiency had recommended him to Grey, Asquith, and Balfour. The story goes that, after several better-known people had refused the job, Clemenceau asked Balfour: 'Who's that young man who always sits behind you?' 'He's my secretary.' 'He'd do,' said Clemenceau. 'He certainly would,' Balfour replied.

Drummond and I got on together right away. With his other Deputy, the American Raymond Fosdick, we set up our headquarters in an old London mansion, Sunderland House, far from the diplomatic squabbles in Paris.

Fosdick, who was soon to leave us when the United States withdrew from the League, has left an account of that time in his letters, published not long ago. He wrote to his wife on July 31, 1919:

We eat and sleep in terms of the League's present status and future development. And of course we do a lot of speculating on how soon it will become a really effective instrument. Yesterday Drummond, in something of a philosophical mood, was inclined to stress the *inevitability* of the League. That is, he feels that with the fast developing interdependence of the world as an economic unit, time is running on our side, and the sheer necessities of the situation will force the growth of some kind of world organization, even if we were to muff this particular attempt.

Monnet and I were inclined to qualify this point of view. We do not feel that time is running on our side, except in the sense of a future too remote to be of advantage to this generation or to the next. This generation is in a race with international anarchy, and Monnet and I stressed the point that the world has very little time in which to set up the framework of international government and *establish the habit of teamwork*. We have far too little time to do a good job before the strains and stresses come. And the danger – the really frightening danger – is that before the nations have learned how to play ball together, they will be overwhelmed by some new emergency – like a football team that has to meet its strongest opponent at the beginning of the season when it is only half-trained.*

II

'In the light of the general interest'

We had to act fast. I realized the shortcomings of the League Covenant, which had not been given any means of enforcing the very serious decision that would have to be taken for the Peace Treaty to be obeyed. The Treaty itself had left a number of problems in suspense. In particular on territorial questions such as the Saar and Upper Silesia, or on the future of minorities and refugees, the victorious Powers were relying on arbitration by the League. It thus not only had to prevent fresh conflicts but also to clear up the chaos left by war. That chaos was immeasurable. In economic terms, there was not only material damage to be repaired: trade was disrupted, and in artificially reshaped countries like Austria or Poland the currency had collapsed. In human terms, millions of refugees were adrift in a continent where frontiers were blurred. And the tasks of reconstruction, which needed a genuine supernational power, were now to be tackled by an organization whose only permanent element was its Secretariat.

The later vicissitudes of the League, when it became the great arena for Briand and Stresemann and a shadow-theatre for the tragedies of Manchuria, Ethiopia, and German rearmament, have tended to obscure the historic task which this unprecedented institution undertook in a world whose international system had crumbled. In charge of what remained of the system were three victorious Powers who had different conceptions of the peace. The Americans, who had intervened to extinguish a far-off war, were looking for untroubled order.

* Raymond B. Fosdick, *Letters on the League of Nations* (Princeton, 1966), pp. 17–18.

Wilson had no selfish ambitions for his country, and was sincerely anxious to create conditions that would make war impossible. The immediate concern of the French was to safeguard, once and for all, their own security: above all, Clemenceau wanted to cut Germany down to size. The British had electoral worries: Lloyd George was bent upon reparations. The fate of tens of millions of Europeans hung in the balance; yet nothing could be settled without the agreement of three great Powers, who in a few months, when the United States withdrew from the League, were to be only two.

Such agreement, we realized, would have to be prepared and effected by the League Secretariat, case by case, in every detail, and in situations ranging from the delineation of frontiers to the stamping-out of epidemic disease. We had therefore to set up machinery that would carry out investigation and research and then intervene in a variety of ways. Yet it must not be top-heavy; and because it could have no power of enforcement, it had to have that of persuasion. As I thought about all this at Sunderland House, I began to work out some principles for action. At the end of May, 1919, I set them out in a memorandum. In it can already be traced the ambitions and the limits of the method that gradually led me to the idea of the European Community.

> Co-operation between nations will grow from their getting to know each other better, and from interpenetration between their constituent elements and those of their neighbours.
>
> It is therefore important to make both Governments and peoples know each other better, so that they come to see the problems that face them, not from the viewpoint of their own interests, but in the light of the general interest. Without a doubt, the selfishness of men and of nations is most often caused by inadequate understanding of the problem in hand, each tending to see only that aspect of it which affects his immediate interests.
>
> But if each interested party in these circumstances, instead of facing another party with opposing interests, is presented with the problem as a whole, there can be no doubt that all parties' points of view will be modified. Together, they will reach a solution that is fair. They will do so all the more readily if they know that the debate is taking place under the eyes of other Governments or peoples who will pass judgement on what they do.

For me, this rule was the key to action: 'look at the problem as a whole and in the light of the general interest'. Certainly, the organization which was set up, and which without major changes went on working in Geneva until 1939, did not always have the strength of its intentions. But in 1919 I was not looking at the system's weaknesses: it went as far as was possible at that time. To me it represented considerable progress, because through it we were beginning to change the relations between peoples. In those days, undoubtedly, I saw the problem of common authority differently from the way I see it today, because in 1919 the Allies saw the restoration of national sovereignty as the keystone of peace.

Even more, in the eyes of the French and the British, the peace was to set the seal on their superiority. The absence of Germany undermined the basic principle of a true League of Nations. But the dangers of international anarchy were so great that any opportunity for common discipline and fair arbitration had to be seized. It was an approach that very well suited the empiricism of Drummond and of the friends who had worked with me on the inter-Allied committees and whom we had now asked to join us in the League Secretariat.

We had no need to change our habits of work. What mattered was to use our common approach to become a guiding light, identifying the common interest and persuading the men in power to accept the appropriate solutions. There was no lack of such men, in peace as in war. Each time that I personally have been convinced of the need for action, I have proposed it to men in power, leaving them to take the political responsibility and reap the reward. Just as I had approached Viviani and Clémentel, and through them influenced the Allied Governments and general staffs, so I now approached Bourgeois and Balfour, who commanded influence in Paris and London. I was already convinced that this very simple, very natural opportunity would recur when the time came. Men in power are short of new ideas: they lack the time and the information; and they want to do good so long as they get the credit for it.

Léon Bourgeois was a leading figure in the Third Republic, nowadays somewhat eclipsed by such national heroes as Clemenceau and Poincaré, but one who took part in every stage of the fight for peace in the first quarter of this century. His achievements and his immense international reputation won him the Nobel Prize in 1920, at about the time when I knew him. He was President of the Senate, and French Delegate to the League of Nations, the idea of which he had always advocated: he had published a book on the subject in 1910. His Radical affiliations, his untidy beard and his flowery eloquence seem old-fashioned today; but he was warm-hearted and clear-headed. I remember the deep impression he made when he spoke at the Peace Conference in February 1919, calling for an international military force in the service of the League of Nations. 'Sudden aggression must not be allowed to take place in the danger-spots of the world without being immediately quenched.' France proposed that contingents supplied by all the nations should be under the command of a permanent international general staff which would also inspect the weapons and fighting strength of every State. This proposal, which Bourgeois tirelessly championed, was rejected by the Americans and the British. 'It would make national militarism international,' said Robert Cecil. From that moment on, the League Covenant had to rely on the goodwill of a handful of men.

Robert Cecil himself, the British apostle of the League, was certainly not lacking in goodwill. 'If nations are basically selfish, greedy, and belligerent,' he said, 'no mere machinery will stop them.' But he believed in the force of public opinion, as did Balfour, Britain's representative at the League, who became a colleague and friend of Bourgeois's. Apart from their basic disagreement about the way to impose the new international order – and already its lack of real power contained the seeds of failure – the two men set an example of confident co-operation. For decisions to be taken, they had to agree; and their agreement sufficed. It was our job to encourage such agreement. Looking back, I can see more clearly how the League of Nations prefigured supranationality – through underlying agreement among men who enjoyed widespread influence in their own countries, so that awareness of the general interest was communicated to the places where national decisions were reached. Later, when Germany joined the League, this complicity came to an end. At that point, institutional arrangements should have been made to replace personal agreements. Some delegation of power would have strengthened a system that had worked only because of the authority and partnership of a few individuals. Without such a change, the machinery proved incapable of dealing with the most inflammatory issue, that of disarmament. Even this might have been settled with a little imagination and courage. But these were qualities that Drummond's successor lacked.

III

Silesia and the Saar: the common interest

The League Secretariat came into being in London in the summer of 1919; but it was not until January 16, 1920, that the League Council held its first meeting, in the Salon de l'Horloge at the Quai d'Orsay, the French Foreign Ministry in Paris. The League, in fact, was one of several aspects of the Peace Treaty that had taken effect on January 10. Throughout the previous year we had been following the negotiations. We now had to deal with the problems that they had left unsolved.

Whenever the Allies failed to agree, the difficulty was passed on to the League of Nations, which thus inherited all the most serious conflicts. When France wanted to annexe the Saar, against the wishes of Woodrow Wilson, the problem was promptly internationalized. When Poland demanded an outlet on the Baltic, against British opposition, we were handed the Danzig question. When there was rivalry over the German colonies, Mandate Committees were formed. Considering the effect of these local problems on world history – Danzig touched off the war in 1939, and the Saar dispute went on until 1950 – considering too how the fate of a town or a strip of territory today can still threaten world peace, it is astonishing how frivolously the signatories of the Versailles Treaty, invested as they were with sovereign power, handed over their weightiest responsibilities to an institution as yet unborn.

That institution, we knew, would have to depend on its Secretariat. Neither the Council, made up of nine sovereign States, nor the Assembly, with its forty-seven nations, could have much hope of solving problems that Wilson, Clemenceau, and Lloyd George themselves had failed to settle in the aftermath of victory. It would be our task to apply the Peace Treaty, first on a continent ravaged by war, and then elsewhere, with a small team of people – in December 1919 there were only twenty of us – on the move from London to Paris and finally, in the autumn of 1920, settling in Geneva. Salter was one of our number: he was in charge of the economic and financial section. Attolico, also from the wartime Executives, took over the transit section. Pierre Comert was head of information, and Paul Mantoux was director of the political section: both had gained their experience on the inter-Allied Committee during the war. All were co-opted individually, irrespective of nationality. What was more – and it was unprecedented – in their work they were released from any allegiance to the countries from which they came.

At that time, however, I was not concerned to stress this idea of a new international authority, and I was not thinking in terms of a transfer of sovereignty. I was anxious merely for efficiency, for better links between Governments and between peoples. To this end, I proposed to André Tardieu, France's Delegate at the Peace Conference, that in each national administration representatives should be appointed to keep in touch with the League Secretariat and to use it as their channel of communication from one country to another. 'This,' I wrote, 'will lead to a broadening of national horizons. As the system develops it will completely transform existing habits in international relations.' Well, it was a step forward; but I was mistaken in setting too much store by this approach. Bringing Governments together, getting national officials to co-operate, is well-intentioned enough; but the method breaks down as soon as national interests conflict, unless there is an independent political body that can take a common view of the problem and arrive at a common decision. I became convinced of this twenty years later. What success we had in Geneva is more simply explained. The important agreements that were reached there became possible only in so far as the Great Powers, in particular France and Britain, thought it to be in their interest to avoid a dispute. When this was the case, we were free to seek solutions. I myself was active in two such instances, both of which added greatly to my experience. One was the partition of Upper Silesia; the other was the rescue of Austria. The mining region of Silesia was a great block of coal on which had grown up a complex of metalworking industries. These were the livelihood of more than two million people, one-third of them Germans, two-thirds Polish. The latter, most of them manual workers or peasants, were dependent on the landed proprietors and owners of industry, most of them Germans. The overall population was inextricably mixed. The Poles claimed the whole region as theirs, but the Germans were determined to hold on to their assets, which made up a quarter of Germany's total output of coal. The two sides agreed on only one point: both refused any partition of the province, since each wanted to have it all.

The signatories of the Versailles Treaty had originally decided to give the whole territory to Poland. After violent protests from Germany, however, they agreed, in accordance with the nationality principle, to organize a plebiscite. Voting took place in March 1921. The results rather favoured Germany; but the voting pattern made only one solution possible: partition on the lines of ethnic majorities. The Germans were in a majority in the towns of the industrial area in the East. Between them and Germany itself lay a zone mainly peopled by Poles. Both Berlin and Warsaw tried to pre-empt any settlement by seizing territorial hostages. The Polish Army occupied the region, and the Germans riposted with the *Freikorps*. Allied forces had to intervene.

This confrontation was serious. But there were many local crises in war-torn Europe; and this would have been no more than one of them, had it not threatened to turn into an international crisis owing to a Franco-British dispute behind the scenes. France sided with her Polish ally, while Britain supported Germany and German economic recovery. In August 1921, Briand and Lloyd George agreed to submit the question to the Council of the League and to accept its arbitration. So fearful a responsibility put our organization on trial. For the first time, the Secretariat was to be in charge of an investigation whose result two Governments were pledged to accept. The decision would determine the fate of more than two million people, and would involve transfers of sovereignty. I resolved to devote myself utterly to making it a success.

The directives given us by the Versailles Treaty and by the Supreme Council's mandate could be interpreted in all sorts of ways. We had to take account of the wishes expressed by the population, but also of the geography and economic situation of the areas concerned. Our task was to draw a frontier between two countries: there was no question of forming a new entity outside the exclusive sovereignty of the two rival powers, although there were geographical and economic arguments for such a solution, which had been recommended by the International Labour Organization, of which Léon Jouhaux* was a member. Upper Silesia was recognized as an ideal 'industrial triangle', as homogeneous as that formed by the Ruhr, Lorraine, and Limburg, which thirty years later inspired the European Coal and Steel Community. But in 1921 the time was not yet ripe for the delegation of sovereignty to a common High Authority. Even so, what was implicitly expected of us was not so very different: we had to work out a formula creating a kind of common statute for people and products on either side of an artificial frontier which, paradoxically, it was our job to draw. It was agreed from the beginning that this statute would remain in force for fifteen years.

The problem bristled with technical difficulties; but the principle underlying it seemed to be simple. Indeed, it could only be solved if a simple principle was applied. What we had to do was identify and organize the common interest. Polish steel needed German coal; Polish workers needed to keep their jobs in German factories. People and products must therefore be free to cross the frontier. To that end we had to devise a certain number of practical measures which for the Germans and Poles would become rules accepted by both States, jointly administered under the supervision and final authority of an

* French trade union leader, 1879–1954.

outside arbiter. This, to say the least, would involve a serious limitation of sovereignty and a form of common authority; but, as I have already pointed out, we were not thinking in such abstract terms. We were acting pragmatically – although it was no accident that the machinery which proved necessary then already pointed towards the more elaborate political ideas that were to grow from later experience. In 1921 we had no occasion to speculate along these lines. Our problem was not so much to mount a frontal attack on excessive nationalism as to persuade sovereign nations to support our efforts.

Even so, it would have been impossible to persuade the Poles and the Germans to sit round the same table and draw their frontiers on the map. This task was given to a Commission of four States which had no part in the dispute: Belgium, Brazil, China, and Spain. Paul Hymans, Dacunha, Wellington Koo, and Quinones de Leon were delegated by their Governments and given very extensive powers. In reality, the work was done by the Secretariat. In this task I was assisted by Pierre Denis, a friend with whom I had worked during the war years in London, and who was to work with me later, and in London again until mid-1940. After that he became Treasurer of the Free French. He was a loyal and able colleague. We pursued our inquiries in the utmost secrecy, with the expert help of M. Hodac, Secretary-General of the Czecho-Slovak Federation of Industry. Our method, recommended to us by Léon Bourgeois, suited me perfectly. 'At no time,' he said, 'must the study take on the character of a negotiation. It must be a common task, arriving by successive approximations at a solution which is fair and acceptable for all concerned.'

The 'approximations' involved not only the two peoples, whose views as expressed in the plebiscite we had to do our best to respect. They also had to do with transport, with the distribution of water and electricity, with the currency, with social security, with trade unions' rights, and so on. I don't know how we did it; but three weeks after the beginning of the investigation our report was in the hands of the Council. I don't think we slept much, and I know that we made heavy demands on the Secretariat's technical services, convinced by us – and like us – that this was the League's first big test.

Our report proposed a frontier line, to be drawn immediately; a transitional regime, based on set principles, for the next fifteen years; and the establishment of two permanent institutions. One was a Mixed Commission, composed of two Germans, two Poles, and a President from the League of Nations; the other was an Arbitral

Tribunal comprising one expert appointed by the German Government and one by the Polish Government, together with a President appointed by the League. I was personally very much attached to the idea of the Tribunal, which was the best articulated element in this first draft of a community authority: its decisions were to be final and directly applicable in the two countries. Naturally, however, these were no more than proposals. They would need to be approved by the Supreme Council, and their details would have to be worked out in negotiations between Germany and Poland.

The French Foreign Ministry raised very serious objections. They were against the limitation of sovereignty – except for defeated countries – and they thought that our project left too much potential power in the hands of Germany. For a while, it looked as if Paris and London might go back on the Anglo-French agreement reached by Balfour and Bourgeois. But Aristide Briand's political sense and generosity carried the day. At that time he was not only the French representative on the Supreme Council, but also its President; and on October 12, 1921, he managed to get our project approved. He thereby confirmed the authority of the League of Nations which his own eloquence was to illumine in later years when it became essentially a great public platform. In 1921, however, few speeches were made. The League was practical and active, as the Secretariat proved in the eight months that followed, counselling and reconciling the plenipotentiaries whose job it was, under the chairmanship of Félix Calonder from Switzerland, to find solutions for the countless questions in dispute. The German-Polish Convention signed on May 15, 1922, contained no fewer than 606 separate items: it was thicker than the Treaty of Versailles. The achievement was greatly admired. Although every step had been difficult, nothing had proved impossible, given the political will to succeed. The technical experts had done wonders in many different fields – co-ordinating rail systems and customs duties, building monetary union, protecting minorities. It was their job. Solutions which had seemed inconceivable the previous day became natural in the broad new context worked out for them. To me, this seems inevitable. I have never over-estimated technical snags.

Of course, the agreement was not accepted willingly. There were stormy debates in the *Reichstag*, decked out in black for the occasion. But both the Germans and the Poles asked for Calonder to stay on as President of the Mixed Commission. The President of the Arbitral Tribunal, the outstanding Belgian lawyer Georges Kaekanbeeck, upheld its authority well into 1937. It was a model institution: we had given it powers that at the time were very novel, as witness such clauses as these: 'The arbiters shall be independent. . . . The Tribunal's interpretation shall be binding upon the tribunals and authorities of the two countries as regards their judgement or decision. . . . When the Tribunal has given its judgement on the substance of a case, the execution or application of its verdict shall take place in the same conditions and with the same formalities as the execution or application of a verdict from a national authority.'

This approach was full of possibilities; yet the fact was not recognized until much later on. At the time, the problem was not so much to start a process of change, but rather to stabilize situations inherited from the war. The constitution of Danzig, with which I was also concerned, could have become a model for international administration. But no one was thinking in terms of models: they were simply applying a peace treaty. So they established a Free City under a High Commissioner, and that was that.

The settlement of the Saar, in which I also played an active part, left me dissatisfied for the same reason: it, too, made no provision for the future. What future was there, indeed, for an international authority that was politically responsible for a piece of land annexed from Germany, but with France given full ownership of the coal that was its main wealth? I wrote to Millerand: 'The Saar cannot remain independent. If the population insists, it will sooner or later return to Germany. With all its coal.' I proposed a referendum, as in Upper Silesia. Poincaré refused. France had its hostage: he saw no further than that.

What was more, a Frenchman was appointed head of the international Commission. French troops had to intervene. Already one could discern the beginnings of a policy – a takeover of the Saar's economic resources. It was doomed to failure, like all attempts at domination; but Paris persisted in it, because it seemed to meet the pressing needs of French industry. This persistence, which led to a near-crisis thirty years later, was mainly due to lack of imagination. Where the economic interests of one nation clashed with the sovereignty of another, people obstinately tried to impose a solution by force. But even under League of Nations auspices, the annexing of the Saar was an insult and an injury to the Germans. I remembered that in 1950, when I saw the same problem arouse the same reflexes in French diplomacy, threatening to perpetuate Franco-German disputes. I came to the conclusion that we must by-pass them, and evolve a new political structure in which national interests would no longer seem to conflict, so that the prize for which they were competing would become a joint Franco-German asset. The 'bold act', in Robert Schuman's words, which created the European Coal and Steel Community in 1950, owed a great deal to the timidity of the Saar settlement in 1922. Long experience had taught us that only by radically transforming the political context could we solve a problem so long beset by equivocation. And in fact, as will be seen later, after May 9, 1950 this ancient conflict became a matter of history.

IV

Austria: collective action

I learned a great deal during this time of intense activity; but I remember most vividly only the handful of tasks that seemed to me to set a lasting example of how to organize peace. One – and it was especially significant – was Upper Silesia. Another, rather less so, was the Saar. A further achievement of the League of Nations was the economic rehabilitation of Austria; and the lessons I learned from that were also to prove very useful. It was there that I realized the value of collective action, and the need to associate in a common enterprise, as equals, both victors and vanquished, both givers and receivers of aid. Austria had been conquered and was receiving aid; but she had no hope of recovery. For three years, the victorious Allies had held at arm's length this tiny republic of six-and-a-half million German-speaking people, a third of whom lived in Vienna, the overblown capital of a vanished empire. Nothing had been done to enable the country to stand on its own feet. Annexation by Germany, itself a desperate remedy, was forbidden by the Treaty of Versailles. Inflation and unemployment condemned the Austrians to poverty and distress. In 1921, to ward off total collapse, the League of Nations was commissioned to restore the country's finances.

What looked like a financial mission was in fact politically vital, both for the stability of Europe and for the future of our organization. Austria was an essential piece of the Central European jigsaw-puzzle created by the Peace Treaty, which had left the League to clear up all its mistakes. I personally doubted whether the fragmentation of Central Europe was a viable solution; but the national rivalries that made it so precarious also helped to maintain it. Not one of these small countries accepted the logical idea of forming a federation – unless it could dominate the rest. A conversation with Edvard Beneš* – if I remember rightly, during a walk on Mont Blanc – had shown me how little this 'Europe of nationalities' would listen to reason. I pointed out what a nonsense it was to chop up this vast central area, which formed a natural economic unit.

'Your countries are too small,' I said. 'Instead of opposing each other, they'll have to agree to unite.'

'Oh, I see great difficulties there,' he answered

'But you know very well that Austria's no longer up to it. . . . You ought to propose a federation: Czechoslovakia could make a start – '

'Never!' said Beneš. 'I'd rather see Austria disappear.'

Such was the state of mind of a young man whose advice was respected in Geneva, and who had already embarked on his great and tragic career as a passionate nationalist.

In March 1921, our task was to prevent an exhausted Austria becoming a prey to other countries. The financial committee of the League Secretariat set to work. All its investigations led to the conclusion that the monetary situation must be put right before seeking credit from abroad. This meant severe budgetary economies, a domestic loan, and the establishment of an independent institute to control note issues. Only then would loans be raised on the international market, against the security of tax receipts and mortgages. This austerity programme was accepted by the Austrian Government, but it remained theoretical so long as there was still any doubt about the country's political future. Who in the world would subscribe to a loan issued by a State whose resources were already mortgaged to foreign powers– which furthermore had withdrawn their aid? This problem delayed matters for a year. Then, one day in August 1922, we saw that the Austrian crown had fallen to one fifteen-thousandth of its gold parity. The League Council was convened, and Bourgeois talked with Balfour. They agreed that the problem must now be dealt with at the political level. That was enough for the Secretariat to return to work with the certainty of success: Salter, as head of the financial section, went to the Austrian capital. 'Vienna at this time,' he wrote, 'was a tragic scene; its great streets empty of traffic; its shops closed; its people of all classes, including scholars of wide reputation, remnants of the older aristocracy and once prosperous businessmen, were visibly starving.'†

* Foreign Minister and later President of Czechoslovakia.
† Salter, *Memoirs of a Public Servant* (London, 1961), p. 176.

Altogether, he concluded, there was great temptation for neighbouring countries to intervene if and when disorders broke out.

It occurred to me then that this real danger of outside intervention might be used, as it were, in reverse. Why not turn it into positive joint action? Why not make the very forces that might have been tempted to exploit the crisis contribute instead to keeping Austria independent? It might be possible to exploit everyone's fear of a move on the part of someone else. A collective guarantee would be the most reassuring solution for everyone, and their common interest would give them the most powerful incentive to succeed. Salter has recalled, as I do, a Sunday picnic by the Lake of Geneva in September 1922, when I expounded this idea to him and to Basil Blackett, a brilliant financial expert from the British Treasury.* We quickly agreed that this should be our approach; and, as usual, each of us set to work to persuade those delegates and national officials on whom we had some influence.

Some weeks later the Committee on Austria, where Great Britain, France, Italy, and Czechoslovakia were represented in the presence of the Austrian Chancellor Monseigneur Seipel, submitted its report. As adopted, this report proposed a preliminary political clause – the so-called 'Disinterested Protocol' – whereby the four signatory States pledged themselves to 'respect the political independence, territorial integrity and sovereignty of Austria, and to seek no special or exclusive economic or financial advantage such as might directly or indirectly compromise that independence'. The Austrian Government, meanwhile, was to apply very rigorous domestic reforms (closing down loss-making State corporations, reducing the number of civil servants, raising the level of tariffs). These steps were the precondition for financial aid in the form of an international loan guaranteed both by domestic revenue (customs and tobacco duties) and by the signatory Governments, which were pledged to pay any interest on the loan not covered by Austria's own resources. The operation was supervised by a Commissioner-General appointed by the League.

Today, such a system is familiar because it has been copied or adopted many times. Then, however, it was a great innovation. It was the first important step in the reconstruction of Europe, a permanent achievement, and no longer a more or less charitable affair. By accepting outside help, not only did Austria lose nothing of her independence: she strengthened it by international guarantees and domestic

* *Ibid.*, p. 177.

94

reforms. So, gradually, new ideas became more acceptable and practical examples, like the spectacular and rapid recovery of Austria's financial and economic affairs, made an impression on people in the old citadels of administration, economics, and finance which the war – in appearance, at least – had not seriously shaken.

One unmistakable sign was that the citadel of citadels, the Bank of England itself, took part in the operation. Today it is hard to imagine the prestige and power that the Bank enjoyed at the beginning of this century. Credit throughout the world more or less reflected its views. We realized this when the time came to float the Austrian loan, and – despite the agreed guarantees – we were met with some hesitation in the largest establishments in Switzerland, Paris, and New York. Someone said to me: 'The reason is that Norman hasn't come in. Once he moves, the others will follow.' Montagu Norman was the Governor of that citadel. He was a formidable man. Once, it was said, he had kept his colleague, the Governor of the Bank of Poland, waiting forty-eight hours before being received. It was his way of preserving protocol. I went to see him: I was lucky enough to be able to persuade him. He invited me to stay with him for several days, and we became friends. The Austrian loan, of $130 million, was oversubscribed several times.

V

Peace based on equality

The League Secretariat and its contacts worked well. We were able to deal one by one with other cases where stability had broken down, as in Hungary, Greece, and Bulgaria. But the precondition for success was itself a limitation: nothing could be done without the agreement of the Great Powers or the benevolent complicity of their delegates in Geneva. Such negotiated agreements formed a kind of international law. But that law was precarious, and it was limited by national self-interest – as is always the case with mere co-operation. Using such methods, how could we ever have achieved lasting order? We had gone as far as possible towards establishing an international economic code of good conduct in October 1920, at the Brussels Conference convened 'to study the financial crisis and seek ways of avoiding and attenuating its dangers'. It was the first Conference that the League had held, and I had prepared it very carefully with Salter, Blackett, Walter Layton, and Robert Brand. It embodied the still lively hopes of our London team. We still believed in the possibility of an organized peace, and we set great store by this meeting of thirty-nine States – including Germany – which together represented 75% of the world's population. They, we thought, might be able to restart some of the machinery that we had put to the test in the wartime Executives. But with peace restored, the driving-force of necessity was no longer there. The only practical result of this first great world economic conference was to establish, at the League, the Economic and Financial Organization, the machinery whereby Salter secured approval of our solutions, as in the case of Austria. All the rest dissolved into bold resolutions – measures against inflation, the removal of quantitative restrictions and price discrimination, the free movement of goods and capital, and above all the organization of financial solidarity. These might have saved Europe twenty years' stagnation and a second world war – if the power to enforce them had been granted at the same time.

Even so, we did not feel like people who were misunderstood or whose actions led nowhere. We got results. We overcame crises that were no less serious than those of Berlin or Northern Ireland today; we administered territories by new methods; we put a stop to epidemics. We developed methods of co-operation among nations which hitherto had known only relationships based on power. We placed great hopes in the development of the League, and the difficulties we encountered acted as a stimulus. It was only later that I realized how we had underestimated them, or rather how we had failed to dig deep enough. At the root of them all was national sovereignty. In the League Council, this prevented the general interest's being seen. At every meeting, people talked about the general interest, but it was always forgotten along the way: everyone was obsessed by the effect that any solution would have on him – on his country. The result was that no one really tried to solve the actual problems: their main concern was to find answers that would respect the interests of all those around the table. In this way, the whole organization fell into the routine of mere co-operation.

This was inevitable in a body subject to the unanimity rule. That rule seemed natural to even the best-intentioned of men. One scene among others sticks in my memory: it was a meeting of the Council to discuss the world distribution of raw materials. The Italian representative, Marchese Imperiale, was pressing for a certain decision to be taken. As usual, the British representative, Lord Balfour, looked as if he were asleep. When his turn came, he got up and said simply: 'His Majesty's Government is against.' Then he returned to his doze. The question was settled. This was by no means uncommon; and yet there can be no doubt about Balfour's good intentions – or those of Bourgeois, despite the fact that I have heard him say in the Chamber: 'There is no question of turning the League of Nations into a super-State or even a Confederation.' People's ideas had simply not evolved very far.

The veto was at once the cause and the symbol of this inability to go beyond national self-interest. But it was no more than the expression of much deeper deadlocks, often unacknowledged. Britain's policy was to seek a balance of power on the continent; France wanted to dominate it; Germany, if not already *revanchiste*, was manoeuvring to loosen the constraints upon her. The fault lay in the Treaty of Versailles: it was based on discrimination. From the moment I first began to be concerned with public affairs I have always realized that equality is absolutely essential in relations between nations, as it is between people. A peace based on inequality could have no good results. I hoped, nevertheless, that the fault could be remedied by goodwill. One might just as well rely on blind chance. One day, Raymond Poincaré showed me the true face of the will to dominate, in circumstances I shall never forget.

We were worried by the problem of German reparations, which we thought was being approached in the wrong way. With Salter, Blackett, and Cellier, who was Director of Capital Movements, I was trying to make realistic sense out of the slogan 'Germany shall pay'.

'She'll pay, yes,' I said to Léon Bourgeois, 'but not an indefinite amount and for ever. I suggest that we replace the idea of an unlimited political debt with that of a limited commercial debt, by means of a loan, floated world-wide, on which the Germans would have to pay the interest. In that way we should no longer be basing Franco-German relations on sheer power: we'd turn reparations into a system of just but reasonable obligations, such as could be undertaken by the citizens of any country.' Léon Bourgeois agreed – and so did his faithful secretary, which was not unimportant. Mlle Millard was a person whom Nature had not favoured, save for her intelligence, which was exceptional. In the shadow of Léon Bourgeois she played an active and useful role: there was something of the osmosis I have referred to in the case of Woodrow Wilson and Colonel House, Bourgeois had wide-ranging, generous ideas; Mlle Millard organized them and made them work. She now proposed a meeting in Bourgeois's apartment near the Place Saint-Sulpice. Millerand, who was already half-convinced, was to be present, and so was Poincaré.

When Poincaré arrived, Bourgeois and Teulis, the Belgian representative on the Reparations Commission, told him that they wanted to consult him about the plan which they asked me to expound. I did so. 'If I understand you aright, gentlemen,' said Poincaré, 'this boils down to reducing the amount of the German debt?' 'Not reducing – fixing. One cannot speak of a debt if it has no limit. I should say rather that we propose to free Germany from an unknown burden.' At this, Poincaré stood up, flushed with rage. 'Never, sir. The German debt is a political matter, and I intend to use it as a means of pressure.' To dramatize his words, he drew from his pocket an extract from the Treaty of Versailles and brandished it before our eyes.

It has often been said that, when the United States withdrew from the League, the breath of generosity went out of it. It is true that Woodrow Wilson was in favour of limiting the German debt; that he had pressed for the establishment of new authorities, in Danzig and the Saar among others; that he fought against economic nationalism wherever it arose; and that he dreamed of disarmament. But it is also true that he was ahead of world opinion, and first and foremost that of his own country. His own failure did not involve the failure of the young League. Powerful as the United States was, it still seemed far off from Europe: the old continent was still the centre of the world. An organization dominated by Britain and France could decide the fate of the planet, above all when both nations, their prestige untarnished, were in agreement. But agreement was hard to reach after centuries of rivalry. I realized that disarmament would never come about when it was clear that Britain wanted to keep her fleet intact, and France was bent on maintaining her army. With these significant exceptions, both were ready to see military systems dismantled. I knew that the League could not go on as it was: but I still hoped to play my part in changing it.

Chapter 5

FROM COGNAC TO POLAND,
FROM CALIFORNIA TO CHINA

I

Back to Cognac

One day in the autumn of 1921, my sister Marie-Louise came to see me in Geneva. 'Father's having trouble with the business,' she said. 'We think you ought to come back to Cognac and take it in hand.' I was not altogether surprised. I knew that the postwar slump, the fall in prices, and the slackening of demand had affected the house of Monnet more than other well-known brands. But what my sister told me seemed serious, and I did not hesitate. My father needed me, so I must go back to Cognac and sell brandy. In Geneva, the League of Nations was working well, and continuity there was ensured not only by the team I was leaving behind but also by the sheer momentum of the Secretariat. Like all institutions, it would outlive its founders. In Cognac, on the other hand, business depended on decisions taken by a handful of men. The world economic situation and the quality of the grape-harvest were certainly important: but it was our job to foresee such fluctuations and in any case to deal with them. My father was old, and he found it hard to adapt to changing times.

I am not in the habit of quarrelling with necessity. I resigned from the League of Nations, although I enjoyed my work there and had the feeling that a great deal more could usefully be done. I certainly did not leave out of disenchantment with the League's weakness. As I have said, I had not then fully realized how weak it was. If I had, I should have gone to great lengths to stay in a job where I could contribute to the maintenance of peace. As it was, I was confident; and my confidence led me to hand over my job to one of my assistants, Joseph Avenol, who had done good work in the political section. It was an error of judgement that I now regret. As later events showed, Avenol was not the kind of man to make a good Secretary of the League.

Others, however, stayed on and continued the work we had begun together. There was the faithful Arthur Salter, who used the financial section to lay the first foundations of economic union, in line with his federalist convictions. There were the conscientious and hard-working Henri Bonnet and Pierre Comert, who in the cultural and information sections respectively set up model systems that have since been copied by all international organizations. There was Albert Thomas, whose powerful, generous temperament gave the International Labour Office an energy that nothing has sapped to this day. His bearded prophet's face was popular with the labour movements of every continent. And there was Ludwig Rajchman, less ebullient but no less influential, at the head of the health section, whose network stretched into every corner of the world.

I should like to enlarge a little on the life and character of this extraordinary man, whose friendship I so much valued. Few people, I think, have had so powerful a sense of the universal. From one continent to another, irrespective of frontiers or political regimes, he maintained warm human contacts that made him both the most disinterested and the most effective of friends. He was born in Warsaw into a family of great classical scholars: he himself became a well-known doctor specializing in bacteriology. When the League of Nations began to combat the terrible epidemics that followed the First World War, he was recruited to set up the health section. I admired its work and the results obtained by his devotion and his organizing genius. He was a great leader of men, and a good friend: we shall meet him again in these pages. When on one of his official missions he saw how great were the sufferings and the potential achievements of China, he devoted himself to that country's development until the Second World War called him back to the United States. Everyone knows how much he did for children the world over, for whom he established UNICEF, the United Nations International Children's Emergency Fund. When Rajchman died in 1965, in the little village in the Sarthe where his body is buried, the achievements of his head and his heart survived him, because he had made them permanent. Rajchman believed in the generosity of human nature, but he had taken care to establish institutions.

The nineteen-twenties were a time for great enterprises, or rather for enterprising minds. If France proved unable to lead the collective effort which might have brought her firmly into the twentieth century, and if she had no time to modernize before the great world crisis put a stop to her development, at least some individuals at that time enjoyed enormous scope. I was at an age when imagination reaches its height, and my need to be up and doing was to involve me in action on a scale that went beyond national frontiers. The brandy business was one example, but I was soon to come up against its limits and its routines. Before long, large-scale economic and financial ventures were to bring me back to problems of which I already had some experience – the internal and external equilibrium of nations that had suffered from the effects of war. It was this persistent need to restore order that brought out my energy, not the incidental profits that I made along the way. Money came and went. I was good at making it, perhaps, but certainly not at keeping it.

Coming back to Cognac, I found that the situation was bad both materially and, still more, psychologically. No sooner had I arrived than I met a friend in the Café du Chalet. 'I must have a word with you,' he said. 'But not here, on the corner of the street.' I had forgotten this side of provincial life. 'I hear that you're going to file a petition in bankruptcy,' he whispered. 'Certainly not,' I replied, 'and you can spread the word.'

I moved into a charming house on the banks of the Charente river, the Alsace, some distance outside the town. There, I made preparations for a struggle which I found very painful, because it was not against things, but against someone I loved; not against events, but against ideas that deserved great respect. There was no doubt about it: my father was trying to run the business against the current of the times. He was more concerned to maintain quality than to expand sales. By quality, he meant sacrosanct respect for the reserves of vintage spirit that were maturing in the depths of our cellars, those dark inner sanctums that were known in Cognac as 'le Paradis'. They held great wealth; but they also locked up an essential part of our capital. My father had long been watching them mature – and grow in value – not as a speculation, since he refused to sell them, but out of sheer professional pleasure and sentimental pride. The house of Monnet was rich: but it lacked the capital to do business, which now more and more depended on less august vintages.

Day after day I fought patiently against the touching obstinacy of a man who was ruining his business to preserve his heart's desire. A firm could go bankrupt in Cognac, even if its product was good and its brand-name respected: all it needed was to go on believing in what had always been true but was true no longer – the virtue of scarcity and the danger of change. Many other firms had been ruined because their founders had stubbornly clung to practices that had won them the esteem of a small and select clientèle. I wanted to save my father from this unhappy fate, and to do so I did not hesitate to go against his opinions, although it hurt us both. I knew that we could diversify our product with a range of good quality brandies for a much broader public. To tell the truth, we had no other option. My father resigned himself to replacing his vintage *eaux-de-vie* with younger spirit which once more made possible widespread sales. At the same time, market prices rose. I believe that I have always been lucky, but I have not always known how much I have helped my luck. On that occasion, in Cognac, I have only circumstances to thank.

I took the opportunity to reorganize the firm. After the death of my brother, my cousins took over its day-to-day administration. I kept some shares in it, but otherwise left myself free. It was at that time that I was approached by a large American investment firm, Blair and Co., which had just established a French subsidiary in Paris. It was a time of great activity on the exchange markets, and the powerful New York investment bankers were extending their interests in Europe. They were floating loans for industrial firms or Governments which themselves were unable to raise the credit they needed for capital investment. The private establishments undertook to float public loans guaranteed by Government pledges. Such pledges had to be verified; and this might even involve the reorganization of a Government's tax or customs revenue. In the case of states that had still not fully recovered from the effects of the war, it might even include reforming and stabilizing the national currency. In such instances the investment bankers had to go right to the heart of the problem, advising Governments on how to balance their budgets, and penetrating the holy of holies, the central bank. Blair and Co. were big enough for such ventures, which were a matter of politics as much as of finance.

II

The zloty and the leu

The Director-General of Blair was Elisha Walker, a very enterprising businessman who already had a substantial reputation. In August 1926 we founded with him the French Blair and Co. Foreign Corporation, based in Paris, with myself as Vice-President. Rajchman, whose influence and inventiveness went far beyond his official role in the international health organization, knew the difficulties that were then facing his Polish compatriots. The weakness of their currency, the zloty, reflected the industrial backwardness of their country, which was only just emerging from mediaeval conditions: it prevented the Warsaw Government from seeking international credit. The first step to be taken was to strengthen the zloty with a dollar loan and to stimulate productive investment with an injection of foreign capital. At the beginning of 1927, Rajchman put me in touch with the Polish Government, and I went to Warsaw. A young financial expert who had been recommended to me by Pierre Comert has recalled how we made our headquarters at the Hotel Europeiski, where our feverish activity astonished the local population. It was René Pleven, later Prime Minister of France. One of the things he discovered there was the inconvenience of the time difference between Warsaw and New York: we had to spend part of the night sending back the results of the day's negotiations.

I think that I was not always easy to live with. I asked a great deal of my colleagues, who found it hard to get used to my methods of work. But they soon saw that these were not really personal idiosyncrasies, because they reflected operational necessities to which I was subject myself. Certainly, René Pleven took a little time to realize that we had to live simultaneously on American time and Polish time if we wanted to start a real dialogue, rather than a succession of monologues between people on opposite sides of the world who were working at the same task. Equally, like many others, it took him some time to agree to rewriting ten or twenty times a note 'of secondary importance' whose text was 'more or less satisfactory'. In fact, nothing that has to be done to attain one's aim is 'secondary'. Nothing should be an approximation, accepted out of tiredness or the lateness of the hour. Pleven also had to learn that to write a letter is not enough: one has to be sure that it has been sent, and to check that it has arrived. Failing observance of these rules, which are not merely details or minor matters, people who are thought to be conscientious are surprised when the results they achieve fall short of their intentions.

I was very glad to have with me this twenty-six-year-old whose intelligence had already mastered all our technical problems and whose feelings were aroused by the human side of our work. I realized right away that Pleven would like to enter public life. He was naturally disinterested, and he saw our financial mission in its broadest context, which was that of politics. The stabilization of the zloty, in fact, was a problem that greatly preoccupied Western Governments. I found myself at the crossroads of rival influences emanating from London, Paris, Berlin, and Washington, since the big central banks all felt it their duty to supervise the parity at which the Polish currency was fixed. These banks were strong, independent institutions, and their governors were powerful men. Montagu Norman, Emile Moreau, Hjalmar Schacht, and Benjamin Strong all faced serious monetary problems of their own which made them form a broadly common front. But when another small European nation was in difficulties, each of them wanted to exert national influence by acting as its financial guardian.

Norman believed that the Bank of England should allow no one else to settle the Polish question. I have already described the way in which he kept his Polish counterpart waiting: he would have done the same with a central banker from Bucharest or Belgrade. He had no great opinion of the Bank of France. For this reason, Moreau did not like him at all. 'This figure from a Van Dyck painting,' he said, 'with his pointed beard and his vast hat, looks like a Stuart cavalier. He's an imperialist: he'd like the Bank of England to rule the world.' I agreed with Moreau, and thought that it was not a good idea to leave the field free for Montagu Norman's superiority complex. The man had charm, and we had become friends; but I was not prepared to see him take in hand the stabilization of the zloty and then make political demands regarding the German-Polish frontier. The will to dominate arouses my deepest feelings. That is why, in agreement with Moreau and Poincaré, I used my friendly relations with Strong to interest the Federal Reserve Bank as a counterweight to British influence.

After long negotiations in Paris and Washington, we reached an agreement putting the Polish economy on a sound footing, with no political strings attached, but in return for severe measures of domestic reorganization. The central banks jointly guaranteed the parity of the zloty, which was stabilized by means of international loans floated by Blair. The agreement, for $70m. guaranteed by customs revenue, was signed at the end of the year. In my mind's eye I can still see the final negotiations, which took place in the Polish President's office. Marshal Pilsudski, in his tight grey military tunic ribbed with red, expostulated against our demands. He refused an interest rate of $7\frac{1}{2}\%$. We got up, ready to break off negotiations. 'Wait a moment,' he said. We sat down again. 'Look,' said Pilsudski, smiling, 'surely you'll let me have half a point for Wanda?' Wanda was his daughter. The loan was agreed at 7%.

Since nothing important is done in the United States without lawyers, we had taken the advice of one of the most brilliant New York attorneys, John Foster Dulles. I had met him at the Peace Conference, and we had become friends. I appreciated his great ability, which proved useful to us in Warsaw and elsewhere. But above all I admired his strength of character and the moral authority that he already commanded outside his professional sphere. In the United States, a great lawyer is a great citizen. His reputation spreads, and he may, without actively entering politics, be called upon to play a national role. Such was patently the destiny of John Foster Dulles, who was deeply religious and profoundly convinced that liberty is essential to civilization. I have always known him as decisive and inflexibly determined, just as history paints him, and at the same time warm, fond of good living, and an affectionate friend. One day the world will come to see him, alongside Eisenhower, as a man of great stature, a symbol of willpower that aroused conflicting passions. But this was not Foster Dulles the man. The Dulles I knew and loved was like many other men, but greater and more upright than most.

Some months later, in January 1928, I was in Bucharest. There, too, political and economic troubles had weakened the currency, the leu, to the point where the Romanian Government could no longer find the credit it needed in Europe, despite its good relations with Paris and London. The negotiations which I began with Vintila Bratianu were concluded in February 1929 with Prime Minister Juliu Maniu, the leader of the Peasant Party, who had come to power after two Government crises due to the financial disorder that it was so vital to halt. The loan consolidating the leu was difficult to negotiate, because even the American market, already affected by the first signs of the coming world crisis, could not absorb all of the $100m. flotation, although it was guaranteed by the Independent Fund of the Romanian state monopolies, which we had set up for the purpose. It was in these circumstances that there appeared in Bucharest a figure who was already legendary. He can truly be said to have sought his fortune throughout the world, after having founded a financial empire on the match monopoly of his native Sweden. This was Ivar Kreuger. He now offered to take up $30m. worth of the loan, provided he were given the monopoly of matches in Romania.

I had already met this disturbing man with his burly figure and his controlled, impassive, enigmatic face. He used to come and see me at the Blair office in Paris: he would sit in an armchair and talk aimlessly about this and that. One day he said to me: 'Come and have lunch.' It was then, for a brief moment, that I glimpsed his true nature. 'You know,' he said, 'I have a Kreuger-Toll company quoted on the New York stock market. I can float loans and get State monopolies practically anywhere in the world. I'm going to start by getting the Polish match monopoly. *And there's no end.*' I knew then that he was heading for trouble. There is no power without limits. There is one limit to everything – death.

So I met Kreuger again in this Romanian affair, where he was offering, by himself, to bring in what the most powerful banking groups in the world were unable to obtain on the European and American markets. Talks with him continued in Paris, but they led nowhere. One day, he saw that we were about to break them off, and he said: 'Give me five minutes, and I'll give you a definite answer.' He withdrew to a corner of the office, and we saw him pull down his starched shirt-cuff and start scribbling on it with his pencil. Everyone waited in heavy silence. After a few moments, Kreuger came back: 'Gentlemen, I agree.' In the general relief, there was no question of asking him what his strange behaviour meant; but a little later I said to him: 'I'd be interested to know what on earth you were writing.' 'It's very simple,' he said, 'I worked out that if I put one match fewer in each box, I should make out.'

The whole Kreuger empire was founded on speculations that were just as rapid and empirical. No one apart from its creator knew anything of its reality or substance. Such an accumulation of secrets is difficult to imagine today. Then, one man could deceive the whole world. But I distrusted his morbid suspiciousness. 'Never use the telephone,' he would say, and he settled business in taxis. The day came when he could no longer conceal the formidable swindle of his fictitious wealth, built on a scaffolding of falsehood. He killed himself in Paris in March 1932. One after another, his giant enterprises crumbled, shaking the financial establishment, and creating stupor everywhere. The liquidation of the disaster was in itself a long and involved international business, on which I spent months in Stockholm in 1932.

III

Banking in San Francisco

Meanwhile, after the signing of the Romanian loan early in 1929, I had gone back to New York. There, expansion was still the watchword; in the general euphoria few people noticed, and no one could then interpret, the growing signs that harder times were coming. Elisha Walker, in search of new outlets, had met another large-scale financier who was also looking for a suitable partner. This was Amadeo Giannini, the son of Genoese immigrants, who on the other side of the United States, starting from the small savings of his Californian compatriots, had built up the biggest banking empire on the West Coast. Elisha Walker was strong and straightforward; Giannini was powerful and wily. At sixty, his imposing figure and his lion's mane of grizzled hair impressed the public. His success seemed magical. Italian children ran after him in the street – they called him 'Gold Touch'. Walker and Giannini thought that if their two groups joined forces each would take on world dimensions. At that time, there was no law separating commercial banks from their investment affiliates. So, in May 1929, the great Bancamerica-Blair Corporation was born. Walker was its president. I became its vice-president and went to San Francisco.

The first reactions, intensified by the publicity surrounding the merger, seemed to confirm our hopes. In a last flash of prosperity, share prices soared. They were soon to fall again, no less suddenly, in the Wall Street crash of 1929: from sixty dollars they dropped to six. Our fate was common to many; but a more serious misfortune was in store for Bancamerica-Blair. At the time of the merger, Walker had not called the accountants in. Now, as we looked deeper into Giannini's empire, we realized that his great holding company, the Transamerica, had been seriously overvalued. It was urgent to put it in order, and since Giannini was always talking about retiring from business, Walker persuaded him at least to take a long vacation on another continent. He promised to go to Austria for two years, and he kept his word. Walker became president of Transamerica, with myself as vice-president. Once installed, we found that it needed total reorganization. In this task we were helped by an exceptionally able lawyer called Donald Swatland. We became and remained friends, and I later enlisted his help on other occasions, in particular when working on big international loans, where his integrity and deep understanding guaranteed that all was well. It has been said that I have often in my life had to clear up difficult situations, but I must admit that I had not embarked on this Californian venture in order to mount a rescue operation. Yet that is what it became.

We worked very hard to put things in order, and by the time we had done so, in 1932, we decided to separate Transamerica from the rest of the group and make it independent, as a deposit bank, from the Giannini empire's other commercial interests. But we had reckoned without the energy and guile of the old warrior, who now returned to California, called together his 200,000 stockholders – the small investors who had helped him make a fortune – and went everywhere proclaiming, with his innate sense of theatre: 'The men of Wall Street have robbed me and are going to ruin honest Californians.' On February 13, 1932, the stockholders' meeting re-elected him chairman, and he ruled his empire once more. Elisha Walker and I had lost. Perhaps we were unlucky, perhaps maladroit. One thing is certain: the banking system that we had tried to control and then to reform was unhealthy. After the 1929 crash, more than 3000 banks closed within a year. Not long afterwards, a federal law was to stipulate that deposit banking must be separate from merchant banking – but not before the crisis had done widespread damage and Franklin Roosevelt had been elected to steer his country out of it with far-sighted determination.

I lived through that crisis, about which so much has been said and written. Looking back, I think the reason for it was simple – a technical fault which triggered off an incalculable series of accidents. At that time, Americans banked their money in two forms – commercial deposits, and savings accounts, which carried a high rate of interest if the money was left in for a certain time. When the New York stock market crashed at the end of 1929, and the depression affected trade, people hurried to the banks to withdraw their money. But, to earn its high interest, the money had been on-loaned in the form of bills, for which there was then no discount system. Since these could obviously not all be called in simultaneously overnight, the whole of America's credit machinery was paralysed. And since the banks called in their commercial loans to reimburse their depositors, the crisis spiralled, and then went out of control. To put an end to it, the Government set up the Reconstruction Finance Corporation, which was authorized to discount bills. Then came the New Deal, which insured bank deposits and forbade commercial banks to use them to finance investments. As always, wisdom and reform came only after great difficulties. Would simple measures, taken earlier, have prevented the slump? To put the question is to forget that people only accept change when they are faced with necessity, and only recognize necessity when a crisis is upon them.

In San Francisco, I made and then lost a great deal of money. Experience was all I added to my capital. At forty, I was still learning – indeed, I have never stopped. In Stockholm, where I went next, as I have said, to clear up the wreckage of the Kreuger trust, I saw the tragic results of excess and deceit in human affairs. In Shanghai, where I spent a further three years, I discovered a civilization whose roots and riches I scarcely had time to fathom. On the subject of China, it is as well to be modest and resist the temptation to generalize. Here, I shall be brief, and speak only of those Chinese men and women that I knew. But before I continue to describe the succession of events that led me again and again to deal with other people's business, I must say something of a personal matter. This was the birth of a long and profound attachment which has been the light of my life.

IV

Investing in China

It was an August evening in Paris, in 1929. An Italian couple were among those having dinner with me. He was a businessman. That night, I saw his young wife for the first time. She was very beautiful. We forgot the other guests.

I think I can trace back to that first meeting the beginning of a love that was mutual and indestructible. I was forty years old; she was little more than twenty. We soon decided that we must be together for life. Many obstacles stood in the way. Silvia was married under Italian law, which forbade divorce. I looked into a number of solutions: I found that divorce and remarriage were possible under Soviet law. We decided on that as a solution. We met in Moscow on November 13, 1934, and everything went as simply as could be. Many years later,

Monseigneur Henri Donze, Bishop of Tarbes and Lourdes and a great friend of the family, married us in Lourdes itself.

We went to live for a year in Shanghai, where I had gone for the first time in 1933. It was Rajchman again, that man of infinite resource, with influence reaching into the furthest and remotest corners, who had introduced me to the unknown world of China. He had come to know it during his official visits on behalf of the League of Nations. He had been so successful in the fields of public health and education that the Minister of Finance, T. V. Soong, had asked him to come back in 1933 as adviser to the Chinese Government. In fact, Rajchman already had very great personal influence in the country: it literally fascinated him, and he was unhappy to see it disorganized, underdeveloped, and at the mercy of Japanese aggression. Japan's invasion of Manchuria had distressed him on two counts, as a humiliation of his Chinese friends and as a threat to world peace. The very existence of the League was at stake, and those who had taken part in its foundation could not allow it to be destroyed by the rise of fascism, wherever it occurred.

Rajchman used every resource at his command to give China a sound economic structure. He had managed to have Salter sent to advise Soong on the establishment of a central body to co-ordinate reconstruction. This was the National Economic Council, set up in 1931, which worked out investment projects for roads, agriculture, education, public health, and so on. So effective were these men of good will that Japan took offence and tried to thwart them by intervening in Geneva; but Soong was on the alert and he protected them. All his energies were concentrated on the struggle with Japan. In this he differed somewhat from his brother-in-law Chiang Kai-shek, who headed the Government. Chiang's overriding aim was to exterminate the Communists – a struggle which wore out China's army and drained her finances. Soong resigned in 1933, but he remained at the head of the National Economic Council. He travelled in America and Europe, which is where I met him. In Geneva, on Rajchman's advice, he asked for me to be sent to China to launch a reconstruction plan that would attract Chinese and international capital. But the League dared not ignore Japanese objections, and when I accepted the job I went as a private individual.

When I reached Shanghai, I quickly realized that I should never understand the Chinese – and that in any case this was not the problem. I found myself face to face with men who seemed far more subtle and intelligent than Westerners, and who were certainly very different.

This difference made them wary; and to tell the truth their pride had been deeply wounded by the intrusion of powerful European firms. So it was much more important to win their confidence than to understand them. How to do so was not something that I learned only from my contacts with the Chinese, but I found it very helpful in dealing with them. The secret was simple: act as you speak, so that there is never any contradiction between what you say and what you do. I believe that the same is true in dealing with any people, despite what the artful may say – and China is the last place anyone should try to be artful. Once you have inspired confidence and established good personal relations, which is essential, then everything becomes simple and there are no misunderstandings. The Chinese friends I made at that time always gave me the best advice and made my work much easier.

Their first piece of advice was this: 'It is no use trying to invest foreign capital in China without Chinese participation.' In the past, undoubtedly, too many European firms had treated China like colonial territory; and the Nationalist Government drew its support from the people's longing for dignity and independence. But it was also true that the repayment of loans could be guaranteed only if the Chinese were brought into the financial operation. This meant starting from scratch, for although Shanghai was the financial and business capital of the country, its only banks were the deposit banks where the South Chinese kept their savings: there was no bank capable of floating loans. For both technical and psychological reasons, therefore, I came to the conclusion that what was needed was a wholly Chinese bank which would take part in bond issues on Western markets. In that way, the Chinese would have an equal stake in the success of the operations that were needed to modernize their country. By June 1934 I had secured the agreement of a large number of Chinese banks, including the powerful Bank of Shanghai and Hong Kong, that they would participate in a China Finance Development Corporation, to inject long-term capital into public and private commercial and industrial concerns.

The China Corporation began remarkably well, mainly in the area where the biggest investments were most urgently needed – railways. In a country crippled by its sheer size and economically fragmented by the inadequacy or decline of its rail network, I believed that it was essential to reorganize and develop communications before financing industry. The Corporation raised money in Europe and in China for a number of projects to open up the country, including the Shanghai-

Hangchow-Minhow (-Foochow) Railway and the important Szechwan line. The 1939 War interrupted a rapidly expanding programme. The modernization of China was not a task beyond human capacity, nor one too big for the material and financial wealth available abroad – provided that the planning of needs and the mobilization of resources could be given the basic tools they lacked, including the Economic Council initiated by Salter and the development bank which I set up myself. But this could only be done with the help of the Chinese, and it took time.

In terms of their own time-scale, the Chinese had embarked on a revolutionary process. Its importance was clear to anyone who had lived through the era of Sun Yat-sen. The whole nation was devoted to the cult of Sun, the Founder of the Republic; his resplendent mausoleum, built alongside the tombs of the Ming emperors, was a place of pilgrimage. Each week at the same time, hundreds of millions of Chinese honoured the leader who had delivered them from bondage. His portrait was everywhere, and his precepts were recited in the remotest provinces: independence with full national sovereignty, total democracy, the common good. Economic progress and industrialization were the watchwords of the People's Party, the Kuomintang. When I arrived in China, it was less than ten years since Sun Yat-sen had brought the Communist Alexander Borodin back with him from Moscow as political adviser. Revolutionary ferment was universal. But, alongside Borodin, Sun had appointed a young military adviser, Chiang Kai-shek, who had completed his training in the Japanese army. Although also schooled in Moscow, Chiang had remained profoundly Chinese. When Sun died, he dismissed Borodin and led a national revolution. In 1927, he captured Peking and began the struggle against the remaining Communist provinces of Kiangsi. Ever since, he had been fighting to subdue these hundred thousand square kilometres, after concluding an unfavourable truce with Japan.

Chiang was unquestioned leader of the army and sovereign ruler of China – or of that half of the country which recognized his Government in Nanking. I knew that I could do nothing without his agreement, and I went to see him in his house on the Yangtze river, where he lived well away from the intrigues of the capital, in somewhat lofty simplicity. He spoke only Chinese, and his ever-present interpreter was his wife, who also watched over his career and his public image. In fact, as will be seen in a moment, she was far more than an interpreter. I remember a remark of her husband's which she translated to me one day: 'The General thinks you would make an excellent general. But he has one criticism: you are too soft with your friends.' Of all the Chinese leaders at that time, Chiang was the most Oriental, the least open to the outside world. Under his wife's influence he had become a Christian convert, but his true ethic was neo-Confucian, expressed through a 'New Life Movement' whose precepts were repeated everywhere. On another occasion, Mme Chiang said to me: 'The General likes you. He says there is something Chinese in you.' From that I was to gather that he agreed with me.

Mme Chiang was the third daughter of a Baptist minister, Mr Soong, who had had all his children educated in the United States. May Ling Soong was a graduate of Wellesley College. Tall and beautiful, she had considerable influence on the General. She shared in the dangers of his adventurous life, and she often acted in his name. The eldest daughter of the Soong family was Mme Kung. Her ambition and cleverness impressed me even more than her beauty and her wit. She had married a rich aristocrat, the seventy-third descendant of Confucius and a former student at Yale, and she had had him appointed Minister of Finance. The Soong family had immense talent and immense appetite for power. Mme Kung was exceedingly intelligent; and it was she who had arranged her sisters' marriages. The second sister, the most beautiful and the most impassioned, had become the wife of Sun Yat-sen. A deeply committed militant, she continued the struggle after the Master's death, and led the left-wing opposition to Chiang Kai-shek within the Kuomintang. Identified by marriage with the leadership of revolutionary power in China, she remained faithful to it, and later, as Vice-President of the Republic, sat alongside Mao Tse-tung. Meanwhile, the proud Mme Chiang shared to the end the old Generalissimo's exile in Formosa. These exceptional women took destiny in their hands, and it was they who commanded power and authority in China while I was there.

Their brother, T. V. Soong, was like them – well-bred, tall, strongly-built and very intelligent. Western in appearance and mentality, he had learned at Harvard to be open to new ideas. Within a few years, he gave China its first organized budget, its first universal currency, and its first central bank. The extent of his contacts throughout the world made him one of the key men of his time. Nothing happened in China without his agreement and his father's participation. The Soong family and their associates were among the main shareholders in the China Corporation. The idea of public service was not yet wholly free from dynastic traditions, and the long march towards democracy had hardly begun.

If it was easy for me to deal with T. V. Soong, whose background was European, I never fully learned the art of negotiating with Chinese businessmen of a more traditional type. It took me a long time to realize that in China one must never ask for an answer – one must guess it. My failure to understand this rule nearly wrecked the China Corporation project, in which I had secured the help of the Shanghai banks, as I have said. When we had reached general agreement, I decided to complete the deal, and the final documents were drawn up. It was now a question of settling the date when they would be signed. I began by going to see Mr Cheng, who headed the great Bank of China, and whose reputation and influence at that time were supreme. We had already met many times to discuss the matter. I had never explicitly asked him to commit himself before; but now that the time had come for action, this was his opportunity to say yes or no. 'Mr Cheng,' I said, 'we propose to sign in ten days' time, if that's all right with you.' 'Oh,' he said. 'I shall be away that day: my daughter's getting married.' I proposed another date, but unfortunately he was going into hospital. For how long he was unable to say.

I took leave of him with the impression that he was no longer prepared to form the China Corporation. I went to see an old Chinese acquaintance, Mr Li Yu Ying, who spoke French and sometimes gave me his advice on how to deal with his colleagues. I told him of my conversation with Mr Cheng, and asked him what he thought. Mr Li Yu Ying looked at me in astonishment. 'Come,' he said, 'I thought you understood China – you've been here quite a while. Did Mr Cheng say no? Well, then, you don't understand the Chinese. Mr Cheng won't give you a precise answer unless you go and see him three times: it would be impolite. So: you must go and see him, and ask him again. In the end, since he hasn't said no, he'll say yes. But you must ask him three times.' I did; and the Corporation was set up. The lesson was not lost on me, because there is something Chinese in many Englishmen, Frenchmen, and Europeans in general.

In Shanghai, I lived in the French Concession, which was rather like Cognac plus the Chinese. The French had the knack of forming sub-prefectures in their most distant outposts. The tramways, the lotteries, and the restaurants – all had the atmosphere of a French provincial town. There were very few firms. On the other side of the street, the Anglo-American Concession was a striking contrast, with its great import–export businesses, its warehouses full of cotton textiles, and its fleets of ships on the Yangtze. Towering over it all was Mr Cheng's Bank of China. There was French capital everywhere, no doubt; but it was anonymous, being deployed by enterprising British and Chinese. My own business address there was that of Monnet-Murnane and Co., the firm I had set up in New York with a skilful business partner, and which at that time was chiefly working with the China Finance Development Corporation. By January 1936 it became clear that I should be more useful in New York; so we left that fascinating world without ever having fathomed it. To do so would have taken several lifetimes or more.

In New York, George Murnane and I worked on a number of different projects of which I have only dim recollections. In fact, I was growing bored with international finance, which ten years earlier had seemed so vast and rewarding. By now, I found the routine monotonous and the horizons narrow. The whole of my attention was directed to the dangers that were piling up in Europe and threatening world peace. The League of Nations' inability to deal with the simplest problems, such as imposing sanctions against odious acts of aggression, showed how inadequate our efforts had been. Arbitration had tried to stem violence, and failed. Even the great economic resources that we had mobilized had not been enough to overcome poverty and injustice. Everywhere, people were afraid. I did not know what could be done by this time to halt the drift and defend freedom; but I was ready to make myself useful wherever I could.

Chapter 6

ARMS FOR THE ALLIANCE (1938-1940)

I

Mission to Roosevelt

One day in September 1935 we were having dinner with Murnane on Long Island, when Foster Dulles arrived with news of Hitler's decrees against the Jews in Germany. I said to my friends: 'A man who is capable of that will start a war. There are no limits to such bigotry and aggression.' If this episode has stayed in my mind among so many others now forgotten, it is because that was the moment when I realized that Nazism would bring war as surely as a hurricane brings havoc. Later, another episode seemed to me equally significant and sinister. I was in New York with Heinrich Brüning, the former German Chancellor. It was March 1936. In the *New York Times*, we read that Hitler had just occupied the left bank of the Rhine. Brüning reacted immediately. 'The Allies must enter Germany,' he said. 'Otherwise, sooner or later, there will be war.' He explained: 'If you don't react, Hitler will think himself invincible, and the German army will believe that he's always right.' The advice was sound, but things worked out differently. The British were unwilling to act – and in those days the French did not act without the British.

I was not then involved in public affairs; but owing to my travels and my varied contacts I was better placed than many men in government to see what was concealed from them by their civil servants, their optimism, or perhaps their fear of crushing responsibility. One only had to open one's eyes to discover how little prepared the Allies were, both materially and morally. As in 1914, when I was a young man, I could see where the democracies were weak, and where once again something had to be done. There were many public debates between partisans of this or that form of national defence. Some were about strategy, such as the role of tanks in modern warfare. Events were to show that we had no lack of tanks: it was simply that we did not know how to use them in the way that Colonel de Gaulle had so clearly foreseen. But we faced a real and serious shortage of aircraft. A veil of silence concealed this fact at the very moment when Hitler and Goering were proudly announcing the birth of the Luftwaffe. By 1937, the Germans already had a thousand Messerschmitt fighters, which were faster than any French or British plane. That same year, the Rapporteur of the French Senate's National Defence Committee declared: 'The German air force is in a position to fly over France with complete impunity.'

At the beginning of 1938, at the house of some mutual friends where I had gone with Pierre Comert, I met Edouard Daladier, who was then France's Minister of Defence. He was a very worthy man, and very human; we became friendly. If he proved no match for the events to come, I cannot bring myself to blame him. Who could be sure of measuring up to a cataclysmic onslaught aimed at everyone by the brute force of Nazism, ready for any crime that could serve its ends? Daladier's only mistake, and one made by the vast majority of Western Governments, was to have understood too late that Hitler would stop at nothing. Once he realized that, Daladier put all his determination into preparing the defence of France. From January 1938 onwards, I witnessed his desperate efforts to overcome our inferiority in the air. He was helped in this task by his Air Minister, Guy La Chambre, who was young and discreet but no less obstinate. The American Ambassador in Paris, William Bullitt, was also anxiously watching the growing threats, not only to France's freedom but to that of the West as a whole. Remembering what I had done in the 1914–18 War, and in particular how we had redressed the balance of power at sea, he asked my advice about the existing imbalance in the air. To both of us it seemed just as serious, and it threatened to be just as decisive.

In the light of this and of the difficulties to be overcome, Bullitt asked me to share my experience with the people who were already working on the problem. That Spring saw the draft of a 'Note on the possible establishment of an aeronautical industry abroad out of reach of enemy attack.' Despite this, no progress was made for several months. It took the Munich crisis that September to get something done. Daladier, by now Prime Minister as well as Defence Minister, came back from the Munich conference filled with a sense of humiliation, rather than the relief that so many of his fellow-citizens felt. On his return, he invited me to lunch with Guy La Chambre and Bullitt. 'If I had had three or four thousand aircraft,' he said, 'Munich would never have happened.' I then learned that General Joseph Vuillemin, Chief of Staff of the French Air Force, had written to the Air Ministry on September 26, telling him that France had only 600 combat aircraft, with a performance inferior to that of the German Messerschmitts, and that only seventeen were of modern design. Daladier had gone to Munich in the certain knowledge that 'the Germans can bomb Paris whenever they choose.' On October 3, 1938, he decided to send me for urgent talks with Roosevelt.

Bullitt cabled to the US President describing the gravity of the situation and suggesting that the man 'best qualified to organize this effort on behalf of France [was] Jean Monnet, who, as you know, has been an intimate friend of mine for many years, whom I trust as a brother.' By October 13 Bullitt was in Washington, and he telephoned me. 'The President is expecting you. Come discreetly.' On October 19 I arrived in New York, and at once took the train for Hyde Park, the Roosevelt family house on the banks of the Hudson River, where the President was spending a few days' holiday. It was an old patrician mansion, but very informal. There were numerous children, and the table always had room for passing guests. If I was impressed by my first meeting with Roosevelt, it was not on account of protocol. The President received me in his study, one of the smallest rooms in the house, where he had worked as a child. Behind a big table, he held out his hands to his visitor with a smile of welcome, apologizing for not getting up. He was in his famous wheel-chair, with a brace on his legs. His disability in no way affected his mind, which was exceptionally wide-ranging, open to all the problems of his great country, but always in a global context. Roosevelt saw the United States in its world situa-tion, and in his view the dangers that were massing in Europe were a threat to democracy in the New World as well as in the Old. That is why he welcomed a Frenchman of whom he knew little save the one thing that mattered to him: this foreigner had ideas about how we could combine to resist the common enemy.

Hitler was not yet the declared enemy of the American people – that came three years later. But already Roosevelt regarded him as the arch-enemy of freedom, and therefore of the United States. A few days before my visit he had been terrified, he said, by Hitler's violent speech at Nuremberg. In Roosevelt's view, Munich had opened the way to war. He had decided to spare his country from ever having to give in under threats, as France and Britain had had to do. For this purpose it was essential to gain overwhelming military superiority. Already he had set his colleagues to work. At present the key factor was air-power. Roosevelt was convinced that if, in that summer of 1938, the United States had had 5000 aircraft, and the capacity to produce a further 10,000 a year, Hitler would not have dared to behave as he had. Roosevelt admitted that he had to reckon with American isolationism, and that if war broke out his plan to supply aircraft to France and Britain would be seriously hampered by the US Neutrality Act. But our job, he told me, was precisely to find ways of overcoming such obstacles.

'We believe,' he added, 'that the Germans can produce 40,000 planes a year, Britain and Canada 25,000, and France 15,000. 20–30,000 more will be needed to achieve decisive superiority over Germany and Italy; and they'll have to be found here, in the United States.' As he quoted these figures, Roosevelt scribbled them down on a piece of White House writing-paper. At the end of our talk, I asked if he would let me have it as a souvenir. Without a moment's hesitation, without even bothering about what I might do with it, he handed it to me. Unfortunately, I no longer have this token of the exceptional confidence he placed in a visitor he had just met for the first time. It was burned by my family in Cognac, together with the rest of my papers from that period, during the German occupation.

We then turned to study how to manufacture the aircraft to be sold to the Europeans, particularly if, as seemed likely, war would break out and oblige the United States to place an embargo on arms exports. The President declared: 'Three factories can be built, each working three eight-hour shifts, which will make it possible to produce 5000 aircraft a year. As regards the embargo, there's a way around it – build the assembly works in Canada.' Roosevelt drew a map of the North-East frontier to show me where he would like to locate the factories, near Montreal. So much attention to detail showed the importance he attached to the problem. It convinced me that we were talking and would always be talking about the same thing, which is the first and perhaps the only rule if two people are to understand one another.

Before I left, Roosevelt telephoned to Henry Morgenthau, Secretary of the Treasury, asking him to see Bullitt and myself right away. We returned to Washington by train, and on Saturday October 22 we dined at Morgenthau's house. He was a solidly-built, hard-working man, not very easy to get on with. His main virtue, and the one that will ensure him a place in history, was his total devotion to Roosevelt, whose orders he carried out loyally in the key post he held for twelve years at a stretch. What was more, he was fully committed to the struggle against Nazism: so concerned was he to eradicate it that he even proposed, when victory was won, to pastoralize Germany. Morgenthau was all for helping the European democracies; but he was startled when I explained what I had come for: 'The French Government would like to order 1700 aircraft, at a cost which I make to be $85m.'

'From what I know of it,' Morgenthau answered, 'there's absolutely no hope of your Government's finding the necessary foreign currency in one year.'

But Bullitt had an idea. 'Four billion dollars' worth of gold has left France in the past four years,' he said. 'Some of it must surely be in the United States. The American Government can help us locate the money, under the Tripartite Agreement of 1936, if you impose exchange controls and oblige French citizens to disclose their foreign assets.'

'An excellent suggestion,' said Morgenthau. Then he turned to me. 'But you'd better not be afraid to send a thousand people to jail. If you have the courage to do something like that, then your country's saved. If not, what's the use of talking about investing in aircraft or anything else?'

During the next few days, the US Treasury did its sums. There was about a billion dollars' worth of French capital in the United States, about five hundred million of which was 'floating' and could be mobilized. So there would be no lack of foreign currency for the operation on which France might have to depend for her survival. At the same time, I found out what types of aircraft were available and what orders might be placed. There, too, Morgenthau opened doors for me in the most confidential quarters, and put naval officers at my disposal – since at that time the US Navy had its own air force.

The results of my inquiries, which I gave to Daladier when I returned to Paris on November 4, were fairly encouraging. By concentrating on one or two existing types of aircraft, American industry could supply us with the numbers of fighters and bombers that we needed in 1939. If the first orders were placed before the end of 1938, the first deliveries could be made in April. Encouraged by this prospect, Daladier was prepared to requisition floating French capital in the United States. But while I had been away, the situation in France had changed. For three days now, Paul Reynaud had been Minister of Finance.

I have always found it hard to fathom Paul Reynaud. In various circumstances I have seen him be bold or irresolute, responsible or capricious, imaginative or conservative. The essence of his lively temperament was probably expressed in his eloquence, which was clear and vigorous, and which he thought could change the course of events. A great patriot, he was prodigal with appeals to the spirit of resistance and the conscience of mankind, which found an echo in France and even more, perhaps, among our allies. But when it came to providing the material resources that resistance required, and in this case seizing the opportunity that America was offering, then he became hesitant. The state of our reserves, he argued, made it impossible; we must not squander our gold. His watchword was: 'Defending the franc is defending France.' As for mobilizing fugitive capital, the idea offended his liberal principles. The military, meanwhile, claimed that French aircraft were better than the American models, and the left-wing parties argued that French industry must be given work. Nevertheless, Daladier held firm. On December 9, he summoned me to see him. In the presence of Guy La Chambre and Reynaud, he asked me to go back to Washington with an expert, Colonel Paul Jacquin, to order a thousand aircraft for delivery by July 1939. The question of payment he would take care of himself. I was to insist on very high technical specifications, to be drawn up by our military personnel.

The only American aircraft that met these requirements, unfortunately, were prototypes still on the secret list; and General Henry H. Arnold, the Air Force Chief of Staff, flatly refused to let us see them. I told Morgenthau, whom the President had recently asked to look after the question of arms supplies for abroad. He might have declined this delicate task, but he knew how important it was for Roosevelt's long-term plans, with the result that the smallest details of my mission were relayed to the President in the White House. So now Morgenthau went to see him and said: 'If it's your theory that Britain and France are our first line of defence, let Monnet have what he needs; if not, tell him he might as well go home. Give Arnold formal orders to show him the planes for reasons of state.' That was on December 21. By mid-January, General Arnold had still not given in. He told Morgenthau: 'If the President of the United States wants these prototypes to be seen by Frenchmen, then he'd better stop counting on the unconditional loyalty of his Air Force Chief of Staff.' But Roosevelt was determined. He believed in people speaking their minds, but he knew that the last word was his. This is how the American system of government works, and Roosevelt was perfectly at ease in it. There is a time for debate, then comes the moment for a decision, which everyone accepts. On January 16, 1939, Roosevelt decided that this moment had come in our affair, and he sent written orders to General Arnold, who obeyed them.

Even so, our difficulties were not yet over. On January 21, the press announced that a 'restricted' army prototype aircraft, the D.B. 7, had crashed at Los Angeles on a trial flight – and that a Frenchman had been on board. What had happened was that Colonel Jacquin and his assistant Captain Chemidlin, who had just been authorized to inspect the famous bomber, had gone to the Douglas factory, and Chemidlin had been taken up for a flight. The American pilot, apparently stung by some remark of Chemidlin's, had pushed the aircraft too hard and sent it into a spin. By a miracle, Chemidlin had escaped with a broken leg. In the rush to help him, and under the stress of emotion, Jacquin had spoken to him in French.

When the isolationists heard the news, they whipped up a storm of protest in the Senate and elsewhere. Roosevelt had to explain himself to Congress and to the press. He had chosen his line of defence: 'Yes, we're selling planes to the French. It's very good business for our air-craft industry, which is in the doldrums and needs the stimulus that these orders will give.' This, in fact, was one of his essential motives in taking such an interest in my mission. Beyond the immediate aid which the American Government was giving the democracies that were its first line of defence, only European orders could revive American military production, which had stagnated in the false sense of security cultivated by the isolationists.

This was Roosevelt's strategy: to advocate in public the cause of solidarity among free peoples, but also that of American self-interest, so that gradually, in practice, solidarity would become total and the common interest emerge. This was the goal that he worked towards, prudently but relentlessly, in a country ill-prepared for an historic task of such proportions. This was why we had understood each other from the start. The orders that I was finally able to place were for some 600 modern aircraft, with a firm option on 1500 more for the beginning of 1940. The American production potential that they set in motion, without publicity and without a premature Congressional debate, was to go on growing until at length it became the great arsenal of the Allies. But this Roosevelt could not yet publicly proclaim. He had first to get the Senate to overcome the obstacle of the Neutrality Act and then, with patient persuasion, to mobilize a whole people. How difficult the task would be he discovered once again on January 31, when the Senate Defence Committee came to see him about these aircraft orders. It was then that he let slip his famous remark: 'The frontiers of the United States are on the Rhine.' Some of the Senators, alarmed by his words, repeated them in public; and he was obliged to deny ever having used them, although reliable witnesses were sure that he had.

I returned to Paris, and to my own affairs. But I kept in touch with those who, like me, were preoccupied by their belief that war was near at hand and that air-power would determine its course and, one day, its final issue. I had the same deep conviction as in 1914: that in any conflict there is one point that makes all the difference between victory and defeat. It is not necessarily found at the heart of the bloodiest battle, where massed forces are locked in a struggle they can barely decide. In 1917, the issue had been determined by mastery of the seas. Now, mastery of the air would one day be just as decisive. When, we knew not; all we knew was that it would be after hard battles, because unhappily we had been unable to secure it early enough to deter the aggressor.

I knew, too, that it would take time to repair the omission, which was the outcome of attitudes which would be slow to change, even when men's eyes had been opened to what lay ahead. In 1916, we had been able to survive the peril of total war at sea. Should we, this time, be able to save French and British armies and cities from annihilation? I doubted it. Our military leaders, as if paralysed, saw how weak we were, but did nothing. 'With our air force, shall be we able to defend French soil?' the French Air Minister asked his Chief of Staff at the beginning of 1939. 'Feebly,' was his reply. He added that all that could be done was to build more aircraft, since there was a shortage of hangars and pilots. I could not help being struck by the contrast between this state of mind and that of America's leaders. With them, the word 'feebly' was taboo. It was clear that the mighty engine I had seen starting up during my visits to America would be heavy to move, but that one day it would carry all before it. It was vital for the European democracies to hold out until then.

By now, I knew how that engine worked; and the network of contacts that I had established in the United States, even more than the results obtained so far, encouraged me to continue my efforts. That network, small and more or less invisible to the public eye, did not correspond to any permanent administrative structure. It was made up of men in whom the President had confidence, and who were wholly devoted to him. Their official positions did not always reflect their real influence; nor did they necessarily match the jobs for which Roosevelt employed them. Like their leader, they were determined to defend freedom and democracy in the United States and – because in their eyes it was the same thing – throughout the world. That is why they were naturally open to my proposals, even though I was a foreigner: I wanted us to fight side-by-side in the common cause.

A great statesman is one who can work for long-term goals which eventually suit situations as yet unforeseen. In 1939, Roosevelt had no idea whether America would have to go to war, any more than he knew whether he would be able to run for a third term as President. One thing he knew for certain: 84% of his fellow-citizens, according to the polls, and probably the same proportion of his Administration, were against joining in the war for which Europeans were preparing. In July, an attempt to repeal the Neutrality Act had been rejected by the Senate. So Roosevelt had to keep to himself his personal conviction that the growing dangers on the other side of the Atlantic were a direct threat to democracy everywhere, and that his country would have to be ready for all eventualities. Never, perhaps, has the role of the President of the United States been so important, or so lonely. During the years that I knew him, Roosevelt was always very human and relaxed; but he was responsible alone for the future of the free world.

II

The Franco-British Council

In the last days of August 1939, when war had become inevitable, the French Government asked me to go back to the United States to negotiate new orders for France's air force – nearly 3000 aircraft and 10,000 aero-engines. Although I realized how urgently these supplies were needed, I saw serious objections to undertaking a third trip. My two previous visits had shown the limits of what could be obtained in the short term from the US Administration and US industry. Both needed time to adapt to developments whose speed the Europeans themselves could no longer control. Our precipitate requests were too much for the United States' present productive potential – not to mention the competing purchases made by the British, and the ambitious defence programme that the Americans themselves were preparing. Moreover, I knew that it was vain now to hope for effective help from Roosevelt so long as he had not solved the problem of the

Neutrality Act, although he would do so soon enough if he were left in peace.

I pointed this out to Daladier and La Chambre on September 3, and stressed a new aspect of the situation which from now on, I thought, was going to dominate all others. It was no longer a question of French needs and French orders: what mattered now was the Allies' common effort. I enlarged on this in a note which I sent to the Prime Minister that same day. On the question of aircraft, I wrote to Guy La Chambre: 'The programme we must present to the American President as soon as the Neutrality Act is repealed, but not before, should aim at increasing American production, which ought promptly to be doubled or tripled. This will have to be achieved by a joint Franco-British effort, as came out very clearly in my talks with Mr Roosevelt.' In conclusion, I suggested that a 'Franco-British Aviation Council' be established, whose staff would maintain a continuing balance-sheet of French and British air strength, and then supervise the necessary purchases. This balance-sheet was the elementary starting-point for any action: it was to come up time and again.

My note to Daladier was of more general scope. Its very title – 'The Organization of Franco-British War Supplies' – revealed my most urgent concern, and the reason for my remaining in Paris at a time when the Allies were mobilizing men and resources. The note began by recalling our experience in the First World War and the risk that the Allies had run, especially at the height of the submarine offensive, by failing to co-ordinate their transportation and supplies. 'France, Britain, and Italy all faced a supply shortage. The problem was to share it out; then, to devote to the most urgent needs those resources that could be procured – and finally to procure such resources on the best possible terms.' The note went on to describe the machinery that had gradually been established – the Inter-Allied Council and the various Executives. 'It is no exaggeration to say that supplies for the armies and the civil population in 1917 and 1918 could be ensured only by a system with almost dictatorial powers, whose strength lay in France's and Britain's agreement to pool their resources and act together in carrying out decisions. . . .' 'This lesson,' I concluded, 'ought to convince the French and British Governments that the same decisions need to be taken now and the same machinery needs to be set up – and that this should be done immediately.'

The argument proved convincing. On September 20, 1939, Daladier wrote to Neville Chamberlain, the British Prime Minister, along the lines suggested in my note. 'I have no doubt,' he said, 'that you like me are anxious for us to avoid at all costs the mistake that was made in the last war, when our two countries took three years to set up the inter-Allied machinery which ensured us our supplies in 1917 and 1918, and helped to overcome our military difficulties in 1918 – in particular by enabling American troops to be brought to France.' It was true, Daladier observed, that there were co-operation agreements between the French and British civil services. But he wanted to be sure that these were working properly, and for this purpose he had asked me to draw up a general report. 'I should be grateful if M. Jean Monnet, who has my full confidence, could be introduced to those responsible for dealing with essential imports, as well as to the Treasury, the Ministry of Shipping, the Air Ministry, the Ministry of Supply, etc.' This was promptly agreed: ideas seemed greatly to have changed since World War I. But habits were another matter.

By September 26 I was in London, where Sir Edward Bridges, the Secretary of the War Cabinet, made all the necessary arrangements. I was accompanied by René Mayer, representing the French Armaments Ministry. For the first time, but not the last, he had to listen to me repeating tirelessly to everyone we met the same simple ideas – the need for joint action based on an overall view of the common problem. 'The first thing to be done is to draw up a continuing balance-sheet of the two countries' needs and resources. For that purpose there must be established, by joint agreement, a Franco-British Executive in the confidence of both Governments, to prepare the joint decisions which the two countries' Ministers will take at their periodical meetings.' Once I have reached a conclusion that I want others to share, I am never afraid to repeat myself – to repeat in the same words the same few, simple-seeming ideas. Why should I do otherwise if the basic question is really as clear as I think it is, and if it seems natural and obvious? I have never been able to explain the same thing in a variety of different ways, because to me words can only have one meaning. I see no way of changing them, and no reason to try. In fact, there are many advantages in getting the same formulae fixed in people's minds. My maternal grandmother used to be known as '*Marie la Rabâcheuse*' – 'Monotonous Mary'. I think she had only a few very simple ideas, and to those she held fast.

By repeating now, as in all my private and public concerns, 'First draw up an overall balance-sheet', I may have been preaching a simple rule; but I know from experience that applying it sets in motion an extremely complex and troublesome process. Simple ideas are often troublesome: that is one reason why they are scorned. The balance-sheet of needs and resources, which ought to be the starting-point of all administration, is often the last thing that administrators think of. That is why I knew that it would take the authority of Heads of Government and the confidence of some key officials to set up and operate the inter-Allied machinery that after long negotiations would produce a balance-sheet capable of being written on one sheet of paper – hence its expressive English name. Balance-sheets of this sort have been milestones in my work: the strength of our fleets in 1916, of our air forces in 1940, of Allied and Axis military power in 1942, of the French economy in 1945, and of the six-nation European Community in 1950. Each time, the need for appropriate action became obvious once the balance-sheet was drawn up.

In these periods of crisis, the balance-sheet most often revealed an overall deficit; and, as I had written to Daladier, the problem was to share it out. Hence the establishment of bodies with the power to decide, in everyone's interest, on the allocation of resources that were no longer national, but common to all. Such bodies cut across civil service habits; but with a balance-sheet in hand it was generally easy to demonstrate that there was no other way. Moreover, the months of work involved in drawing up the balance-sheet made civil servants themselves aware of the need to co-operate and exchange information between different Ministries and different countries. So much so that the teams needed for joint action were already formed when the time came for decision. This is the dynamic of the balance-sheet, a page of figures which looks very like those great account-books that my father taught me to read in Cognac when I was sixteen.

The people I talked to in Britain were very receptive to my proposals – to set up joint purchasing bodies in the United States so as to avoid competing against each other, and to draw up a continuing balance-sheet of the two countries' aeronautical and other needs. Before going further, I corresponded privately with Sir Edward Bridges to make sure that we really understood each other: that what we were talking about was a joint organization of equals, and that nothing stood in the way of formal agreement between the Heads of Government – a precaution which is advisable before undertaking any joint action with the British. When I returned to London on October 17, we saw entirely eye to eye. To avoid the mistakes made in the last war, I had an explicit commitment from the British to the effect that all the tonnage at the Allies' disposal – French, British, and neutral alike – would be used to implement common import programmes. What was more, if our joint resources proved inadequate, any cuts to be made in the Allied programmes would be fairly shared between the two countries. In this way, we began in 1939 where we had left off in 1918.

On October 18, Daladier and Chamberlain agreed to establish five permanent Executive Committees, for food, armaments and raw materials, petroleum, aircraft, and shipping. These were to draw up a programme of what was needed and an inventory of what was available, 'to ensure the best use, in the common interest, of the two countries' resources of raw materials, means of production, etc., and to share fairly between the two countries any cuts that may be imposed by the need to reduce the programmes'. Finally, they were to work out joint Allied import programmes to be effected by a single purchasing agency. The Executives were to be under the authority of an Anglo-French Co-ordinating Committee with eight members chosen from among their own senior officials. Above this, at Ministerial level, there was to be an Anglo-French Council, which would meet periodically, and an Economic Section was to be formed within the Supreme War Council. The real power, however, would lie with the Co-ordinating Committee, since it would be in permanent session and would have the technical staff. It was to be based in London, and it seemed natural that its Chairman should be French. Four weeks later, I was appointed to that office by the two Governments acting jointly, and a British newspaper went so far as to write: 'Salute to Mr Monnet! He is the first federal official of the New World.'

This was certainly an innovation, at least as regards traditional civil administration, and I hoped that it would set a precedent. I persuaded Daladier and Chamberlain to confirm my role in terms which I had suggested to them and which I was to remember in other circumstances later on. 'You will note,' they wrote to me, 'that the Chairman of the Co-ordinating Committee is to be an Allied official; and while in no way an arbiter, you must use your best efforts to smooth out differences and bring about joint decisions by adopting an Allied rather than a national point of view.' For 'Allied' read 'Community' and there is no better definition of the role to be played later by the President of the European Coal and Steel Community's High Authority – which is doubtless no coincidence.

The first task was to make a list of all Allied orders that required an allocation of shipping, and to draw up a programme of imports up to March 1940, as well as an estimate of aircraft and armaments output for the same period. In other words, I had to produce a picture of the essential needs and resources of two countries which did not even have the same rules of public administration or the same weights and measures, and neither of which was in the habit of confiding to its neighbour even the fragmentary knowledge that it had of its own economy. But there was no point in wondering whether the job would be difficult or impossible: I only knew that it was essential. To help me, I had outstanding colleagues. My immediate associates were René Pleven and Pierre Denis; René Mayer was in charge of the Armaments and Raw Materials Executives; and the Food Executive was headed by Jean Laurent, who some months later became *chef de cabinet* to General de Gaulle, and played an important part in forming the Free French.

Our team was small – too small, it might seem, to do what was expected of it. In fact, however, it was perfectly suited to its task, which was to persuade innumerable departments to bring out from their files the technical information that was essential to political action. I knew from experience that the information was always somewhere to be found, but that it was shrouded in mystery by its custodians, who used all their ingenuity to make it incomprehensible. Authority alone is never enough to dig out information. Before it can start to circulate, the practical psychological conditions must be established; and the only way to do that is to ensure that those who know and those who decide – those who have all the figures and those who need only round totals – speak the same language. Persuading technical experts to divulge their secrets is so difficult that I can well understand why some men in Government give it up as a bad job and act in ignorance of the real situation. This is why so many mistakes are made in perfectly good faith. But in serious situations, where mistakes can be fatal, it is inconceivable to me that action should be thwarted by misunderstandings about a few basic and decisive facts, such as what resources are needed and what may be available. This is the point at which I have often intervened, to propose to men in power a simple method which they generally accept because they are glad to be offered a way out – and to enjoy the benefit.

It was this method that was to be used by the Executives, firmly linked with national civil services, where we had set up *ad hoc* committees. Once the machinery was established, I was able to spend more of my time on the problem of aircraft, which more than anything else would be decisive in the battles that lay ahead. Since the enemy were working to build up their own assault forces, they had given us some respite, and we still had time to catch up on their head start. But it was urgent to bring some order into our relations with Government and industry in the United States.

The problem that was becoming serious was the proliferation of French and British overseas purchasing missions, either already established in Canada and the United States or on the point of setting out. The Co-ordinating Committee that we were setting up in London looked like having a very hard time catching up with all the purchasing missions which had been sent here, there, and everywhere, and which were vying with each other to find public or private suppliers. Their rivalry even interfered with the orders placed by the American Army itself. Roosevelt was annoyed by this dispersion of effort. He himself wanted to supervise the negotiations, and to deal with a single interlocutor. The Neutrality Act was modified on November 4, 1939, and since we had waited so long the President now expected us to lose no time in sending a joint high-level purchasing team. On November 16 I went to London to discuss the problem with Chamberlain's influential adviser Sir Horace Wilson, and we agreed that the French and British Purchasing Commissions in Washington should be merged under the chairmanship of the British delegate, Arthur B. Purvis, with the French delegate Jean-François Bloch-Lainé as Vice-Chairman. Purvis was a Scottish industrialist who had settled in Canada and been very successful in a number of important business ventures. He served the Allied war effort magnificently until his death on an official mission in 1941.

So no time was lost. The establishment of the Anglo-French Purchasing Board coincided with Roosevelt's appointment of a presidential advisory committee which enabled him to follow Allied supply arrangements very closely, independently of the Army and the Treasury. Morgenthau, however, far from being kept out of things – which he himself had proposed – continued to be the faithful executant of Roosevelt's aid policy. In this way, the most direct and high-level links were established, and vast prospects for action were opened up. On November 23, Guy La Chambre, William Bullitt and I met Daladier in his office. 'We must have absolute superiority in the air,' the Prime Minister declared; 'and to obtain it the Allies must buy 10,000 aircraft in the United States. The first deliveries must be made at the beginning of 1940, and the rest continue into the spring of 1941. I know that American assembly lines are already working to full capacity. But there are automobile factories that can be converted.' Daladier thought big, and he was right – a few years too late, perhaps; but who in the autumn of 1939 would have said that it was already too late to act? Indeed, the future was to show that World War II was partly won in the automobile factories of America, and that the initial impetus came from these first Allied orders.

III

Roosevelt: aircraft for Europe

Roosevelt was not shocked by such Allied pressure. He saw very clearly that the free world was one, and that the United States had duties to it that went beyond any legal commitments. All he asked was that the Allies should not upset the internal balance of the American economy by interfering with military priorities or forcing prices up. This stipulation he made perfectly clear. For the rest, once the embargo was lifted, it was a matter of orders and foreign investments for private industry – or so it appeared in public, for in reality everything was secretly dealt with via the White House. Had France the resources to finance her share in this huge programme? 'I'll find the money to buy these planes,' Daladier said, 'even if I have to sell Versailles.' I proposed that Pleven should be sent to open the great negotiation.

Daladier's firm determination was not fully backed by Chamberlain. He, in reply to a pressing letter from the French Premier, had the following message sent by telephone: 'Prime Minister agrees on the need to achieve air superiority. But believes this can be done by using possibilities for manufacture in Britain and Dominions. Also, Great Britain would not have the required foreign currency.' This answer reflected the illusory British belief whose stubborn effects we were to see later – the belief that 'Britain can look after herself alone, and therefore must hang on to her gold.' This was the watchword in London, where people took a monetary view of the war. The Treasury had laid down a principle: 'Whatever happens, never export more than £150m. a year.' I had expected these difficulties, and I did not even try to persuade the British, who are only moved by the results of action. If the French mission succeeded, they would join in. In fact, it was not long before it was joined by one of the foremost British experts, Colonel J. H. M. Greenly. Pleven left on the Clipper on December 14, for one of these wartime journeys on unpredictable routes that made all our official missions extremely tiring, and often dangerous. He reached New York on December 21, and at once saw Morgenthau. All his talks were held in the utmost secrecy.

America, in fact, was entering presidential election year, and men like Colonel Charles Lindbergh, the national air hero, were intensifying their campaign in the country. On a trip to Europe just before Munich, Lindbergh had been greatly impressed by the superiority of the German Luftwaffe over the Allied Air Forces, and he had persuaded many Americans that they must at all costs keep out of European affairs. Roosevelt kept a close watch on this powerful wave of isolationism, and he conducted his negotiations with the Allies behind the back of the State Department and the Department of Defense. Pleven found the President just as well-disposed, however, and it was agreed that more than 8000 aircraft could be delivered in October 1940, provided that aero-engine capacity was doubled once again. The cost would be one billion dollars, half to be paid by France and half by Britain. At the end of January, Pleven came back to France to face the difficulties we had come to expect. The same old ritual was repeated every time: objections from the Treasury departments and scepticism on the part of the military – to say nothing of the unyielding counter-offensive that General Arnold was mounting in the United States.

It was Paul Reynaud once more who declared that such expenditure would empty the Allied Treasuries. He was supported this time by the British Chancellor of the Exchequer, Sir John Simon. Their idea was always the same – to enable our economies to come out of a long war with their reserves intact. At this point, Daladier talked of dismissing Reynaud. The objections raised by the military were no less specious: 'If, as is likely, the enemy delays his offensive until 1941, these American aircraft will be obsolete.' 'There's nothing more obsolete than having no aircraft at all,' replied Pleven. But I was now in a position to advance a still more convincing argument. At the beginning of January I had asked for the balance-sheet of Allied air strength, which we had just completed and which was now to incorporate the results of Pleven's mission, to be compared with the estimates of German air strength made by Allied intelligence. Apparently, our intelligence services were not in the habit of exchanging information, for the Prime Ministers themselves had to give special orders for those responsible to meet in London. Their respective reports, it must be admitted, told the same story. They revealed that in April 1940 enemy bombers would outnumber those of the Allies by two to one, and enemy fighters by three to two. At the present rate of aircraft production, it would take the Allies five months to match the enemy in fighter planes and two-and-a-half years in bombers.

At last I had the figures before me. They filled a big sheet of paper, 21¼ inches by 15¾ inches, which I have kept ever since, because its simplicity and mathematical rigour express all the tragedy of an unequal struggle. In an accompanying memorandum, I drew the following conclusions:

This report shows:

1. The formidable mass of striking power that could be let loose upon us from one moment to the next.

2. The odds against us: they may be improving, but time will be needed for us to establish superiority.

3. In the event of attack, our people will be encouraged and comforted in their plight by knowing that the immense resources of America are firmly and surely available to help them.

4. How can we, their Governments, relax our efforts until we have secured for them, however late in the day, the assurance that their vital defence supplies will continue to be produced even if our own factories are destroyed?

5. Present capacity in the United States is limited and probably fully taken up. We must now build up new potential there, which will produce results this year and will afterwards remain at our disposal to be used when the need arises.

Such were the thoughts prompted by three columns of figures summarizing months of hard work. I am not at home with statistics, and their intrinsic significance has always escaped me. But I have never lacked experts to interpret them and above all – after much insistence on my part – give me the relative orders of magnitude that reveal either balance or disequilibrium. Finally, a single figure speaks for itself and makes action imperative: the result in the right-hand column at the foot of the page. For me, it was enough to know that our aircraft balance-sheet was in deficit. If it stayed that way, we ran the certain risk of being dominated in the battles to come, not only militarily but economically and psychologically as well. So the balance had to be redressed, or rather reversed. Our deficit had to be turned into an ample surplus, for the same military, economic, and psychological reasons. The enemy had to be made aware that we were building, beyond his reach, a huge additional potential which would give the Allied people grounds for hope and the United States the proof of our determination. The memorandum ended with a quotation: 'Where there is no vision, the people perish.'

It was this vision that I was trying to communicate to Daladier and Chamberlain, men absorbed by the everyday problems of government and faced with miserly Ministers of Finance, unimaginative military men, and public opinion lulled by the illusions of the so-called 'phoney war'. To resist an enemy possessed by the will to power and organized for conquest, material and moral forces had to be built up, backed by a vision as yet far off. In 1940, as winter drew to a close, it was still possible to believe that these forces would stand firm on our soil and patrol our skies. Even so, we could only be optimistic if we were certain of American support. That support was needed whatever happened, and so much was at stake that we had to prepare for the worst. The measures that I recommended to the two Heads of Government were concerned most urgently with strengthening our military power. But already my thoughts were turning towards more fundamental political action, which would strike at the root of the problem and express the Allies' common will to face the future as one. I have described at the beginning of this book how these ideas developed in the spring of 1940, and how they came to a head that June. In view of the events to come and the way our efforts were to end, the last few months' work of the Anglo-French Committee may seem tragically futile. Nevertheless, it was this that laid the indestructible foundations of the great democracies' solidarity against the common foe.

Churchill, whom I was able to influence through Sir Horace Wilson, was convinced by our arguments and overrode British objections to the purchase of American aircraft. On February 5, 1940, the Supreme War Council took up the recommendations of the Pleven mission, which a study of the decisive balance-sheet had made more urgent still. Even then, it took three precious weeks for the Supreme Council's agreement to be translated into joint action – a further illustration of the almost structural difficulty that the British and the French seem to encounter in tackling problems together from the same point of view. I have seen this happen many times in the course of my life. For the French, the common approach is settled by the terms of the agreement, and it applies at once. For the British, it involves lengthy debate, and agreement is reached through a constant adjustment of positions. Daladier and Chamberlain had reached a common viewpoint on a crucial question: the Allies were to mobilize the formidable American arsenal. But for one side this meant a commitment to immediate joint action, while for the other it meant a decision jointly to envisage the possibility of action. Not without difficulty, we persuaded our partners to join us in a firm programme for the purchase of 8000 aircraft.

The second Pleven mission did not reach Washington until March 4. It met with the same active support from Morgenthau and the same obstruction on the part of General Arnold, who refused to let the Allies have the latest American models – the very type we most wanted, because they were a match for the new Messerschmitt 109s. Once again the same tale was repeated. Morgenthau went to see Roosevelt and asked him to exert his authority. The President summoned his Chiefs of Staff and, as Arnold confessed later, 'looking in my direction, he said that he knew places where officers who did not play the game might find themselves – Guam, for example.' In fact, Arnold was not playing the President's game: he was stirring up the Senate and the press against the priority given to Allied aircraft orders. But Roosevelt untiringly continued his campaign of public explanation. 'These orders,' he said, 'are an important factor in United States economic activity in general, and in developing the aircraft industry in particular. They mean prosperity as well as security.'

What they meant in practice was a further doubling of aero-engine capacity: we had helped to quadruple it within a year. This had been the bottleneck in the American aircraft industry, which now had to employ twice as many workers and technicians. That gave the necessary boost to production, which now began in earnest and took on gigantic proportions once the United States had abandoned isolationism and come into the front line. When the German offensive began, in May 1940, the results of so much effort on our part no doubt seemed tardy and inadequate. Only a few hundred American aircraft faced the Germans in the Battle of France. A larger number took part in the Battle of Britain, and helped decide the war on the Western Front. Most of them were lost, with their crews, in these heroic struggles; but others at once arrived to take their place. What counted was sheer quantity – those 'clouds of aircraft over the Atlantic to crush the demoniac force that is dominating Europe', for which Reynaud appealed desperately to Roosevelt on the night of June 3. When the time came, they poured from the factories which our needs had helped to develop and set up at a time when America was still unaware of the danger. I knew that we were only at the beginning of a long effort; but the machinery for action was in place, and it would never stop. Trust had been established between the men in power, born of a common will and strengthened by experience. We could wait on events, and make use of them. They would certainly not overcome us. That was my deep conviction in those spring days of 1940.

The problem of aircraft was not the only subject that our Co-ordinating Committee dealt with, although in my view it had absolute priority.

We were in charge of supplies; we had access to all sources of information; and from February 1940 onwards I began to hope that it might be possible to draw up a comprehensive balance-sheet of Allied needs and resources for defence as a whole. An ambitious balance-sheet of this kind was indispensable for the conduct of the war; it could be drawn up, and so it must be. I pressed for the intelligence services to be asked to estimate Germany's present strength and productive capacity in armaments of all kinds. 'Decisions must proceed almost inevitably from a presentation of the facts,' I wrote. I have never underestimated the power of such evidence: but it has to be presented so as to make an impression. I knew that it would take our military authorities, British and French alike, several months to make a coherent inventory of our own strength. As I had guessed, and incredible as it may now seem, no such inventory existed – except, of course, for aircraft, and that was only two months old. In this state of ignorance, no strategy, no plan of production or purchasing, could be anything but arbitrary. While waiting for the 'statement of the facts' that was indispensable, I spent a great deal of time on coal and shipping problems. All preparations were made for a war of attrition.

Hitler decided otherwise. In April came the Battle of Norway, a first serious warning. On May 10, the German invasion of Belgium and Holland surprised everyone – except, as I have said, General Ismay and all our grand strategists, who planned to catch the enemy in a trap. The German breakthrough at Sedan nonplussed them, for they had no alternative plan. With the enemy now at our gates, were we to go on hoarding our gold in the vaults as we had withheld our troops? Were we to go on fighting two separate wars, from Paris and London, with two War Ministers and two administrations handling our economic affairs? Were we to remain two separate nations, each following its own star? For some time already I had begun to think otherwise. Necessary as it was, our work of co-ordination no longer seemed adequate to the approaching peril. We were working hard, with care and determination. What we were doing was necessary and would prove useful whatever happened. But we were not prepared for the sudden speed of events. In this first phase of our war effort, we lacked nothing except time.

IV

The last attempt

The first striking successes of the German *Blitzkrieg* in no way altered my conviction that one day the war would be won by the superior strength of Allied armaments. France and Britain had their own resources and those of their Empires; they had territory at their disposal throughout the world; and they had the powerful assistance of the United States, on which they could count so long as they continued the struggle. All this strengthened my confidence and encouraged me to go on as I had begun. Hitler was in a hurry. Space and time were against him. At all events, our only hope, since we were not prepared to resist lightning attacks, was to build up beyond the enemy's reach a potential strength superior to his. There would be no miracle. No acts of mercy, no anguished appeals for American intervention could suddenly produce what had to be worked for, month after month, by deliberate, methodical organization, backed by formidable energy.

Two new leaders were now in charge of the Alliance. In France, Paul Reynaud had succeeded Daladier, and in Britain Winston Churchill had replaced Chamberlain at the head of the War Cabinet. The men of Munich had been pushed aside. At the centre of the stage now were two men, both eloquent and both fervently patriotic, who symbolized the spirit of resistance: both had fiercely opposed the Munich settlement. But that was where their similarity ended. There was no one to compare with Churchill, a true man of war, the legendary incarnation of John Bull. Power was his inheritance, and supreme power his instinctive goal; yet he was profoundly democratic. Did he see beyond the interests of Great Britain? I think not – but for him, as for many of his compatriots, British interests were those of vast areas of the world. Wherever the Union Jack flew, Britons ruled the waves. My relations with Churchill were good; but in the nature of things, as he saw them, my influence could only reflect my role, which was not political. He respected political power; and, while he appreciated the form of power that I had been given, it was not worthy of the same regard. I often had to find roundabout ways of securing his attention.

As Chairman of the Anglo-French Co-ordinating Committee, I was directly responsible both to Churchill and to Reynaud. On May 20, I sent them both a letter repeating the essentials of the arguments which had convinced their predecessors, and which I was now hoping patiently to preach to them. Now that they had the supreme responsibility, they would find that events left them little option, and that the claims of a balanced budget or the superiority of national weaponry were no longer relevant:

> Hitherto, France and Britain have concentrated their main efforts in the United States on the question of aircraft. But now that we can expect imminent and intensive bombing-raids on essential factories and production centres in France, it has become urgently necessary to extend our efforts in the United States in order to ensure that the most essential types of arms and munitions are manufactured without delay, and on as large a scale as possible. This will be made easier not only by America's increased desire to assist us, but also by the rapid growth of her own armaments programme. If we can state without delay what supplies we most urgently need, we can probably persuade the United States to concentrate on these the effort they are making to increase their productive capacity. This should enable us to get practical results in a matter of months.
>
> Anxiety to conserve foreign currency has been overtaken by the events of the past week. Now, it is much more important to convert our dollars as fast as possible into military strength, rather than to save them for some future occasion, by which time we risk losing the war if we cannot increase our military capability. Furthermore, the danger that America might refuse to supply us if we can no longer pay cash on the nail has now become negligible.
>
> The potential productive capacity of the United States is almost unlimited. It is greater than Germany's, and much greater than the joint capacity of France and Britain, especially since both our countries are exposed to enemy bombing. American capacity, moreover, is capable of immense expansion: this was shown in the last war, when shipbuilding increased from less than 200,000 tons a year to more than 3m. In the new circumstances of the present war, the United States can become the Allies' main source of supply, and the expansion of American production will be decisive. But to obtain that production, we must act at once. I suggest that a joint programme be drawn up without delay.

I quickly secured the agreement I was seeking; and on May 24, 1940, I cabled Purvis, asking him to study with Morgenthau the possibility of developing in the United States a vast capacity for producing arms and munitions, as had already been done for aircraft. Could the output of heavy tanks and anti-tank and anti-aircraft guns be increased, or would further factories need to be converted? How long would it take? Events were hurrying on. In the days that followed, the British

Army fell back to Dunkirk, and with great difficulty withdrew from the continent. On land, the Alliance now lacked substance; and its morale was sapped by mutual reproaches. This, of course, was just what Hitler wanted.

Nazi propaganda so successfully misrepresented the Dunkirk evacuation that many Frenchmen came to see it as a symbol of selfishness on the part of Britain. Yet I myself can testify that there was no lack of solidarity between the Allies in those dramatic days. On June 2, Silvia telephoned me at the office: she had just read in the paper that a trainload of French soldiers was arriving in London. 'We must invite some of those boys to lunch,' she said. Most of them were officers, and the three who joined us at lunch seemed like characters out of *La Grande Illusion*, the film by Jean Renoir that had so much moved us a few years before. One was Jewish, one was an aristocrat, and one was from the lower middle class. Salter and Pleven, who were also with us, could confirm that these French soldiers had no grudge against the British. 'They're embarking in orderly fashion,' they said; 'but on our side there's no organization: our soldiers are clinging to British boats that are already overloaded. It's tragic to see them forced off. . . .' We decided that we must do everything we could. Together with Salter and Pleven, we went to see Churchill.

Humanitarian as he was, in this terrible hour he was a military leader issuing stern orders: 'The evacuation of our troops will be completed by midnight tonight.' 'But there are more than 25,000 French troops left on the beaches.' 'We've done all we could. We've sent every ship we have, including sailboats and barges. . . .' Churchill had supreme power: the order of battle on land and at sea depended on him. We succeeded in persuading him, and he modified his orders. The Dunkirk operation went on, despite the exhaustion of British sailors, and thanks to their courage. By 2.23 p.m. on June 4, when no more could be done, 26,000 French soldiers had been evacuated to Britain.

That day, I still believed that a new joint line of defence could be established. But for this to be possible, each country must avoid seeking its own safety alone. I suggested to Churchill that Britain should recruit a pioneer corps to build fortifications on her own soil, while the expeditionary force should go back to France, where steps were already being taken to re-equip it. On June 6, in the further letter which I quoted at the beginning of this book, I returned to the need for joint action:

While Germany is concentrating all her forces on her immediate objective, the gravest danger would be if our power of resistance were to prove inadequate because it was dispersed. . . . The most important decision that circumstances immediately require seems to me to be the joint use of our two countries' air forces.

Our latest balance-sheet showed that the ratio of the combined Allied air forces against the strength of the Germans was one to one-and-a-half. But if they were not treated as a single force, French and British aircraft would simultaneously be fighting unequal and desperate battles under separate commands.

It was too late, no doubt, for such radical reorganization – and too late for the General Staff to realize how deep the cracks in our defences were. But in my view one thing was certain: the rift in the Alliance was as much the cause as the consequence of our misfortunes. That rift was as dangerous psychologically as militarily. It must at all costs be remedied before it became irreparable; and that could only be done by a bold stroke that would fire the imagination of two peoples on the edge of despair. I had had this in mind already when I was working on the gradual and to me inadequate co-ordination of our war effort. Now, it took on new significance: for while in recent months my British friends and I had imagined closer links between our two countries – perhaps a confederation – today it was total union, an immediate merger, that seemed necessary if we were to face together the choice between tyranny and freedom that was now being thrust upon us. France and Britain must join forces, in war and for the future.

In exceptional times, anything is possible – so long as one is prepared and has a clear plan to put forward when all else is confusion. The union of two peoples is a simple idea which men resist in normal times, but which reveals its value when they face the worst. It is all a question of timing. I have already described the plan for Anglo-French union; and if I put it at the beginning of my story, this is because it marked the high point of a continual effort to achieve unity among men. Joint Franco-British citizenship might have become an unprecedented reality, matching the unprecedented challenge that the two peoples faced. The men with the power to decide were not difficult to convince, because they were offered a constructive idea at a time when everything around them seemed to be crumbling. Even then, the idea had to be put before them. That this was done proved the value of confidence gradually built up in frank and friendly day-to-day work.

I had many British friends who trusted me because I had accustomed

them to the fact that in our joint work there was never any equivocation. They listened to me at a time when people were generally deaf to
advice. Arthur Salter, Desmond Morton, and Horace Wilson staked all
their credit with Chamberlain, Vansittart, and Churchill to bring to
fruition a proposal made by a Frenchman who had no political mandate. Churchill, indeed, did not accept it at once: he realized its significance only when he saw the enthusiasm of his Cabinet colleagues, men
like himself. He admitted as much, very fairly, in his memoirs:

> My first reaction was unfavourable. I asked a number of questions of a
> critical character, and was by no means convinced. However, at the end
> of our long Cabinet that afternoon the subject was raised. I was somewhat
> surprised to see the staid, solid, experienced politicians of all parties en-
> gage themselves so passionately in an immense design whose implications
> and consequences were not in any way thought out. I did not resist, but
> yielded easily to these generous surges which carried our resolves to a
> very high level of unselfish and undaunted action.*

On the French side, the project was not known until the last minute.
We have seen earlier how Reynaud was convinced – by a single
telephone call from de Gaulle, who was not. I can testify that on that
day, June 16, 1940, de Gaulle overcame his scepticism and joined in
all our efforts to bring about a total pooling of sovereignty between
Britain and France.

V

Continue the struggle

By now, I think, everything has been said about those June days.
There is no mystery left. Affairs of state have little need of the secret
machinations, the busy emissaries and ingenious stratagems, with
which they are surrounded in fiction even more than in fact. The most
important things are generally simple – at least, if one wants them to
be. Certainly, mixed motives and murky conspiracies sometimes
exist. But I have always ignored them, and they never did me any harm.
In Bordeaux, however, I found the atmosphere stifling, heavy with
intrigue. I only stayed a few hours, as I have said, and I was relieved
to come back to Britain with my friends, in the big flying-boat that had

* Winston S. Churchill, *The Second World War* (London, 1948), Vol. II, pp.
180-1.

been intended to evacuate the whole French Government to North Africa. In London, I found once more an atmosphere of calm determination, unshaken by the defection of Britain's ally. When the curtain of illusion was ripped aside, it revealed the unchanging moral strength of a people who had no need of wishful thinking to make them confident that they would never be conquered: civic courage was enough. The many French people who came to Britain to continue the struggle were welcomed with moving warmth.

André and Amélie Horré, the couple who looked after our house, had remained with us. When they heard of Pétain's messages to the French people, they wept and wanted to stay indoors. 'We're too ashamed to go out,' they said. Finally, Amélie went to the butcher's shop, and came back even more overwrought. 'Just imagine!' she exclaimed. 'Do you know what he said? He said "*Vive la France!*" ' In a London bus, Silvia and Hellé Bonnet met an elderly gentleman wearing a black tie: he came up to them when he heard them speaking French. 'Don't be too disheartened about France, ladies,' he said. 'Everything will come right in the end.' He added: 'I lost my son at Dunkirk.' Everywhere we met this same dignity – or rather, we sensed it, because people concealed their private grief. Our great friend Bob Brand kept to himself the loss of his only son. One day, he simply said to us: 'You mustn't think it's made me bitter.' That was all he ever said. Life went on in a nation that was now exposed to all the forces of destruction. One night when we came home from the shelter after an air raid, our caretaker met us: he was looking sad. 'You missed it,' he said. 'We had a very nice cup of tea.'

I was disappointed at our failure to keep the French Government in the war; but I had no regrets about having gone to Bordeaux. The experience removed a doubt that would have weighed on my future actions if I had not seen for myself the disarray and impotence of the men on whom we had mistakenly relied. I was still convinced of the aim to be achieved: but I was obliged to re-examine the means. The aim was still to unite the Allies' resources, including those of the French Empire. The means could no longer include the present Government of metropolitan France, which had become as it were a voluntary prisoner; but there was hope still for the French authorities overseas, whose incumbents had been appointed by the previous regime.

Men like General Charles Noguès in North Africa and General Eugène Mittelhauser in Syria derived their authority from a legitimate Government, which at the time of their appointment had still been free. Noguès had announced that he was continuing the struggle. De

Gaulle had cabled him on June 19: 'AM IN LONDON IN DIRECT UN-
OFFICIAL CONTACT WITH BRITISH GOVERNMENT. AM AT YOUR DISPOSAL
EITHER TO FIGHT UNDER YOUR COMMAND OR FOR ANY ACTION YOU
THINK FIT.' So there was no doubt then about the line to be followed.
The French and British Empires together, 'drawing without stint upon
the immense industry of the United States', as de Gaulle had said
over BBC radio the day before, provided the only chance, but a
sure one, of overcoming Hitler's dictatorship, which they could
shatter with their combined moral and material strength. But the
union of the two Empires had to be ensured, and on the broadest
possible basis: their immense but as yet inchoate common will had to be
organized and given legitimate shape.

De Gaulle's first moves were in this direction, and as soon as I
got back to London I had a number of talks with him. But it did not
take long for me to realize that his ideas did not quite tally with what
might have been assumed from the appeals he had just made. At the
same time as he was offering to place himself under Noguès's command, he had been envisaging a French National Committee operating
from London in agreement with the British Government. He made no
secret of his intention to run this committee, which in the eyes of the
Allies and of all free men would represent the legitimate authority of
France, as against the Pétain regime which had lost its freedom of
action.

De Gaulle secured from Churchill the British Government's recog-
nition of the National Committee as the sole legitimate French autho-
rity, in the name of which he, de Gaulle, would address the French.
So there was no interval between the breaking-off of relations with the
Bordeaux Government and the establishment of the London Com-
mittee: both decisions were published simultaneously by the British
Foreign Office on June 23. At the same time, I saw the text of what de
Gaulle was proposing to say that night over BBC radio:

> The French National Committee will take under its jurisdiction all French
> citizens at present on British soil, and will assume command of all French
> military and administrative authorities in this country now and in the
> future.

I could understand this haste, dictated by the desire not to leave French
authority vacant now that in the eyes of the free world the Bordeaux
Government was stripped of power and no longer legitimate. But at
the same time I saw the danger of prematurely freezing a situation
that was still completely fluid, and one in which the main pole of

attraction was not necessarily in London. What would be the reaction to this appeal from one man, speaking in the name of a Committee set up in London under the aegis of the British Government? Would it be listened to overseas by those for whom it was intended? Who was likely to believe that the London Committee was really independent? Who among France's proconsuls, her colonial civil servants, or her seamen would obey orders emanating from a body supposedly bound up with British interests? Anything might happen. It depended on powerful leaders, conscious of their power, whether immense territories and innumerable ships would rally to the legitimate republican cause that they had never abandoned, and which they now in fact held in trust – for they could perfectly well ignore the orders of a Government under constraint. The die was still not cast – in North Africa, in the Levant, in the Far East, on the seas. That was why, on this day of June 23, 1940, I believed that one isolated man, however convinced he might be of his historic mission, could not yet claim that he alone represented fighting France.

De Gaulle had reacted honourably against the humiliation of the armistice; but who could say whether other leaders, with more powerful resources, might not react in the same way? Noguès, in fact, was on the point of sending to Bordeaux a scathing message accusing the Government of 'not having made an objective appreciation of the possibilities of resistance in North Africa'. He was asking Weygand to reconsider his armistice orders. It was hard to understand why de Gaulle had first offered to place himself under Noguès's command and then, a few days later, had set up a French Committee on his own authority and asked Noguès to join it. How did he think he could reconcile the power he had assumed in London with the role he proposed for Noguès in the Committee? He knew full well how suspicious Noguès was of Britain – so suspicious, in fact, that he rejected all proposals coming out of London.

I explained to de Gaulle the reservations that I had about his ideas on how to continue the struggle. I should have preferred a less dramatic attitude and a less personalized form of action, which would not have hindered various developments that I still thought possible. However, realizing that my words were falling on deaf ears, and that the decisions were going to be announced over the radio on the evening of June 23, I decided to write to de Gaulle that same day, to give the fullest weight to considerations of which he was already aware. My colleague Pierre Denis handed the letter to him at the BBC:

My dear General,

After our meeting I talked with Sir Alexander Cadogan*, and I told him what I had said to you and to Brigadier Spears.

I believe that it would be a great mistake to try to set up in Britain an organization which might appear in France as an authority established abroad under British protection. I fully share your desire to prevent France abandoning the struggle; I am convinced that the Bordeaux Government ought to have sent the Head of State, the Presidents of the two Chambers, and some members of the Government to North Africa, in order to establish there, in agreement with General Noguès, a bastion of French resistance.

I still believe that even now General Noguès's decision to fight on could rally all those in France who want to continue the struggle and remain faithful to France's solemn pledges to her Allies. If resistance can be organized in North Africa, that is to say on French soil, under the authority of leaders properly appointed by a Government which was not virtually under enemy control when it was formed, I am sure that there will be a massive response in France and in all French colonies overseas. But this task of resurrection cannot at present be undertaken from London. If it were, it would appear to the French as a movement under British protection, inspired by British interests, and therefore condemned to a failure which would make further efforts at recovery all the more difficult.

As I say, I have put this to Sir Alexander Cadogan. I have repeated it to Sir Robert Vansittart and the French Ambassador. Like you, I have only one aim: to reawaken the energies of France and convince her that she cannot end like this. I wanted you to know my thoughts to the full.

P.S. – It goes without saying that it would be extremely useful to establish a Committee to help mobilize all Frenchmen who wish to continue the struggle alongside Britain. As I said to Spears and yourself, I am at your disposal at all times to discuss this question further.

I still hoped that the London Committee would not immediately assume too formal a character, prematurely freezing in their present roles the forces still available to France – those in Britain, and those overseas. But de Gaulle's broadcast appeal was followed by the British Government's message recognizing the Committee as representing all French units that were determined to continue the war in fulfilment of France's international obligations. This message, too, was the result of haste. The British Cabinet had not had time to discuss it. This was realized, and its publication was stopped. I had proposed to de Gaulle that we should discuss the matter again, in the hope of convincing him that

* Permanent Under-Secretary at the Foreign Office.

the question of France's role in the war remained open. De Gaulle agreed to see me, in order to persuade me that France's role and his own were already indissolubly linked. Next day, I received from him this letter:

My dear friend
    At such a time as this, it would be absurd for us to cross one another, because our fundamental aim is the same, and together perhaps we can do great things.
    Come and see me, wherever you choose. We shall agree.

In fact, we met several times more. But our good personal relations were not enough to overcome our disagreement about what should be done in the face of pressing danger. Britain was preparing to resist a formidable attack whose outcome was far from certain. The men and women, British and others, who were called upon to fight in this last bastion of freedom would not be found wanting in honour or courage. All that they lacked were the armaments and other resources to fight the war. Individual efforts and national character counted for little against this overwhelming need. In the weeks to come, when it began to be possible to hope that the Allied war was being won overhead, in the Battle of Britain – when it became clear that all was not lost and all might at length be saved – then, our energies must be bent towards a single goal: to confront the enemy with a single force equipped with superior arms. Pending the moment when this force would become that of the whole free world, the world's most powerful arsenal must be opened up. This was now my sole concern.

I said as much to de Gaulle, as frankly as he in turn explained his own conception of the historic role he felt called upon to play. But there was no meeting of minds. He criticized my decision, which would take me away from the nerve-centre where he intended to ensure that France would share in eventual victory. Victory, I replied, would not be achieved by heroism alone, or by strength of character: we must see about securing the essential material resources that we at present lacked. I intended to help in that task, and was willing to go wherever I could best contribute to winning the war. There was no room for subjective considerations in a decision of that kind.

We parted – or rather, the separate paths we chose to reach the same ultimate goal soon gave us no further occasion to meet, at least in London. It was three years before I saw de Gaulle again, in Algiers, where free Frenchmen found themselves once more facing difficult choices. There, once again, personal problems were important – too

146

important – but again the need to fight dictated a common solution. If I was able to play a useful role in Algiers, it was because I had maintained a position of independence, in which I could give de Gaulle advice and assistance which he knew were disinterested. Now, in London, he respected my choice as I admired his determination. I knew that it had taken great strength of character for him, a traditional soldier, to cross the great dividing-line of disobedience to orders from above. He was the only man of his rank with the courage to do so; and in the painful isolation felt by those Frenchmen who had decided to continue the Allied struggle, de Gaulle's rare example was a source of great moral strength.

Myself, I had no problems of conscience. As soon as I had realized that all the combined resources of the free world would be barely sufficient to resist Nazi hegemony, I had decided where I must work. The fall of France in no way changed the direction of our efforts: it simply meant that they must be redoubled. The war would be lengthy: there was no doubt of that. But the key to liberation was the same as always – the broadest and most complete alliance. For me, however, one formal detail had changed: the Anglo-French Co-ordinating Committee was no longer needed, and I had to wind it up. On July 2, 1940, I sent a purely formal letter to Marshal Pétain:

> Prime Minister,
> In letters dated November 20 and December 2, 1939, the French and British Prime Ministers asked me to accept the post of Chairman of the Anglo-French Co-ordinating Committee, whose task was to co-ordinate the economic war effort of France and Britain, as well as to supervise the Anglo-French Purchasing Board in the United States.
> As a result of recent events, it is clear that the Anglo-French Co-ordinating Committee, and other Allied machinery both here and in the United States, must now cease to exist. I therefore have no alternative but to offer you my resignation.

I sent the same message to Churchill, adding this:

> I have hitherto acted in an Allied capacity, serving the two countries equally. In present conditions I am deeply convinced that not only the future of this country but the liberation of France depend upon the successful prosecution of the war by Great Britain. I wish you to know, therefore, that I should be extremely happy if the British Government would give me the opportunity of serving it, and in doing so, of continuing to serve the true interests of my country.
> I therefore place my services at the disposal of the British Government in such capacity as they can be most useful.

My last act as Chairman of the Anglo-French Committee was to send to Bloch-Lainé in New York a cabled order from the Prime Minister in Bordeaux, instructing him to suspend all negotiations and the signature of all contracts on behalf of France, and then to try to cancel existing contracts, although some of them might be transferred. 'In the absence of further details,' I wrote to Bloch-Lainé, 'I take it that this means transferring to the British Government *all* the various armaments contracts signed by us and covered by the exchange of notes between General Weygand and the British Ambassador.'

On July 16 I received the following reply from Churchill:

Dear Monsieur Monnet,

I accept your resignation as Chairman of the Anglo-French Co-ordinating Committee, which you placed in my hands in your letter of July 2.

I am glad to note your desire to serve the British Government and thus the true interests of your own country. I have been in consultation with the Minister Without Portfolio* about how to give full scope to your qualities and knowledge. We both of us think that it would be best for you to proceed to the United States of America and there continue, in association with the head of the British Purchasing Commission, those services in connection with supplies from North America which have been so valuable to us during the time when you were Chairman of the Anglo-French Co-ordinating Committee,

Yours faithfully,
Winston S. Churchill.

It was everything I had wanted. Even if – or perhaps because – my mandate was not too precise, I was going to be able to continue my efforts to persuade America's leaders to realize the gravity of the real situation in Europe and the danger that would threaten them in their turn if the Nazis' totalitarian onslaught was not stopped. I knew that the task would be made easier by the brutal destruction of so many illusions, but that it would also be made more difficult by isolationist reactions to the great disappointment of the fall of France. I was glad to join Purvis again in Washington, and I knew that I should find it easy to work with him, as the British Government expected. More than that, I saw an advantage in his having the administrative responsibilities, so that I could devote myself entirely to the patient effort of persuasion for which I had already prepared.

Before taking leave of my colleagues in London, I summed up the

* Arthur Greenwood, who as acting leader of the Labour Party in the House of Commons had helped to precipitate Chamberlain's declaration of war.

lessons of our joint work in a paper which concluded as follows: 'The enemy cannot establish a reserve of weapons beyond the range of the bombers. You can. You cannot win by force of arms without overwhelming superiority in the air and without machines of at least equal performance. This cannot be achieved by British production alone. It is therefore no exaggeration to say that not a day must be lost in establishing this reserve, which may make all the difference between defeat and victory.'

Chapter 7

THE VICTORY PROGRAM
(WASHINGTON 1940-1943)

I
On the side of freedom

At the end of August 1940, Silvia and I left for Washington on the Clipper. When we landed *en route* in Bermuda, a British customs officer looked at my French passport suspiciously. I showed him my instructions from Churchill. His suspicion turned to bewilderment. 'It just doesn't make sense,' he said, 'for a Frenchman to hold a British job at this point.' From his point of view, he was right. My administrative situation was certainly anomalous, and even more so than he could have realized. Until recently, Purvis had been responsible to me; now, I had to choose what position I should occupy with him. Purvis was Canadian, I was French: we were now to be loyal servants of Britain. Given our great mutual trust and the scale of what we had to do, I was sure that there would be no problems. Purvis's exceptional character and ability had won him considerable influence at every level of the Administration in Washington. My role at his side was to be political. I now knew the machinery of decision-making in the United States, the engine, the transmission – and the brakes. I had taken the measure of Britain's needs, and I could testify to her determination.

I realized when I arrived that it would be hard work to ensure that the Americans and the British took the same view of the war and its immense demands, although they spoke the same language and wanted to make common cause. From his air-raid shelter at No 10 Downing Street, Churchill was sending moving appeals to Roosevelt, who received them on his ocean cruiser and sent back messages of sympathy. For the time being, there was nothing more he could do. Even sending fifty old destroyers in exchange for British bases in the West Indies and Newfoundland, as Roosevelt did in September 1940, raised constitutional and psychological problems. Both time and courage were needed to overcome them – which was why he chose such seemingly insouciant places of refuge in which to concentrate his mind. When he received me at the White House, he was full of anxiety. 'How soon will there be fog in Britain?' he asked. Nothing else, he thought, could prevent a German invasion. I found the same pessimism everywhere. I set out to dispel it by showing how confident I was in Britain's physical and psychological ability to resist an invading force. I was certain that the Nazis could no longer win the war: what concerned me already was how to defeat them. They were going to lose the Battle of Britain; our next task was to fight the Battle of the Atlantic, and win it. What I gradually discovered was how ill-prepared America still was.

Although the Selective Service Act had been passed, making it possible to raise 800,000 men from a total of 16m. fit for military service, there were in fact only 55,000 soldiers on a war footing, and very few aircraft in service. The rest existed only on paper – in estimates like that which Roosevelt had scribbled in my presence in 1938. But as the danger took shape, the estimates swelled. A few days after the German offensive in May, Roosevelt had asked Congress for a billion dollars for defence expenditure and the manufacture of 50,000 aircraft. Within a month, the programme had increased to three billion dollars. Once past the first shock, public opinion grew accustomed to these astronomical figures, and gradually accepted the idea of defence efforts commensurate with the size of the United States. Inevitably, people began to wonder how far such efforts were compatible with the supply of aid to Britain. This question of priorities was already being discussed when I arrived; but it seemed to me absurd. First, because Allied orders had been and still were the key to American production; but also, and in my view conclusively, because far from choosing between two alternatives it was a question of adding or rather integrating them both. The defence of Britain and that of America were indissolubly linked.

Despite the lack of preparedness, and although so much was still in the air, I myself was not pessimistic. The problem had been stated, and the means of solving it were being discussed. To understand America, it is important to realize that before any problem is solved in the United States there has to be a period of public debate. The opinions of qualified people are listened to without formalities. Then comes the decision – and a decision is always reached, because no one would dream of leaving a problem unsolved, and no one wants discussion for discussion's sake. Once taken, the decision is no longer questioned: good or bad, it is carried out by all concerned. In the autumn of 1940, I was far from surprised to find the United States full of controversy, in Congress, in committees for and against isolationism, in the press, and in the Administration itself. I realized that this was one of those periods of gestation from which, when the time comes, great decisions proceed. And the country needed to take an historic decision. Roosevelt, attentive as always to public opinion, watched and waited, intervening without ever forcing things. When the time was ripe he would be ready to turn the debate into action.

With the election a few months off, the President had to reckon with a powerful isolationist movement, and this might have sufficed to explain the caution with which he refrained from making spectacular gestures of the kind for which the Allies hoped. But over and above electoral considerations, I believe that his behaviour was dictated by his deepest concern as a statesman: never to divide his country. Whatever his private convictions – and he could certainly have imposed them on the whole nation – the decisions to be taken were too serious not to require unanimous support. He studied the opinion polls, and saw them regularly shifting in the direction he wished. In September 1940, 67% of Americans believed that the country was heading for war. If they had had to vote for or against fighting, 83% would have voted against. This was readily understandable, since they had not been directly provoked and had no personal experience of Nazi aggression. 'Our dangers are internal,' Lindbergh told his fellow-countrymen. 'We need not fear invasion unless Americans bring it through their own quarrelling and meddling with affairs abroad. If we desire peace, we need only stop asking for war. Nobody wishes to attack us, and nobody is in a position to do so.* The majority of Americans were agreed, however, about aid for Britain – aid short of war. In this area, Roosevelt could go ahead. He did so by handing over the destroyers, as well as large quantities of arms and ammunition drawn from US Army stocks. But his political instinct made him hasten slowly, his every move watched by opponents who knew as well as he did that commitments 'short of war' would one day merge into war itself. That day was undoubtedly coming: what mattered was to approach it imperceptibly under the pressure of necessity.

This reluctance did not worry me: it would fade away as the shock waves from the collapse of Europe at length reached the heart of the United States. More worrying, it seemed to me, was the resistance I

* Robert E. Sherwood: *Roosevelt and Hopkins* (New York, 1950), p. 153.

encountered in the structure of the American economy and the habits of the Administration. Purvis showed me the very disappointing results of the survey I had asked him to undertake at the end of May. There was all too little productive capacity for the guns, tanks, and ships that Britain needed, unless new factories were built – which meant delays of twelve to eighteen months. American industrialists were uneasy about the long-term risks attached to wartime investment. What was more, the British persistently failed to understand the obvious advantages of procuring their supplies from the United States, out of reach of the bombers. In London, under the pressure of immediate needs, priority was given to the purchase of American machine tools, in order to produce rapidly, on the spot, and without any loss of foreign currency, the British armaments that were considered best.

Orders placed in the United States, although they were a first-class guarantee of being able to fight on until victory was won, immobilized this machine-tool capacity. They also greatly worried the British Treasury, which was always anxious about its gold and currency reserves. In other words, there was some confusion about what means of defence to choose – confusion that was in marked contrast to the Government's and the British people's clear and vigorous determination and will to win. There was a similar contrast between the aims and the actions of the American Administration. Clearly, the Allied war machine was slow to gather momentum.

There was one good way of tackling these apparent contradictions; and that was to state them in simple terms and bring them into the wide-ranging discussion that I referred to earlier. That was to be my main contribution to the war effort during the months that followed my return to Washington. This time I had no difficulty in finding men who were ready to listen and to turn into practical decisions the plans that we worked out together. Some were already old friends; others were those to whom they introduced me. They belonged to Roosevelt's circle of advisers. This was a quite informal group, united by mutual trust. Among the people who played an important role at that time, I would single out for first mention Felix Frankfurter, the Supreme Court Justice. Austrian by birth, he had learned English at the age of twelve and been a brilliant pupil at the Harvard Law School, where he later taught after practising as a lawyer. He left his mark on generations of American jurists, many of whom worked with him in Roosevelt's circle at the time of the New Deal. Now he once again lent his great authority to the struggle against totalitarianism. We were soon united by deep friendship as well as common ideals, and I was able to count on his full support. It was Frankfurter, incidentally, who after Roosevelt's Inaugural ceremony in January, 1941, had passed on to the President a note from our small daughter Anna, enclosing ten dimes for the Infantile Paralysis Fund. 'It is very little, but it is all I have,' she wrote.

Justice Frankfurter, clearly, had no official post in the presidential entourage; but the President's door was open to him whenever he thought fit. Roosevelt, unlike European statesmen, set no store by formalities. I myself needed no official title to go and see him. He knew very well that I would only do so for good reason, and I never abused the privilege. Problems of prestige had no place in Washington at that time, where the only concern, essentially, was to make a workmanlike job of organizing the war in a country still at peace. Frankfurter, like the others, was completely disinterested. He was not seeking any political position, and those people who had taken official jobs, like Stimson, McCloy, Harriman, and Dean Acheson, saw themselves as on active service on behalf of the United States. Their true career was in the service of law. It was as lawyers that I had first come to know and respect them – members of that characteristically American profession, in which ability and technical skill are carried to the highest degree that I have ever seen. The power and material advantages that flow from it do not detract from its disinterested nature. No one who was not disinterested, in fact, would have given up his lucrative practice and answered the President's call as these men did.

Stimson had already been Secretary of War under a previous President, the Republican William Howard Taft, thirty years earlier. He too had been trained at the Harvard Law School. As a lawyer he had a great reputation, and he had neither the temperament nor the ambition for a political career. Stiff and self-willed, he was said to be a difficult man; but his energy and enthusiasm as Secretary of War won him great loyalty. My friend Jack McCloy, who was his Assistant Secretary, was a 'fighting lawyer' like his chief. Thirty years younger than Stimson, he had the same strong personality, the same integrity, and the same burning patriotism. But the warmth of his feelings was more obvious – so much so that he commanded affection as well as respect. He had had a difficult time as a young man, brought up by his mother in modest circumstances, and had had to work his way through law school. His brilliant intelligence made his reputation as a lawyer, but his deep humanity led him naturally into public life when he saw freedom threatened. A Republican like Stimson, McCloy served his

Democrat President loyally and enthusiastically. It was undoubtedly the love of freedom that prompted these remarkable men to lend their careers and their talents to a cause that was still unpopular, but which should, and one day they thought would, be that of the whole nation. Surrounded as he was by such powerful people, Roosevelt nevertheless exercised to the full his presidential function, which was to take decisions. Even his closest associate, Harry Hopkins, whom I gradually came to know, never abandoned his role of loyal servant and faithful executant, however great an influence he came to exert on American political life and on the course of the war. This, however, was so exceptional and so striking a case that I shall return to it at greater length later on.

Among these people there was a ceaseless exchange of information and ideas. We dined together – often at our house in Foxhall Road; we telephoned each other; we exchanged notes at all hours of the day or night. Military men joined in our talks: General James H. Burns, and Lt.-Col. H. S. Aurand, who was somewhat suspected by the Army on account of his links with this anonymous, informal group whose influence on the White House was well-known. It was there that I grew accustomed to working on a basis of total trust with outstanding newspapermen such as Walter Lippman and James Reston, who could be brought in on the most serious discussions, where their experience was useful, without ever being tempted to give away secrets. The secret elements in these talks, in any case, were less important than the public debate, which helped move men's minds towards our objective – throwing the weight of American power into the struggle.

Robert Emmet Sherwood, the playwright and wartime assistant to Harry Hopkins, described this period in his fine book *Roosevelt and Hopkins*: 'One adviser who remained in the background, but who exerted considerable influence, was the Frenchman, Jean Monnet. He was no New Dealer. He was, in fact, a coldly calculating businessman who had seen his own country suffer terrible defeat and Britain come close to it because of the refusal or the inability of industrialists and soldiers to face the facts of total war. Monnet was the great, single-minded apostle of all-out production, preaching the doctrine that ten thousand tanks too many are far preferable to one tank too few.'[*] If such was the impression I gave and the conviction I held, I must say that in the matter of tanks we were far from having such a surplus at the end of 1940.

[*] Sherwood, *op. cit.*, p. 288.

Purvis and I explained to London that the Americans would launch a big enough rearmament programme only if they were strongly pressed to do so, and that many people in Washington were waiting for this pressure to take the form of precise requests. When it did, something positive might be done, or it might not, and we should draw the appropriate conclusions. It was for this purpose that Sir Walter Layton, Director of Programmes at the British Ministry of Supply, came to Washington at the beginning of October with an impressive list of orders – all the equipment needed for ten new British divisions, and 9000 more aircraft in addition to the 14,000 already on order. Obviously, Britain could no longer afford the three billion dollars that she would have to pay for these supplies under the Cash and Carry law, which was still in force. But we had decided to turn on its head the argument advanced by the financial experts, who wanted needs to be adjusted to match resources. When the needs in question amounted to the survival of the free world, the argument was absurd. When so much is at stake, resources can always somehow be found. What mattered was to demonstrate our firm resolve and to fire men's imaginations with the magnitude of our requests.

This was also the attitude of Lord Beaverbrook, the British Minister of Aircraft Production, whose dynamism was gradually overcoming the doubts of British industry. Beaverbrook was a powerful character who reigned over a press empire and whose friendship with Churchill had led to his being appointed, very shrewdly, to important posts in the War Cabinet. He shared our idea of 'all-out production', as did Edwin Plowden, Under-Secretary at the same Ministry. Plowden was a first-rate administrator whom I was often to meet again, both officially and as a friend. Beaverbrook and Plowden fully supported Layton's mission; and it seemed to have succeeded when Roosevelt announced in Boston on October 30 that he was ready to fulfil British orders for 26,000 aircraft, and that he wanted to make the United States 'the greatest air power in the world'. Six days later, Roosevelt was re-elected: isolationism had had its day. Even so, nothing could be solved overnight. In the absence of appropriate machinery, the best will in the world ran into obstacles. We needed to change the over-bureaucratic form of relations between Britain and the United States, and invent more intimate and open-handed methods of co-operation. It was no longer a time for tough negotiations, such as Layton had just conducted. I said as much in a letter to Salter, who was Parliamentary Secretary to the Ministry of Shipping and in charge of Anglo-

American supplies. Its purpose was to prepare my British friends for the new scale which the war effort was now to assume:

> [Our] goal has now been reached in the main, namely: a greater air program has been launched; orders for an additional 1500 planes a month from the end of 1941 are now being placed, these types to be such as to serve both USA or England. The basis for a large amount of army supplies has been established. The USA has agreed to supply the equipment of ten divisions to Great Britain, thus integrating British supplies in its own program....
>
> This has been done, but done with slowness and on a scale that is yet too small....
>
> Indeed one of our main troubles since the beginning of this war is that we 'install' ourselves in certain situations either military or industrial and are content to 'administer' them as if the war was a new normal condition for us to live in, instead of being a catastrophic condition that needs to be ruthlessly brought to an end with all speed. The Maginot line and the British supply program planned in 1939 for 1942 are bloody examples of this....
>
> This I suggest was in turn caused by the lack of realization in London generally, including the top, that the British production was insufficient to enable Britain not only to resist but to win the war....
>
> The time has now come to change completely our line of approach and to treat this country as a partner willing to provide England with all that she needs to finish the job....
>
> But I am anxious you should feel deeply 'in your bones' as we do ourselves that we are entering a new period of the war as far as this country is concerned. The defence of England is for this people the defence of America. They therefore will be willing to do whatever England requires them to do. They will not, however, for the moment go to war – in time they may – I personally believe that they will some time next year, but the Government is going to try not to, and indeed if this war would be won by Great Britain with all the material help from the USA, but without its active war participation, then it would be the greatest internal political triumph F.D.R. could win.

In conclusion, now that the time was ripe I proposed to act as follows:

> It is for England to speak, to state clearly what she wants from this country, and state it in big terms.... The moment has come to face the President and the Administration with the complete requests of what England requires to 'win the war'.... The 'gap', and there will be a large one, will have to be managed by F.D.R. in the way that he chooses. My belief is that if properly handled it may result in USA making to England a gift of the material she needs, and the people of this country

would be almost unanimously united behind such a policy – and be proud of it.*

This letter, dated November 15, 1940, shows the lines of thought which we were exploring at that time and which led on to the crucial decisions of 1941: the urgency of solving the financial problem, if only by subterfuge; the necessity for a general balance-sheet of needs and resources – and for putting needs first, which meant a change of attitude in Britain and a gamble on the chance of mobilizing American production. All these difficulties were met by a swift succession of measures, each following naturally from the one before – a sign that everyone's ideas had matured. First came Lend-Lease, which removed the financial obstacle. With that out of the way, we could look un-flinchingly at the deficit in our war resources, and soberly calculate our real needs by drawing up a new balance-sheet. Once America had been drawn into the war, new forms of dialogue with Britain were needed: hence Hopkins's mission to London and the fruitful understanding that grew up between Roosevelt and Churchill. Finally, and inevitably, the full weight of the American economy was thrown into war pro-duction: the state of emergency enabled normal priorities to be re-versed. The way was clear for the Victory Program, which was to unleash upon the dictatorships in Europe and Asia the greatest military power the world had ever seen. I worked without stint to help plan and promote this irresistible process. Its mainspring was simple: the unflagging determination of a group of men united to serve a President with unheard-of power and responsibility, who in turn could count on the widest popular support.

II

The arsenal of democracy

At the beginning of December, Roosevelt embarked on the USS *Tuscaloosa* for a two-week cruise in the Caribbean. He took with him only a few colleagues, and he seemed to be leaving behind him all the most worrying problems. The worst of these was the British dollar deficit, which called for urgent and energetic action. All Britain's liquid assets in the United States had been requisitioned, and her

---

* Letter to Sir Arthur Salter dated November 15, 1940; in English in the original.

credit would soon be exhausted. The constraints of the Cash and Carry law, whereby the British could take away only what they could carry in their own ships and pay for with their own cash, had to be by-passed by some device which only the President could initiate and impose. It was his responsibility: we knew that he was aware of it and was looking at a number of possible solutions. His indecision alarmed Churchill, who on December 8 decided to send him an impassioned letter. A flying-boat took it to Roosevelt's yacht. It was a long, noble, uncomplaining message, not even appealing for armed intervention by the United States. Instead, Churchill appealed to the common destiny of two countries facing a common danger. Britain would bear the brunt of the human effort, he said, if America could supply the arms and aircraft and protect the convoys. 'You may be sure that we shall prove ourselves ready to suffer and sacrifice to the utmost for the cause, and that we glory in being its champions. The rest we leave with confidence to you and to your people, being sure that ways and means will be found which future generations on both sides of the Atlantic will approve and admire.'*

Roosevelt was deeply impressed. He read and re-read the letter, casting about in his mind for the 'ways and means'. The question was not so much technical as one of psychological presentation: how to make acceptable to Congress and to American public opinion his firm decision to give Britain all possible aid without asking anything in return? The solution he came to was Lend-Lease. Like the Marshall Plan eight years later, it was a simple idea, such as can only result from exceptional strength and exceptional generosity in a man and a people. In addition, Roosevelt had a genius for expressing his ideas. It enabled him, as soon as he was back in Washington, to persuade America to make a gift by presenting it as the hiring-out of goods that were never in fact to be returned.

> Suppose my neighbour's home catches fire and I have a length of garden hose four or five hundred feet away. If he can take my garden hose and connect it up with his hydrant, I may help him to put out the fire.
> Now what do I do? I don't say to him before that operation, 'Neighbour, my garden hose cost me $15; you have to pay me $15 for it.'
> What is the transaction that goes on? I don't want $15 – I want my garden hose back after the fire is over.

That explanation was a stroke of genius: it left a lasting impression on people's minds, and got off to a good start the great national and

* Churchill, *op. cit.*, Vol. II, p. 501.

Congressional debate on Lend-Lease. As Roosevelt said,

> There is absolutely no doubt in the mind of a very overwhelming number of Americans that the best immediate defence of the United States is the success of Great Britain defending itself.

I was delighted to hear him condemn out of hand taboos that I had been attacking for years:

> In all history, no major war has ever been lost through lack of money. . . . What I am trying to do is eliminate the dollar sign.*

The alliance of the two great democracies was now cemented, and there was nothing to prevent the better endowed of them from using all its resources to strengthen its more exposed partner. 'The United States,' I said one evening to a group of friends, 'must become a great arsenal, the arsenal of democracy.' Felix Frankfurter interrupted. 'Very good,' he said; 'but promise me not to use that phrase again.' 'Why not?' I asked in astonishment. 'Because I think I can soon find a very good use for it,' he replied. A few days later, we listened together to Roosevelt's famous radio 'Fireside Chat' of December 29:

> A nation can have peace with the Nazis only at the price of total surrender. . . .
>
> Such a dictated peace would be no peace at all. It would be only another armistice, leading to the most gigantic armament race and the most devastating trade wars in history. . . .
>
> We cannot escape danger, or the fear of danger, by crawling into bed and pulling the covers over our heads. . . . We must produce arms and ships with every energy and resource we can command. . . .
>
> We must be the great arsenal of democracy†

After our conversation, Frankfurter had gone to the White House to slip that phrase into the speech, which Hopkins was drafting for the President. ' "Democracy?" ' someone objected: 'does that mean that Russia won't benefit from Lend-Lease?' 'Never mind,' came the answer: the phrase was too good to be stopped by quibbles.

The first great obstacle was gone: the verbal problem had been solved. It took three months of legal and political battles to get from words to deeds. But when words were the public expression of a President's determination, they amounted to an international pledge, and they brought action in their train. Roosevelt used the magic of

* Roosevelt, press conference of December 16, 1940; Sherwood, *op. cit.*, p. 225.
† Sherwood, *op. cit.*, pp. 224–6; Edward R. Stettinius, Jr., *Lend-Lease* (London, 1944), p. 69.

words with great skill. In a world where decisions made by a few people might mean life or death for millions of men and women, his speeches were events, awaited with hope or with dread. Sherwood, who had helped in the careful drafting of the December 29 Fireside Chat, has described how that night the Nazis subjected London to one of the most violent bombing raids of the war – it devastated the City and only spared St Paul's by a miracle – in order to drown the message of hope that the British were hearing from Washington. Lend-Lease was a psychological and material turning-point in the war, as was illustrated in an unusual way by a story I was told some years later. An American soldier parachuted into Normandy in 1944 was welcomed at a nearby farm-house, and there he was surprised to see a calendar showing the date as March 11, 1941. 'You're a bit behind the times,' he told his hosts. 'We stopped the calendar,' they answered, 'on the day we heard on the radio that the United States had voted for Lend-Lease. That day, we knew that Germany had lost the war.' No one could invent a story like that, and I believe the man who told it me. Those Norman farmers set their clocks by the BBC, and they had undoubtedly heard Churchill's words: 'Give us the tools and we will finish the job.'

We were now in a position to tackle the second great obstacle: calculating the industrial effort needed to turn into an arsenal what for the time being was still only scattered production. To do so, we had to set targets, based this time not on available resources but on needs, conceived in the broadest terms and on a scale big enough to over-whelm the enemy. Such a calculation meant changing people's attitudes in Britain, but not in the United States. There, no one is ever afraid to think out what is needed before asking whether it be possible: what is needed *must* be possible, by definition. That was why, in a memorandum written at the end of November, I had listed the following priorities:

1. Decide the scale of armaments needed;
2. Decide what form they must take;
3. Then, and only then, work out how to produce them.

This last point was an industrial problem, and it in no way worried me. I was not naive enough to believe that American potential was unlimited; but, knowing the United States, I was certain that a very great deal of productive capacity was under-used. More important still, I suspected that this energetic nation was capable of creating new capacity: all it needed was the stimulus of a major challenge.

Logic might have suggested that we should begin by asking industrialists what they felt able to produce; but most of them could not have told us. They would only be able to do so, I felt sure, if they were put to the test – committed, that is, by firm orders on a growing scale. This, of course, would imply transfers of resources and the limitation of civilian production, for which the President would have to prepare public opinion.

The question of what armaments to manufacture was strategic, a matter for the military to decide. But the first of our three points – how much to produce – required an overall view which only Purvis and I could provide, because it depended on a balance-sheet of needs and resources; and if we did not yet have the precise figures, we at least had the method and the experience that were necessary for digging them out. I knew that a further balance-sheet comparing the combined strength of Germany, Italy, and Japan with that of Britain and the United States would show a considerable deficit. This, I was convinced, would strike the imagination of the American Government and people, and persuade them to accept the inevitable sacrifice of some civilian production.

The first step was to calculate the deficit. Purvis worked on this in London until the end of the year. The British were alarmed when they saw the enormous gaps between what they needed to win the war in the next two years and what they had set themselves as supply targets. They refused, in fact, to present so negative a balance-sheet – not so much to avoid alarming the Americans, as for fear that the United States would take it upon itself to fill the gap, and would withhold raw materials and machine tools from Britain. It was the same old notion of a finite, zero-sum world with limited resources, in which one ally could be strengthened only at the expense of the other. So we drew up the balance-sheet ourselves, and presented it in the starkest terms, knowing that the American Administration needed a shock, and that Roosevelt was only waiting to be spurred on by big demands. He accepted without hesitation our figure of ten billion dollars as the amount of aid to be offered to Britain up to June 1942. He knew as well as we did that it could not be attained, at least within that time-limit – but he was reassured, as it were, by that order of magnitude. The figure that he fixed for the Lend-Lease appropriations was seven billion dollars. In October, Congress voted six billion more.

The very large scale of the new supplies covered by these figures revealed the full inadequacy of the programmes on which Britain had previously based her hopes of winning the war. Originally, she had ordered sixty merchant ships from the United States, to be delivered by the end of 1942. Under Lend-Lease, these now became 1200, and the total tonnage on order increased from 400,000 to 6m. tons. Deliveries of aircraft – mainly heavy bombers – were to be doubled, to total 50,000 in the next two years. Orders for tanks were also doubled; orders for machine-guns were quadrupled. We were far from the '10,000 tanks too many' that I was credited with seeking, but we were now seriously approaching the scale of the total war which the enemy had forced upon us. What the American decision meant, and what a demoralizing effect it had on the Nazis, can readily be understood. In the light of these figures, Churchill's allusion to 'the most unselfish and unsordid financial act of any country in all history' no longer seems exaggerated.

Even so, we had to recognize that the scales would be dangerously tilted against us throughout 1941, and that a balance-sheet was a measuring instrument, not a cure. I knew from experience that it took four months to draw up an accurate balance-sheet, two months to prepare a programme, and a further eighteen months for supplies to come off the production line. That was why I always seemed to be in a hurry, and to be hurrying other people. All my notes at that time were punctuated by the word 'now', usually underlined. Countless human lives depended on how fast we could go. 'If this gap can be filled up,' I wrote to Roosevelt at the beginning of January, 'the war may be shortened by a year.' In fact, most of the new orders were not met until 1942. The bombers built in the United States in 1941 were in fulfilment of the contracts we had signed at the beginning of the war. Yesterday's efforts, which might have seemed useless when France fell, were bearing fruit today, enabling Britain to fight on. In the same way, efforts made today would ensure victory tomorrow.

During these months it was very difficult to match British needs against American capabilities, and above all to reconcile the attitudes of two separate civil and military administrations. The experience convinced me that our liaison machinery, formerly the British Purchasing Commission and now the British Supply Council, no longer met the needs of what was becoming a total alliance. True, the American Government had long taken the precaution of pretending to keep at arm's length from the British war effort; and the British, understandably proud, asked only for technical assistance, which our officials were active and able enough to negotiate. What was surprising, however, was that political relations between the leaders of two powers united in so many ways were still ruled by protocol and conducted by occasional correspondence through diplomatic channels. Churchill had never met Roosevelt: he wrote him frank and courteous letters which he always signed in the same strange way, as 'Former Naval Person'. Roosevelt had invented this transparent code name as a joke, and Churchill used it throughout the war. But beyond this touch of familiarity there was no personal link between the two men.

In December 1940 the British Ambassador in Washington, Lord Lothian, suddenly died. He was a man of great distinction and high intelligence: he had been a very effective intermediary, and had helped to establish growing confidence between Roosevelt and Churchill. With his death, both lost a mutual friend. It was then that we learned that Roosevelt was sending Hopkins to London to look at the situation on the spot and establish direct contact with the British Government. I realized that, by sending his closest associate, Roosevelt was in effect going to London by proxy, and that if the right psychological conditions could be created Atlantic relations could be put on a far more satisfactory footing.

Like everyone in the small world of Washington, I had met Hopkins; but we had not made really personal contact. At that time he was living in the White House, in a suite which Roosevelt had put at his disposal. He was unpaid, and had no official position, having resigned as Secretary of Commerce on account of ill-health. In fact, he had never really occupied that post. For many years now he had been Roosevelt's most influential adviser: the President had recognized his exceptional intelligence, integrity, and loyalty in the early days of the New Deal, when he had been working as a charity and relief official. Hopkins came and went at the White House as his health permitted. His illness affected only his body: his mind was as vigorous as ever.

He was respected not only because of his privileged position with the President, but also and above all because his influence was good, disinterested, and discreet. Between him and the President there was true osmosis of two minds and characters, such as I have rarely seen. Roosevelt was open, genial, and generous, with a very lively imagination. Hopkins was reserved, and on the surface seemed cold: at times, he had a caustic tongue. He looked fragile; but those who knew him well found him full of concentrated, passionate, and unselfish energy. He and Roosevelt were sufficiently alike to be real friends, but different enough for their complementary characters to be a remarkable driving force at the head of affairs.

Roosevelt habitually talked in general, imprecise terms: Hopkins turned his words into precise action. The alleged intellectual from the New Deal was in reality a man of practical organization and decision. At least, that was what he had become in order to serve the President he so deeply admired and to whom, in this time of great trouble, his presence was indispensable, day and night. There were always people, of course, who criticized the relationship as over-exclusive. Wendell Willkie, Roosevelt's unlucky rival for the Presidency, reported him as saying:

> I can understand that you wonder why I need that half-man around me. But – someday you may well be sitting here where I am now as President. And when you are, you'll be looking at that door over there and knowing that practically everybody who walks through it wants something out of you. You'll learn what a lonely job this is, and you'll discover the need for somebody like Harry Hopkins who asks for nothing except to serve you.*

To serve, as Hopkins understood it, was to bring to grips with reality the imaginative thoughts of Roosevelt, who was always exploring the most far-reaching ideas. The Oval Office in the White House reflected the character of its occupant: it was a miniature maritime museum, full of souvenirs from the far corners of the world, of which Roosevelt had astonishing geographical and political knowledge. Hopkins, a native of Sioux City who had never travelled abroad, was there to pilot the President's wide-ranging ideas into the administrative channels that he knew so well how to navigate. No one doubted the authenticity of the orders he gave: everyone knew that he would never use for his own ends the authority so liberally delegated to him. In fact, he was the unofficial Chief of Staff of the American Government.

It was in this capacity that the British Government was preparing to receive him, and contacts had been arranged with various Ministers and civil servants in order to give him the fullest information. I was rather surprised that at such a critical time Roosevelt's *alter ego* was going on what amounted to a ministerial mission – a task that a Secretary of State could have undertaken – whereas the real gap in the Alliance was the lack of direct and constant communication between the two men at the top. Since it was still too early for Roosevelt and Churchill to establish a close personal relationship by meeting publicly, as both would clearly have liked to do, everything pointed to the need for Hopkins to initiate the transatlantic dialogue without delay. I remarked on this to Felix Frankfurter.

* Sherwood, *op. cit.*, pp. 2–3.

'Hopkins will be wasting his time,' I said, 'if he only talks to Bevin and people at that level. He ought to concentrate on Churchill.'

'Would you be prepared to tell him that?' Frankfurter asked.

'Of course.'

A few days later, 'Mr Justice' invited us both to his house, and I told Hopkins what I thought.

'I've seen how things work in Britain. Believe me, don't look for authority there except in Churchill. Churchill *is* the War Cabinet. Everything will be simpler if you can establish a close link between Roosevelt and him.'

Hopkins could not hide his surprise at my insistence on this precise point, and I realized that he had some prejudice against Churchill: he was tired of hearing about the Churchill legend.

On January 10, 1941, he arrived in London and went at once to No 10 Downing Street. 'From this hour,' wrote Churchill in his memoirs, 'began a friendship between us which sailed serenely over all earthquakes and convulsions. He was the most faithful and perfect channel of communication between the President and me.'* As early as January 14, he cabled to Roosevelt: 'I am most grateful to you for sending so remarkable an envoy who enjoys so high a measure of your intimacy and confidence.'† On the same day, Hopkins wrote to the President:

Churchill is the gov't, in every sense of the word – he controls the grand strategy and often the details. . . . I cannot emphasize too strongly that he is the one and only person over here with whom you need to have a full meeting of minds.‡

Hopkins's mission lasted more than a month. During that time, he and Churchill had many talks, by day and by night. It was a turning-point in Anglo-American relations. The two countries' destinies were now linked at the highest level of responsibility.

Hopkins was greatly impressed by the stoicism with which his hosts endured incessant bombing. During his reception at Buckingham Palace, the Royal Family quietly went down to the shelter with him to continue their discussion, which was about the possibility of imminent invasion by the Nazis. He determined to use all his influence to increase American aid to Britain: for him, it was no longer a matter of figures, but of human lives to be saved. This experience convinced him that I had been telling the truth when I had spoken to him of the British Government's and people's unconquerable determination; and he now listened to me more attentively. One evening, he asked if he could come round to our house, and he spent the evening with the family.

* Churchill, *op. cit.*, p. 21.　† *Ibid.*, p. 23.　‡ Sherwood, *op. cit.*, p. 243.

Before he left, I asked him:

'Did you want to talk to me about something?'

'No, no,' he answered. 'I just wanted to get to know you a bit better.' The trust and friendship that grew up between us greatly helped me in my work.

No one in Washington found it strange that I worked at all hours and in any sphere where I could be useful; and no one worried about whether I was exceeding the very elastic limits of my role as a member of the British Supply Council. I put forward ideas: if they were accepted, so much the better. I have never tried to work in fields outside my experience – although there are many which I might have been induced to enter, if I had not always followed the rule of doing only one thing at a time. It seemed natural to try to convince Churchill, Roosevelt, and Hopkins personally, in that the most direct way to get things done was to go through them – as in the case of Viviani, Millerand, and Clemenceau twenty-five years earlier. I had no inhibitions about suggesting to the President's special envoy how he should act, and I thought less about the risk of annoying him than about the need to give him good advice. Likewise, to give Roosevelt ideas for his speeches, and to work over countless drafts of them, was in my view neither incongruous nor pointless, whether the attempts succeeded or failed. People knew that I wanted nothing for myself, and that I was not looking for a job – which enabled me to be both insistent and demanding. My efforts were not always successful, and they rarely succeeded at the first attempt. I was satisfied if there was a chance of succeeding; and there certainly was. I had further proof of this from Roosevelt a few days after the 'arsenal of democracy' episode.

Although I was not especially consulted as a Frenchman, I was more readily listened to on European matters than my Washington compatriots. Those Frenchmen who were on the side of the Resistance were comparatively rare in the United States, and were divided by intrigues; those who represented Vichy had no credibility. I frequented neither. I could see, however, that the effort to help Britain, which had absolute priority, was causing the United States to take no immediate interest in the future of France. I had never given up hope of seeing the French Empire enter the war alongside the Allies, but under the influence of internal propaganda and general discouragement, the prospect was growing fainter every day. For those who wanted to remain free, Britain was a symbol of hope, but under constant threat. They needed firm reassurance from the United States.

At the end of December 1940, I wrote a note to Roosevelt, who was preparing his annual Message to Congress. 'France,' I wrote,

is now subjected to the greatest possible pressure by the Germans, who are relentlessly pursuing their settled policy – namely, obtaining from France her willing adherence to the new 'European Order'; her giving up of the North African bases, and of the remainder of her Fleet. So far the Germans have failed to obtain these results essential to them. Pétain has refused, supported and probably guided by two forces of resistance in France – French public opinion which is more and more opposed to 'co-operation' with Germany, and Weygand and other authorities in North Africa who have stated that they will resist any foreign intrusion into any part of the French African Empire.

These two forces are of course encouraged by the British resistance, but in the last analysis they *look to the USA for final hope and guidance.*

What is the attitude of the USA and of President Roosevelt, not only towards helping England but towards *Europe as a whole* and, therefore, towards France, that vital part of Europe? This is the question that French men and women and General Weygand are surely asking themselves.

Roosevelt's silence on these questions might be misinterpreted. He was on the point of making a speech for which the whole world was waiting. 'One cannot exaggerate,' I wrote,

the importance of his statements and the repercussions that they will have not only in this country, but in England, in the countries of the Axis, and especially in France. . . .

[They] should be completed by a statement of the USA's position towards what Hitler is now trying to force on Europe – 'the new totalitarian order'. . . .

Without French acquiescence no 'new' European order can be created. . . .

Therefore, if, on the occasion of his statement, the President linked together the security of the USA, the providing of weapons to Great Britain, and the refusal of the USA to recognize any 'new Order' forced on Europe, he would very likely galvanize the forces of resistance which in France and in Europe are now making it impossible for Hitler to achieve the first part of his goal.'*

The message of January 6, 1941, known as the declaration of the 'four freedoms', made a considerable stir. Roosevelt promised men a world founded upon four essential human freedoms: freedom of speech and expression, the freedom of every person to worship God in his own

* Max Freedman (ed.), *Roosevelt and Frankfurter: Their Correspondence 1928–1945*, (London), 1970, pp. 566–8 reprints this Memorandum, dated December 18, 1940.

way, freedom from want, and freedom from fear. 'This kind of world,' he concluded, 'is the very antithesis of the so-called new order of tyranny which the dictators seek to create with the crash of a bomb.

'To that new order we oppose the greater conception – the moral order.'

The promise was not merely formal. Roosevelt declared:

'I ask this Congress for authority and for funds sufficient to manufacture additional munitions and war supplies of many kinds, to be turned over to those nations which are now in actual war with aggressor nations.

'Our most useful and immediate role is to act as an arsenal for them as well as for ourselves.'*

III

Overwhelming superiority

Not until May 26, 1941 did Roosevelt bring himself to declare a state of 'Unlimited National Emergency'. This put an end to the fiction of 'business as usual' and enabled the Government to impose priorities, cutting back on production for civilian use. I had known for a long time that this would have to happen if Britain was to be helped while America's own defences were made secure. But the real question, in my view, was a different one; how far should America herself take up arms to help defeat the enemy? As yet, no one could say; and in the absence of any such target the military authorities were peacefully equipping an army of two and a half million men, which was obviously not designed to attack Germany in the European theatre of war. Myself, I had little doubt that in 1942 the United States would be drawn into the war by the sheer force of events. When that happened, the military authorities would demand supplies which would not be delivered for six months or a year. It was therefore essential to anticipate the inevitable. The state of Unlimited National Emergency paved the way for a great victory programme. On May 28, McCloy and I drafted orders for Stimson to give to all the relevant departments, with a view to compiling a comprehensive Anglo-American balance-sheet comparing our resources with our estimates of German strength.

---

* *The Public Papers and Addresses of Franklin D. Roosevelt, 1940 Volume,* (London, 1941), pp. 668, 672.

In one of the many bodies that Roosevelt had established to advise him, I had come across a brilliant economist who had left the Rockefeller Foundation to offer his services to the Government in preparation for what he thought was an inevitable war. His name was Stacy May. He was in the prime of life, a born enthusiast, and he seemed to me the very man to build the immense edifice of figures from which we should have to draw our conclusions. How to persuade the military authorities to answer our voluminous questionnaires, when the smallest item was top secret – that was our own secret, and one which I have used on many other occasions. It is so simple that most people overlook it: the trick is to ask the right questions, and to seek out the goodwill that can always be found somewhere. What is simple is not usually easy; and in practice this means taking very great pains. I made that my business. Stacy May put the figures together, and arrived at a first overall estimate. It seemed quite out of line – except to those who already suspected that America was still a long way from making the necessary effort.

These were 'hectic days', as the Americans say. The time for reflection was over: action had begun. The Administration's thoughts had to be concentrated on a single objective – how much must we produce to overhaul and defeat Germany's material strength by the end of 1942? We should only know the answer when our gigantic inventory was complete. During the summer, Stacy May went to London. He came back with a full balance-sheet sixty pages long. It was one of the most confidential documents ever produced during the war, and one which would have given enemy spies a complete picture of what the Allies needed and what they could produce. But since no secret service at that time paid any attention to an inoffensive economist, either to kidnap him or to protect him, he came back alone at the end of August by the normal route, with his document under his arm. When it was read in Washington, there were some unpleasant shocks.

Rarely has a balance-sheet come at so opportune a moment or been so effective as a revelation and a spur to action. When it was realized that America was producing fewer arms than Britain and Canada, that she would not catch up with them until the end of 1942, and that her weak points were in heavy bombers and tanks, the disappointment was very deep. As I wrote to my friends, 'It is clear that we have not yet earned the right to call ourselves the arsenal for the democracies. . . . The facts disclosed by this balance-sheet clearly demonstrate that our present effort is proportionate neither to the goal we must set ourselves nor to our actual or potential resources.'* In fact, no one could prescribe a particular level of production at a time when Allied strategy itself was uncertain. Who, in a year's time, would be fighting whom? Already, Hitler's attack on the Soviet Union on June 22 had transformed the terms of the problem.

The excesses of the Nazis had reached their culminating point. They were certain to lose; but no one could say how soon. I gave Silvia a moment's false hope when I woke her and said: 'We've won the war!' For a second or two, she thought a miracle had happened. I have never experienced a miracle, or even a fortuitous stroke of good luck – only circumstances that are propitious or less propitious to action. In every case, effort is needed: only effort can give circumstances any significance. The war was won, because great sacrifices and a lot of hard work had given the Allies, with the USSR now among them, the chance to control events. In September, Roosevelt sent Hopkins to see Stalin, who received him like a Head of State. Hopkins, who had taken over all Lend-Lease operations, offered American aid to the embattled USSR. For the time being, this generous gesture could not but affect aid to Britain; but she in turn felt German pressure slacken now that the Soviet Union was in the war.

The US General Staff had only an approximate idea of the Red Army's battle strength; but in this connection I came across an example of how simple commonsense could sometimes deduce information that the secret services find it so hard to obtain. An expert on Soviet affairs, Mr Carter, said to me one day:

'I can tell you how many tanks the Russians are building.'

'Really? We'd certainly like to know. But what are your sources?'

'That's easy. My secretary, Miss Moore, speaks Russian; and she reads the economic documents published in Moscow. She's noticed that the statistics on tractor production have suddenly stopped. It's obvious: the production lines are now making tanks – at full capacity, and we can work out how many that means.'

On August 8, 1941, Roosevelt and Churchill met for the first time. Each came in a naval ship to the meeting-place, in Placentia Bay, off Newfoundland. Despite the presence of Lord Beaverbrook, more impatient than ever, this 'Atlantic Conference' made little impact on our production problems. However, the strategic discussions on how best to defeat Germany – there was already serious talk of a 'second front' – gave the officials in charge of the armaments programme

* J. M. Haight, *Jean Monnet and the Opening of the American Arsenal of Democracy*, Part II, p. 58.

something more precise to work on. Here once again we did not have to look far for the best man to solve the technical problems raised by questions of policy. One of Stacy May's team, my friend Bob Nathan, a shaggy-looking force of Nature, was the inventor of the way of calculating national income that became general after the war. He gathered up the bulky mass of statistics in our balance-sheet and began by summarizing them on one page. It was all that Roosevelt needed to know. Armed with these simple and striking figures, and in agreement with General George Marshall, the President took a crucial decision. On September 25, 1941, he gave his official approval to the Victory Program for the Army and the Navy. This meant an immense increase in American strength and, by implication, a decisive American impact on the future course of the war.

The key decision was taken. The next job was to work out how great an effort the United States could make, bearing in mind their national resources, their financial equilibrium, and the availability of raw materials. This was a task for which the British have a useful and expressive term – 'feasibility study'. It was the task that fell to Bob Nathan in October and November – a gigantic labour that was essential if the American economy was to be mobilized to the full. It is striking, if not altogether surprising, to see how a small group of people, and on occasion only one of them, without official mandate and without publicity, can have so decisive an influence on historic events. We all know that great occasions call forth great qualities; but these are not always where they are thought to be, or where official credit is given. In trying to recall the events in which I took part, I should like to put on record my continuing admiration for those men, and my gratitude for what they did. Their blend of ability and enthusiasm enabled them to take the measure of a situation where everyone else was baffled, to invent ingenious machinery which no one else had thought of, or to act as a link between two incompatible national systems. Bob Nathan, like Stacy May and Colonel Aurand, was among their number. Nor can Arthur Purvis ever be adequately praised for the part he played in uniting the Allies' war effort. At this crucial moment, alas, he was no longer with us. The aircraft bringing him back from Britain with a copy of the balance-sheet crashed in Scotland on August 20, 1941. I remember that he had a premonition of death, and that the last hurried notes that he made before the crash were a kind of testament. Tommy Brand, our loyal colleague in London, rescued them so that our friend's work might live on. Purvis had just enough time to complete that work. It ensured, through the

British Supply Council, that London and Washington henceforth spoke the same language in every sense.

It was in December 1941, in fact, that the British and the Americans really began to talk about the same things on the basis of the same facts. The facts left no choice but to make an unprecedented, fully co-ordinated effort. For the civil and military authorities, there were no more technical obstacles. On paper, the projects were ready, and the Victory Program had been declared feasible. Roosevelt, however, could not take the initiative of declaring war, and he hesitated to put the economy on a war footing. On December 7, 1941, the attack on Pearl Harbor put an end to this oppressive indecision. But while it took so startling a shock and so great a danger to bring America fully into the war, it is fair to ask where the United States would have been if the preparations for immediate action had not been worked out in advance. While the American people and the rest of the world were taken by surprise, we in Washington were already in a position to give the orders that would at once bring into action the great American arsenal.

Bob Nathan's calculations showed that the Victory Program might amount to 150 billion dollars by the Spring of 1944, and that the greater part of it could be attained by September 1943. This would mean doubling the effort so far made. Half the national income would have to be spent on armaments, instead of a fifth as at present, and civilian consumption would have to be severely pruned. General Marshall's staff translated these figures into the types of munitions to be produced. Once again, however, I saw that the military were thinking in defensive terms, and that they had a narrow view of the war. Their plans for 1942 in no way provided for the overwhelming superiority which was the only way to overcome the enemy's material strength and morale. On December 10, three days after Pearl Harbor, I told Roosevelt that in my opinion the munitions programme worked out by the General Staff could be increased by 50%. I had no difficulty in convincing Beaverbrook, who had come to Washington with Churchill for talks with Roosevelt and Hopkins at the White House over Christmas 1941 – a meeting known by its code name as the 'Arcadia conference'.

On the basis of what I had told him, Beaverbrook produced figures which to the American experts seemed fantastic: 45,000 tanks in 1942 instead of 25,000; 24,000 fighter aircraft instead of 5000; three times the number of anti-tank guns, and so on. Only Roosevelt listened to these requests without demur. 'All that's out of the question,' he was told.

'It's not a matter of what we *can* do, but of what we *must* do,' he replied. I recognized in his attitudes and decisions that same philosophy of action that I myself had acquired from very different experience. Events were to show that this philosophy, which concentrates on what is necessary, is more realistic than one that takes account only of what is possible. On January 6, 1942, in his Message to Congress, Roosevelt announced his ambitious Victory Program to the American people. 'The superiority of the United Nations in munitions and ships,' he said, 'must be overwhelming – so overwhelming that the Axis nations can never hope to catch up with it.' He made no secret of his military production targets: 60,000 aircraft of all types in 1942, and 125,000 in 1943; 45,000 tanks in 1942, and 75,000 in 1943; 8m. tons of shipping – in short, he had taken the boldest of our suggested figures. Nor did he disguise the implications: 'This production of ours in the United States must be raised far above its present levels, even though it will mean the dislocation of the lives and occupations of millions of our own people.'* That day, more than at any other time in my life, I felt the satisfaction of having contributed to a decision that would change the course of events.

If 'satisfaction', however, implies something satisfactorily accomplished, then the word is quite inappropriate, because there is always a long way to go between a decision and its implementation. I knew that Roosevelt had set his sights a little too high, for psychological reasons on which we fully agreed. It was now time to justify his gamble by setting up a permanent organization. In those days there were no computers, and everything was done by means of a vast network of consultations involving the Army, the Administration, the industrialists, and the trade unions. At the centre of the network for this decisive phase, Roosevelt put the effervescent Donald Nelson, the very prototype of the 'all-outer', or advocate of 'all-out' production. Nelson and his War Production Board were to form the greatest productive apparatus the world had ever seen – something for which the elderly Bernard Baruch had long been calling. He too had remembered the lessons of World War I.

From then on, with the help of men from the New Deal and *laissez-faire* industrialists, the United States mobilized their whole economy – a result that the dictatorship never achieved. The paradox was noted by Albert Speer, architect of the Nazi war effort. 'One of the most surprising aspects of this war,' he wrote in his memoirs, 'is that Hitler

* Leland M. Goodrich (ed.), *Documents on American Foreign Relations*, Vol. IV, World Peace Foundation, Boston, 1942, pp. 48–9.

wished to spare his own people the privations that Churchill and Roosevelt imposed without hesitation on theirs.' Speer explains that the Nazi régime was afraid of losing public support. That is perhaps one of the reasons why it failed. What seems to me certain is that Churchill and Roosevelt won because they appealed, at home and abroad, to a deep love of freedom that justified any sacrifice.

A second daughter was born to us in November 1941, and we wanted her to bear a name that would reflect the time of hope in which she was born. Should it be 'France' or 'Victoire'? We chose 'Marianne', which summed up everything – the symbol of the French Republic that was to be reborn when our country again became free.

Of course, difficulties remained. The American military authorities, once they had been given an arsenal bigger than they had ever dreamed of or desired, were not very willing to share its output. From my place on the British Supply Council, I had to fight to secure for the defence of Great Britain a fair share of what I had helped to obtain for the war effort as a whole. These tensions reflected the strategic indecision that lasted throughout 1942, up to and including the choice of Operation 'Torch' – the landings in North Africa. Colonel Aurand, whom his superiors thought too sympathetic to our needs, was replaced by a more difficult partner, General Brehon B. Somervell; and there was a lack of co-ordination between the various British and American bodies concerned with war production. All this brought me back to my constant preoccupation, which had taken me to London in 1914 and again in 1940, and from there to Washington: the need to take a common view of common problems, to combine the resources of the Allies, and to organize a unified defence effort – in short, to see that we all waged and won the same war. Roosevelt and Churchill had just set up the Combined Chiefs of Staff to deal with strategic questions. It seemed obvious that there should be a similar organization to deal with the production of arms, aircraft, and ships.

When what is needed is also obvious, there is no time to hesitate or relax. The struggle to establish what came to be called the Combined Production and Resources Board went on until the beginning of June. I used the same arguments, and in some cases the same notes, that had convinced Daladier and Chamberlain in 1939 – and when one remembers that they referred back to the experience of the Supreme War Council of 1916, one can see how little my preoccupation had changed. Why should it change, if men were still taking up the same attitudes and making the same mistakes? Only circumstances change, so that the forms of organization devised to deal with them must be different every time. What I proposed to Oliver Lyttelton, Beaver-brook's successor, and to Hopkins, and what they in turn, after many vicissitudes, persuaded Churchill and Roosevelt to accept, was a new structure, but one that for me at least embodied the same principle. I think I have already said enough on that score; and the present story would gain nothing from a detailed description of how the Combined Board worked. Nor would there be any point in describing the vicissitudes that attended its creation, since they were in no way different from those that had had to be faced in Washington to carry through any of the initiatives that seemed to me to be needed.

From then on, nothing could stop the vast munitions production machine that so many efforts had set in motion. It is the efforts that I have described, because they seem to me to illustrate what a few determined men can do, together, to unite peoples who are separately threatened by the same danger. Even where solidarity is obviously essential, it still does not come naturally. It needs organization. That organization is never complete; but there is a great difference, to my mind, between the time when it is conceived and established – out of nothing, or out of chaos – and the time when it is ready to be operated and run. Once the Victory Program had emerged from the phase of its long, uncertain, and disputed conception, it became a common task, the uncontested duty of all Americans. I was on the various committees which supervised its execution, and I had occasion to intervene again at a critical moment towards the end of 1942, when it became clear that the demands of the US Army were threatening to encroach on vital supplies for Britain. Our Combined Board was not powerful enough to counter-balance the influence of General Somervell, and the British sent Lyttelton to Washington. His mission, which he performed with great authority, was in response to our appeal. It had a decisive effect on the pooling of American and British war efforts. From then on, there was total solidarity.

The military situation, which in the first half of the year had gone against the Allies, began to improve as American production rose and the vast and heroic Soviet armies regrouped to block Nazi expansion. Between January and May, we had had to endure Rommel's victories in Libya, the surrender of Singapore, the capture of Rangoon, the German offensive in the Crimea, and the fall of Corregidor. German submarines were patrolling not far from the American coast. In June, the Allies lost 600,000 tons of ships. In August, the Wehrmacht drew near to Stalingrad. But it had reached the furthest point of its advance. The tide was about to turn. Then came El Alamein, the North African landings, and Guadalcanal.

When the total came to be counted at the end of the war, aircraft production had increased from a trickle in 1940 to the astonishing figure of 300,000. Once run-down automobile factories had produced 100,000 tanks. Shipyards hit by the Depression had built 184,000 ships. America's arsenals had manufactured 2·7m. machine-guns; her blast-furnaces had made 430m. tons of steel. That a country's economy could have expanded so rapidly in so few months seems obvious only to those who regard the power of the United States as a fact of Nature. No doubt, Americans have a natural bent for organization and expansion. But this does not exempt them from the need for effort and discipline. And their natural gifts become active only when they are led by energetic and responsible men. I had chosen to live among such men, and I was lucky enough to be able sometimes to suggest what they might do.

I therefore feel that they should share the tribute paid by John Maynard Keynes, who himself played an active part in these affairs as the British Government's economic adviser. Afterwards, he told his friend Emmanuel Monick:

> When the United States of America entered the war, Roosevelt was presented with an aircraft production programme which all the American experts thought would require a miracle. Jean Monnet was bold enough to find it inadequate. . . . The President came to agree with this point of view. He imposed on the American nation an effort which at first seemed impossible, but which later was completely fulfilled. This crucial decision may well have shortened the war by a whole year.*

* Monick, *op. cit.*, p. 67.

Chapter 8

FRENCHMEN UNITE (ALGIERS 1943)

I

A political mission

With the Allied landings in North Africa on November 8, 1942, the period of Liberation began. Once Roosevelt and Churchill were assured of a powerful and virtually unlimited armoury, they could choose from among several bold moves suggested by their strategical experts. Public opinion was impatient for direct action against Germany, and the Russians never stopped asking for a 'second front' to weaken German pressure on themselves. Finally, during the summer, it was decided to launch an oblique attack and make French North Africa the springboard for further operations. The plan was reasonably bold, and it gave the American Army under General Eisenhower, which bore the brunt of the task, a chance to test its fighting strength and organizing ability.

Until the very last moment, the secret had been well kept. For security reasons, the Americans did not inform the French in London, whom they regarded as too talkative – which naturally annoyed General de Gaulle. For the same reason, they kept to a minimum their advance contacts with the French in North Africa, and even surprised some of the friends on the spot whom for months they had been encouraging to hope for Allied landings. These friends were well organized, thanks to the very effective work done in Algiers by Robert Murphy, an American diplomat who was well versed in French and African affairs. Murphy was not content merely to observe events: he intervened to change their course. He had exceptional knowledge of human nature, and a remarkable taste for dangerous adventures. Although he had done everything to make himself master of the situation, and although he had many active agents, helped by patriotic Frenchmen at every level of this complex local society – colonials, civil servants, and military men in the Vichy Army – his plans were upset at the last moment, and the Allies met with greater resistance than they had expected.

The vicissitudes of that operation have so often been described by those who took part in it, and retold hour by hour by so many historians in more than thirty books, that I shall not dwell on them myself. At the time, I knew little more than I read in the American newspapers. These, I must say, devoted a lot of space to the operation, in which drama and folklore shared the honours. So much so that they gave only a confused idea of rather disquieting events. Here we were, a month after the Allied landings, and the situation still seemed hideously equivocal. Civil power was in the hands of Admiral François Darlan, on the fictitious pretext that he represented 'the captive Marshal', Pétain; and although General Henri Giraud had been specially brought from France by Murphy with the agreement of Roosevelt and Eisenhower, all that he had been able to secure was the title of Commander-in-Chief of the French forces. The proconsuls appointed by Vichy had formed an 'Imperial Council': it included Yves Chatel, the Governor of Algeria; Pierre Boisson, who had given orders to fire on the Free French; and Charles Noguès, who had ordered his troops to resist the Americans. Vichy laws were still in force; and not only had political prisoners not been released, but new prisoners had been sent to join them. Darlan, finally, had signed an advantageous agreement with General Mark Clark, Eisenhower's Chief of Staff, whereby the French Army was to receive equipment for eight divisions and nineteen squadrons, 1400 aircraft, and 5000 tanks.

Reading the dispatches that Roosevelt received from Murphy, his personal representative in Algiers, McCloy and I were able to form a rather more accurate idea of the situation than then appeared, and still appears, in many accounts of it. True, the Vichy administration and its army remained in power, supported by the Americans whom in several places, on Vichy orders, they had tried to drive back into the sea. But we knew Eisenhower too well to suppose that he had acted without good reason. He was soon to reveal the exceptional organizing ability that the new types of warfare required; and already he was displaying the human and moral qualities that were to make him a great statesman. At his level, military command involved diplomatic duties which may have made him seem weaker than his fiery subordinates, men like Mark Clark, Omar Bradley, or George Patton. It was simply that he had greater responsibilities. The public was not deceived: people were aware of his magnetism, and they knew that he was sparing with the lives of his men. His task in North Africa was delicate. The whole world was watching this advance-guard of the Liberation army. Already, it had encountered unexpected obstacles; and I must dwell on them for a moment if later events, in which I was involved personally, are to be understood.

Operation Torch – the North Africa landings – did not involve large numbers. Only 110,000 men landed on November 8, covering about 2000 kilometres of coastline. But 500,000 would have been needed to neutralize all the bases in North Africa, including those in Tunisia. From the start, Tunisia had to be left out, and so the Germans dug in. At several other places, especially in Morocco, sporadic French resistance seriously worried the Allies. Eisenhower had insufficient resources either to conquer or to occupy Algeria and Morocco: his plan had been for them to provide a friendly base and a reservoir of men and munitions for the invasion of continental Europe. Political success was therefore essential to his mission, and he had not concealed from the President that 'the African operation was too risky to justify on purely military grounds.'*

The policy he was to follow, however, was to be entirely subordinate to military needs. He had not come to 'liberate' French North Africa: the problem did not present itself in those terms, in so far as the area was not, or would no longer be, under German or enemy occupation – a condition fulfilled in Algeria a few hours after the Allied landings. Eisenhower had to ensure that no disorders upset his lines of communication and, ideally, that he could count on active support from the authorities and the local inhabitants. The civil and military authorities had rallied to the Allied cause – moral judgements were left till later – and the population, most of which regarded them as legitimate, had followed them with relief in this change of sides. There was no doubt that all French North Africa was firmly committing itself to the struggle against the Nazis. Whether it was as firmly committed to democracy was another question.

Immersed as he was, without a moment's respite, in the difficult Tunisian campaign, General Eisenhower could afford to ignore this moral and political issue. I could not, because what would very soon be at stake was French unity in the war and, later, in the Liberation. Every time that I have been able to bring men together, I have done so, as a matter of course. I am not concerned with political calculation or personal ambition, although I do not criticize them in others: it is simply that for me they would be a source of great complications.

* Robert Murphy, *Diplomat Among Warriors* (London, Collins), p. 136.

Experience has taught me, on the contrary, that unity can only be achieved by a simple and objective approach. In 1943, those Frenchmen who were in a position to fight were embroiled in complicated quarrels which divided the effort that France had to make to come back into the war. Allied policy threatened to accentuate the quarrels; and while I could understand the immediate practical considerations that dictated it in this hour of need, my task was to preserve the chances of bringing together all those who wanted to take part in their country's liberation.

With the Victory Program pursuing its course, I was convinced that Germany would be defeated within a matter of months. What was important now was to look ahead to the moral and material reconstruction of Europe, for the stability of which a strong and united France would be essential. On this, I had no reason to suspect the intentions of Roosevelt and Churchill. They had committed themselves very clearly to French independence once the war was over – and why should the Americans have joined battle if this was not their firm intention? But it was obvious that in their concern to win the present battle they would not necessarily be punctilious about their choice of temporary allies – and the arrival of Darlan was a major asset to the military, because the French North African army obeyed him. The American Government accepted this temporary compromise with many misgivings: on November 17, Roosevelt declared that Darlan was a 'provisional expedient'. The Americans' democratic concern for the future inclined them in a quite opposite direction, and they insisted on not pre-empting in any way the choice that the French people would eventually make by means of free elections. Until then, no one could claim to embody French sovereignty or to exert governmental authority. To do so would have been to prejudge the will of a people who had not yet recovered control of their own future.

In December 1942, in fact, we had no way of knowing how the French imagined their future – except that they were waiting for the Liberation and that the great majority of them were ready to fight again alongside the Allies wherever they could. I had no other reliable information on which to base my thinking; but a simple approach was preferable to the flood of contradictory intelligence that was reaching us from France, Britain, and Algeria. It was this simple approach that we now tried to work out. Just before Christmas, I summarized my ideas in a note which I have kept, and which has already seen the light in Hopkins's papers.* It both suggested and

* Sherwood, *op. cit.*, pp. 680–1.

reflected Roosevelt's own ideas.

The note set out three principles. First, the recruiting and equipping of a large French army in North Africa. This army, under the command of a general it trusted, Henri Giraud, would form a part of the Allied forces, and would be at the service of the French Government to be set up after the Liberation of France. For the moment, the fact that it was fighting alongside the Americans, who represented the hope of Liberation, would be a powerful psychological asset. The rebirth of French military power would capture people's imaginations and recreate moral unity.

A second principle was to preserve the French people's right to decide for themselves, when the time came, what Government they should have. 'No French political authority can exist or be allowed to attempt to create itself outside of France. . . . The French people as well as the world must receive that solemn assurance.' The 'legitimacy' claimed by Darlan could not in any circumstances be used as a basis for establishing a French authority in North Africa. The Pétain regime, set up under the pressure of disaster and fear, was not legitimate. As for de Gaulle, he symbolized the French will to continue the fight against the Nazis.

This line of argument led naturally to a third point: there was no longer a French Government, but only limited authorities, whose role was confined to local civil administration, and who would have to account for themselves to the future French Government. Darlan, therefore, was not the political leader of overseas France, but the provisional administrator of French interests in those of our territories that had resumed the struggle. A further conclusion was that the authority of de Gaulle's London Committee was limited, and for the duration would continue to be limited, to the territory of Free France. Any rivalry for Allied recognition that threatened to develop between London and Algiers must be discouraged from the start. The most urgent priority, in our view, was to give the French the fighting resources that the 'arsenal of democracy' was producing. This would strengthen the Liberation army, help merge within it the various elements of Fighting France, and ensure the presence of our country among the victorious Powers.

This approach seemed to me reasonable, and I was able to persuade Frankfurter and Hopkins to agree with it. On these problems, they were Roosevelt's most influential advisers: Secretary of State Cordell Hull and the State Department as a whole were kept quite outside of White House policy on France. At that time, of course, I imagined that victory would soon be won, and that this line of policy could be maintained until the liberation of France, which I thought would come some time in the following year. Later events naturally changed my mind somewhat, but they did not alter the essential objective, which was to unite the French and ensure that they shared in the victory. Roosevelt's attitude was more rigid. He stuck to the principle of local authorities long after it had been superseded by the need to organize for a more protracted struggle.

The memorandum went to the President on December 23, 1942. On Christmas Day, Darlan was assassinated. Giraud took his place, appointed by the Imperial Council, which as I have said consisted of the Vichy proconsuls still in power; and he assumed the curious title of 'Civil and Military Commander-in-Chief'. Marcel Peyrouton, Pétain's former Minister of the Interior, who had been dismissed by Laval, had already been summoned back from South America by Darlan to the post of Governor-General in Algeria. No changes had been made in the administration inherited from Vichy, and there was still the same ambivalence about the authenticity of orders given in the name of 'the captive Marshal', whose portraits still adorned the walls. Everyone on the spot seemed happy enough with this ambivalence; and Eisenhower had no reason to complain about a state of affairs that maintained order in the rear of his arduous Tunisian campaign. In the United States, however, I found that the American newspapers were giving a very different impression. The maintenance of Vichy laws, and in particular of discrimination against the Jews; the failure to liberate political prisoners; monarchist intrigues; and the reactionary nature of the regime itself – all gave rise to violent press campaigns. The appointment of Peyrouton caused a scandal. I was more than ever convinced that the authorities on the spot could never become in any way representative, and I also doubted very much whether they could long help to maintain law and order. It seemed to me unhealthy to equip an army that was open to anti-democratic influence, however ardently it wished to fight for the liberation of Europe. That army must not be in the hands of a faction: it was at the service of France, and all Frenchmen capable of fighting had their rightful place in it.

Now that the Victory Program had passed the point of no return, I judged that my most useful role would be at the heart of French affairs, and I asked Hopkins to send me to Algiers. He spoke to Roosevelt about this when they were both on their way to meet Churchill in the Anfa Hotel for the famous Casablanca Conference on strategy in January 1943. I do not know why on this occasion, contrary to his custom, Roosevelt consulted Cordell Hull; but his telegram reveals what was on his mind at the time:

> General Giraud arrives here tomorrow and Mr Churchill and I have arranged that General de Gaulle shall be brought here on Monday. I feel sure that the British can be brought around to our point of view and it appears that we must get a civilian into the administrative picture here. Apparently Giraud lacks administrative ability and the French army officers will not recognize de Gaulle's authority. Since there are no French civilians readily available in this area, what would be your opinion of having Jean Monnet come here? It appears he has kept his skirts clear of political entanglements in recent years and my impression of him is very favorable. I believe that Morgenthau knows and trusts Monnet. It had been my hope that we could avoid political discussions at this time, but I found on my arrival that American and British newspapers have made such a mountain out of rather a small hill that I should not return to Washington without having achieved settlement of this matter. All well here and I send you affectionate regards. I am particularly anxious that the mention of Monnet be kept completely secret as everything will be spoiled if there is any leak.*

Curiously enough, Hull answered that I was not the man for the job, on account of my supposed Gaullist connections, which were alleged to be 'closer than anyone suspected'. Roosevelt must have ignored these reservations because, according to Giraud, it was at Casablanca that the President described me to him as 'the man in North America who best represented France and the French spirit'. As soon as Hopkins returned, he took steps to ensure that I was sent to Algiers on behalf of the Munitions Assignment Board, of which he was the chairman. His letter of accreditation ran as follows:

> The question of equipping the French troops in North Africa has been considered at the Casablanca meeting between the President and General Giraud.
> This is a question of the greatest importance to all parties – General Giraud, the United States, and the British Government, and in which their interest is common. . . .
> You will acquaint General Giraud with the situation here, review this matter with General Eisenhower and General Giraud, and generally give through appropriate channels every assistance to the solution of questions arising in connection with the rearmament of French forces.†

* Sherwood, *op. cit.*, pp. 678–9.
† Hopkins, Letter to Jean Monnet, February 22, 1943.

In reality, starting from this important and urgent task – Roosevelt had promised Giraud considerable military aid – I knew very well that my mission would necessarily involve the whole political context of the war in which the French were once more fighting.

II

Republican legality

I left Washington on Tuesday, February 23, 1943. Owing to the dangers of the transatlantic crossing, I had to go the long way round, via Miami, Georgetown in British Guiana, and Natal in the northeast corner of Brazil, where I spent the whole of Thursday. On Friday evening I landed at Dakar in Senegal, French West Africa, and on Saturday afternoon at Marrakesh in Morocco, arriving in Algiers that evening. McCloy had reserved an apartment for me on the rue Michelet, and I moved in right away. My first visit was to General Giraud, whom I had not yet met. 'I confess, to my great shame,' he wrote about me, 'that I had never heard of him.' About Giraud, I must say, I already knew all there was to be known: it could be summed up in a few words. He was tall, with a clear, blank gaze: he was conscious of his own prestige as an officer and a hero; he was inflexible on military matters, and hesitant on everything else. I venture no judgement on his intelligence, which was that of a general with long experience of desert warfare, and inclined to simplify things. He had shown his mettle by escaping from captivity in both World Wars in order to go on fighting the enemy. His only thought was to rebuild his shaken army, without changing either its spirit or its structure. For the rest, he has described himself with touching candour: 'In matters of politics I was incredibly incompetent, clumsy, and weak. The cobbler should stick to his last.' This lack of self-confidence about anything outside army affairs made him open to influence, despite his obstinate nature. I realized at once that where he was obstinate he had to be respected, and where he was hesitant he could be steered.

He had moved into the Summer Palace – or rather, he was camping out in its Oriental grandeur, attended by a small personal staff which had come with him by submarine, plus a few other loyalists. Among the latter was Lt.-Col. de Linarès, an open and upright man who was to have very good influence on his chief. Most of the officers in the

Algerian Army, however, had not welcomed Giraud – and this fact, which was painful to him, should not be forgotten when trying to recapture the atmosphere then reigning in North Africa. If Giraud found it hard to assert his authority over civilian and military officials who blamed him for having deserted Pétain, it is difficult to see how de Gaulle could have come in and assumed power with the support of a handful of more or less clandestine Free French militants. It was true that at Casablanca he had claimed the right to do so, but on conditions which he knew could not be met overnight – in particular the elimination of the Vichyites and the Vichyite spirit. The fictitious reconciliation that Roosevelt and Churchill had imposed on the two generals in front of the photographers had in no way altered the situation. Things were no better when I arrived in Algiers, and I at once set about looking for ways to ease the deadlock.

Giraud's account of our first meeting, which left him with 'an unhappy impression', is accurate. I shall not go over it again, partly because the substance of it is to be found in statements he made shortly afterwards – and what counts is not so much what I said or wrote to Giraud as what he publicly endorsed. He was a thoroughly honest man; but if I was unable to alter his personal convictions, I was at least able to persuade him, in France's interests, to keep them to himself and give his public blessing to others that were more in line with the democracies' war aims. He was deaf to any argument based on political morality, and would accept only the practical considerations I put to him: that the Americans would refuse to equip an army with reactionary ideas which was supporting a racist regime. To justify his verbal concessions, he said that if Paris had been worth a Mass, Allied munitions were certainly worth a 'progressive' speech.

I negotiated that speech with him, word by word, during my first two weeks in Algiers. Its purpose, in my view, was far more than just to win over American opinion. Irritated as Americans were by the 'Darlan deal' and then the 'Giraud deal', they had virtually no other choice. In fact, Giraud's speech was both the prologue and the first act in reuniting the French. Nothing could be done until the spirit of Vichy was exorcized and the continuity of the Republic reaffirmed. The day fixed for the speech was Sunday March 14, 1943, at a general meeting of French families from Alsace and Lorraine. At 6.00 p.m., in front of 500 people, but above all in front of the international press and the radio microphones of the free world, carefully forewarned, Giraud read out what he described with bitter irony as 'the first democratic speech I ever made'. He was constantly interrupted by applause.

It mattered little whether he believed in what he was saying: the speech had to be made. As he confessed, it was no easy task. Until the very last minute, under the pressure of his own convictions and of his Algiers advisers, he went on trying to water down my text. The notes with which Linarès and I bombarded him bear this out.

One of these notes, which I have kept, is dated Saturday night, March 13. By pointing out how much was missing from the version of the speech that Giraud wanted to make, it showed how great a gap there was between the spirit of a France conquered and divided and that of a France reunited and ranged among the victorious Powers. Behind the disputed words lay a deeper dispute, in which our whole future was at stake. 'We have reviewed your text and compared it with the one we prepared for you during the evening,' I wrote. 'I am profoundly convinced that, if France is to get the benefits we all want from it, your speech must take an unequivocal stand on the essential points.' The note then set them out:

1. The formation of the Provisional Government is left hazy. There is no mention of the Laws of the Republic. It is essential to mention them, for otherwise there is no legal basis, and the Provisional Government could be set up by plebiscite, or assume some other arbitrary form.

2. The text on Vichy legislation is reduced to a statement without any firm conclusion. There is no declaration that such legislation is null and void, which is essential.

3. There is no reference to rejection of the armistice.

4. The French Resistance, a crucial point in the speech, is treated far too summarily.

5. The appeal to French unity is made on a colonial basis, whereas it is essential that such an appeal be national. In this connexion, given all the previous disputes, and the latest memorandum from General de Gaulle, I consider that you must take a firm and unassailable stand – firm about the fact that you are ready to co-operate, and precise about the fundamental principles on which you will do so.

Reading this eleventh-hour criticism, one may well wonder how much Giraud's text still contained of his long-awaited message to the Alsace–Lorrainers, beyond perhaps a homily to their faithful little colony in Algiers. I had little time; but haste helps those who know where they are going. This was one of the many occasions on which I was able at the last moment to substitute a patiently-worked-out text for one that an indecisive or careless politician has failed to perfect. When Giraud got up next morning, he found my note and my draft. He had no time to do anything but accept it and send it for duplication before going to Mass. When he went on the platform that evening, General Maurice Bergeret, a former Minister under Pétain, was not in his appointed place, and before nightfall several of Giraud's most reactionary advisers resigned. The rest were to leave soon afterwards. The ambiguities that had kept them in power were dispelled. Giraud declared:

> The people of France have not accepted the armistice. The heroes of the Resistance, those who remained loyal in hard times, those whose faith survived the most desperate hours, express and still express the true France. Those who died in mortal combat, those who are suffering in torture camps and prisons – they are the advance-guard of the nation. Tomorrow, in our village streets, alongside the war memorials to those who fell in battle, men will bow their heads before monuments to members of the Maquis, to the saboteurs, the hostages, the deportees, the heroic multitudes who laid down their lives in the cause of freedom. . . .
>
> From now on there will be only one French Army fighting Nazi Germany, whether from Algeria or from Libya. All France will share with her allies our victory in the cause for which she has suffered so much. In this way, France will recover her place among the victorious Powers. . . .
>
> Disunion is the mark of defeat; union is the sign of victory. This union must be real and open-hearted. It will gather together not only Frenchmen in France at present under the enemy yoke, but also those who, like ourselves, are outside of France. For our country, this is a matter of life or death.

These few phrases were enough to break the chain of events that had followed the fall of France, the armistice, and the policy of collaboration. But they would have left the problem of legitimate authority wholly unsolved if we had not persuaded Giraud, against his will, to envisage institutional developments that would give the same sense of purpose to all French men and women engaged in the struggle. I had never had a moment's doubt about what that struggle meant; but so long as the physical prerequisites for Liberation were not attained, I had always refused to imagine what France's political future might be after the war. Civil and military supplies were the priority, for the French as for their allies; and until now I had made this my main and even my sole preoccupation. I do not like – or rather, I am unable – to concentrate on two problems at once. And when one of them was as simple and as urgent as the need to win the war, the other – organizing the peace – had to be put off till tomorrow. Now, however, the situation had changed. Our armies were being regularly equipped by the Victory Program, channelled through Lend-Lease. By this time, in the early months of 1943, supplies were no longer a problem, but simply a matter of good administration and liaison work. On the other hand, however, every day brought new and more worrying evidence of political confusion about the future of France. The ensuing dissensions were dividing ally from ally, Frenchmen from Frenchmen, and the Allies in general from the French themselves. I realized that we must go further than simply stating very general principles, further than I had imagined when I was in Washington, and further perhaps than the Allies thought necessary and sufficient for the immediate conduct of the war.

In trying to clarify my ideas about the future of France, I had sought the opinion of eminent men like Charles Ettori, a member of the Council of State, and Louis Joxe, whom I had persuaded Giraud to recall from Constantine in Eastern Algeria, where he had exiled him for 'Gaullist intrigues'. Together, we had induced Giraud to undertake clear commitments, putting a stop to all insinuations and discouraging all political manoeuvres:

> The expression of the French people's sovereignty has been interrupted by the German occupation. It will be resumed only when France is liberated. I give the people of France my most solemn pledge that their sacred right to determine for themselves the choice of their Provisional Government, under the Laws of the Republic, will be upheld. I promise that conditions will be established to enable them to make this choice, without disorders and with liberty restored. I promise that this shall be done as soon as France is liberated. I am the servant of the French people; I am not their commander. Tomorrow, we shall be the servants of the Provisional Government that they will freely set up. To that Government we pledge ourselves to hand over our powers.

'I am not their commander': this phrase applied to everyone, including de Gaulle – not in any polemical spirit, but because at that time problems of persons had no place in the debate. Tangled as they were, such problems would be that much easier to deal with if everyone recognized a few fundamental rules. Could the whole of France be liberated under the hybrid régime of a 'Civil and Military Commander-in-Chief'? I thought not. Would de Gaulle's London Committee and the authorities in Algiers join forces? I hoped so, and I was going to work for that end. Meanwhile, we had to draw the logical and legal conclusions from Giraud's speech. He himself announced the re-establishment of Municipal Assemblies and General Councils representing the electorate. This opened up a constitutional possibility that was much discussed, although eventually abandoned – that of using the long-standing 'Tréveneuc Law' of February 15, 1872. The Tréveneuc Law laid down that, in the event of a power vacuum, the General Councils should appoint a Provisional Government, whose duty it would be to prepare constituent or legislative elections. But that was for the future. What seemed to me more urgent was to abolish the laws against the Jews. That went without saying. Yet I was unable to budge Giraud from his obstinacy over a crucial point, the so-called 'Crémieux Decree'.

This, also issued in 1872, had given Jews in North Africa rights of citizenship that had not been accorded to Moslems. Vichy had repealed it; but by rights it should now have been restored. Giraud refused, on the pretext that to do so would have meant racial discrimination, although the real reason was his fear of public disorders. 'I thought I knew more about North Africa than anyone who had just arrived,' he wrote later. Perhaps he did; but he certainly knew less about Allied public opinion, which refused to let such an error pass. It took several months of pressure and a complete change of political climate before the Crémieux Decree was restored. With this exception, Giraud's March 14 speech was everywhere hailed as a major event, as were the implementing decrees announced that same day: 'Constitutional acts, laws, and decrees passed after June 22, 1940, are declared null and void'; and 'Executive acts shall use the following formulae: "French Republic" and "In the name of the French people".' In London, de Gaulle declared: 'The Algiers statements in many respects mark great progress towards the doctrine of Fighting France.' It was the beginning of a move towards unity which, despite many difficulties, would never stop. In Algiers, I had the portraits of Marshal Pétain removed from public places. Finding Republican busts to replace them was another matter: they had all disappeared. After long searches one was discovered, thick with dust. It still stands on the mantel-shelf of my study.

Next day, March 15, Giraud wrote to General Georges Catroux, whom de Gaulle had recently sent to Algiers as his personal representative:

> I was anxious to state publicly yesterday the principles guiding my action. So no misunderstanding remains between us. The time has come for all Frenchmen of good will to unite. I am ready to welcome General de Gaulle in order to give unity practical expression.

The reply from London was immediate:

> I have received your message and I count on being able to come to North Africa soon.

All seemed to be going well and quickly; but to believe this was to misunderstand the nature of the wholly political battle that de Gaulle was preparing to fight. His objective, which was power, implied advance calculation. Ambition had taught him to be patient and prudent. He feared a trap. 'This unexpected *coup de théâtre*, followed by an immediate invitation to confer,' Catroux wrote, 'aroused his mistrust. . . . He therefore resolved to wait and delay his visit.'

Catroux and I both agreed with de Gaulle's decision, although we thought his motivation more imaginary than real. If there were misgivings, rightly or wrongly, then the time was not yet ripe for a confrontation. The two generals had already discovered how incompatible they were when they had met at Casablanca. We must therefore postpone problems of persons and first clarify the principles that were in dispute. What these were we already knew. On the one hand there was a long memorandum which de Gaulle had sent to Giraud at the beginning of March; on the other, there was Giraud's speech of March 14. These two documents must first be reconciled: the men themselves could come later. There were still serious differences on matters of substance, even after Giraud's great concession to democratic opinion in the free world. These differences concerned not only de Gaulle or the invitation to Algiers, as de Gaulle affected to believe. In obtaining the restoration of Republican liberty and legality, my purpose had not been merely to satisfy Roosevelt, any more than it had been to make overtures to de Gaulle. I was neither fulfilling a particular mission nor answering a particular memorandum. I was simply acting on my convictions, in the certainty of thereby preparing the climate that was needed if we were to continue the war and build the subsequent peace. But there was even more to it than that. My convictions also made me vigilant against any premature bid for power and any *fait accompli* that might be presented at the Liberation, from whichever quarter it might come.

As far as Giraud was concerned, we had put a stop to any attempt by his supporters to impose a continued Vichyite regime or a restoration of the monarchy. But on de Gaulle's side we were being asked to join the National Committee in London, enlarged for the purpose and transformed into a central power with all the attributes of a Government. True, de Gaulle's memorandum gave firm assurances about the free expression of popular sovereignty once Liberation was achieved. But it also clearly stated that de Gaulle intended as soon as possible to assume the leadership of a Provisional Government, which would negotiate with the Allies and establish itself in France, when the time came, in order to prepare for elections. I found it hard to accept de Gaulle's attempt to freeze, in his own interests, a situation that was still fluid, and to politicize an effort at wartime reorganization that had scarcely begun. His attitude, unfortunately, confirmed Churchill's and especially Roosevelt's misgivings. To me, quite frankly, their fears seemed exaggerated. De Gaulle was not by nature a dictator. But he was openly a candidate for power; and his impatience and intolerance seemed to incline him towards certain forms of personal authority. Slight as the risk might be, it had to be averted in the interests of France.

Giraud's answer, which he sent to de Gaulle on April 1, distinguished between the period preceding the Liberation of France and that which would follow when the Liberation was complete. First, a Council made up of representative public figures, including the governors and commissioners responsible for the administration, would be placed in charge of areas as they were liberated, in partnership with the General Councils. Then, when the time came, the Council would hand over its powers to a Provisional Government set up under the 1972 Tréveneuc Law, which had provided for just this type of situation. 'Thus,' said Giraud's memorandum, 'it will be possible to avert the temptation either to seize personal power or to establish a revolutionary Government, either of which might be encouraged by circumstances.' The fear of this never left me. In my mind's eye I could see France torn apart or thrown into a state of sullen rebellion. What would happen when the French people were once more able to express their will? If there were a power vacuum, with no legitimate authority, who would say what risks they might run? The name of the man who could hold power mattered less to me than whether he would acquire it legally and wield it democratically. In those early months of 1943, common sense, law, and patriotism all seemed to me to argue for the system of republican authority established in Algeria now that this French territory had resumed the war effort, and for that system to be somehow combined with de Gaulle's National Committee, which itself had sprung from a deeply republican act of rebellion. Once the Allies landed in France, the Tréveneuc Law or some better legal instrument could be used to ensure continuity.

To trust in this happening, however, was to ignore the character of the two rival claimants, who did their level best to thwart attempts to reconcile them. On April 20, Catroux returned from London, bringing with him de Gaulle's reply. This very skilfully attacked the weak point in Giraud's position:

1. Monnet, about five years old, in Cognac (Monnet Private Collection)

2. Monnet in 1922 (Monnet Private Collection)

3. Monnet with parents, standing (Monnet Private Collection)

4. Monnet with parents, sitting (Monnet Private Collection)

5. Monnet, Geneva 1922, League of Nations (Monnet Private Collection)

6. Monnet and Sylvia, in China in 1929. Monnet was twenty-two, Sylvia just twenty (Monnet Private Collection)

7. Monnet and Sylvia, 1935, Wakefield, Rhode Island (Photo by Underwood & Underwood)

8. Amélie and André, Monnet's cook and maître d'hôtel for many years (Photo by N. R. Farbman, *Life* Magazine © 1950 Time, Inc.)

9. Monnet, Sylvia, Anna, Marianne at Orly in 1945, returning from the United States (Photo by M. Rosenthal)

10. Monnet, Charles de Gaulle, Winston Churchill, Henri Giraud, Anthony Eden, etc., Algeria, June 5, 1943

11. Signature of Lend-Lease Agreement, February 28, 1945. Monnet with Bonnet

12. Jean Monnet

13. Monnet and family in 1950. Marianne's eighteenth birthday (Monnet Private Collection)

14. May 9, 1950, Salon de l'Horloge at the Quai d'Orsay

15. Monnet and Walter Lippmann, Houjarray, 1951 (Photo by Carl Perutz, Magnum)

16. Monnet and Harold Macmillan receiving honorary degrees at Cambridge, June 1961 (Photo by Christopher Angeloglou)

The proposed Council again involves too many confusing elements. A distinction must be drawn between the central authority and the administrative bodies responsible for carrying out its orders. The governors cannot belong to the central authority: they are subordinate to it. The same principle must apply to the Commander-in-Chief. It is a basic principle of democracy.

De Gaulle stated the problem of Giraud's role in terms of alternatives: either he could continue to exercise civil authority and give up his military command, or he could keep his command and acknowledge obedience to the civil power. De Gaulle was indeed calling for a 'governmental body' in the name of the 'fighting and resistance forces inside and outside of France', and no longer solely on behalf of those in liberated territory. His attack was sudden and well aimed. Everyone knew that Giraud was a military man in every fibre of his being. He would never resign his command. However, even if he had little taste for politics, would he – a five-star General – agree to take orders from the two-star General de Gaulle? When the problem was put in those terms, which was how Giraud himself saw it, no solution seemed possible.

Those on either side who basically wanted to unite the warring French factions had only one course to follow: to try to bring about a gradual change, if not in the minds of the two rival leaders, at least in the context within which they were operating. During the difficult weeks that followed, Catroux was a great help. Fortunately, he had enough stars to be listened to with respect by both the other generals. He was a good general himself, but also a good diplomat: he had needed the qualities of both in his career as a soldier in North Africa and the Far East. De Gaulle made use of his subtlety and put up with his independent ways. In Algiers, he allowed him to move forward a little, ready to disown him if he compromised more than necessary. What was essential, in de Gaulle's eyes, was to avoid anything irreparable while skirting the danger of a breach. Catroux, on the other hand, disliked the pressure to which he was subjected from London, and asked for more time to negotiate – which made de Gaulle suspect him of disloyalty. I myself was likewise suspected, for not going to absurd lengths in support of Giraud, who at times really touched on the absurd in his theatrical refusal to recognize the realities that were slipping from his grasp.

All this was happening in the strange atmosphere of a city riddled with intrigue and apparently devoted to plots. Senseless rumours went the rounds. I had to stamp on allegations that I was to be arrested in a counter-revolutionary Army putsch. At the same time, there was a constant influx of emissaries from the London Committee, all more or less official, all more or less secret. Sporadic demonstrations by Gaullist groups kept people on edge. Eisenhower looked on in amazement. None of this really interfered with his Tunisian campaign; but he was by no means eager to see crowds rioting while his troops were fighting for their lives. He let this be known. But he left political affairs to the two advisers whom Roosevelt and Churchill had seconded to work for him.

I have already mentioned the first of them, Robert Murphy. He knew his way about in all the Algiers factions better than anyone, as he did in the world of Vichy and in all the other places where he carried out his difficult and important missions. He seemed the exact opposite of a secret agent. Brilliant, friendly, and warm-hearted, with an expansive Irish temperament, he loyally tried to perform his conflicting tasks: to support Giraud and yet reassure American democrats, to set up a French authority and yet not allow de Gaulle to take over the government of France. A time was coming, however, when it would no longer be possible to reconcile such contradictions. When that time came, Murphy swallowed his disappointment and took off for fresh fields of action.

General Eisenhower's other adviser was Harold Macmillan, one of Churchill's men, who had been a Conservative Member of Parliament for some sixteen years. Better known as a publisher than as a politician, Macmillan plunged with great assurance into these exotic intrigues, which appealed to his cultivated tastes. I had met him in London in June 1940, at the very moment of the French armistice, when I had been arranging for French arms orders in the United States to be transferred to Britain. He and I were friends; he and Murphy were accomplices. At times, they found it hard to follow the same line when Churchill and Eden backed de Gaulle more than Roosevelt would have liked. But nothing between us was really secret, as is shown by the detailed accounts that Murphy and Macmillan have given of this period, which largely confirm each other. We exchanged what information we had, and we adjusted our positions in the endless meetings that were a feature of life in Algiers. Macmillan and I used to take refuge in Tipasa, a seaside village some 45 miles west along the coast road. There, walking among the Roman ruins near the sea, we quietly made plans for the future.

It was in Algeria, too, that I was fortunate enough to meet again a man whose personality had impressed both Silvia and myself and whom we had come to know and like in Washington, where he had gone as a refugee from the Nazis. Antoine de Saint-Exupéry had a taste for grandeur and independence that kept him on the margin of organized endeavour. He was determined to fight in his own instinctive way. Instinct had led him first to the United States, where he was free to write again. There, he set out to expound to the Americans the values that all the democracies would have to defend, and the reasons for their common struggle. He would sometimes join our group, and Silvia remembers the card tricks that he performed for her and her women friends while the men were talking in the next room. They would call us in, and Saint-Exupéry would repeat his mystifying legerdemain in front of McCloy and Frankfurter, who were completely baffled. We asked him to explain his secret. 'I shall carry it with me to the grave,' he said. One day, he told us: 'I've come to say goodbye. I'm going to the front to fight.' We knew that the Air Force had turned down, on account of his age, his application to serve as a fighter pilot. 'You could be just as useful doing other things,' we said. But his mind was made up. 'There's no other way. I want a plane, and I'll get one.' When I met him again in Algiers, he had succeeded in this courageous plan, and was going off to face his destiny with his eyes open. The solitary hero who had so many friends disappeared on a solo flight on July 31, 1944. I shall never forget one sentence that he wrote: 'Man's finest profession is that of uniting men.'

III

De Gaulle and Giraud

As the Tunisian campaign began to take a favourable turn, Eisenhower saw fewer objections to de Gaulle's coming to Algiers. At the same time, on April 20, 1943, Catroux was authorized to put to Giraud a constructive proposal which seemed to me acceptable. The Central Council, it was suggested, should have seven members chosen by de Gaulle and Giraud; it should have collective responsibility; and the two generals should take it in turn to preside. In official ceremonies, Giraud would have precedence. Under pressure from us, the Civil and Military Commander-in-Chief finally accepted this proposal. In fact, we had been expecting some measure of disagreement, and had been prepared to put up with a few misunderstandings, which we thought would sooner or later be ironed out. It was at this moment that de Gaulle chose to dramatize in his own way a situation which by itself was developing well.

Giraud had written: 'I invite you to come and meet us at Biskra [in Eastern Algeria] or at Marrakesh so as to put the finishing touches to our agreement in a peaceful place out of reach of any factitious demonstrations. . . . From there we can go to Algiers together.' De Gaulle answered: 'It must be Algiers. That is where we must hold our talks. You no doubt fear that I shall be welcomed by a mass movement. But I guarantee that my supporters will abstain from any misplaced demonstration.' This quarrel delayed de Gaulle's arrival by a further month. Catroux wrote to him: 'Do you or do you not intend to reach agreement with Giraud? If you do, a favourable climate must be created. If not, say so.' In fact, de Gaulle's real answer was neither yes nor no, but something else: he already saw a prospect of winning hands down. Having just received from France the support of the new National Resistance Committee set up by Jean Moulin, he was convinced that time was on his side. By a subtle alternation of public attacks and secret negotiations, he could begin to unseat his rival. At the same time, Giraud was now tempted to break negotiations off. He had the army under his command; he enjoyed real popularity – he had just been acclaimed by crowds in Algiers and in newly-liberated Tunis; and he was assured of American support. Never was the unity of Frenchmen at war so gravely threatened as in those Spring days.

We could not allow our two generals to go beyond the point of no return. After a few weeks, when the situation had developed sufficiently, Macmillan and I withdrew to Tipasa to draft a new version of a text that could be accepted by what Roosevelt and Churchill called their 'two prima donnas'. This was Giraud's letter of May 17, which Catroux and Macmillan took to London in a Flying Fortress made available by Eisenhower. It maintained the idea of the alternating co-presidency and of collective responsibility. The Executive Committee was to consist of two members proposed by Giraud, and two by de Gaulle: it in turn was to organize a National Consultative Council and a Resistance Committee; it was then to appoint the Commissioners. Giraud's letter went on to reaffirm that the procedure laid down by the Tréveneuc Law should be followed at the Liberation. 'We cannot ignore the fact that ours is a purely *de facto* authority,' Giraud wrote. 'We are not, and we cannot be, the Government of France.' This draft made few concessions to de Gaulle's original objections; but he accepted it, as we had thought he would. 'There are some debatable points,' he told us, 'but at first sight I do not believe that we disagree on anything essential.' In reality, he regarded the draft as something to be torn to pieces; but he felt strong enough now, and was in enough of a hurry, to prefer to attack from within. And in fact he was telling the truth, for what mattered to him was an invitation to Algiers; and that he had secured. He arrived on May 30, 1943, accompanied among others by André Philip, René Massigli, and Gaston Palewski. Giraud and Catroux were waiting at the airfield – at Boufarik, some twenty miles south of Algiers. A band played the French national anthem. 'As for the cars,' de Gaulle wrote in his memoirs, 'they were French.'* In my eyes, de Gaulle stood for the spirit of the French Resistance, united at last, and overwhelmingly supporting him. His place was indeed here, where the authority of the French Republic was being restored.

At 9.00 on the following morning, June 1, the Executive Committee held its first meeting, in the Lycée Fromentin. Both co-Presidents were there, each with his own men. De Gaulle arrived with Philip and Massigli; Giraud with myself and the elderly General Joseph Georges. Catroux was welcomed by both parties. Why General Georges should be there was a mystery that only Churchill could explain, for it was on his insistence that his old friend had been brought from France. He was a respected soldier, but a survivor from a defeated General Staff. As a relic of the past, he was more of a burden than an asset to Giraud. Altogether, there were seven of us around the table. Some of those present undoubtedly saw this as the first Cabinet meeting of the new legitimate Government of France. Those same people, no less certainly, foresaw profound changes in the present team. But for me this was not what mattered. We were merely entering a new phase in the slow and difficult unification of the French. Great progress had been made; now it must be consolidated. What had been achieved was the establishment of the Executive Committee, whereby for the first time the men of London and the men of Algiers would be able to speak with one voice. I had therefore prepared a very simple plan; that the Committee be convened and publicly presented right away as a single unit, instead of as a body within which negotiations would take place. The Committee, I thought, should issue an official proclamation. Then would begin a preliminary period of four or six weeks, to merge the respective administrations that had hitherto worked for the Civil

* Charles de Gaulle, *Mémoires de guerre*, Vol. II, *L'unité* (Paris, 1967), p. 126. The contrast was with the American vehicles that had met him at the Casablanca Conference four months earlier.

and Military Command in Algiers and for the National Committee in London. It would take at least as long as that to bring together the various officials and work out a common policy. Twelve Commissioners should be appointed (for National Defence, Resistance, the Interior, Foreign Affairs, etc.), and consultative bodies set up. It would then be time to deal with important and delicate questions such as the High Command, the unity of the Resistance in France, and questions of persons such as appointments of governors, military leaders, and so on.

Over and over again in my life I have seen joint organization and action blocked by questions of persons. I have never been able entirely to avoid such obstacles, or to overcome them. But I have always refused to regard them as preconditions, and I have dwelt on them only when I have been forced to, after exhausting every possibility of dealing first with questions of principle and method. This rule, obviously enough, applies in the first instance to myself. Seeking no job and no favours, I have never been embarrassed to ask other people to be a little unselfish or modest – or, more simply, to be reasonable. In Algiers, in those early days of June 1943, I realized that reasonableness was not on the agenda. That is why I wanted to give it the benefit of time.

> It is essential [I wrote] that matters be discussed calmly and in a way that enables all members of the Executive Committee to become aware of the realities of the situation, both in France and in North Africa, which some of them, necessarily, do not know in detail. For this purpose a certain amount of time is required. If we proceed in this way, there is no doubt that solutions will be found which will secure everyone's agreement, and that when they are made public they will guarantee sound administration and real political unity.

Giraud more than anyone else had an interest in seeing matters follow this course. I am sure that I had convinced him on that point; but when he opened the meeting of the Executive Committee he asked ingenuously: 'Has anyone anything to say?' De Gaulle certainly had, and in plenty, beginning with questions of persons. I already knew his speech: he had had me read it on the previous evening in the villa, *Les Glycines* (Wistaria House), where he had set up his headquarters. His character had not changed since I had seen him in London in 1940: it was the same mixture of a practical intelligence that could only command respect, and a disquieting tendency to overstep the bounds of common sense. He was by turns intimate, using his undoubted charm, and distant, impervious to argument when carried away by patriotic honour or personal pride. I agreed with his analysis of things, but only up to a point: beyond that point I could no longer follow him in his bursts of egocentricity. His conflict with Roosevelt, and in a lesser degree with Churchill, had become an obsession. At the beginning, he had some justification; but towards the end he was clearly in the wrong, exaggerating the persecution of which he claimed to be the victim. And yet he was most often right in his criticism of Giraud, whom I myself could not support in every respect.

De Gaulle was right, for example, on the morning of June 1 when he demanded that the men of Vichy – Noguès, Boisson, and Peyrouton – be dismissed. He was right, too, in insisting that the military command must be subordinate to the Government. But this frontal attack on Giraud's views, as I expected, ran into stone-wall opposition. 'I took these powers,' retorted the Civil and Military Commander-in-Chief, 'because they were there for the taking in exceptional circumstances – which, incidentally, still prevail. To hold both civil and military office is not at present unconstitutional; and besides, it is not forbidden by the terms of our written agreement.' The debate got stuck in this groove. Massigli and Catroux were perturbed, and they tried to persuade the two generals to say that their ideas were fundamentally the same – an attempt at compromise that was not helped by mutually contradictory statements from André Philip and General Georges. I tried several times to bring the debate back to its starting-point. This, I reminded my colleagues, was the establishment of the Executive Committee, with no preconditions, but with all its implications, including the changes that we all wished to see. But for the moment it was clear that Giraud would not give way on anything, and that de Gaulle wanted him to give way on everything. Finally, in exasperation, de Gaulle picked up his documents. Without another word, he got up and left, slamming the door behind him. Having provoked the storm he wanted, he withdrew to *Les Glycines*.

The atmosphere in Algiers was now electric. For two days there was intense agitation: there were even rumours of a putsch. All this took place in the presence of Churchill, who had come with Anthony Eden, the British Foreign Secretary, for strategic talks. What was more, a 'Peyrouton affair' had just broken out, as a result of obscure manoeuvres by Gaullist agents, who had persuaded Peyrouton to resign as Governor-General of Algeria – and to place his resignation in the hands of General de Gaulle. De Gaulle had accepted it, and had announced it himself, without a word to General Giraud, from whom Peyrouton held office. The move was both shrewd and clumsy. But what did de

Gaulle care if he annoyed Giraud or alienated Catroux? He was at least disturbing the ranks of the old administration and displacing the magnetic pole of power. At the same time, the temptations and promises showered on the North African Army by Free French recruiting officers were making the climate worse. It was high time to put the whole civil and military system under a single authority. After further pressure, the two generals agreed to meet again at the Lycée Fromentin on June 3.

There, right from the start, they clashed over the 'Peyrouton affair', making the atmosphere as bad as it had been two days before. But soon, in agreement with André Philip, I made a brief statement: 'At a time when unity is about to be forged, this discussion has no more than retrospective interest. I submit that the new Committee should be established at once.' It was what I should have done at the first meeting. In an instant, the decision was taken. De Gaulle confirmed Massigli and Philip as his representatives; Giraud nominated Georges and myself; we all agreed in co-opting Catroux. From that moment, administrative measures could be decided on. The first was to appoint Catroux Commissioner for Moslem Affairs and Governor-General of Algeria. The second was to appoint as Secretary of the Committee Louis Joxe, whose remarkable ability I had come to recognize. He continued to fulfil this role for many years afterwards, under the title of Secretary-General of the Government. The Minutes of the meeting added:

> It has been decided to recall General Noguès to Algiers as a matter of urgency. He is to be replaced as Resident-General in Morocco by M. Gabriel Puaux. After a discussion in which various opinions were expressed on the subject of General Bergeret, General de Gaulle proposed to the French Committee of National Liberation that a vote be taken. By five votes to two, it was decided to retire General Bergeret.*

From that moment it was clear that on most such questions, where the past and the future were in conflict, Giraud would be in the minority. This first vote foreshadowed many others. De Gaulle took the point. At the end of the meeting he rose to his feet. Going up to Giraud, he embraced him.

---

* General Maurice Bergeret, a former Vichy Minister, was a member of the Algiers 'Imperial Council'. The 'French Committee of National Liberation' was the formal title adopted by the 'Executive Committee'.

IV

The French Committee of National Liberation

Under the headline 'A DECISIVE DAY FOR FRANCE', the *Echo d'Alger* published our first official communiqué:

> The Committee of National Liberation is the central authority of France. It directs the French war effort everywhere in all its forms. As a result, it exercises French sovereignty in all territories not under enemy control. It is in charge of the administration and defence of French interests throughout the world. It assumes responsibility for the territory and the forces on land, at sea, and in the air that were hitherto under the authority of the French National Committee or of the Civil and Military Commander-in-Chief.
>
> The Committee will hand over its powers to the Provisional Government that will be established in accordance with the Laws of the Republic as soon as the liberation of metropolitan territory makes this possible, and at the latest on the total Liberation of France.
>
> The Committee solemnly pledges itself to re-establish all French liberties, the Laws of the Republic, and the republican régime, utterly destroying the régime of arbitrary and personal power at present imposed on the country. The Committee is at the service of the people of France. Their struggle, their resistance, their ordeal, and their deliverance demand the union of all our nation's strength.

This proclamation, dated June 4, 1943, contained many echoes of Giraud's speech on March 14. Since then, by 'altering the appearance of the Civil and Military Command' – a process which de Gaulle said that I had 'inspired' – I had no doubt helped to create conditions for a peaceful meeting and natural confluence between two currents of French life which France's misfortunes had divided and made incapable of understanding one another. Would anyone have dared to assert, two and a half months earlier, that this could have been done without violent clashes and hatred? To tell the truth, not all equivocations had been dispelled. The two generals continued to dispute possession of a power that they were not wise enough to share. But at least the armed forces could gradually be merged – the few but seasoned fighters of the Free French and the large reorganized contingents from Algeria itself. On the one side were 15,000 men in already legendary fighting trim; on the other, 300,000, two-thirds of them Moslems, eager to continue the war and fresh from their triumphs in Tunisia. Together, they were to play a vital role in the Italian campaign. Here, in the domain where he excelled, it is only fair to recognize the importance of General Giraud's leadership of an army to which he had devoted his life. He was in his element in army camps, not in political councils: indeed, he had become involved in politics almost against his will. He had agreed to come to North Africa in the hope of becoming Commander-in-Chief of the Allied expeditionary force there – a hope that Eisenhower had had to disappoint when they reached Gibraltar. It was by chance that he had been entrusted with the civil Government after Darlan's assassination. If his ingrained sense of hierarchy had not made it unbearable for him, a five-star general, to take orders from a two-star general only recently promoted, he would willingly have confined himself to purely military command. But the honour of his caste was too much for him: in the end he lost everything because he wanted to concede nothing.

All summer long, his inevitable retreat continued; but so too did the gradual organization of public authority in France at war. The seven-man Committee met again on June 5 to decree an increase in its membership. It was time to fill out the framework that we had prepared, by including people who had proved their worth in London or Algiers. I was convinced that they would bring no spirit of faction to their work. I knew that René Pleven, who had become one of de Gaulle's close associates, would still be the loyal friend that he had always been and, incidentally, continued to be in the future. I was sure that Maurice Couve de Murville, who had arrived some months ago from France and who was carrying out important tasks in Giraud's administration, would be able to co-operate closely with de Gaulle and the men from London. The future showed that I was right. My friend René Mayer, another of Giraud's nominees, surely had enough intelligence and character to win de Gaulle's respect and make his mark on the team that was to rebuild France. Mayer brilliantly proved that he had. As for Henri Bonnet, nominated by de Gaulle, I knew him well enough from League of Nations days to realize how loyally he would devote himself to our work. Of the other new members of the Committee I could say little, since I hardly knew Adrien Tixier and André Diethelm, whom de Gaulle had co-opted, or Dr Jules Abadie, a local dignitary chosen by Giraud.

The new Committee, then, had fourteen members. Massigli, a conscientious and hard-working career diplomat, was in charge of

Foreign Affairs. The imaginative and impulsive André Philip, whose untidy appearance contrasted with his remarkably clear diction and didactic skill, was in charge of the Interior, i.e. internal politics. I am not sure that he ever really controlled the police – and certainly not the secret services. Of these, Giraud's was no less powerful than de Gaulle's. Each of them, and sometimes each against the other, played a major and disturbing role in Algiers at that time. Couve de Murville was put in charge of Finance, René Mayer of Transport and Public Works, Pleven of the Colonies, Diethelm of Economic Affairs, Tixier of Labour, Abadie of Justice, Henri Bonnet of Information, and I myself of Armaments and Supplies. Catroux and Georges were given the title of Commissioners of State. It was a good, well-balanced administrative team, in which a consensus could be secured for decisions in the general interest. The line-up was less Machiavellian than some people have supposed. One of those people was Murphy, who hurried to see Giraud and express astonishment at the way the General had let himself be deprived of power. On Murphy's reckoning, de Gaulle had secured a majority on the Committee. Matters were not as simple as that; but there is no way of preventing skilled politicians from seeing power-struggles everywhere. They tend to look at the character of men rather than the nature of problems. They are not always wrong, and Murphy was right – if, that is, one believes the subsequent interpretation that de Gaulle gave of his own action: 'In the certainty that this group was prepared to support me, I embarked on the next round in the game. But before making my throw, I shook the dice very hard.'*

Even so, I repeat, matters were not as simple as that. Murphy could not resist colourful speculations, any more than de Gaulle could resist fine phrase-making. My own recollection is that at the time there was less perspicacity and less cynicism among both players and spectators: instead, there was great uncertainty about how to consolidate the unity that we were beginning to forge. It was then, no doubt, that I answered Murphy's reproaches, when he came to see me with Macmillan, by saying in effect: 'We have enough trouble on hand setting up a complex piece of machinery to unite all French forces. Diplomatic relations can be arranged through the normal channels by Massigli.' Murphy drew the correct conclusion that a new epoch had begun, but also the unjustified inference that I had somehow tipped the scales. 'Monnet thus politely declared French independence,' he wrote.†

* De Gaulle, *op. cit.*, p. 138.
† Robert Murphy, *Diplomat Among Warriors* (London, 1964), p. 227.

Myself, I never believed that French independence could be 'declared'. At that time, as always, I was convinced that it could only be brought about by the united efforts of the French. This was what I set out to achieve, together with those men of whom I have spoken, who for the most part worked without any ulterior motives to perform the Committee's tasks.

In fact, when de Gaulle 'shook the dice very hard', he was counting on the fact that the vast majority of those who were responsible for the war effort in North Africa, and who were also concerned to prepare for peace, were wise and sensible men. The whole affair was too serious to be treated as a game of poker dice; and if we constantly intervened in the discussion, it was not in order to save what either of the two rivals had at stake, but in order to maintain the role of common sense. Common sense required that Giraud should cease to exercise both civil and military power: de Gaulle was right to recall that in principle these should be separate. But he was wrong to turn a reminder into a brutal demand, and wrong to press that demand to the limit by trying to have Giraud dismissed. I gradually realized that what de Gaulle found intolerable was not just the constraint of having to work with Giraud: it was that of working with the Committee itself, which exercised collective responsibility and had a certain spirit of independence. A week after the birth of this first Government of the revived French Republic, the stage was set for a major political crisis. This was precisely what I had sought to avoid by asking everyone, on June 1, to agree to four or six weeks' delay during which posts could be filled and the two commands merged. But a crisis, of course, was just what de Gaulle wanted for his own ends. On June 9 he withdrew from the Committee, halting its work. It was the 'empty chair' tactic, whose only outcome must be either a compromise or a total break.

Some accommodation was necessary; and de Gaulle understood this sooner and better than Giraud. He returned to his place on the Committee without obtaining any satisfaction other than that of having stirred up public opinion and given us a great deal of trouble. But the basic problem remained unsolved, and without fail de Gaulle raised it again. Giraud, he said, should look after ôperations in the field: he should make war, not policy, which was the Government's prerogative. As soon as he left for the field, he would have to leave the Committee. 'The Committee knows nothing about the North African Army,' retorted Giraud, 'and the Army trusts only me.' It was true that he knew the army better than anyone; but for this very reason he was too much involved to be able to reform it, and above all to rejuvenate it. With the help of General Alphonse Juin, who was in a position to speak frankly and effectively to both Giraud and de Gaulle, we made various acceptable suggestions. But was there any real need for them now, with the Allies preparing to land in Sicily and a risk of disrupting French forces in the field? The American General Staff obviously thought not. Once again, Eisenhower intervened.

On June 19, he invited Giraud and de Gaulle to see him. 'I purposely came in last and spoke first,' de Gaulle wrote afterwards.* Eisenhower listened patiently, and was impressed by the General's dignity and spirit. But his mind was firmly made up.

'We are on the point of launching important military operations,' he declared, 'and I want there to be no change in the present organization of the French command. I shall continue to deal only with the Commander-in-Chief, General Giraud, who is in charge of all French troops and all French means of communication. If not, I'm afraid that arms deliveries will have to be suspended.'

This might be called Allied pressure: but in reality it was the pressure of facts. Eisenhower had no choice, and the orders he had received from Roosevelt and Churchill were fully in line with his duty as a military commander. It was our job to work out a compromise between the two French generals, who were obliged to work together for some time to come. The solution we hit upon was a 'Permanent Military Committee', an idea to which, together with General Blanc, I put the finishing touches on June 22.

Precarious as it was, this agreement safeguarded what was essential: the unity of the republican system set up in liberated territory, and the American commitment to equip the French Army. I had never ceased to bear in mind this latter point, because as soon as I reached Algiers I had realized that there were snags, despite the assurances that Roosevelt had given Giraud at Casablanca. After summit agreements, it often happens that practical measures are left vague and nothing is done. In this case, the problems of transportation had been greatly underestimated. Thanks to my direct links with Hopkins and McCloy, however, I was able to speed up deliveries. The first massive shipment had arrived on April 13. The next few months saw the arrival of supplies for at least four infantry divisions, two armoured divisions, and four tank battalions – a total of more than 450,000 tons of military equipment, plus a large quantity of civilian supplies. These efforts, which were vital to France's recovery and hence to her independence,

* De Gaulle, *op. cit.*, p. 140.

were no less urgent and important than the establishment of power structures; and I was concerned with both. That was why I had no faith in hasty solutions or personal preferences. Giraud had a great achievement to his credit: he had rebuilt an army which, before he took it over, had been demoralized and unarmed. No one but he would have received such substantial aid from the United States; and this was a fact of which I was obliged to take account.

On the other hand, Giraud was incapable of rejuvenating the army – it had 185 generals – or of eradicating the men of Vichy. It had been struggle enough persuading him to dismiss Boisson in July. He had neither the inclination nor the ability to run the large-scale administration that we had to prepare for postwar France. But de Gaulle could do just that; and here was another fact of which I had to take account. In the end, things worked out as I had hoped – that is, reasonably slowly. The few weeks that I thought the readjustment would take passed peacefully enough, despite de Gaulle's efforts to hurry matters along. His spectacular gestures achieved less, in this respect, than the mistakes made by his maladroit competitor. In July, Giraud committed his last and biggest error: he left on a long trip to the United States, Canada, and Britain. Perhaps he hoped that it would confirm his authority; but all that it gave him was transitory glory. He was received everywhere as a war hero, and his hosts studiously avoided talking politics. His own few inadvertent political remarks were inept. He was amazed at the youth, strength, and modernity of the US Army that was being built up. The lessons this taught him came too late to be applied on his return. However, he did bring back substantial promises of further supplies for the forces of France.

In Giraud's absence, the Algiers Committee had established efficient habits of work. Each of its members had so much to organize in his own sector that protocol problems seemed to be forgotten. This breathing-space, however, only made more obvious how impossible it would be to carry out our duties in the atmosphere of confusion created by two rival leaders. It was no longer a matter of deciding who was right and who was wrong, but of fixing on a clear and effective form of power. Since Giraud had no changes to propose and would agree to no diminution of his own role, which he thought his travels had reinforced, the natural result was that the compromises proposed by de Gaulle began to seem reasonable. They left Giraud with enough apparent civil authority and enough real military power for him to accept being hemmed in by a system whose very complexity made it easier to expel him later on. Certainly, he remained co-President and co-signatory of the Committee's decrees, but de Gaulle chaired the meetings of the National Defence Committee. There was to be a National Defence Commissioner, General Paul Louis Legentilhomme; and Giraud was Commander-in-Chief of the reunified French forces. But he was to exercise his command in the field: he was no longer a member of the Government.

In reality, these legal niceties escaped him – unless he had decided to ignore them. He still had considerable power, owing to his authority over the whole army and over those secret services which, so to speak, were his. He used his power to maintain special relations with the Allies in the conduct of the war in Italy and Corsica, where he alone decided on and carried out important military operations. But his very real successes could not excuse his cavalier behaviour. De Gaulle took umbrage at the former and was indignant at the latter. He resolved to have done with his troublesome rival. Aided by the general weariness and by an increased majority of his own intransigent supporters newly arrived from France, de Gaulle struck. On October 1, he persuaded the Committee to vote for the election of a single President to whom the Commander-in-Chief would be subordinate. Even so, de Gaulle had to make a second effort before he could rid himself entirely of Giraud. He achieved this only in April 1944, long after I had left Algiers, by a final decree stripping Giraud of all political power.

There can be no doubt that this unhappy sequence of events deeply disturbed many consciences, especially in the army, to judge by the long apologies that the main participants have felt obliged to make. There has been much talk, understandably, of obedience, honour, discipline, loyalty, and sacrifice. I respect all these; but I cannot help thinking that the interests of France might have been better served by a little more self-effacement and a little less Messianic fervour on either side. In egocentricity, Giraud had nothing to learn from de Gaulle. Each spoke of himself in the third person. Each believed that he had a sacred mission. Both were obsessed by the need for France to be independent; and I can testify that Giraud felt no more committed to the Americans than de Gaulle to the British. Each exploited the main Power which seemed likely to bring him, and France, to the top. In fact, the fate of both remained undecided for a long time. If history finally tipped the balance in favour of General de Gaulle, who was better able to make and carry out a political plan and to imagine what the postwar period would be like, he owed his success in part to powerful support from outside, in the form of Churchill's loyal and stubborn friendship, as well as to the patient intervention of men of good will in Algiers.

These men have been described as the 'Algiers moderates'. I dislike this expression, and I know that several of those concerned have no recollection of having played a moderating role. However, if matters remained in flux for months without resort to the ever-present threat of force, and if they finally matured once the armies had been united and men's ideas had converged, all this was possible only because we actively assumed our responsibilities. I had come to Algiers to help reunite the French – to help them work together for victory and for the recovery of France. That was my only ambition; and, beyond my democratic convictions, I had no other preconceived ideas. I was bent only on this goal; and since I owed no allegiance to any individual I did not have to change sides to achieve my purpose. This was very clear to the two Allied observers, Harold Macmillan and Robert Murphy, who had somewhat divergent reasons for being satisfied with the way things turned out. No detail escaped them; and in their respective memoirs, each in his characteristic manner has treated the motives and results of my action in a way that I can accept.*

I now faced a new question. Where could I most usefully continue the varied but continuous effort that I had been making for more than four years? Forging the weapons of victory was now the business of the US War Production Board's huge arsenals, which under Donald Nelson were implementing the Victory Program. Allocating supplies among the Allies was the job of Harry Hopkins and Lend-Lease. Supervising their delivery and deployment in North Africa was the task of my own Commissariat for Armaments, Supplies, and Reconstruction. Once again, I found myself facing the problems of administrative routine, which naturally follow the creative phase and are a proof of its success. Other people were better able than I was to deal with these problems, day in, day out – so long as the source did not dry up. I had the feeling that I ought to go back to the nerve-centre of the war effort, to consolidate the machinery that would surely bring us to the end of the war, and to prepare now for the reconstruction of France after the Liberation.

On September 15, 1943, I put before the Committee a rearmament

* Murphy, op. cit., pp. 223–4, 225, 227–8; Harold Macmillan, Memoirs, Vol. II, The Blast of War (London, Macmillan, 1967), pp. 297–8, 300, 312, 317–19, 321, 325, 328–31, 338.

balance-sheet which showed that Giraud's Casablanca agreements were being scrupulously carried out. The deliveries already mentioned – over 450,000 tons of supplies, enough to equip six divisions and several heavy artillery regiments – were to be supplemented before the end of the year by 600,000 tons, intended for three infantry divisions, two armoured divisions, four tank battalions, and three more heavy artillery regiments. In a few months' time, our air force would have 600 fighters and bombers. The allocation of this flood of supplies had caused immense problems, but these were now solved. It was now up to the army, I thought, to deal with matters on the spot. On September 20, I asked the Committee to relieve me of my duties in respect of armaments:

> In the present circumstances it is important that I should be able to devote myself fully to the problems of civilian supply and immediate aid to France together with postwar reconstruction. Now that the Liberation of France is approaching, it is vital to take all necessary steps to restore the country's supplies, to restart essential industries, and to prepare for the return of prisoners of war.

I therefore proposed to the Committee that I should go back to the United States to negotiate for the continuation of existing programmes and the initiation of new ones.

Already, large-scale machinery was being set up in Washington to give emergency aid to the liberated countries. This was the United Nations Relief and Rehabilitation Administration, UNRRA. As far as was then possible, estimates had been made of what prostrated Europe would need. France's share had to be determined: which was why the Committee sent me as its plenipotentiary delegate to the inaugural session of the United Nations on November 9, 1943. What was at stake was the recovery plan for the whole of France, because over and above any measures of first aid, I had to lay the foundations for bilateral Franco-American agreements to safeguard our economic and financial future. We had been concerned with these problems since the summer, in a small informal group based, like so many others, on friendship and on attachment to a common ideal. The group included René Mayer, Robert Marjolin, and Hervé Alphand. Numerous memoranda produced at that time, in which everyone left the mark of his imagination, bear witness to an eager and sometimes prophetic concern for France's future and that of the new Europe.

I recognized again in Robert Marjolin the lively, sparkling intelligence that had struck me when I had first met him as a young economist in London. It was obvious already that he would be one of the most gifted minds of his generation. His elegant reasoning gave us clear solutions, felicitously expressed. René Mayer brought to our work his great administrative experience and that remarkable ability to master technical dossiers which was to underpin his political authority later on. As yet, his only ambition was to deal effectively with those things for which he was responsible, but it was easy to surmise that his character would one day make him want to govern men. Hervé Alphand was not only an outstandingly brilliant diplomat, a many-sided past-master of the art of negotiation: he also had the courage to involve himself in very important projects for which, without hesitation, he risked his career. Different as they were, these men were my friends, and we fell into the habit of working together. At about that time we were joined by Etienne Hirsch, who already, under his London code-name of 'Commandant Bernard', had won a reputation for mastering and simplifying the most complex difficulties. His engineer's training was partly responsible; but in my opinion it is above all his moral strength and legendary calm that help him, as it were, to dissolve problems that are wrongly called technical, when they are really a matter of common sense.

Our plans for the future were based on a knowledge of French affairs which grew more confident as men and women of the Resistance, and politicians summoned to form the Consultative Assembly, continued to arrive in Algiers. From what these courageous men told me, I realized both the sufferings of occupied France and its potential for recovery. I understood more clearly that the vast majority of the French people rejected the reality of German domination, and shared more or less passionately, more or less actively, in the spirit of Resistance. If the organized Resistance was a minority affair, I was neither surprised nor disappointed when I discovered, from the accounts that they gave us, the strength of character of these leaders of the underground army, whom we had snatched from the battlefield to prepare the reorganization of France. Most of them dreamed only of returning to the dangers of the fray.

Since the Occupation began I had known and admired the story of those extraordinary men and women of the Intelligence Service who had gone alone into battle to set up, with a few courageous and forgotten Frenchmen, the first networks of resistance to the Germans. I knew also of the incredible feats performed by the officers of the secret army, whom Giraud sent on the most perilous missions, to work of their own free will in the shadows, hidden for ever from the public gaze. But I had yet to meet the Resistance in the shape of such extra-ordinary characters as Henri Frenay, who now became our col-league. What he did, with others, more than others, and on a par with the greatest, fills me with admiration. His unshakeable strength and his open-heartedness survived the adventures that had revealed them, and were never really matched in French politics after the war.

Other men of the Resistance, however, found their natural place without effort in the Consultative Assembly or on the Committee, which more of them joined from November 1943 onwards. I appreci-ated the good sense and parliamentary experience of Henri Queuille and Félix Gouin, on whom de Gaulle relied for his new constitutional position. I got to know Communist leaders, through the powerful personalities of men like François Billoux and Fernand Grenier. I was impressed by their patriotism and their realism. Provided that they were dealt with clearly and directly, I knew that they would help un-reservedly in the reconstruction of the country. My approach won their confidence, and I was able to bring them usefully into our work in Algiers and later in France. No doubt they on their side remembered that, as soon as I had arrived in Algiers, I had helped to liberate com-rades of theirs whom the French administration had kept in concentra-tion camps since Marshal Pétain's armistice.

I left for Washington on November 15, 1943, on a mission which I knew would last for the rest of the war, since it was in Washington that decisions would in due course be taken on the massive aid pro-grammes which France so badly needed. But I also had another mission, to seek moral as well as material support. This was something of which de Gaulle stood in need – Roosevelt's recognition of his Government. True, the Committee of National Liberation had a Commissioner for Foreign Affairs, René Massigli. Since August, he had enjoyed recognition of a sort on the part of several States. The USSR had accorded it in fairly broad terms; but Britain and the United States had used a deliberately qualified phrase: 'The Com-mittee is recognized as administering those overseas territories that acknowledge its authority.' De Gaulle was disquieted by these reser-vations on the part of the Allies: he suspected.the United States, in particular, of wishing to rule the liberated territories in its own way until the end of the war. He thought that I might have some in-fluence on Roosevelt's decision. I was less certain. Clashes of character are impervious to reason. This one was to resist my efforts of per-suasion for a very long time.

Part Two

A TIME FOR UNITY

Chapter 9

PEACE (1945)

I

The Provisional Government

After the atmosphere of Algiers, Washington was a tonic. I could see, too, how much the American outlook on world problems had broadened in the intervening months. Looking back to four years earlier, when at about the same time of year I had arrived in the capital while the United States was still at peace, I realized how readily Americans adapt to change. Four years ago, the country had been rather introverted, hesitant to use its power, and uncertain of its responsibilities. Now, the President had imbued it with his own calm strength, and it was ready to take up any challenge. The most serious of all, dominating everything else, was the war of Liberation. It was the first time in history that a nation had faced a truly world-wide task. The furthest points of the globe were linked with Washington's underground war rooms, where it was never either day or night, and where the commanding figure of General George Marshall was the symbol of America's calm, methodical energy. Already, the Americans were looking ahead to the challenges of peace and postwar reconstruction. While still in charge of the war effort, even in its details, Roosevelt and Hopkins were at the same time planning a new, postwar world. They had begun to confer with Stalin and Molotov no less than with Churchill and Eden. They held their meetings in out-of-the-way places, under heavy security. It was very difficult to discover what they thought about Europe, and about France. It was more difficult still to intervene. I recognized that my task would not be easy.

Although that task was my sole preoccupation, in the eyes of the American Government it was only one problem among many. In my new role as an official representative of France, I hardly expected that my friends in the Administration would give me so much of their time, in spite of our two years of very close co-operation. In fact, however, I found them just as open-minded, just as ready to listen to me and help me: we quite naturally resumed our working habits in a friendly, family setting. While I had been away, they had given Silvia and the children a great deal of moral support. I also discovered that, at Silvia's request, Jack McCloy had arranged protection for me when American newspapermen in Algiers had been reporting exaggerated rumours of a putsch. As well as being Assistant Secretary of War, McCloy was now also Chairman of the Combined Chiefs of Staff's Civil Affairs Committee, which had been set up to study the immediate problems that would follow Allied landings in Europe. Already in Algiers we had made an inventory of what France would need in this first phase, based on the mass of valuable intelligence that had been smuggled out. Very complex technical arrangements were required if we were not only to prevent life in France being totally disrupted while the fighting continued, but also to provide for public services in the liberated areas. These crucial plans were studied very sympathetically by the American departments concerned, to which I was given liberal access by Hopkins, Stimson, Dean Acheson, and McCloy.

At the same time, with the help of UNRRA, the Relief and Rehabilitation Administration, we worked out a plan for the reconstruction of liberated France. UNRRA was a mammoth undertaking, which was to cover all countries laid waste by war and occupation. It prevented a breakdown in supplies, which would inevitably have caused appalling famine, disease, and political disorder in Europe. To ensure that the French people's real needs in that still indefinite future were known and recognized was a task for men who were skilled both in economic forecasting and in negotiation. Alphand, Hirsch, and their experts performed it admirably. When the time came, the experience enabled them to take in hand without a hitch the revival of French industry after the war. Fearing that the battle to liberate France would be very destructive, and hoping that her three million prisoners and deportees would rapidly be brought home, we built up in the United States, North Africa, and Britain the large stocks that a country of France's size would need for six months – from coal to woollen blankets, from locomotives to footwear, from medical supplies to baby-linen. As it turned out, our estimates were partly wrong: physical devastation was less catastrophic than we had imagined, and human suffering more cruel. But at least all due steps had been taken to limit our country's plight.

So long as we were dealing with concrete problems – which are

vital in the lives of nations and the establishment of peace – I was able
to influence matters and could send good news back to Algiers. But
we soon fell foul of questions like who should do what and at whose
bidding – or, more simply, the muddles that are inevitable in any relationship as complex as that between allies. Agreements negotiated
in Washington on behalf of Algiers had to be carried out in London,
where Hirsch was the contact man; and when Eisenhower moved the
nerve-centre of the war effort to the West I asked for Alphand to be
sent there to use his negotiating skill. Instructions and reports crossed
and sometimes conflicted; now and then, communications were even
cut off altogether by the necessities of war. The civil and military
authorities might thus be dealing with a single problem in three
different places, which gave rise to many misunderstandings in the
period preceding the Liberation of France. The question of paper
money, with which we grappled for more than six months, is a good
illustration of the difficulties we faced.

I was told when I arrived in Washington that the US Treasury was
preparing special military banknotes, with 'Allied Military Command'
printed on them, for use by the expeditionary force in France. Nothing
was planned as yet for civilian currency, although the manufacture of
banknotes took a considerable time. Economically and psychologically,
the large-scale issue of money for use by the occupying forces would
have very serious results. I said as much to General Hillding, who
headed the civil section of the 'Nord Department', as well as to Morgenthau. They agreed; and since there was still time, we looked into the
idea of issuing French banknotes marked '*République française, Trésor
public*'*, to be used by the expeditionary force and then to be exchanged
for the French notes issued during the war under German control.
Discussions on this subject went on interminably. We were hoping
that the French Committee of National Liberation would be officially
recognized soon enough to enable the notes to be issued under French
rather than American auspices. Alternatively, if this hope failed to
materialize in time, we hoped that the banknotes would clearly appear
to be of French origin, which would be tantamount to official recognition of the Committee somewhat in advance of the fact. At the
beginning of June, Pierre Mendès-France, our Finance Commissioner,
came to negotiate with Morgenthau. Perhaps he imagined that he had
secured what I had failed to obtain. However that may be, he was
greatly surprised a few days later, when the Americans landed with
banknotes bearing a tricolour flag and the words '*Liberté, Egalité,*

* French Republic, Department of the Treasury.

Fraternité', but no mention of any French authority. De Gaulle at once declared that he would not recognize this 'currency imposed by force'.

We were in the thick of the political problem about which I had been negotiating, apparently without success, since my return to Washington. There was no French currency because, in the eyes of the Allies, there was no French Government. Roosevelt actually said in a press conference: 'When there is a free French Government, naturally it will issue money.' But the Committee of National Liberation had just published a decree proclaiming itself the Provisional Government of the French Republic. Why did Roosevelt not see it as the legitimate authority of France? Why did he still resist widespread pressure to recognize the Government established in Algiers? Newspapermen had already questioned him on the point. 'No one,' he had answered, 'not even the French Committee of National Liberation, can possibly know what the French people really think. For the United States, the question remains open.' This, I believe, was his profound conviction, and it tallied with his democratic principles: the American expeditionary force would not be allowed to present the French people with a Government ready-made. It was obvious, too, that he suspected de Gaulle of not being a good democrat. But Roosevelt's attitude toward any other claimant to French leadership would undoubtedly have been the same. Haste seemed to him suspect. He was fighting a war, and he could not fathom why people in Algiers spent so much time on politics and questions of persons.

Many of us, however, thought that the necessities of war itself made it urgent to establish and proclaim a legitimate French governmental authority as soon as the Allies landed. I had realized, when I arrived in Washington, that the whole civil and military war effort was concentrated on plans for invading continental Europe before very long. I certainly did not share de Gaulle's constant anxiety about a possible seizure of power. But it seemed to me natural that the organization set up in Algiers, strengthened by its refusal to capitulate, its pioneering spirit, and its links with the Resistance and the whole free world, would eventually be in a position, with Allied help, to take over the affairs of France which the defeated Government had abandoned. Daily, we were discussing with the Americans all the practical problems involved in the Allied landings and the administration of liberated territory, some of which were directly concerned with sovereignty, like the currency and public services. There was a contrast between this *de facto* recognition, at all levels of the administration, and the refusal to establish a legal relationship at the top. True, the diplomatic vacuum was not total; but the supreme rites had not been observed, and these were the only ones that counted in the liturgy of international affairs. Theoretically, the Allies could deal at will with any other French authority they chose – except the Vichyite collaborationists, whom they were strictly pledged not to approach. In reality, it seemed to me, this danger had ceased to exist on the day when the Algiers Committee had begun to act like a government. Eisenhower had no hesitation on this point, and the French Committee never had a more loyal friend.

Ever since my arrival, I had been trying to establish a working relationship between the US Administration and the staff of the French Committee, so as to make permanent our existing daily contacts on the vital, concrete questions involved in fighting the war and preparing the peace. Rather than make a frontal attack on the problem of diplomatic recognition, which for the moment was insoluble, I believed that by seeking the maximum common interests, both material and psychological, it would eventually be possible to create a *de facto* situation, which of necessity would soon become *de jure*. In the course of my life I have known and helped to create a number of such situations, which to my mind are the most natural way for men to improve the form their mutual relations take. When I have failed, it has been through running into obstacles of doctrine or character – which are very often linked. In Washington in 1944 I had to acknowledge such an obstacle, which took the form of majestic silence on the part of the White House in the face of haughty demands made in Algiers. Nevertheless, I continued on the same pragmatic course, since my prime concern was that the operations to be mounted together on the European mainland should be successful. This in turn required that the citizens of liberated areas in France should be supplied, communications restored, and factories put back in production. International recognition might come as a bonus, or it might not. I should add that the lack of formal recognition never prevented me from obtaining whatever it was reasonable to seek.

On the other hand, everything in politics that depends on symbols or myths, and on the necessary principles of strict legality, suffered from this lack of diplomatic recognition – so much so that fresh storms broke between de Gaulle and the Allies at the time of the Normandy landings. In view of the colossal gamble now being fought out on the beaches and battlefields of France, these quarrels were heartbreaking. I urged my friends to intervene as forcefully as they could. Stimson, McCloy, and Eisenhower pointed out to Roosevelt how much the work we were engaged in together, and the Committee's ability to maintain order in France, depended on at least *de facto* recognition. Their arguments carried weight. At Churchill's request, de Gaulle came to Washington. He came alone, and he asked me to return to Algiers during his visit, no doubt to demonstrate that he had not come to negotiate and that he was in no one's debt. Roosevelt received him hospitably and showed him every courtesy. But he accorded him only qualified recognition. Not until October 23, 1944, was the Provisional Government acknowledged to be what by now it had undoubtedly become – the legitimate authority in France.

This, when it came, was not the result of negotiation or recrimination, but the culmination of practical work. If I managed to help matters along, it was in so far as I was able to persuade those who had all the resources for victory, and all the responsibility for taking decisions, that France's fighting forces had been effectively united by democratic means. To understand America's policy in wartime, one has to remember that the aims for which that great nation was fighting and making sacrifices were the destruction of dictatorship and the restoration of freedom in the world. Europe, which had seen its freedom so appallingly crushed, or had not known how to defend it, was called upon to offer the strongest guarantees of its return to democracy. France, in particular, whose Government had betrayed its allies to collaborate with the totalitarian enemy, was expected to adopt an attitude that reflected her true traditions. All too often, however, the Free French seemed to be taken up with factious squabbles and rivalry for power. In the eyes of those to whom he addressed his imperious claims, de Gaulle appeared less interested in the conduct of the war than concerned for his own role afterwards.

To me, this judgement seemed unfounded. The French Committee was a collective body, more and more open to various political groups: it had recently been joined by the Communists. Unfortunately, misunderstandings between de Gaulle and Roosevelt continued long after the recognition of the Provisional Government. This in itself was merely a minor episode; but like a recurrent fever it has troubled Franco-American relations for the past thirty years. Many of the attitudes that we shall observe later would be inexplicable, were it not for illusions born of wounded pride in a memory that never forgot.

II

The shape of the peace

At the beginning of the summer, I was visited in Foxhall Road by a reporter from *Fortune* magazine, John Davenport. 'We want to tell your story,' he said. 'I've all the time in the world, so let's begin at the beginning.' For the first time, I turned to look back on my past life, and was presented to the magazine's readers as 'M. Jean Monnet of Cognac'.* I was fifty-six years old; and my career looked variegated and spasmodic. This disconcerted the authors of 'profiles' or *curricula vitae*, who were anxious to put me in some familiar category: politician, businessman, economist, diplomat, etc. I cared little for such definitions; but I must say that I found the title which Davenport gave me rather apt. Cognac has always been a point of reference in my reflections, which develop slowly, like those of all men from the Charente, who have a healthy respect for the work of time.

It seemed to me, looking back, that I had always followed the same line of thought, however varied the circumstances, and no matter where I was. My sole preoccupation was to unite men, to solve the problems that divide them, and to persuade them to see their common interest. I had not set out with this intention, and it was only a long time later that I came to any such conclusion. Only then, urged by my friends or by newspapermen to explain the point of my work, did I come to realize that I have always been drawn towards union, towards collective action. I cannot say why, except that Nature made me that way.

Now that the war in the West seemed to be leading rapidly to the Liberation of France and perhaps to the final defeat of the German Army, I began to realize that circumstances were going to bring me new tasks. There was no point in wondering what course my life would take. There would be many things to change: first, in the structure of France, then in the organization of Europe, as economic and political order was restored with the return of peace and the reclamation of the ruins. If, as I believed, the Provisional Government proved capable of preventing anarchy or a Communist takeover, there

* John Davenport, 'M. Jean Monnet of Cognac', *Fortune*, Vol. XXX, No. 2 (August, 1944), pp. 121–216.

would soon be a tendency to return to the old order. In that case, the greatest danger would be that of rebuilding a Europe made up of sovereign States, each exposed to the facile temptations of protectionism. As I have said, there had been much discussion of these questions in Algiers, with René Mayer, Alphand, Marjolin, and Hirsch; each of us had made his contribution to examining what the National Committee's European policy might be. Hervé Alphand had studied how to establish a European economic union going well beyond a mere customs union. René Mayer had been thinking in terms of an industrial 'Lotharingia' – a single economic entity in the coal-and-steel producing areas spanning the French, German, and Belgian frontiers. As for myself, I had already reached the conclusions that have inspired my work ever since. In a note written for the Committee of National Liberation in Algiers on August 5, 1943, I had said:

> There will be no peace in Europe if States re-establish themselves on the basis of national sovereignty, with all that this implies by way of prestige policies and economic protectionism. If the countries of Europe once more protect themselves against each other, it will once more be necessary to build up vast armies. Some countries, under the future peace treaty, will be able to do so; to others it will be forbidden. We experienced such discrimination in 1919; we know the results. Alliances will be concluded between European countries: we know how much they are worth. Social reforms will be prevented or delayed by the pressure of military expenditure. Europe will be reborn yet again under the shadow of fear.
>
> The countries of Europe are too small to give their peoples the prosperity that is now attainable and therefore necessary. They need wider markets. . . . To enjoy the prosperity and social progress that are essential, the States of Europe must form a federation or a 'European entity' which will make them a single economic unit. The British, the Americans, and the Russians have worlds of their own into which they can temporarily withdraw. France is bound up in Europe. She cannot escape.

I concluded:

> The solution of the European problem is all-important to the life of France.

The *Fortune* interview a year later showed that by now the question of Germany was uppermost in my mind. What I was thinking of was a system whereby the former *Reich* would be stripped of part of its industrial potential, so that the coal and steel resources of the Ruhr could be placed under a European authority and used for the benefit of all the nations involved, including a demilitarized Germany. 'But this in turn,' Davenport quoted me as saying, 'implies a Europe far more unified than before the war. Here he would like to see not merely a "switchboard" association,* but a true yielding of sovereignty by European nations to some kind of central union – a union that could cut down tariffs, create a great internal European market and prevent that race of nationalism "which is the curse of the modern world".' But that was where my certainties stopped. 'Where to begin? And how far to go? And could England be brought in' so that Germany did not once again become preponderant in the European system? All I knew was that this was what we had to do.

The problem was urgent because, however slowly its solution might emerge, every decision reached now in the reconstruction of Europe had to take account of the future. The unification of Europe might be delayed, but the revival of nationalism would not. From now on, this was my deepest concern. It was not yet precise enough to act upon; but it was so deeply-rooted that the worry never left me. I knew that it would come to the surface again as soon as there was an opportunity for something constructive to be done. Meanwhile, I could devote myself exclusively to more immediate tasks – to the implementation of France's supply programmes, which were being held up by the shortage of ships.

I returned to Paris at the end of September 1944, after an absence of four years. My heart ached to see how impoverished and exhausted people were, once the excitements of the Liberation had passed. On the way to Cognac to be reunited with my mother and sisters, I saw the extent of the destruction and deterioration in a country whose weakness had already impressed me before the war. Throughout the Occupation, the Germans had requisitioned most of our family house as billets for their officers. One of them, I learned, could not bear noise and had forbidden anyone to raise his voice – with the result that my mother, who was almost stone-deaf, had to spend months in a gloomy silence that no one dared break to talk to her. Her manservant François, who had fought courageously in the war of 1914, had his own way of resisting the occupying power: when he had to polish the commandant's boots, he put on all his medals. The Germans had left Cognac only to fall back on Royan, a few kilometres away; and they were not driven out until some months later. People in Cognac, as in most French towns, were mercilessly paying off old scores. I thought of the

---

* Davenport had quoted Monnet as fearing that the United Nations Organization, like the League of Nations, would 'be only a "switchboard" through which nations can communicate with each other.'

years of effort that lay ahead for Frenchmen, who had already endured so much, if they were to recover and surpass their prewar standard of living and re-establish themselves in the world. They would be able to do so, on condition that they faced the future together. But it was too soon to prepare for the future. All our resources and all our energies were going to be absorbed by the continuation of the war and the struggle for survival. I realized that I had no choice: at all costs we must keep up the flow of supplies from overseas. Without them, the economy would founder; in which case anarchy, already latent, would become rife. I went back to Washington, where I had left Silvia and our two daughters, Anna and Marianne.

Since September 9, 1944, I had no longer been a member of the Provisional Government. De Gaulle had reshuffled it to give stronger representation to the French Resistance. I still had the title of 'Commissioner on special assignment', which enabled me to use the services of the French Supply Council, some five hundred strong, whose job was to make purchases through the US Government under the provisions of Lend-Lease. My official mandate was to see that the Lend-Lease agreement was implemented and, if necessary, modified or renewed. It was therefore a negotiating job; but in fact I also had to look after the day-to-day running of the supply programmes, which were nominally the responsibility of the Financial Attaché, Christian Valenski. This administrative task was not entirely to my taste; but I saw it as my duty to complete an assignment which events had prolonged well beyond my optimistic forecasts. A further winter of war lay ahead of us, and one that threatened to be particularly hard, owing to the pressure of military needs on limited resources and disrupted communications. We were no longer dealing with estimates, as in 1943: we were facing harsh and immediate realities. The great ports of Dunkirk, Saint-Nazaire, and La Rochelle were still in enemy hands; Nantes and Bordeaux were out of reach. What remained of our merchant fleet was requisitioned for war. We had fewer than three thousand locomotives. We had little coal, no steel, and no prospect of iron ore for months ahead.

Fortunately, I had colleagues whose outstanding technical ability was allied to an intimate knowledge of the French and American administrative machines. The active presence of Marjolin in Washington, Hirsch in London, and Alphand in Paris, guaranteed us anything that could be obtained by the exercise of administrative authority or political power. I relied also on the tireless organizing activity of Léon Kaplan, whom I had been glad to meet again in Washington. He had a highly developed sense of teamwork – a quality which is rare, and also underestimated, because by nature those who possess it are usually modest. Kaplan was later to play an important part in France's industrial recovery. Finally, while in Paris I had secured the services of a young *Inspecteur des finances,** Félix Gaillard, who had been warmly recommended to me by Emmanuel Monick. For several years, Gaillard was my *chef de cabinet* or chief executive assistant. His intelligence and his exceptional ability to master difficult subjects enabled him to find brilliant and rapid short cuts. He soon afterwards went into politics, the only possible outlet for his impatient and exalted ambition. This team of very able administrators knew how to handle the immediate, transitional problems. But my real hope was to set them to work on building the future, when everything would have to be refashioned and rethought.

Until the early days of December 1944 we spent most of our time re-examining with the French authorities the supply programme drawn up before the landings in France and therefore based in large measure on mere hypotheses. On the one hand, there had been less physical destruction than we had expected, and industrial capacity had remained at about 80% of its prewar level. The Germans had retreated so rapidly that they had been unable to carry off all our stocks. On the other hand, the paralysis of communications led to unforeseen shortages – with the result that some imported supplies proved less useful, while others, which were essential, could not be shipped to where they were needed. It became clear that the Liberation of France would not put an end to privations of various kinds. German resistance stiffened in the Vosges and on the Rhine, and French territory continued to be the Allies' main Western base. The repatriation of prisoners and deportees was delayed, and our soldiers and workpeople remained subject to conscription. All our careful calculations were thrown awry. I went back to Washington with a totally revised six-months' programme, for which I negotiated with Secretary of State Edward R. Stettinius on the same basis as the British and Soviet Lend-Lease agreements – unprecedented forms of unrepayable or low-interest credit, which Stalin acknowledged as having enabled him to win the war. In return, France was able to make important contributions in the form of work and services: hence the term 'Mutual Aid', applied to our agreements of March 13, 1945. These were valid until July 1946; they covered such basic materials as oil, metals, textiles,

---

* Lit. 'Inspector of finance', in fact one of the élite corps of France's senior civil servants, with an economic as well as an administrative training.

phosphates, fats, and railway equipment.

Never had France concluded a foreign agreement on such a scale. The total value of these consumer and investment goods was more than two-and-a-half billion dollars – virtually a gift for the duration of the war. Now, the problem was no longer to secure the supplies, but to ship them: once again, freight problems had become the main bottleneck. In addition to the European theatre of war there was also the Pacific, which became the top priority after the German ceasefire. The paradoxical outcome was that the end of the war in Europe created new difficulties for France.

The capitulation of Japan three months later brought the abrupt cessation of Lend-Lease, which legally lapsed as soon as hostilities were over. All the aid not already delivered was to be turned into minimum-interest loans. With peace restored, a new relationship was to be established between the United States and its allies, and new negotiations were needed. Even to transfer and liquidate existing contracts was a considerable task. We were now dealing with the Export-Import Bank, with which I later concluded new types of loan agreement. Our purchasing missions also had to change their methods, since in future they would be negotiating with private firms instead of with the US Administration. The necessary reorganization of our staff led to my taking over the chairmanship of the French Supply Council at a time when I had counted on completing my American assignment. This unfortunately delayed my going back to France and starting on my projects for the future.

Meanwhile, our job was threefold. First, we had to tackle the immediate problem of preventing the French having a worse winter in 1945 than under the Occupation. Secondly, we had to ensure the flow of supplies up to the end of 1946. Thirdly, we had to lay the foundations of France's longer-term recovery. Altogether, it was a challenging task; and it was complicated by the fact that we had returned to a market economy. This gave our purchasing missions more flexibility, but also greater responsibilities, to which they were no longer accustomed. We had both to alter our working methods and to replace some of our people, reintroducing notions of competition and cost-effectiveness that had seemed less important during the war. We could no longer meet our needs by drawing on a free and almost inexhaustible source: instead, everything had to be balanced by exports or paid for in hard cash. It was true that the United States had not simply cut off all aid to its allies when the war came to an end: Lend-Lease had immediately been replaced by very generous substitutes. But the new

226

contractual relations were based on the supposition that debtors could meet their obligations by their own efforts. France had therefore to set about re-establishing her economic autonomy. So, beyond the immediate question of supplies for the French, I was concerned to give them the means with which they could recover their strength and independence for themselves.

To achieve this, it was essential to rebuild the country's stocks of raw materials and to replace capital investments that had been run down or destroyed. But I realized that a mere return to prewar production levels would be inadequate if the French were to regain their position in the modern world. Already before the war they had lagged behind their main competitors; and during the Occupation they had been overtaken by many more. While France had stagnated, the belligerents had made immense technical progress – not only materially but psychologically: men's minds had been stimulated by the quest for novelty and power. In every area there was a lot of leeway to make up; but the technological gap and the lack of productive drive seemed to me the most serious problems. These were matters on which our purchasing missions could do nothing to help. Even ways of measuring and analysing our relative decline were beyond our grasp. I met no one in Paris, with the notable exceptions of Alfred Sauvy and Jean Fourastié, who were capable of forming an overall view of the French economic situation; and even they did not possess the modern measuring instruments that the Stacy Mays and Bob Nathans of this world used with such skill. One of the latter, Silbermann, was seconded from the Massachusetts Institute of Technology to introduce our pioneer French planners to the new techniques.

At the same time, I asked a young lawyer friend of mine, George Ball, to give our team the benefit of his experienced legal and political advice. I had met George Ball in the Lend-Lease administration; later he had played an important role in planning the strategic bombing campaign. Powerfully built, he exuded strength and level-headedness, like many Americans of his type, whose massive appearance matches their striking command of both physical and intellectual resources. His wisdom, his boldness in taking decisions, and his loyalty to his friends gave him great moral authority, even then. But the time had not yet come for him to aspire to a political role, and his only ambition was to do his present work well. Better than that, he gave excellent advice, and I profited greatly from his talents as a lawyer, blending the most concrete practicality with the very broadest concern for the general interest. For him, the general interest was that of the whole Alliance, within which, he thought, a rebuilt and united Europe would have an essential role to play.

In August 1945, de Gaulle came to Washington on the invitation of President Harry S. Truman. I had not seen him for the past six months, and I took the opportunity to expound to him my ideas about the future of France.

'You speak of greatness,' I said; 'but today the French are small. There will only be greatness when the French are of a stature to warrant it. That is how they are. For this purpose, they must modernize themselves – because at the moment they are not modern. They need more production and greater productivity. Materially, the country needs to be transformed.'

During the past year, de Gaulle had realized the limits of French power, and had perforce become aware of economic realities. On the previous day he had begun talks about the loan I was to negotiate with the Export-Import Bank, which was essential to the continued flow of our supplies. Would such credits be renewed, and if so for how long? The United States had just dropped the atom bomb on Japan. America's dazzling prosperity, de Gaulle confessed, had astonished him since his arrival: his knowledge of this enormous country had previously been limited and imperfect. He listened to me very attentively.

'You are certainly right,' he said. 'But do you really want to try?'

'I don't know what I shall be able to achieve,' I answered; 'but I'll certainly do my best.'

The months that followed were taken up with reorganizing the French Supply Council, which I was soon able to leave in the reliable hands of Léon Kaplan. Then, when the agreement with the Export-Import Bank was well on the way, I came to the conclusion that I no longer needed to stay in Washington. The loan agreement was for $550m., at a very low rate of interest – a little over 3%. That would see the French economy through the winter. But it was urgently necessary to exploit this breathing-space; and that was why, in November 1945, I came back to Paris and gathered together our faithful team. We made our headquarters in a suite of rooms at the Hotel Bristol. There, Marjolin, Hirsch, Gaillard, and a few others took counsel about how to modernize France. The old-fashioned décor of this requisitioned mansion, where we worked in bathrooms and the beds were covered with documents, astonished the visitors whom we asked to come and discuss the future. Everyone was preoccupied with immediate affairs. It was over a year since the Liberation, but the

French were still subsisting on fewer than 2000 calories a day. Preparations were being made to reintroduce bread coupons and to ration meat, which made for a prosperous black market. The Government and the civil service were struggling with these day-to-day difficulties. Intense political activity – there was a succession of elections and referenda – discouraged longer-term considerations.

I was glad not to be immersed in that atmosphere, and not to be responsible for the problems of the day. If I had, it would have been impossible for me, as for others, to look ahead to lasting reforms. But I by no means underestimated all this political activity. It showed that democracy had returned to France, and it gave expression to a number of ideas that would bear fruit in the future. The new men who were trying out their strength and their talent before the public, and in the recently-elected Constituent Assembly, would for a long time hold the future of France in their hands. On them would depend what had to be done, or rather what had to be engineered, to modernize France. In these circumstances, might it not have been safer to become one of them, or at least to join their ranks? The idea came to me quite naturally when I returned to France, and I thought about it for some time. I had no need to consult many people, because it was not the choice of a party or a constituency that concerned me then, but the problem of knowing whether in this way I should have a better chance to act in accordance with my character and in pursuit of my chosen goal. In reality, it was a question that I had to settle with Silvia and with myself. The answer soon followed: once and for all, it was no. I have never regretted it.

Now, at the age of 57, I was in a position to take stock of my past experience and of the tasks that lay ahead. My life so far had involved a series of actions at the level where contemporary issues are decided, whether by men's willpower or by default. I had constantly been concerned with public affairs; but my work, unlike that of the quintessential politician, had not required an endless succession of fresh choices to be made in the infinitely complex situations that face the Government of a State. What I had undertaken, at every important turning-point in my life, had been the result of one choice and one choice only; and this concentration on a single aim had shielded me from the temptation to disperse my efforts, as from any taste for the many forms of power.

That is how my mind works, and I am incapable of acting otherwise. But I also believe that some things have to be tackled in this way in order to achieve results. The rule does not apply to those who are responsible for all the affairs of state, because they have to look at the whole range of problems. The ability to do so, which is essential to a statesman, itself limits his power to control events. If he were obsessed by only one idea, he would have no time for others, which are also his responsibility; by concerning himself with everything, on the other hand, he risks missing the opportunity for action, which comes only once. In the face of this dilemma, I realized that I had better things to do than to seek power for myself. My role for a long time past had been to influence those who held power, and try to ensure that they used it when the opportunity arose. What could I possibly gain by joining their ranks or trying to take their place?

At the same time, I knew that to attain such a position I should have to do violence to my own nature. For a statesman, the permanent long-term aim at any time is to be in government – and to be at its head. This endeavour is bound up with a certain way of presenting things, which often counts as much as, or even more than, the things themselves. In the end, everything revolves around the struggle for power; and the problem to be solved, which is the purpose of power, is forgotten. I have never met a great statesman who was not self-centred, and for very good reason: if he were otherwise, he would not have made his mark. I could not have done it – not that I am modest: simply, that one cannot concentrate on an objective and on oneself at the same time. For me, that objective has always been the same: to persuade men to work together; to show them that beyond their differences of opinion, and despite whatever frontiers divide them, they have a common interest.

Furthermore, I knew that I lacked the gifts for a political career. I should have liked to be an orator; I was not. As a young man, I longed to be a boxer – let anyone draw the conclusions he prefers. I soon resigned myself to being content with, and using, what abilities I had. My temptation to engage in politics at this late stage resembled my youthful ambitions. I did not even have to take the test of joining an organized party – a test that I should certainly have failed. Never having done so, I cannot imagine how I could affiliate myself to a system over which I had no control and, on some subjects, no chance to exert any influence. The very expression 'belong to a party' puts me off. To belong, to follow the party line, to act without total conviction, or before one is totally convinced – of that I should have been incapable. At the same time, however, as if by contrast, I was beginning to see quite clearly what I could usefully do via the political organization that was being set up by referenda and repeated general elections.

If there was stiff competition around the centres of power, there was practically none in the area where I wanted to work – preparing the future, which by definition is outside the glare of present publicity. Since I did not get in statesmen's way, I could count on their support. Moreover, although it takes a long time to reach the men at the top, it takes very little to explain to them how to escape from the difficulties of the present. This is something they are glad to hear when the critical moment comes. Then, when ideas are lacking, they accept yours with gratitude – provided they can present them as their own. These men, after all, take the risks; they need the kudos. In my line of work, kudos has to be forgotten. I have no particular taste for secrecy, despite what some people say; but if I can best expedite matters by self-effacement, then I prefer to work behind the scenes.

Having settled that problem in my own mind, my next task was to think out the forms of action which would enable France's new political institutions, and the man who ran them, to help in the work of modernization, and enable the French once more to be masters of their fate. How to lead an immense collective effort without being in control of decision-making in the State or in industry, and how to pursue this long-term effort with some guarantee of stability – these were questions that we were going to have to study in our temporary billets at the Bristol. We were starting from scratch: what we were attempting was virtually without precedent in any democratic country. But at least I was assured of the support of General de Gaulle, whose ambition for France would break down any obstacles that the past might erect. In fact, as will be seen, the past put up no resistance. There was nothing to break down, although there were many people to convince. France had in fact become a new country, full of fresh energies which lacked only a setting to work in, a method of action, and objectives on which to converge.

Chapter 10

THE MODERNIZATION OF FRANCE (1946)

I

A method

It was obvious to everyone that France had emerged from the war severely weakened. Less well known, or less willingly acknowledged, was the weakness from which she was already suffering when war broke out. This, no less than military or moral shortcomings, explained her sudden collapse in 1940. A few weeks after my return to France, Marjolin, Hirsch, and I looked at the figures. No one had previously put them together and faced the grim picture they revealed: the slow and regular decline of our economy. Fierce controversies about the neglect of spiritual values in recent years, and the ardent professions of faith in the future made by the country's new leaders – none of these touched the fundamentals of France's problem. Its origins lay far back in time, and its solution would not be found overnight. The Liberation had given us back our freedom, but with all its liabilities and with heavy debts. When I had promised General de Gaulle in Washington that I would tackle the modernization of France, I had had no idea how huge a task it would be. Now, I realized that it was vital: it would occupy all my energies and those of the men who had worked with me on the war effort. To sustain a comparable effort in peacetime, we should once again need to take an overall view and to mobilize all available human and material resources. The arsenal of victory and the powerhouse of reconstruction had this in common: each in its turn was engaged in the same fight against fatalism.

Since the beginning of the century, indeed, the French seemed to have become unconsciously fatalistic about the technological race. It was as if they were content to rest on the laurels won by past generations, whose immense hard work and creativity had fuelled the industrial revolution. It had long been thought that the shock of the first Great War had made France fall behind other industrialized countries; but her comparative backwardness was in fact already discernible between 1900 and 1914. The loss of 1,400,000 men in World War I had certainly retarded French production even further, so that it only slowly regained the level it had reached in 1913. In 1929, output rose to a new peak – but the world recession quickly put a stop to growth, and by 1938 the country was exhausted: it had lost a third of its investment capacity in a decade of crisis and social change. Then, once again, the scourge of war attacked an already weakened constitution; and by 1945 France's national income, in real terms, was little more than half what it had been in 1929.

Such was the sombre picture painted for us by the few exceptional men who had thought about the problem, and who were capable of using the economic measuring-instruments that were still little-known in France: men like Alfred Sauvy, Jean Fourastié, and Jacques Dumontier. Their diagnosis was crisp: by modern standards, France was appallingly backward.

But the low level of production and national wealth was itself only a symptom of our enfeeblement, which the two world wars had merely made worse. The deeper reason was undoubtedly the lack of enterprise, which had led to a serious neglect of productive investment and modernization. This in turn had affected the level of economic activity, which was now barely enough to meet the needs of domestic consumption. The French were buying abroad more than they sold. Already before the war they had been paying for a third of their imports with revenue from long-standing overseas holdings. In an equilibrium as precarious as this, there was no hope of new capital investment: what capital was ploughed back scarcely covered the replacement of antiquated machine tools, whose average age in France was twenty-five years, compared with five or six in the United States and eight or nine in Britain, where there were already twice as many as in France. Etienne Hirsch, who had long experience in industry, told me that France's most modern steelmaking plant dated from 1906 – and even that had been installed by the Germans during their annexation of Lorraine. Similar examples were brought to our notice every day as soon as it was known that we were determined to look at the problem seriously and to try to put it right.

In a static world, the result of such backwardness might just have been tolerable. But wartime destruction had made them worse; and the challenge of war had actually stimulated those countries that had gone on fighting after the fall of France. Even in normal circumstances, we seemed to have become resigned to using only a half or a third as much energy per head as our immediate rivals: now, we were going to find it impossible to compete. And how could we bear the additional burden of postwar reconstruction? From their inventory of our backwardness, the experts worked out the size of our 'productivity gap'. In 1938, they said, an American workman had produced three times as much as the average Frenchman, and a British workman one-and-a-half times as much. A French farmworker was now producing enough to feed five consumers; an American, fifteen. This was hardly surprising, when in France there was one tractor for every 200 people on the land, while in the United States there was one for every 43. There was no mystery about our plight, and no miracle could cure it. That was the great discovery we made in the closing months of 1945, when for the first time the French were faced with the consequences of their past neglect.

I realized that we should have to disappoint those who believed that the Liberation would bring prosperity. For four years, they had lived on idealized memories or impatient hopes; but the basis of the prosperity they dreamed of had been forgotten for too long to be restored so quickly. A long campaign of explanation would be needed before the country could be persuaded to invest in essential capital goods rather than squander its resources on immediate satisfactions. But we had to do more than just return to prewar standards, which had been modest; and there was a danger that the country would slacken before it fully caught up. This psychological problem seemed to me all-important, and I spoke about it to General de Gaulle. He too, I found, was anxious to ensure that we should not relax our efforts.

'It will take time,' I said, 'to rebuild our cities and ports and to repair the railways. But all this will be done, because there is no alternative. On the other hand, it will take very great willpower and an immense effort of explanation before people realize what is really wrong – which is that our capital equipment and production methods are out of date.'

'That is a task for the authorities,' he answered. 'Make a proposal to them.'

'I don't know exactly what has to be done,' I said; 'but I'm sure of one thing. The French economy can't be transformed unless the French people take part in its transformation. And when I say "the French people", I don't mean an abstract entity: I mean trade unionists, industrialists, and civil servants. Everyone must be associated in an investment and modernization plan.'

'That is what has to be done, and that is the name for it,' de Gaulle concluded. 'Send me your proposals before the end of the year.'

We set to work in what was essentially virgin territory. True, some plans existed already: every department of the administration brought us its own. In their separate areas, the civil servants had worked very well, each doing his best to develop that sector of industry for which he was responsible. But while they had incidentally consulted a few industrialists, they had not collated their respective inquiries, with the result that their plans were neither well co-ordinated nor ranged in any order of priority. On the contrary, all were competing for the same limited resources of energy, manpower, and foreign currency, which at this rate would soon be exhausted. Yet in fact the various sectors were interdependent: the plans for industry determined those for transport, while hydro-electric dam projects would clearly be affected by the targets set for cement production. No such correlations had been made; everyone was working contentedly in his own separate compartment. People in different administrative departments or different branches of industry spoke to one another, but their respective intentions remained secret and unco-ordinated. Everyone was entrenched in his own position. And even if priorities had had to be established, would anyone have come forward to argue that cement should be used for dams rather than houses, and that farm machinery was more urgently needed than automobiles? Neither was evident at first sight, because on the contrary the most obvious shortages seemed to be in housing and consumer goods.

The question was: where to begin? Once again, I realized that this was the only question that mattered. Once you have made a start, all you need do is continue. But in order to begin, one needs to have clear ideas and decide on the simplest way forward. Common sense is not enough, even if in retrospect the decisions taken look obvious. In fact, without Hirsch's and Marjolin's great economic and technical expertise I should have found it difficult to identify so accurately the key sectors – those which, once set in motion, affect the whole economy. Today, economists are very familiar with this kind of interaction. In 1945, we had to take a leap in the dark. Admittedly, we could hardly go wrong by concentrating on energy and steel, where shortages were visibly paralysing France's recovery. But even there we had to keep within bounds: we had to bear in mind the nation's available resources of raw materials, capital, foreign currency and, above all, manpower. Yet there was no overall balance-sheet to help us. It was a situation which I had already encountered on several crucial occasions in France, Britain, and the United States. But while it neither surprised me nor worried me, it nevertheless had to be tackled in a totally new way.

Now that the war was over, that is, circumstances had changed. We were no longer fighting an external enemy, whose menace aroused the instinctive reflex of self-defence. The internal danger that now faced us was no less serious a threat to our independence and our way of life; but it was not perceived vividly enough to mobilize the country by decree. What was more, a peacetime economy would no longer tolerate the wide safety margins which had been accepted for war production, and which had made possible the 'overwhelming superiority' achieved by the Victory Program. If in 1940 I had been credited with saying 'Better ten thousand tanks too many than one tank too few', such an attitude no longer made sense in 1945. Production must be adjusted to requirements, or else there would be economic and social chaos. Such precise adjustment, allied to such massive efforts, at a time when there were no computers, could neither be decreed and supervised by a few civil servants nor be left to the judgement of thousands of entrepreneurs. Our action had to be at once less dictatorial and more specific: we had to persuade, not compel, private enterprise to act in accordance with public needs. The best way, surely, was to bring together all the parties concerned, so that they could jointly seek the common interest, which no one of them could determine alone, but in which all of them had a share. We agreed that what mattered above all was to work out a democratic method of action along these lines.

From that moment onward, the underlying philosophy of the French Plan was clear in my mind. What remained was to give it practical form: a method of concerted action whereby everyone could see where his own efforts fitted in with everyone else's. We had to ensure that everything – the most pressing needs and the most distant ambitions – obeyed the rule we had set ourselves: always start with an overall view. The experts who brought us their statistics, the industrialists with their dossiers, the trade unionists with their programmes – all went away with extracts from our 'Treatise on Method'.* We wanted them to digest it first and come back later, when we had established the framework within which we could all confer. Nor did it merely have to be established: it had to be invented. As I have said, civil

* A tacit allusion to René Descartes's eponymous *Discours de la méthode* (1637).

servants, producers, and workpeople had never sat down together around the same table. If they had sometimes negotiated, they had done so bilaterally, on opposite sides of the table and in an atmosphere of confrontation. There had been a winning side and a losing side, so that the underlying problem had merely been postponed. The idea of a plan belonged to the realm of ideological controversy over the Soviet Five-year Plan; and I knew that only action could dissipate misunderstandings about the entirely new type of planning that we had in mind.

This was as far removed from the Soviet *Gosplan* or State Planning Commission as it was from the unique system that Sir Stafford Cripps, the British Chancellor of the Exchequer, had established to organize a concerted national effort on the part of the United Kingdom. We had studied the operation of Cripps's 'working parties', which brought together industrialists, trade unionists, and technical experts; but this democratic attempt to steer the economy seemed to us seriously handicapped by the absence of civil servants representing the public interest, as well as by its lack of general objectives. Improving on this precedent, we quickly hit upon what seemed the right formula, that of our 'Modernization Commissions'. These we saw as the king-pins of the whole planning system; and we rapidly committed it to paper. At the beginning of December 1945 I was already in a position to meet General de Gaulle's deadline, and I sent him a five-page Note entitled 'Proposals for a Modernization and Investment Plan'.

Three of its pages were devoted to a diagnosis of the French situation and an outline of the remedies required. First, it was essential for France to catch up with the technological revolution that had begun to leave her behind even before the war. 'Modernization and reconstruction,' the Note said, 'must go hand in hand.' Secondly, France must produce more, and at lower prices, in order to pay for the raw materials that were vital for her export industries. Thirdly, there was no time to be lost:

> All France's manpower and available industrial resources will very soon be fully employed. Our domestic needs are such that there will be no difficulty in selling at home all that we can produce. At that point, interested parties of all kinds will insist, not on transforming the productive capacity they are using, but on protecting it. If we bowed to these demands, it would prevent any progress and any improvement in the standard of living. It would reduce France to the level of a second-class power.

There was a very real danger, indeed, that France might content herself with frugal mediocrity behind a protectionist shield. This, after all, had been a national tradition. But I knew that the mere allusion to such a possibility would be enough to win support from the new, Resistance generation and to carry the day with General de Gaulle. He was following our work very closely. He could not falter on any course that meant greatness and independence for France, and I should have no difficulty in convincing him that this was the only way. But I made no secret of the fact that it would require foreign loans if we were to move quickly – and that to move slowly would be extremely dangerous. 'Without these loans,' I wrote, 'modernization would still be needed, but the conditions for achieving it would be different. It would necessarily take longer, and the French people would have to be asked to accept greater cuts in domestic consumption.' To tell the truth, we never seriously imagined adopting this second course, which not only would have delayed France's recovery, but would have distorted it, and would perhaps have led the country in a different direction altogether.

A fourth section of my Note described the proposed method:

> The whole nation must join in these efforts. People will accept the measures to be taken, but only in so far as they know and understand the real situation. The proposed Plan is not only a tool for the administration and the public authorities: it concerns all Frenchmen. It will give them the facts about where we stand, and directives to guide them in their own individual decisions.

Accustomed as we are to the talk of 'participation' which now accompanies all steps of any importance, we may well underestimate the significance of that passage. But it has to be given its full weight, because it led directly to the method which made possible the modernization of France:

> Since the implementation of the Plan will require everyone's collaboration, all the vital elements in the nation must help to draw it up. That is why the method of work proposed is to bring together in each sector the administrative department concerned, the best qualified experts, and the representatives of industry and the trade unions (workpeople, white-collar workers, and employers).

The idea of having people share in setting the economic targets they would then be asked to attain seemed in those days a figment of the imagination. But it was also the precondition for action; and I knew that the idea of co-operation, which was then the subject of so much political controversy, would be accepted by everyone if it were presented in this way. The time was propitious for experiments in collective effort: the patriotic impulses released by the Liberation were still powerful, and they had not yet found an adequate outlet. The nationalization of various industries, long awaited and recently achieved, was no longer a goal, but a vehicle for making collective progress in ways that now only had to be defined. Everyone felt that progress was possible, but no one knew precisely what to do. In this situation, the Plan could be a genuinely 'national enterprise' – an expression that could at last take on practical meaning. I was determined to make the Modernization Commissions a living reality, and the description of them that I prepared for General de Gaulle was in my view crucially important:

> The Planning Council will decide which French industries are to be the subject of modernization studies.
>
> For each group, a Modernization Commission will be set up, comprising representatives of the civil servants, experts, employers, trade unionists, and white-collar workers concerned. The Modernization Commissions will be empowered to form sub-commissions for the study of particular questions.
>
> A representative of the Planning Commissioner will sit on each Modernization Commission as Chairman, Rapporteur, or Secretary, in order to facilitate co-ordination.
>
> The Planning Commissioner and his staff will draw up general directives for the Modernization Commissions, monitor the progress of their studies, and ensure that each of them takes account of needs or limitations brought to light by the others. The Commissioner and his staff will be responsible for the overall results.

The ultimate aim of this system was to draw up 'an overall balance-sheet' which would enable the Planning Council to set 'priorities' and to submit to the Government 'practical proposals concerning France's essential industries and the targets to be attained within a stated time.' No dates were set for the completion of these tasks or for the duration of the Plan. The first instructions were vague: 'To determine French productivity and the arrears to be made up; to propose production levels to be attained' – it might be, to regain those of 1929. In fact, the most important feature of this description was its flexibility, enabling plans in any sector to be constantly readjusted in the light of the others. Comparing notes and continual adaptation were the cardinal rules. We were putting into administrative practice the notion of interdependence which is fundamental in the world of business.

I sent my proposals to General de Gaulle on December 5, 1945. Two weeks later, the French Cabinet approved them; and on January 3, 1946, it issued a decree establishing the Commissariat-General of the French Modernization and Investment Plan. The first article of the decree stated:

> Within six months a first overall Plan for the modernization and eco-nomic equipment of metropolitan and overseas France shall be drawn up.

The aims of the Plan were then defined under four headings:

(1) To develop national production and foreign trade, particularly in those fields where France is most favourably placed;
(2) To increase productivity;
(3) To ensure the full employment of manpower;
(4) To raise the standard of living and to improve the environment and the conditions of national life.

The decree went on to lay down the membership of the Planning Council. Its Chairman was to be the Head of Government; twelve of his colleagues were Ministers, and twelve were to be public figures chosen for their expertise. Finally, the Planning Commissioner's role was described. He was to be the Head of Government's permanent delegate to all Ministerial departments; he was given extensive powers of inquiry, and the Commissariat which he headed was empowered to enlist help from the staff of all Ministries and in particular from the statistical institutes. The Commissioner was also authorized to set up working committees and, of course, the Modernization Commissions. The decree was signed by nine Ministers, of whom two belonged to the Christian-Democrat *Mouvement Républicain Populaire* (MRP), two were Radicals, one a Socialist, and four Communists.

I was grateful to General de Gaulle for having followed my recom-mendations so completely. The success of the Planning Commissariat would depend on its structure and the position it occupied in the country's political and administrative life. To command the widest authority, it had to be attached to the Prime Minister's office; but this was by no means a matter of course, as I was to discover now and on many subsequent occasions. Traditionalists would have placed the Commissariat under one of the economic Ministries, and the whole weight of civil service tradition tried to drag it back into this state of subordination every time there was a Cabinet change. Although I had never cared about questions of rank, I was convinced that the effectiveness or otherwise of my work as Planning Commissioner would depend on the level at which it was carried out. It was not that I wanted any particular position for myself; but my colleagues and I had to be able to influence the whole range of Departments that would be involved in implementing the Plan. No Ministerial post would have offered as much scope as the indefinable position of Planning Commissioner, attached to the Prime Minister's office. I was taking no one's place and becoming no one's superior. I was moving into territory that had hitherto had neither occupant nor name.

In administrative terms, that territory would have to be modest. I asked Gaston Palewski, General de Gaulle's *directeur de cabinet* or chief executive assistant, for a small staff and some conference rooms.

'This will be the Government's smallest administrative budget,' he remarked.

'It has to be,' I said. 'That way, no one will be jealous, and we shall be left in peace. We shan't be tempted to do everything ourselves; we'll get others to do the work. And I shan't be bothered by administrative problems.'

In fact, there were never more than thirty senior officials on the Planning Commissariat, and the whole staff, including secretaries and doormen, was no more than a hundred or so. My own working team was smaller still – just four or five people who were with me all the time, including Hirsch, who took charge of the technical side. But I had asked for large rooms, because I intended to bring together there the many people whose expertise we needed, but whom we did not want to add to our small permanent staff. On one particular point I was insistent: I had to have a small dining-room so that work could continue uninterrupted – or rather, so that every day it could include a period of relaxation, making it more human and informal. I had already learned in Britain and the United States how much depends on personal relationships, even in the face of the sternest tasks. In Paris, the innovation raised some eyebrows – as did the frugality of our meals, which disconcerted more than one Minister and more than one trade unionist. But our dining-room certainly encouraged progress and mutual understanding and I believe that it started a trend.

Gaston Palewski's friendly efficiency and subtle intelligence were of immense help to us when we began. He made it his business to find us somewhere congenial to work: a small private house on the Left Bank at No 18 rue de Martignac, just by the church of Sainte-Clotilde, an island of peace in the midst of Ministry buildings. The state rooms at the top of the main staircase were large enough for the Modernization Commissions, while my colleagues and I moved into the smaller rooms on the floor above, in a baroque setting riddled with unexpected corridors and stairs. It made a strange contrast with the intellectual order and rationality that we were supposed to represent. In reality, in the words of J. F. Gravier, the caustic wit who was lodged under the tiles in a small office next to Jean Vergeot and Paul Delouvrier, of whom I shall say more in a moment,

> This absurd setting has at least one advantage: it's so cramped and labyrinthine that it creates a sense of intimacy and familiarity, like an old Italian family mansion. It's as unbureaucratic as could be, which is just as well, since we insist that we're not a bureaucracy.

The absurdity must have some inner logic, because for the thirty years that the Planning Commissariat has been in existence, stimulating new ideas everywhere and launching so many carefully thought-out projects, it has never felt the need to leave its inconvenient quarters in the shadow of Sainte-Clotilde. The inconvenience has at least saved it, as I had hoped, from the dangers of bureaucratic proliferation.

Félix Gaillard, who stayed on as my *chef de cabinet*, strongly recommended to me one of his friends, Maurice Aicardi, whom he knew to be very adept in all fields of practical organization. I saw him, and found that he was indeed very able. He made an excellent job of setting up the small and efficient administration that I wanted, and helped me for years with the routine problems of No 18 rue de Martignac. He is still there, still plying his remarkable skill, compounded of political finesse and satisfaction in work well done. Gaillard had a sure touch, because among the people he brought into our team was a fellow-*inspecteur des finances*, Paul Delouvrier, at that time *directeur de cabinet* to René Pleven, who was now de Gaulle's Finance Minister. Like Pleven himself, Delouvrier was all strength and appetite for life. He too had been tested by the Resistance and was impatient to throw himself body and soul into action for the public good. His intelligence and magnanimity were just what our venture needed from this new generation of Frenchmen. Delouvrier went to work with a will on the Plan's financial problems, and began a very distinguished career.

Sauvy and Fourastié, who lent us their help at the beginning, were unable to stay on; and their place in the economic and statistical section was taken by Jean Vergeot, a senior official from the Ministry of Economic Affairs who had worked with the well-known economist

François Perroux. 'Monsieur Vergeot', as we always called him, out of a mixture of respect and friendship, was meticulous about everything, with a precision of mind and expression that made him a remarkable expositor of our ideas. His capacity for steady work, and his unruffled good humour throughout our inevitable teething troubles and later difficulties, never ceased to astonish me. I have always had great regard for this modest man who hid behind his dossiers – out of which, day after day, he made clear and simple reports, all written with his old-fashioned 'Sergeant-Major' pen, endlessly dipped in the inkwell. The Plan owes a great deal to Monsieur Vergeot: it certainly owes to him the fact that it was read and understood by so many of his compatriots.

In his orbit, three young economists – Jacques-René Rabier, Jacques Van Helmont, and Jean Ripert – practised the style which for years was to be that of the Planning Commissariat's publications: short sentences, numbered paragraphs marking the transition from one idea to the next without clumsy bridging passages, a limited number of concrete words, and few adjectives. It was an austere art, of which all three became pastmasters. Some people thought it the opposite of art, because it lacked virtuosities of form or wit. At that time there was a fashion for brilliant dialectical displays. Myself, I fancy that the reports of Monsieur Vergeot's team may well have worn better than some of the period's far more subtle writings. At all events, they can be re-read today. They expressed the necessity of the time – and necessity can always dispense with artifice. Newcomers, anxious to shine, got their drafts back with the comment: 'Too intelligent; rewrite.' In the end, all our documents went to and fro through a common filter which reduced their style and content to essentials.

At the beginning, to help me train the new team, I also had with me such tried and true colleagues as Pierre Denis, Roger Auboin, and Léon Kaplan. They all knew my methods – Denis since the League of Nations and Silesia, Auboin since Romania, and Kaplan since Washington. They soon went their separate ways, however, and Marjolin and Hirsch stayed with me to handle the central feature of the planning system, setting up the Modernization Commissions. We had to select both the sectors and the people, and we could not afford to make mistakes. Together, we took the responsibility of making our leap in the dark – of giving priority to one line of development rather than another, and of saying in effect: 'These people will do better than those.' The month of January 1946 was filled with consultations, and a number of very notable figures came to No 18 rue de Martignac.

Having been out of France for six years, we met for the first time the new men – industrialists, trade union leaders, and civil servants – who had emerged from the war with an exemplary record of resistance to the invader. They were often unknown to each other. It took many discreet approaches, and many talks, to form an idea of their weight and their worth.

Hirsch was very good at discovering first-rate experts with abilities outside their own fields. As a former mining engineer, he knew his way about in the world of industry, and was able to spot the coming men. At forty-five, he was reassuringly calm and competent; but I knew that his cool exterior concealed deep sensibilities. He was as sure in his estimate of men as he was level-headed in his judgement of things. I relied on him to balance our overall production targets, and I put him in charge of our technical staff.

Marjolin was influential among economists, and the brilliant impression he had made during his spell at the Ministry of Economic Affairs had given him great authority in civil service circles, where he pointed out to us the most effective people. He was also trusted by the Socialist trade unions, with which he had worked as a young man. He was still barely thirty-five, and looked like a tall student in the grip of theoretical ideas. Self-taught, he had become the favourite pupil of the economist Charles Rist, and as a young Socialist militant had caught the eye of Léon Blum. Under these two influences he had learned to think for himself; and the war had confirmed his conviction that thought without action was not enough. With the title of Deputy Planning Commissioner, he worked out the general economics of the Plan. With him and Hirsch at my side, I could not have asked for a better combination of complementary skills.

We had given ourselves a month to make a first survey of the problem, and we had six months to work out our proposals. Events forced us to take a little longer. No sooner had General de Gaulle signed the decree setting up the Planning Commissariat, and turned the note I had sent him into an instruction – the full text is in his *Memoirs* – than he suddenly resigned from the Government on January 20, 1946. Thanks to him, the venture was safely launched, and he deserves the political credit. He was succeeded by Félix Gouin, a shrewd statesman whom I had known since Algiers, when he had come as a representative of the Resistance and had been President of the Consultative Assembly. I had access to him, and could appeal to his common sense. I was obliged to do so at once, when a fresh attempt was made from on high to have the Planning Commissariat made subordinate to the Ministry of Economic Affairs. I have already pointed out how much importance I attached to this apparently formal question: the very nature of the French Plan would have been called in question had it been made the subject of permanent negotiations between the major Ministerial departments. Determined to resign if necessary, I went to see Félix Gouin.

'I have a high regard for the French civil service,' I said, 'but it is not equipped to produce a plan for changing the face of France. On the contrary, its job is to maintain the state of affairs entrusted to it. The senior civil servants who run it have every quality – except the spirit of enterprise. To transform France, we must first transform the French Establishment, and perhaps also the training that produces it. I do not propose to entrust the Modernization Commissions to civil servants, and still less to accept civil-service tutelage over the Plan. The Commissariat will be attached to your office or it will be nothing.'

'I'll speak to André Philip,' said Gouin.

I heard no more of the matter, for a year at least. And I must say that we were left completely free to appoint the non-Ministerial members of the Planning Council. As representatives of the trade unions we quite naturally chose their General Secretaries – Benoît Frachon and Léon Jouhaux for the General Confederation of Labour (CGT) and Gaston Tessier for the French Confederation of Christian Workers (CFTC). But otherwise we chose for ourselves, independently of all outside influence, those men whose ability and authority we had recognized: leaders of industry like the Chairmen of Citroën and of the Saulnes Blast-Furnace Company, or the President of the Wool Committee; in agriculture, a landowner from the Aisne and another from the Gard. The latter's name was Philippe Lamour. His dynamism and eloquence were a tonic. Near him sat a quiet Member of Parliament, a specialist in agricultural questions: it was the Communist leader Pierre Waldeck-Rochet.

We also brought together other public figures representing various economic groupings: Léon Gingembre, already heading the confederation of Small and Medium-sized Businesses (PME), and Pierre Ricard, a steelmaker who was influential in the National Council of French Employers (CNPF). Men of system, they were later to adopt attitudes hostile to change; but at the time they were carried along by the general trend, quite as much as their counterparts in the CGT. One of these was Pierre Le Brun, who later played an important part in our work. He was one of the brains of the trade union movement. A former engineer, essentially an intellectual, he was influential as the

CGT's economic adviser, and he had very extensive contacts, somewhat belied by his cool, self-effacing appearance. A convinced Marxist, he was always on the left wing of the CGT, although it was impossible to say what links he had with the Communist Party. So long as the Party was represented in Government, it formed a very useful link, and was a loyal and even friendly partner in our work: our joint discussions were always open and frank.

The Modernization Commissions, we realized, could be formed in the same way as the Planning Council; but first we had to decide on the priority sectors. Our prime task, undoubtedly, was to draw up an overall balance-sheet of France's needs and resources; but unlike some people I did not believe that we should treat all sectors alike. Although we set up a total of eighteen Modernization Commissions, all of the same type, this was to enable us to form a complete and consistent picture. When the time came to act, I knew that we should have to concentrate on five or six decisive points: the others would act as landmarks to help guide, encourage, or restrain activity in other less important or less urgent fields. Once again, and not for the last time, I had to explain and defend the choice of priorities – not only to producers and consumers, but also to the public authorities concerned. Everyone's natural tendency was to continue doing everything at once: people seem to find nothing more difficult than to decide on priorities for what they have to do. But it was surely obvious that we ought first to concentrate on the powerful driving-forces that would set in motion the rest of the machine. Theoretically, this was undeniable: yet it was hard to apply in practice because it meant changing set habits and patterns of work, as well as making temporary sacrifices.

Everyone agreed, for example, that one absolute priority was to develop sources of energy: but they disagreed when the logical conclusion was drawn that cement and steel must be used to build dams rather than housing. To improve our balance of trade, should we export automobiles or expand our own agriculture and import less food? The latter was the obvious choice: but then we had to decide whether it would be better to produce fertilizers or agricultural machinery. Our job was to make choices – which in the end meant displacing manpower, natural resources, capital, and imported supplies. It was not simply a matter of ensuring that sacrifices were fairly shared: at this the French had become very adept. We had at the same time to find ways out of France's present poverty, to use her inadequate resources for the new investments that would eventually make her rich, and to do this without imposing fresh privations. For everyone involved in the

Modernization Plan, that had to be the long-term objective. My essential task was to persuade them and ceaselessly remind them of that fact. Objectives are all too easily forgotten in the process of action itself.

In my view the Modernization Commissions were not only a means of communicating our ideas to those responsible for the economy, and through them to the general public: they were also, and equally, sources of information for ourselves. It was with this in mind that we sought out those men who were most enterprising and influential in their various fields. Gradually, we learned their names and came to know their faces; eventually, they devoted themselves completely to the Plan, which for months became their overriding concern. In all, more than a thousand people worked on this great collective task during the year 1946, either in the Commissions or sub-commissions, or as experts to be consulted at all hours. They became one huge team, led by the Planning Commissariat. Without our leadership, the team would have produced a plethora of ideas but no conclusions; yet without the team, our conclusions could never have reached every level of the population. In this sense, the French Plan was a genuine collective achievement.

By the beginning of February, 1946, the Commissions on Coalmines and Electricity had been established and set to work; a few weeks later came those on Steel and Building Materials. This order of events reflected the list of priorities which I had drawn up, but which was not officially endorsed until later, in May and June, when the Commissions on Transport and Farm Machinery were formed. These completed the famous 'six basic industries', which for years were the cornerstone of our modernization plans.

The Chairman of the Coalmines Commission was a powerful figure, Victorin Duguet, Secretary-General of the Underground Workers' Federation, and at that time also Chairman of the French Coal Board, since the mines had been nationalized in December 1944. As in the other Modernization Commissions, the Vice-Chairman was a specialized senior official, the Director in charge of mines at the Ministry of National Production; while the Rapporteur was an expert, an instructor at the School of Mines. As Chairman of the Electricity Commission we appointed a leading technician from the industry, Roger Boutteville. His Deputy was the Director of electricity at the Ministry, Roger Gaspard; and the Rapporteur was Pierre Le Brun. There was a similar arrangement on the Steel Commission, which was headed by the Chairman of the Longwy Steelworks, Etienne Roy.

We quickly realized how effective such arrangements were. Certainly, nationalization made matters easier when it came to setting targets for energy. But in that field, as in others, the men in question came from very different backgrounds, and before the war they had been at loggerheads in their firms – if they had met at all. Yet when the Coalmines Commission had to meet with the Steel Commission to agree on coal quotas for the blast furnaces, labour leaders like Duguet and Le Brun had no objection to sitting on the same side of the table as industrialists like Roy and René Damien, Chairman of the Denain and Anzin Steelworks.

'Of course,' said Hirsch, 'they can look back to the Resistance. They were also on the same side then. But you can't put it all down to camaraderie.'

'It simply bears out what I learned a long time ago,' I said. 'When you take people from different backgrounds, put them in front of the same problem, and ask them to solve it, they're no longer the same people. They're no longer there to defend their separate interests, and so they automatically take a common view. You'll see: the Plan will work without imposing anything on anyone.'

The machinery was already in place. The Electricity Commission had twenty-two members, including six heads of firms, three trade unionists, two white-collar workers, five experts, and four civil servants. The Steel Commission had five heads of firms, two trade unionists, two white-collar workers, three experts, and three civil servants. The same proportions applied elsewhere.

By March 16, 1946, we were ready for a meeting of the Planning Council. It was held in the biggest room at No 18 rue de Martignac, under an imposing copy of François Rudé's relief sculpture *La Marseillaise* on the Arc de Triomphe, which Palewski and Aicardi had had made to symbolize the Republic calling on Frenchmen to practise the arts of peace. Opening the first session, Félix Gouin declared:

A real technological revolution is urgently needed. Reconstruction and modernization are inseparably linked. We can only succeed if the whole nation is fully alive to the importance of its part in this task.

I then proposed that the Council include in the Plan the targets which we believed could be attained if conditions were right: to get back to our 1938 production level by 1948, and to the 1929 level, 25% higher, by 1949; then, in 1950, to improve on the 1929 level by a further

25%. To this end, the Council approved the target which the Coal-mines Commission had set itself: 65m. metric tons by 1950, plus guaranteed deliveries of German coal. Hydro-electricity output was to be doubled. Steel production was to reach 12m. metric tons. 50,000 tractors were to be produced annually in the next five years.

Finally, I had to recognize how limited our exports were by comparison with our vital import needs:

> Not until 1950 can we hope to re-establish lasting equilibrium in our balance of payments on current account. Until then, we shall need outside help in order to meet the deficit. Even if we were to use all our official gold and currency reserves, and to mobilize private holdings abroad, we should still need several billion dollars more in the period 1946-50.

And I added this sentence, which at the time had political significance, but which I knew to be utterly hollow:

> Part of this sum should be supplied by Germany in the form of reparations.

Everyone knew where we should have to look for the remainder – that is, for the bulk of what we needed; and everyone knew where we had the prospect of obtaining it. If we were discreet in what we said that day, it was because delicate negotiations were already in progress 3000 miles to the West.

II

Continued efforts

On March 19, 1946, a few hours after the Planning Council meeting ended, I flew to Washington to join Léon Blum, who had arrived two days earlier as the French Government's Ambassador Extraordinary. The purpose of his trip was to settle the financial problems still pending with the United States since the termination of Lend-Lease, and to negotiate for fresh credits to take over from the $650m. loan that I had obtained in November. This time, we had done our sums well, and we made no secret of the fact that, whatever efforts we might make, our foreign currency deficit would continue for a number of years, and that even then it would not be phased out except by the judicious use of considerable overseas aid. Blum's trip had been decided on at the beginning of February, but it had been put back on account of his ill-health. The delay was very unfortunate, because Congress had meanwhile approved a large loan to Great Britain, and the US Administration had had to promise never again to offer foreign borrowers such advantageous terms. So we had come at the worst possible time. On the other hand, two months earlier we should clearly have been unable to present so well-documented a case. Then, there had been no balance-sheet of France's needs and resources; no firm projects had been approved by the Planning Council; and the United States might well have refused to renew its aid without making most pressing recommendations about how we should conduct our affairs. It was not that the Americans wished to curb our independence: on the contrary, they wanted us to be able as soon as possible to do without their help. In this respect, the Plan anticipated their concern, and perhaps also any conditions which they might have imposed on less responsible borrowers. That was why I felt more confident in going to Washington with the Planning Council's decisions under my arm.

How closely the Plan and overseas aid were linked was something I realized more clearly every day – so much so that our assignment took an unexpected turn. Originally intended to last two weeks, it in fact went on for eleven, all of them spent in practical and constructive dialogue. Naturally, the long delay led people to imagine that there were serious difficulties; and public impatience in France turned into suspicion with the approach of the May 5 referendum on the draft Constitution. After the vote – by which the Constitution was rejected – the election of a new Constituent Assembly was scheduled for June 2; and the same suspicions arose again. The press alleged that Léon Blum wanted to return with a success in his pocket; and some people wondered whether he might not be buying it by means of political concessions.

The truth was both simpler and more complex. The difficulties were not political, but technical. Indeed, I have no recollection of difficulties, but rather of very detailed joint work, which is not the same thing. Nothing serious is easy; and when one has to liquidate several years of wartime accounting and embark on enormous credit operations for a still uncertain future, weeks pass quickly. From Paris, my colleagues urged me to have done. I ignored their tactical arguments, which were irrelevant to the task in hand. Things have their own rhythm, and one can never spend too long on a job if by taking a little more time one can do it better. What matters is to know how to stop at a certain moment; but I meant to be free to decide when that moment had come. If I had listened to arguments about French or American domestic politics, the agreement would have satisfied no one. Instead, it finally satisfied everyone: the new French Assembly ratified it on August 1, 1946. In the election of that Assembly, I might add, the Socialists lost ground, despite Léon Blum's success. For me this was further proof that one must deal with each main difficulty as one comes to it: nothing is gained by looking for over-ingenious solutions in an effort to tackle several problems at the same time.

The success of our negotiations was a triumph for that great humanist Léon Blum, who had staked on them his considerable reputation. He deserved the credit: it had needed courage to undertake this journey into the unknown so soon after recovering from the ordeal of wartime captivity. At seventy-six, Blum had never before been to the United States, and he was boyishly excited by the spectacle of New York. Everyone received him with great respect; he was indeed no ordinary ambassador. I relieved him of the burden of negotiating, and he seldom had to intervene in the talks; but he greatly helped them by his noble speeches to members of Congress. He was able to touch a chord of trust and generosity in these men, even in the sober setting of the National and Consultative Committee on Foreign Loans. To the texts of the speeches we prepared for him he added a human dimension that appealed to his most hardened listeners. Over and above the language common to all politicians, which is certainly effective, Léon Blum had the same high ideals of liberty and democracy as the very different men to whom he spoke. It was easy to believe this veteran Socialist leader when he declared that France would take on the commitments required by the charter for international free trade which was then being prepared at Hot Springs:

> It is perfectly right and proper for nations to apply planning or State control at home, as is the case or the tendency in most of Europe, while their external transactions, on the contrary, form part of an international system based on unqualified freedom and equality.

This was an official commitment, against which the French Government was requesting the aid that would enable it eventually to abolish all restrictions on foreign trade. But Blum added a further and more political argument:

> If we were unable to pay for the imports that are vital to our economy, you must realize that France would be placed, through material poverty

and a sense of having been abandoned, in a situation from which one could not expect any reasonable way out.

The men who then governed the United States understood what he meant.

Roosevelt had been dead for a year, and the spirit which had moved him, and which he had communicated to his great team, and through them to the whole nation, was no longer to be felt. Hopkins was no longer with us: after devoting his last remaining strength to the service of his country, he had followed his friend to the grave. We had seen each other in Washington when he had come back from his last visit to Stalin – for which, at Truman's request, he had left hospital for a few days. The ceremonial with which he had been received had not blinded him to the facts: the era of diplomacy between brothers in arms was over; so was the charm of intimate conversation. Hopkins had lived just long enough to see the atomic bomb. Other men would have to administer the armed peace; and at their head was the quiet former Vice-President, whom I had met in Roosevelt's entourage. Harry Truman was certainly no ordinary man, and his years in Congress had given him great experience of America's internal affairs. But, against almost everyone's expectations, he showed himself capable of dominating the world scene. The essential reason was a quality with which he was exceptionally well endowed: the ability to decide. Whether by nature or because the role of President had transformed him, he never hesitated in the face of great decisions. Once he had the supreme responsibility, questions about the depth of his intelligence or his knowledge became irrelevant. Only one thing mattered: that he did his duty, which was to give orders after listening to advice. In the nature of things he could not always be well-informed, and he was capable of making mistakes; but he knew how to make his mind up, which is the sign of a genuine statesman.

In Truman's entourage, a new team had taken over for the transition from war to peace. Fred Vinson at the Treasury and James Byrnes at the State Department were conscientious negotiating partners. After I had renewed contact with the many departments on which our success depended, and after the various Lend-Lease accounts had been sorted out, we concentrated on the future. What I said about the French Plan was received with such great interest that we were soon engaged in active co-operation: the modernization of France became an objective common to both borrower and lender. Both became committed to the success of the operation – an attitude which is certainly in everyone's interest, but which is too often forgotten in negotiations, where each side tends to measure its own advantage in terms of the loss inflicted on the other.

Day after day, we worked on estimates of the opportunities for rapid recovery that the Plan would give to French production and exports. Beyond the financial guarantees that they offered our creditors, these opportunities also affected the way in which Europe's economic and political recovery was conceived. The more we could convince our partners, the better would be the conditions attaching to the final agreement. In this way, by a continual exchange of information across the Atlantic, we improved the first indications I had brought with me, so that the Plan had made considerable progress by the time I returned to Paris, where the Modernization Commissions had been kept very alert by our incessant questionnaires.

How much did we hope to obtain by way of fresh credits once we had liquidated our past debts? Léon Blum was not afraid to reveal to Congress the very substantial figures that emerged from our calculations:

> We are entering a transitional period, after which we hope to achieve satisfactory equilibrium in our balance of payments, but during which we shall have to import those goods that are needed for the modernization of France. Our total import needs would appear to be in the region of 11 billion dollars, including 5 billion from the United States. To pay for them, we shall use every available resource. We shall mobilize our last remaining gold and currency reserves; we shall increase our exports as much as we possibly can. But, even so, we shall face a total deficit of about 3 billion dollars for the next five years. It would scarcely be reduced even if, against all reason, we were to give up our modernization programme – because in that case our exports would obviously fall, as well as our imports. This is the problem that I am asking you to examine with us in all its aspects and as a single whole.

This frank, direct appeal made an impression; but if that impression was favourable, even among representatives of the American taxpayer, who had returned to 'business as usual', it was because we had at the same time put forward a bold programme of action for the five deficit years. A further advantage of that programme was that it enabled overseas aid to be spread over a period. I knew, in fact, that there was no hope of obtaining massive credits in one lump. We should have to come back year after year and prove what efforts we were making. As the terms of the agreement became clearer, Léon Blum made no secret of his disappointment.

'I can't have appealed powerfully enough to their feelings,' he said.

I assured him that he had done all he could. The agreement could not go beyond the realities of the time. Feelings were no longer so important; and in any case, if all the clauses of the agreement were taken together, they added up to a very generous political gesture. In effect, it wiped out what remained from Lend-Lease, and with it the very principle of 'war debts', which has so often poisoned the return to peace. Of the 3½ billion dollars of debts still on the books, the Americans agreed to cancel three-quarters in return for 'services rendered'. All that remained were $420m., to be repaid in 35 years at virtually nil interest. $300m. were lent to us to purchase American surplus goods at low prices. We had finally liquidated our share in the cost of our own Liberation.

There remained the burden of the future, which could not be relieved so swiftly and decisively. On May 28, 1946, the Chairman of the Export-Import Bank told us that he was opening a new line of credit of $650m., intended for French purchases of capital goods and raw materials. At the same time, we were promised a loan of $5–600m. from the International Bank for Reconstruction and Development. In addition, we were to receive 75 Liberty Ships on deferred-payment terms – a 50% increase in our merchant fleet. The total value of all this was about 1½ billion dollars. It would cover only part of our estimated needs between now and 1950; but that, in my view, had not been the aim of our mission. What I had come for, and what was now assured us, was the guarantee that we could embark on the Plan without fear of having to stop halfway. Once it was set in motion, its own impetus would create the internal and external conditions that were essential to its success.

Those weeks in the company of Léon Blum added mutual warmth to the friendliness he showed me and the respect I felt for him. His moral authority, which extended well beyond the militants of his own political party, had been increased by the war and by his time in captivity; but it was essentially inborn, a product of his deep human feelings. He liked people, and he knew how to forge direct links with them. They in turn felt his affection, and there is no need to look further than this to explain the power he had over his contemporaries. Perhaps he had too many qualities.

'I envy you your ability to concentrate,' he said to me once. 'Personally, I can't help being interested in everything that goes on.'

I cannot judge whether his policies were better or worse than those of anyone else. But I know that he had the ability and the strength to base his policies on the dictates of his conscience, and to win people over with his noble and generous feelings. No one can ask much more of any statesman.

Back in Paris, Blum warmly defended the Plan, which we had patiently explained to him; and now he described it better than we did – as statesmen often can. After the French Assembly had approved the Washington agreements, he wrote an editorial in the Socialist newspaper *Le Populaire* whose conclusion admirably summed up the problem of the time:

> Do we or do we not want liberated France to be abreast of modern science and technology? Or do we see her future as a niggardly affair of mediocrity and routine? That is the choice that faces our country. And remember that the French economy, even if it were kept at a mean and mediocre level, still could not do without imports: it would be stifled to death. To import, we must export. To export, we must produce on terms more or less comparable with those of our rivals. In other words, we must rebuild and modernize our industries. So one thing leads to another: there is no third alternative, whichever way one looks. But according to which choice we make, and which state of mind prevails, we shall either do what we have to do, courageously, decisively, and boldly, or find ourselves condemned to timid, close-fisted, penny-pinching prudence. If we choose aright, we shall be able to call on the nation's confident and eager efforts. If not, our efforts will be slow and insignificant, and they will be met by scepticism and indifference.

Today, that may sound like a piece of rather high-flown literature. At the time, it was a simple, clinical description of the pitiless reality confronting us in this first year of peace. Even the choice of words reflected the choice that faced the country: boldness or mediocrity. We ourselves used a similar expression: 'Modernization or decadence'. For years, that was the motto of the Plan. But behind the slogans, everyone was aware of the practical reality: it was a part of our daily life.

The French Communist Party alleged that the loan agreement contained secret political clauses; but most people believed Léon Blum when he denied any such thing. In fact, we had had to make a concession on one point; but there was nothing secret about it, since Byrnes made much of it with his California voters: France was to increase its imports of Hollywood films. The Communists, who grew ever more aggressive as the electoral timetable became more pressing, made fierce attacks on this addition to the loan agreement. At the same time, they were campaigning for higher wages – which they were granted shortly afterwards at the great conference of business, peasant, and trade-union representatives called together by Georges Bidault, the new Prime Minister, at the Palais-Royal in July. The endless race between wages and prices had begun.

The Communists and the CGT remained unwavering, however, in their attitude to the Plan. Their desire to take part in the rebuilding of France was categorical and sustained. The appeal for more production which the Communist leader Maurice Thorez had made in a speech at Albi had been widely followed. But no progress could be achieved without increasing real working hours beyond the statutory forty-hour week. The President of the Planning Commissariat's Manpower Commission was a Confederal Secretary of the CGT, André Tollet, who had played an important role in the Liberation of Paris. When he saw the figures that revealed France's real situation, he had no hesitation in calling for a forty-five-hour working week; and although we did not then go back to a forty-eight-hour week, this was not on account of trade-union opposition, but because French industry had not enough resources to make it possible.

Benoît Frachon was a member of the Planning Council, and it was in this capacity that we met, both at No 18 rue de Martignac and at the headquarters of the CGT. Our personal relations were friendly, and I remember spending working evenings with him at my house outside Paris, where we enjoyed discussing all manner of things. He was a man of wide experience; and so long as we had the same fundamental concern – to improve the French economy – he was a co-operative partner with an open mind. But these relaxed contacts, I soon realized, depended on political circumstances, in which he was not free to follow his personal bent. When the Communists decided to stiffen their opposition, and even before the non-Communist minority broke away from the CGT in December 1947 to form the CGT-*Force Ouvrière* (FO), the CGT's representatives on the Planning Commissariat gradually drew back. Then, one day, without any open clash, they ceased to appear at all. In this way I gradually lost contact with Benoît Frachon, and with another useful man with whom I had had very good relations since Algiers, François Billoux. Billoux was Minister of Reconstruction at the time when the important choices had to be made; and under the pressure of public opinion and of his own staff he might well have demanded that housing have absolute priority.

'That would be an irrational policy,' I said. 'If we used up our available resources at once on housing, we should soon have to stop, perhaps for several decades. We must first rebuild our steel and cement industries. Reconstruction and modernization are not alternative options: on the contrary, they go hand in hand.'

Not without courage, Billoux endorsed this fundamental choice.

My experience with the Communists was therefore limited to that relatively short but decisive period when everything had to be subordinated to the undeniable needs of production. By 1948, the Plan had become national policy, and everyone rallied to its call, which was widely echoed because it was so tirelessly repeated. But before this unanimous effort could fully bear fruit, electoral preoccupations and ideological battles once more became predominant; and the implementation of the Plan was soon threatened by social conflicts and inflation. From the Spring of 1947 onwards, we could no longer count on the Communists to help maintain discipline, and my usual contacts in the Party avoided me. Politics had introduced a point of view incompatible with the principles underlying the Plan, which were to seek the common interest and to accept collective decisions. True, I have always encountered political resistance, from many different quarters; but so long as the discussion remains open, I respect disagreements and do my best to overcome them. Thanks to Pierre Le Brun, the CGT continued to be represented on the Modernization Commissions for some time, and we never had any open clash. Then one day Le Brun too ceased to attend; but by that time the Plan was firmly rooted in the customs of the country.

The year 1946 was when we worked out the main modernization programmes; and since everything had to be synchronized there was intense activity at No 18 rue de Martignac, where the 350 members of the Modernization Commissions and a further 500 in their subcommissions were all working toward the same goal. Hirsch and Marjolin brought together the Rapporteurs and collated their proposals. They knew better than I did how to prepare the programmes, and I made no attempt to interfere with their work or with that of their experts and statisticians. My concern was with general objectives and orders of magnitude: I had to maintain an overall view. Industrialists, engineers, and trade unionists always thought they knew better what was feasible. They were usually right about their own subjects but wrong, more often than not, about the problem as a whole. The most difficult job was not to verify this fact, but to convince them that it was so. We took no vacation that summer. As the conclusions reached by the different Commissions were gradually co-ordinated, with much toing and froing of information in no fewer than 160 meetings, my

colleagues set to work on the overall Report. After countless modifications, it reached its final form in November, 1946.

For five years, this 200-page Report was the reference-book for the
French economy – not so much in its technical recommendations, which
had constantly to be adapted to changing circumstances, but rather by
virtue of its approach, which combined this necessary flexibility with
a few basic and permanent requirements. In fact, as far as I was concerned, it could all be summed up in the few pages describing its method
– or even in just one, page 33. If anyone came into my office ignorant
of that page, he had usually been shown it by the time he left. What
had to be understood was this: that while the Plan set production and
other targets for 1950 according to the resources that were then expected
to be available, the six crucial programmes – those in the basic sectors
– must at all events be implemented between now and then. They
alone were paramount. Clearly, resources of energy, metals, currency,
and manpower had to be procured and utilized in the pursuit of general
objectives. No additional State control was proposed; but existing
regulations, which provided for the allocation of raw materials and
credit, gave the Government powerful enough means of encouraging
and monitoring what had to be done. Even so, it was not on these that
I counted the most. One reason was that they were not directly under
my control, but in the hands of the Ministerial departments; and they,
although bound by the Plan, were reluctant to accept the predominance
of the Planning Commissariat. But the other reason, and perhaps the
more important, was my continued belief that nothing works so well as
persuasion.

I was certain, now, that the Plan could be implemented only by
methods like those that had been used to prepare it. 'Our methods,' I
wrote, 'should be based on those that were used in drawing up the
proposals made in the present Report. A collective effort requires
collective organization and constant joint consultation.' I proposed
that the Planning Commissariat should be made permanent in its
present shape and size, and that this new but already indispensable
body, modest but all-embracing, a rival to no one but a mentor to all,
should become a national institution. 'The Plan,' I continued, 'is
essentially a method of convergent action and a means whereby everyone can relate his own efforts to those of everyone else. It is concerned
as much with orientation as with control.' On page 101 of the Report
there appears the phrase 'concerted economy', which has since become
fashionable in France. I was not very keen on it, but I could see that
Hirsch was anxious to keep it in. I understood why when he told me

that his family played chamber music together. It was as a violinist, not an economist, that he had chosen the term. I finally agreed to it when somebody pointed out that the poet and essayist Charles Péguy had called the French 'an unconcerted people'. We had to bury that legend.

'Frenchmen today,' I said, 'are no different from those who were born when France was a great power. But in those days we were ahead of our time. It depends on us whether we pull ahead again. In any case, we have no choice. The only alternative to modernization is decadence.'

As always, I was repeating myself. I left my visitors no respite. It was as much by hammering home a few simple ideas as by virtue of its weighty reports that the Plan became a household word. The key to the whole undertaking was perhaps a sentence in the introduction to the Report, and one which at first seemed surprising: 'Modernization is not a state of affairs, but a state of mind.' In France, neither as yet existed; but it was clear that the French people could only recover and maintain their past wealth and influence if they acquired in their work the attitude of a modern people. Where should we begin? We could hardly go wrong, as I have said, if we started by dealing with the great shortages of energy, steel, and building materials. For agriculture, we began with farm machinery because, as Hirsch put it, 'a farmer driving a tractor will no longer think like a farmer following a horse.' These priorities were undeniable: the very idea of them had a powerful psychological effect. And it was more urgent to make a start than to spend ages discussing what the first steps should be. Mistakes could be put right later, because flexibility was an essential feature of the Plan. Some people wanted it to involve more State control:

'What is your philosophy?' they asked.

'The answer is simple,' I said. 'Life itself is a matter of uncertainties, hopes, constant changes, and disappointments; but it also involves continuity and achievement, provided one doesn't give up. The Plan, like life, is a continuous creation.'

This empirical attitude, however, did not obviate the need for great vigilance: quite the reverse. There was nothing automatic about the implementation of the programmes. Our November 1946 Report was studded with serious warnings:

> We have only a short respite.... Once our overseas credits are used up, our economic independence will hinge on our ability to export – i.e., to produce at competitive prices.

But the immediate danger was inflation. Between July and December 1946, French domestic prices had increased by 50%.

> Of all the preconditions essential to the success of the Plan, none is more fundamental than the stabilization of prices and of the currency.

From that moment on, it became clear that I could not limit my action to the administration of a Plan which, although it would determine the future, was at the same time so dependent on the economic policy of the day. Whether we liked it or not, we should have to intervene in the business of Government. I took no pleasure in bombarding Ministers and senior officials with notes and telephone calls; but they at least grew accustomed to being badgered at all hours. They claimed that it was the result of my eccentric temperament; but what would really have been eccentric, in my view, would have been to watch the country's economy rapidly deteriorate and still do nothing about it. True, most of these people and those who succeeded them soon overcame their initial irritation and took notice of my own and my colleagues' advice. Even so, none of them ever accepted as natural a method of work which on occasion ignored official hierarchies and upset normal routines – although in a crisis, when action is needed, this is often the only way.

The crisis facing France when we launched the Plan was not merely a matter of wartime devastation and long-standing under-investment. It also took the form of growing monetary and political instability. Our Report was submitted to the Planning Council, then chaired by Premier Georges Bidault, on November 27, 1946. It was unanimously approved by the Ministers and by the industrial and trade-union representatives. On the very next day, however, Bidault's Government fell. It was succeeded by a Socialist Government under Léon Blum. This approved our Report on January 14, 1947; but it was finally a coalition Government under Paul Ramadier which, from January 17 onward, had the task of putting the Plan into practice. All this turmoil was not without its compensations. It gave us the opportunity, with each successive investiture debate, to have the nation's commitment to the Plan restated, and thereby to associate Parliament with it. Many were the Ministerial speeches we drafted at No 18 rue de Martignac, in the hope that at least a few sentences would survive in the final version. Many, too, were the parliamentary leaders whom we tried to convince before each debate. Governments changed, but our ideas took root. The essential thing for us was not to be constantly called in question. Léon Blum had promised me to keep the Planning

Commissariat attached to the Prime Minister's office. He forgot. I submitted my resignation: once again, matters were put right. I worked under ten Prime Ministers, and had battles with all of them. Government instability was harmful to France, but little more than a nuisance to the Plan. In the twenty years that followed, three Planning Commissioners outlived twenty-eight Governments.

By the very fact of having been approved, the Plan had truly become everyone's concern. The Communist and Christian trade unions (CGT and CFTC), the farm unions in the General Confederation of Agriculture (CGA), and the industrialists of the National Council of French Employers (CNPF), all accepted the Plan's objectives and urged their members to fulfil them. In particular, the Manpower Commission's proposals were adopted, and the forty-eight-hour week eventually became the norm. This could never have been done if it had not been accepted by the workforce. It was a crucial factor in French recovery. Similarly, the six basic programmes were launched because they had been acknowledged as essential by the industries concerned. For the year 1947, work was put in hand at once: the Donzère-Mondragon dam, the Usinor strip mill, and the Rhône Valley project were spectacular first steps in modernization for industry and agriculture alike. 'Directly or indirectly, more than 30% of the French economy has now started toward the 1950 targets,' we announced. But at the same time the basic economic balance still had to be maintained.

In reality, it was under threat. On January 1, 1947, Léon Blum decreed a compulsory 5% price cut – a vain attempt to stem the flood of inflation that was swelled by the budget deficit and the increase in money supply resulting from higher wages. Throughout the year, successive counter-inflation measures failed. Not only was the Plan in danger; the country's morale was undermined. The black market, the spread of speculation, the flight of capital, and the standstill in productive investment were together putting France back by several years. Action was needed: but what? Economists trained in the traditional schools were silent, and the Government seemed to be waiting for a miracle. After the hard winter a disastrous wheat harvest, the worst for 150 years, only added to our troubles. Even if no remedy was in sight, we at least had to try to evaluate the extent of the threat and to isolate its worst features.

A young graduate of the *Ecole Normale Supérieure* had recently joined the staff of the Planning Commissariat. His name was Pierre Uri. After taking his fellowship examination, his *agrégation*, in philosophy he had been taught by the celebrated Princeton economists. Later, he had worked with François Perroux and been an adviser to the CGT. At thirty-five, he had a reputation as an unrivalled dialectician: young people admired his brilliant articles in Jean-Paul Sartre's magazine *Les Temps Modernes*. But he also had another quality that was more solid, and in my eyes more valuable because more rare: an exceptional ability to think out new and rigorous solutions to the most complex problems. Uri often approaches technical difficulties from an unexpected direction, and gets to the heart of them, where everything is simple; but this can only be done after going through the maze of details in which very intelligent people seem almost to enjoy losing their way. Uri is supremely intelligent. He is capable of brilliant insights, which I often have to damp down somewhat to make them less dazzling and more convincing. In the early days, his fine intellect found it hard to accept the constraints of common sense. But no matter: it was he who loosed the Gordian knot of the French economic crisis, with the aid of the latest analytical instruments, which he had learned how to use, and the synthesizing spirit which was all his own.

I saw that if I gave Pierre Uri the chance to examine the public and private accounts, he would be able by himself to master the whole problem of the country's overall needs and resources. He would produce a balance-sheet which would show the gaps where inflation was getting in. From it we should even be able to deduce what remedies to apply. But if work of this kind were done in solitude, what spin-off would it have? How could it become a national plan of action? If, on the other hand, it was conducted according to the methods of the Plan, and if all the parties concerned were involved in it from the start, then its conclusions would automatically be understood and accepted. I set about forming a 'Balance-Sheet Commission'. It included Le Brun, Martial Brousse the agriculturist, and Ricard, as well as Jean-François Bloch-Lainé, now Director of the Treasury at the Finance Ministry, together with more than sixty of their colleagues from the CGT, the CGA, the employers' federation, and the civil service. Uri was its omnipresent Rapporteur. A decree dated October 1, 1947, was the starting-point for the inquiry, the first of its kind in France. By the beginning of December, I was able to submit to the Government a 100-page Report which was both intellectually rigorous and perfectly clear – qualities that go hand in hand, as Uri quickly learned after a few months at the Planning Commissariat.

This first national balance-sheet revealed that there would be a large inflationary gap in 1948. But more important than the figures themselves was the method whereby they had been reached, and the experience this had given to those responsible for the French economy. Once again, the balance-sheet necessarily led to action; and because the duty to act was incumbent on those who had taken part in the inquiry and subscribed to its conclusions, the resultant decision was both implicit and unavoidable. The inflationary gap must be closed. To increase the country's resources was difficult: to cut back demand was possible. All it required was courage. On January 16, 1948, Robert Schuman, now Prime Minister, and his Finance Minister René Mayer persuaded Parliament to vote into law an exceptional levy, which could be avoided by taking out Government bonds, and the withdrawal of 5000-franc banknotes. At the same time, the franc was devalued by 80% against the dollar. I must add that the preparation of these measures was in no way commensurate with the achievement of persuading Parliament to vote for them, which was a very great ordeal for René Mayer.

The same series of laws, at my request, set up a National Modernization and Investment Fund, designed to finance, without interruption and without contributing to inflation, the investments required under the Plan. I managed to have the Fund receive one-third of the exceptional levy; but I was never able to overcome the Finance Ministry's resistance to its acquiring real budgetary autonomy. At the same time, however, we were in the process of winning a far more important battle – securing for the Fund the franc counterpart of Marshall Plan donations. The domestic financing of the 'Monnet Plan' was thereby assured until 1952, as were its overseas supplies – thanks in both cases to the same source of credit. This, as will be seen, was doubly providential for France.

Chapter 11

EUROPE IN THE DARK (1947-1949)

I

The Marshall Plan

So we had at last concerted our efforts to halt France's economic decline; but now, once more, everything seemed to be at risk. Two years earlier, we thought that we had plumbed the depths of material poverty. Now we were threatened with the loss of even basic essentials. The year 1947 should have seen the end of major shortages; and although the Plan called for short-term austerity measures, it had certainly promised a rapid rise in consumption, and was preparing for future prosperity. We had perfected our method, and set up machinery whereby the whole nation felt involved in the Plan, just as we had wished. The main corporate entities were on our side. Any obstruction could only be the result of accidents. Some of them were predictable; but others now took us by surprise. We knew, for example, that we should have to overcome short-term difficulties in our balance of payments, since the credits we had been granted under the Blum-Byrnes agreements would not last until we were self-sufficient. But now our dollar resources were melting away at an alarming rate, because we were having to buy American wheat to replace the crops we had lost during the winter. This alone cost us $200m. instead of the $30m. we had expected to pay. In addition, we had to increase our coal imports at a time when prices had risen in the United States. In June, we met the cost with gold bullion from the Bank of France; in August, we cut off inessential imports. A further American loan was soon exhausted.

Nor was this grim situation confined to France. Britain too had come to the end of her resources. In February 1947 she had abruptly cancelled her aid to Greece and Turkey, whose burdens she had seemed able to assume in 1945. Overnight, this abrupt abdication gave the United States direct responsibility for part of Europe. Truman did not hesitate for a moment: with the decisiveness that was to mark his actions as President, he at once asked for credits and arms for both Turkey and Greece. Congress was now once more opposed to financial and military commitments overseas; but the President declared:

> I believe that we must assist free peoples to work out their destinies in their own way.
> I believe that our help should be primarily through economic and financial aid which is essential to economic stability and orderly political processes. . . .
> We must take immediate and resolute action.*

With these words, he announced the Truman Doctrine of March 12, 1947. Its significance was general: it meant that the United States would prevent Europe from becoming a depressed area at the mercy of Communist advance. On the very same day, the Four-Power Conference began in Moscow. There, for a whole month, George Marshall, Ernest Bevin, and Georges Bidault argued with Vyacheslav Molotov about all the problems of the peace, and above all about Germany.

When Marshall returned to Washington, he knew that for a long time there would be no further genuine dialogue with Stalin's Russia. The 'cold war', as it was soon to be known, had begun. At about the same time Will Clayton, the Under-Secretary of State for Economic Affairs, came back from Europe with a very alarming secret report. 'It is now obvious,' he said, 'that we have grossly underestimated the destruction to the European economy by the war.' He proposed that the United States should supply aid 'based on a European plan which the principal European nations . . . should work out.'† Information from a number of sources convinced Marshall and his Under-Secretary Dean Acheson that once again, as in 1941, the United States had a great historic duty. And once again there took place what I had witnessed in Washington a few years earlier: a small group of men brought to rapid maturity an idea which, when the Executive gave the word, turned into vigorous action. This time, it was done by five or six people, in total secrecy and at lightning speed. Marshall, Acheson, Clayton, Averell Harriman, and George Kennan worked out a proposal of unprecedented scope and generosity. It took us all by surprise when we read the speech that George Marshall made at Harvard on June 5, 1947. Chance had led him to choose the University's Commencement

* *Public Papers of the Presidents of the United States: Harry S. Truman*, 1947 (Washington, DC, US Government Printing Office, 1963), pp. 178–9.
† Ellen Clayton Garwood, *Will Clayton: A Short Biography* (Austin, University of Texas Press), pp. 119–21.

Day to launch something new in international relations: helping others to help themselves.

I had first met General Marshall when, as US Chief of Staff, he had put his full weight behind the Victory Programme. Few men have earned such great respect, doubtless because authority came as naturally to him as modesty and humanity. When these qualities are combined in one person they leave a mark on men's minds. The history of the United States provides several fine examples of such leadership, which commands allegiance without oppressing anyone. Marshall proved during the war that he had a genius for organization, which he also displayed in his work for peace. Roosevelt could not do without him – which is the only reason why Marshall is not remembered as the hero of Europe's Liberation. The President told him: 'I feel I could not sleep at night with you out of the country', and after long hesitation appointed Eisenhower Supreme Commander. Truman turned Marshall into a diplomatist, sent him to China, and then put him in charge of the State Department, where postwar policy was still in the melting-pot. Although unfamiliar with Europe, Marshall sized up at once the dangers that were gathering:

> In considering the requirements for the rehabilitation of Europe, the physical loss of life, the visible destruction of cities, factories, mines, and railroads was correctly estimated, but it has become obvious during recent months that this visible destruction was probably less serious than the dislocation of the entire fabric of European economy. . . .
> The rehabilitation of the economic structure of Europe will require a much longer time and greater effort than had been foreseen.*

This lucid statement was not in itself enough to convince American public opinion. There was a great temptation to return to isolationism; and the Democratic Administration had to face a Republican majority in Congress, including the powerful Senator Arthur H. Vandenberg. Marshall could hardly ask his compatriots to make yet another sacrifice for a Europe yet again on the road to ruin. Or at least, since that was the situation, he had to produce a new and creative idea:

> Assistance, I am convinced, must not be on a piecemeal basis as various crises develop. . . .
> The initiative, I think, must come from Europe. The role of this country should consist of friendly aid in the drafting of a European

* George C. Marshall, Speech at Harvard University, June 5, 1947, in *In Quest of Peace and Security, Selected Documents on American Foreign Policy 1941–1951* (Department of State Publication 4245, 1951), pp. 93–5.

program and of later support of such a program so far as it may be practical for us to do so.

Thus, for the first time, responsibility was to be shared, and Europe was asked to come together to draw up a balance-sheet of its needs and resources:

The program should be a joint one, agreed to by a number of, if not all, European nations.

That was the basis of what at once came to be called the Marshall Plan – an American offer to contribute to an essentially European effort. We promptly answered:

France has never lost sight of the need to see her own recovery as part of the recovery of Europe.

Bevin and Bidault at once dispatched an invitation to Molotov, who arrived in Paris with a retinue of eighty advisers.

I myself played no direct part in the diplomatic negotiations which culminated in the Soviets' refusal to join in an overall programme, on the grounds that it would infringe national sovereignty. As is well known, the USSR's satellites followed suit, cutting a deep divide down the middle of Europe. The results were profound and lasting; but the sixteen countries that finally met in Paris in July 1947, at the invitation of Great Britain and France, had at least all reacted in the same way, determined to resist economic decline and thereby preserve political freedom. How far they would be able to pursue, and pursue together, the bold efforts that were needed, remained a question. So far as France was concerned the answer was already clear: the French Plan was the most elaborate of the contributions made to the programme launched by the Committee of Economic Co-operation. Marjolin left the Planning Commissariat to join it, eager to test his mettle in a vast and complex enterprise where his gifts could have full scope. I was sorry to see him go, because as I have said the Plan was a continuous creation, and it still needed brains of his calibre; but I realized that, at his age and with his temperament, he was eager to spread his wings. He was going to apply his knowledge and our methods of work, which had grown out of so much shared experience, to a similar venture in the international field, the success of which was essential to that of the French Plan.

It has often been said that I used my ingenuity to place colleagues in jobs which amounted to forward outposts for my future battles, and that by this means I gradually infiltrated all the positions of power. This is untrue. I never like losing anyone whom I have recruited for my small team, often after long hesitation, and who has entered into its spirit. I like to see familiar faces around me; but if new tasks bring in new men or take others from me, I bow to the inevitable. That is why, while never casting anyone off, I have had to ask a succession of people to help me. Circumstances, rather than my own wishes, have usually brought about the changes I have had to accept. Very often, the same circumstances have put colleagues of mine into useful administrative or political positions; but that has been in the nature of things rather than a matter of calculation. At the end of 1946, Félix Gaillard was elected Deputy for the Charente, and he later joined the Government as Under-Secretary of State to René Mayer at the Ministry of Finance and Economic Affairs, where he was responsible for overseeing the Plan. At about the same time, Paul Delouvrier became Mayer's *directeur de cabinet*. When in 1948 Robert Marjolin was appointed by the sixteen Marshall Aid countries as Secretary-General of the Organization for European Economic Co-operation (OEEC), which he had helped to set up, Etienne Hirsch succeeded him as Deputy Planning Commissioner. In the end, I wonder which is more striking – the succession of different people who appear in these pages, or the fact that the same names so often recur again and again.

The scope of the inquiry undertaken by the Sixteen, and the difficulty of obtaining genuine and comparable data, made it impossible to produce a full picture of Europe's situation before the end of September 1947. No other European country had the equivalent of the French Plan, which from the beginning had not only formed the basis of France's answers to the Americans' questions, but also helped serve as a model for the questionnaire itself. Despite intensive work, the cure had to wait while the malady grew worse. Something had to be done while the Marshall Plan was still facing administrative and Congressional obstacles. At the end of December 1947, therefore, Truman signed the legislation for Interim Aid, which enabled Italy and France to import the wheat, coal, oil, and cotton which they so desperately lacked. Shortly afterwards, the President submitted to Congress 'A Programme for United States Support to European Recovery' providing for seventeen billion dollars to be made available to the 'sixteen countries between then and June 1952. Not without many difficulties and a great deal of valiant effort, the Economic Co-operation Act was voted by Congress on April 3, 1948. In Paris a few days later, the Sixteen signed the Convention establishing OEEC. For hundreds of millions of people, this was a guarantee that they would have the resources and raw materials that were vital if their standard of living was to be raised. But there was no certainty that this relief would last. Their independence and prosperity would prove dangerously deceptive, unless we used this breathing-space to learn to dispense with outside aid. The very facilities that now enabled the French Plan steadily to develop made the constraints on it all the more evident. Time was limited, although the deadline was now postponed till 1952. Resources were also limited – just under three billion dollars to last for fifty months. There was no margin for waste.

Once again, inflation might engulf everything. We needed both dollars, to be spent on raw materials, and francs, to be spent on investment; but there was no automatic link between the two. How could we ensure that foreign aid stimulated internal effort? There was one very simple answer: to finance the Plan with the francs we earned by selling the supplies which we had obtained free. This was the solution to the problem of 'counterpart funds', which occupied us for months: in the end, it made possible the modernization of France. But, as always, the most obvious solution aroused the greatest opposition. Not unreasonably, the Americans wanted these 'counterpart' francs to be frozen, lest they contribute to inflation. The French Government – like all European Governments – was strongly tempted to use them as a source of revenue. But there was one form of productive expenditure which would not be inflationary; and that was investment to develop the basic industries which were the driving-force of the Plan. The Plan, after all, was the Americans' guarantee that Marshall Aid would be used for the recovery of France.

The logic of this argument seemed to me inescapable. Clear as it was, however, it might not have prevailed without a stroke of good luck. Chance had brought to Paris two men of exceptional vision and good-will – Ambassador David Bruce and his financial adviser William Tomlinson. David Bruce was already a friend of mine, and the mutual trust between us has helped solve many political problems. I should describe him as essentially a civilized man, because for me this general term has a very precise meaning. Bruce always takes account of others, and listens to them without trying to impose his point of view or insist that he is always right. He is always anxious to be fully convinced before attempting to convince others. He has fulfilled many important and difficult missions, and is free of political dogmatism – although himself a Democrat, he has served Republican Administrations – and he never sees his country as a dominating force. Instead, he looks for ways in which the United States can help other countries; and he is always trying to help others himself. That, to my mind, is what being civilized means.

David Bruce is an ambassador in the best American tradition; like some others I have known, he helps to formulate the policies he is called upon to represent. Very influential in his own Government, he has sometimes helped draft his own instructions. At that time, we worked together to perfect those that concerned the Marshall Plan. In charge of it in Paris was a young representative of the US Treasury, William Tomlinson. Tommy, as we called him, was twenty-eight years old, and he looked like a conscientious student. His shyness and frail appearance masked a warm heart and unflagging energy. Since his teens he had known that he was suffering from serious cardiac trouble, but he gave himself no rest. No one but Tommy himself would have imposed on him the effort he made during those creative years, when he played so vital a part in helping David Bruce and myself. He was one of those people who give their loyalty to an idea; and he naturally thought in terms of teamwork. Familiarizing himself with our economic affairs, which were his official concern, he realized both their technical effectiveness and their political importance. He trusted me completely, and I concealed none of our problems from him, because he made it his business with the US Administration to help us solve them. He loved France, and made many admiring friends there, as he did later when he became the first US Ambassador to the European Community, among the pioneers. He died at the age of 36, worn out by his efforts. We owe him a very great debt.

In 1948, without the help of Bruce and Tomlinson, I should never have succeeded in persuading the US Administration to allow hundreds of billions of francs' worth of counterpart funds to be used by the French Government; and I should have found it hard to persuade the latter to allocate them to the Plan. As it was, in 1949 some 90% of the Modernization Fund's resources came from this unhoped-for source, and 50% in 1950. Even more, the certainty that so prolonged an effort could be financed without fail gave a sense of confidence to the whole French economy. And the economy, at that time, was not just a matter of material well-being: it was the necessary basis for national independence and the preservation of democracy.

II

National limits

In April 1948 I was once more in the United States. The official purpose of my trip was to obtain additional allocations of wheat to tide us over until harvest-time. But to understand America, its people, and its leaders, one has to go back regularly and form some idea of the changes that ceaselessly carry it forward. I have some general notions about America and the Americans, acquired over decades of friendly contact; but when it comes to action I rely on my judgement at the time. That was the real reason for my regular visits, which always began with calls on well-informed friends. In places like London, New York, and Washington, where the big decisions are made, my first talks have always been with men who cannot afford to make mistakes – bankers, industrialists, lawyers, and newspapermen. What others say may be coloured by imagination, ambition, or doctrine. I certainly respect their influence; but I base my judgement on the wisdom of practical men.

One of them, André Meyer, I have known for forty years. I have been to see him every time I go to the United States. The same is true of Pierre-David Weill, George Murnane, Floyd Blair, and Dean Jay. The scale of the subjects they deal with in their banking houses necessarily gives them very broad horizons. Nor did I fail to seek the opinion of Felix Frankfurter, until his death in 1965. I also went to see laywers like Dean Acheson and George Ball, or university teachers like Robert Bowie, Walt and Gene Rostow, or McGeorge Bundy. None of them was ever far from public affairs and government: at any moment they might be called to some political post. Finally, I learned a very great deal from talks with friends in the press world – Phil and Kay Graham, Walter Lippmann, Joe Alsop, James Reston, David Schoenbrun, and Robert Kleinman. I gave them news of Europe, it is true; but in return they shared with me the world panorama they enjoyed from such vantage-points as the *New York Times*, the *Washington Post*, or C.B.S.

It was while I was in Washington on that occasion that the Convention establishing OEEC was drafted and signed in Paris. When I studied it, I could not help seeing the intrinsic weakness of a sytem that went no further than mere co-operation between Governments. One single line in Article 14 of the Convention prevented any kind of joint action: 'Unless the Organization otherwise agrees for special cases, decisions shall be taken by mutual agreement of all the Members.' In a letter to Georges Bidault, I wrote:

> Efforts by the various countries, in the present national frameworks, will not in my view be enough. Furthermore, the idea that sixteen sovereign nations will co-operate effectively is an illusion. I believe that only the establishment of a *federation* of the West, including Britain, will enable us to solve our problems quickly enough, and finally prevent war. I realize how difficult it is – it may even be impossible – but I see no other solution, if we have the necessary respite.

If this idea had struck me so forcibly again, it was not because of the inadequacy of what was being done in Paris. I had not in any case expected much from that. What really concerned me was what I had seen during the past few weeks in the United States, after two years' absence. In another letter, this time to Robert Schuman, I said:

> This country is always animated by a dynamic force that derives from the very nature of every individual. America is on the move, but it is neither reactionary nor imperialist. It does not want war, but it will go to war if need be. Its determination on this point is very firm. But that determination is not blind. A great change occurred here recently: preparation to make war has given place to preparation to prevent it. The idea that détente may be possible is beginning to emerge.

Accustomed as I was to the American temperament, I was disturbed at so strong a will to act and so great an impatience to see convalescent Europe stand on its own feet. These seemed likely to lead to instability and future misunderstanding. And in the same letter to Schuman I broached an idea which was to go on developing at the back of my mind for the next two years:

> I cannot but be struck by the relationship that threatens to develop between this great and dynamic nation and the countries of Europe, if they remain as they are, in their present state of mind. In my opinion, Europe cannot long afford to remain almost exclusively dependent on American credit for her production and American strength for her security, without harmful results both here and in Europe.
>
> Everything I have seen and reflected on here leads me to a conclusion which is now my profound conviction: that to tackle the present situation, to face the dangers that threaten us, and to match the American effort, the countries of Western Europe must turn their national efforts

into a truly European effort. This will be possible only through a *federation* of the West.

There could be no truly European effort without a federation of the West, but there could be no federation unless it were backed by such an effort. The two seemed indissolubly linked: so where should we start? It was a question that was to be asked by more and more people, ceaselessly trying to revive the old federalist traditions in Europe, which war had so often interrupted. Most of these people belonged to political movements, and sincerely believed that union could be achieved by concerted goodwill. At the time of my letters to Bidault and Schuman, preparations were being made for a great Congress at The Hague in May 1948, under the chairmanship of Winston Churchill. Many of our friends attended it: Anthony Eden, Lord Layton, Harold Macmillan, Paul Van Zeeland, Paul Reynaud, François Mitterrand, Pierre-Henri Teitgen, André François-Poncet. There were also others, less well known – a German party leader named Konrad Adenauer, and a Professor from Frankfurt, Walter Hallstein. In the profusion of ideas that typifies such meetings, I am sure that despite many vain aspirations there were also some fruitful lines of action. But I confess that I paid little attention to the Hague Congress; and the fate of its enthusiastic resolutions, which a year later led to the founding of the Council of Europe, confirmed my belief that this approach would lead nowhere.

Nor would the more pragmatic methods of OEEC bring unity, because there it was laid down that anyone could be exempted from decisions that he found difficult. It was the opposite of the Community spirit. Still, provided that the limits of co-operation were recognized for what they were, OEEC could certainly help the European economy, which in the past had been too compartmentalized. The removal of quota restrictions, and the later agreement on intra-European payments, would encourage and facilitate trade; and better knowledge of each other's plans and resources would enable everyone to improve the thrust of his own efforts. It would be a mistake to ask more than that of a system which entailed no delegation of sovereignty. Very soon, OEEC had become simply technical machinery; but it outlived the Marshall Plan because it provided a mass of information which everyone found useful. I realized that neither this organization, with its headquarters at the Château de la Muette in Paris, nor the parliamentary meetings in Strasbourg that resulted from the Hague Congress, would ever give concrete expression to European unity.

Amid these vast groupings of countries, the common interest was too indistinct, and common disciplines were too lax. A start would have to be made by doing something both more practical and more ambitious. National sovereignty would have to be tackled more boldly and on a narrower front.

I had to wait many months before I found the opportunity to act along these lines, which seemed to me the only ones that might work. It was too soon to do anything with Germany, an emergent political entity whose economic backbone was becoming more and more solid and powerful, but which was still subject to careful supervision. This supervision, exercised jointly by the French, the British, and the Americans, gave rise to occasional friction between ourselves and our Allies. They were naturally anxious to develop the 'Bizone' formed from the British and American occupation zones – which included the main Ruhr coalfields – so that the costs of occupation could be met by the Germans themselves. What was more, the Marshall Plan's production targets aimed at restoring the German economy, like that of Europe as a whole, by 1952 – but without allowing it once again to become autarkic. In August 1947, in some Allied documents which Marjolin had passed to me, I found some disturbing facts. The German steel industry would soon be absorbing all the coke produced in the Ruhr, with the result that steel production in France and the rest of Europe would have to be limited. In these circumstances, it was hard to see how Europe's global targets could be attained. Economically and politically, this would be unacceptable; and I saw no solution except to propose linking the growth of German steel production to an increase in Ruhr coke exports, by means of some sophisticated sliding scale. Only in this way could we maintain France's steel production targets, which were the key to the whole French Plan.

I had few illusions about the effectiveness of such expedients; and it was with growing anxiety that I saw our policy towards Germany beginning to slip back into its old ways. True, in 1948 we were no longer demanding that the former *Reich* be politically dismembered; but, in varying degrees, all shades of public opinion, all public authorities, and all private interests in France were supporting our diplomatic rearguard action against Germany's inevitable rehabilitation. There was something pathetic about the growing isolation of Georges Bidault, who at one conference after another obtained only a further delay or a little more coal. I liked and admired Bidault's goodwill, intelligence, and courage: he performed great services in these postwar years. It was not his fault if France was weaker than her international partners. For France to have influence, the world had to be certain that she would complete her own modernization – and, because Bidault realized this, he used all his authority to ensure the success of the Plan. He made very energetic efforts during those difficult years when we had to raise our voice to make our claims heard. Perhaps it was this that gave him the crabbed attitude which gradually made him seem a man of the past.

If Georges Bidault firmly backed the Plan, I must say that he in turn had my full support in the incessant negotiations we had to conduct to obtain the outside resources we so vitally needed: American, German, and Polish coal, raw materials for our industries, capital equipment, and above all credit with which to pay for them. I devoted a great deal of my own efforts to this in 1947 and 1948, while at the same time working day after day to ensure the uninterrupted financing of the Plan – in particular, as I have said, by means of Marshall Aid counterpart funds. Even more demanding was the battle against continuing inflation, which as I well knew would threaten our whole venture until French production had outgrown the decay that was undermining it. The Planning Commissariat's successive reports were punctuated with warnings which are still just as valid today. And all the time we had to fend off criticism from Malthusian economists who regarded investment as the source of inflation, while winning over Members of Parliament who would have preferred to give the public short-term satisfactions. We had to fight simultaneously on all fronts. When Paul Delouvrier went to work with René Mayer in the citadel of the Treasury, which was not always on our side, the young economist Paul Delcourt took his place at No 18 rue de Martignac. In continual arguments with the French civil service, Delcourt ardently and effectively championed the cause of investment. His moral and intellectual integrity made him universally liked and admired. Sadly, he died before his time.

Although we were continually battling with the economic problems of the day, the Planning Commissariat's machinery worked with scarcely a hitch – so much so that it began to attract attention abroad. Its flexibility enabled it to adapt to changing external circumstances, without in any way altering its basic principles or its method. We were thus able to prolong for a further two years the arrangements we had planned to run until 1950, so that they coincided with the duration of the Marshall Plan, due to end in 1952. We decided to add agriculture to the priority industries, with the aim of becoming exporters from 1952 onwards. At the time, this was a revolutionary idea, since it meant that France would have to give up a tradition of protectionism dating back to the 1880s and to the policies of the then Minister of Agriculture, Jules Méline. To help bring about this major technical and psychological mutation, I relied on a young agronomist colleague, Libert Bou. A man of Herculean strength and practical energy, he seemed naturally suited to undertaking great things. But he worked stealthily, with the patience of a peasant; and this was undoubtedly the secret of his continual success. I sent him to see David Lilienthal, whose work on the Tennessee Valley Authority had greatly interested me as a possible object-lesson for France and Europe. Libert Bou came back with the idea of the Bas-Rhône-Languedoc project, which he carried out with the help of his friend Philippe Lamour: it became a model of French and European agricultural progress. He still recalls his astonishment when he realized that we had no power to put his project into practice.

'But we have the power,' I told him. 'The power is the power to persuade, to make clear our desire to carry out the Plan. If the Plan weren't practicable, it wouldn't be put into practice. We don't carry out the Plan, nor does the Administration. It's not imposed by orders from above: it's the work of manufacturers, traders, and farmers. But if it fails, then that's our responsibility.'

By 1949, that fear could be set aside. For the first time, I reported to the Government: 'France has rejected the decadence that threatened her.' That sentence alone is a measure of the uncertainty which pervaded this long postwar period. Today, the gravity of what was at stake can hardly be imagined: the question was whether our standard of living would improve or totally collapse. We could not afford to stagnate, because we were still dependent on overseas aid with a firm time-limit attached. Jean Fourastié told me:

'Our industrial production may be 20% higher than in 1938, but you must realize that we have achieved this by working longer hours. In reality, we have scarcely recovered our prewar level of productivity – which as you know was lower than that of the major industrialized countries of the world.'

So we had only half fulfilled the watchword of the Plan: 'Produce more and produce it better.' It was easier to replace machines than to alter attitudes.

'What do you propose?' I asked.

'Set up machinery capable of dealing with the problem, and start a campaign of information and education which will gradually change people's minds,' he replied.

Fourastié was clear-headed and far-sighted: I trusted him. His ever-growing influence on his readers and his pupils accounts for only part of the effect he has had on the generations that have helped to modernize France. Through the Planning Commissariat and the Productivity Commissions which it established, Fourastié was able to apply in practice his idea of more effective, more rational, and more useful production, liberating modern man from the most laborious tasks. Liberated as we now are, we may be tempted to forget the fact. But that liberation was the great achievement of the 1950s; and it was Jean Fourastié at No 18 rue de Martignac who worked out the plan of campaign.

By the end of 1949 I could look back for the first time on a year of stable prices and firm currency after thirteen years of uninterrupted inflation. At the same time, the major shortages had come to an end – which was very largely the reason. But this was still no time to relax. French production could look forward to a more settled future: but other problems would soon arise out of the very achievements that we had helped to make possible. It was at that time, I well remember, that I came to realize the limits of what any one nation could do. The French could not become modern or great by themselves, alongside European neighbours and competitors who themselves would soon discover the limits of their home market and the cramping effect of national barriers. Tomorrow, our steel production might be at the mercy of German coke deliveries; later, our agriculture might depend on the whims of European importers. Disquieting signs began to appear on all sides. There was anxiety about market outlets for our brand-new rolling mills. French manufacturers were preparing to demand the imposition of import controls. But what at that time worried me most was an experience I had just had, which had shown how hard it was to establish a community of interests between economies and peoples, however much they seemed to belong to-gether. From this unsuccessful experiment, which I shall now describe, I had rapidly to draw positive and practical conclusions.

III

No reply from London

At the beginning of March, 1949, Maurice Petsche, the French Finance Minister, invited me to dinner with his British counterpart, Sir Stafford Cripps. They were trying to harmonize the plans that their respective countries had submitted to OEEC. All too obviously, these plans bore no relation to each other – which hardly helped to increase intra-European trade and reduce the need for dollars.

'You won't reach agreement,' I said, 'unless you make it your ultimate aim to merge the British and French economies.'

They were certainly not ready to accept this solution; but they were interested in the method I proposed for reaching it. I suggested holding informal talks to exchange ideas about the position and the real intentions of either side. Petsche and Cripps thought of such talks as something that could always be brought to an end: I, on the contrary, hoped that they would lead a very long way. What mattered was to break with the tradition of bilateral negotiations, which for the past two years had been conducted under amicable agreements, but which had not prevented either side's pursuing its own separate economic policy, punctuated by surprise devaluations of the pound or the franc. This time, we must get to the heart of the matter, and above all we must talk about the same things. Even though we had all the available data and statistics, we did not really know how the British ran their affairs, or how they viewed the future. Experience had taught me that no one can claim to understand other people's problems unless he can be sure that they are using words in the same sense as himself. For that reason, I always came back to the same method – getting people to sit round the table together.

This was what had happened just one year earlier, when Sir Stafford Cripps had asked me to explain the French Plan to him. He was curious to know how we had managed to bring together so many people who had never previously met, and how we had persuaded the trade unions to accept the forty-eight-hour week. I replied:

'I shall be glad to come to London; but I must bring with me Marjolin, Roy the steelmaker, and Le Brun of the CGT. On your side, you should be accompanied by civil servants, manufacturers, and trade unionists.'

These meetings had proved so interesting that Attlee and several of his Ministers had attended them, and Cripps had expressed the wish to come to Paris and see how a Modernization Commission worked. But that was where matters had stopped. However, it was as a result of our visit that the British Government had set up a sort of central planning organization, with Sir Edwin Plowden at its head.

I had known Plowden in London at the beginning of the war, when he had been recruited to the Ministry of Economic Warfare on account of his long industrial experience. He was a man of great insight, energy, and organizing ability. When anything in Britain had to be planned or changed, people turned quite naturally to him. He did his job quietly and efficiently, and then made himself available for fresh tasks. When it became apparent that the shortage of aircraft would be the major problem in 1940, Plowden was made Under-Secretary at the Ministry of Aircraft Production; and from Washington I kept in close touch with him. His was never a spectacular role, but he had great authority in Government circles, whether Conservative or Labour, as well as with Members of Parliament. We met frequently, and it seemed to me that he would be an essential link in any closer association between Britain and France. Because we were friends, and because I wanted to talk with him candidly and in confidence, I invited him to come to my house at Houjarray outside Paris, with two colleagues of his own choice. He brought Alan Hitchman and Robert Hall. I had Hirsch and Uri with me; and we all spent four days together at the end of April 1949.

France's aims were clear and required little discussion: all that was needed was to read the Planning Commissariat's Report and the national Balance-Sheet, where everything was set out with Cartesian clarity – our progress, our setbacks, our targets, our resources, and above all our methods of work. British planning was neither so ambitious nor so rigorous: it set a number of short- or medium-term objectives which, on examination, differed little from those in our own basic sectors – although in Britain's case the stress was on coal, while we emphasized agriculture. This was no great revelation; but at least it showed that the fog hanging over the British economy concealed nothing untoward, and that we could try to make fast some lifelines between our two countries. What was more, our visitors seemed more open to trade and competition than their official attitudes had suggested. This first survey of the problem was encouraging; yet I found it difficult to steer the talks round to those broader issues for which, in my view, they were merely the point of departure. I raised the German problem; but this only revealed that for the British it was not a matter of current concern. They did, however, admit that the growth of their foreign trade was due in large measure to Germany's temporary eclipse as a supplier of capital equipment.

'We must think seriously about that,' Plowden admitted; 'and we must think about it together.'

Uri, I noticed, kept coming back to the British farm pricing system, which he attacked with verve. He had put his finger on one of Europe's major political problems.

'Your producer subsidies are a heavy burden on your economy,' he said. 'We could contribute to your food supplies; but to do that we should have to increase our own production, mainly of meat. And for that we should need guaranteed long-term outlets.'

Characteristically, he at once went on to invent strict and complicated devices for solving several problems at a time. In the end, it was on such practical subjects as this that we made the greatest progress; and I came to the conclusion that we should have to exchange a lot more information, and tackle many more concrete problems, in order to get our visitors used to the idea of a new Franco-British union based on common interests, which I hoped would be the first step towards a European federation.

I had the impression that Plowden was very interested and full of goodwill; and if the rather technical nature of our talks prevented me from enlarging on these political ideas, I thought that I had said enough to make clear their long-term significance. And yet I later learned from Plowden himself that he had by no means realized all that was in my mind at the time. He was certainly open to joint action, and he saw the advantages of reciprocal trade. He was prepared to enlarge the framework of our bilateral agreements and to move away from protectionism. But at the same time there was no place in his philosophy for delegating any of Britain's national sovereignty.

'We'd won the war,' he told me later, 'and we weren't ready to form special links with the continent. That prevented my understanding what you were really getting at.'

Had I been insufficiently explicit? Had he been too little prepared to grasp the point? Looking back, I find it impossible to say. Whatever the reason, our talks went no further. At the end of the year, Plowden wrote to me:

> My dear Monnet,
>
>   Robert Hall has mentioned to me his recent conversation with you in the course of which you reverted to the idea of exchanging UK coal for French foodstuffs in a manner which would make plain to the world the reality of Anglo-French co-operation.
>
>   Without challenging your underlying idea, I think we must take account of the facts as they exist at present which suggest that there is at present little basis for an arrangement of the kind you suggest outside the ordinary commercial exchanges.

It could not have been more clearly or authoritatively stated that the British Government had no desire to commit itself, however loosely, to an economic relationship which might have led to closer union with France – or, indeed, any other country. I cannot help thinking that the

British had understood more thoroughly than they admitted the risk of starting on the far-reaching process that I had in mind. At all events, their instincts made them wary.

Time was slipping by, and my attempt to create a nucleus around which a European Community might be formed had met no response from the one great power in Europe which was then in a position to take on such responsibility. Not counting Germany, which would have no Constitution before May and no Chancellor before September, only Italy and the three Benelux countries – Belgium, the Netherlands, and Luxembourg, already economically linked – could effectively enter into a form of union with France. But the efforts to bring this about were fitful, and I followed them only at a distance. The Franco-Italian customs union project, a Treaty for which was signed on March 26, 1949, certainly provided for real economic unity through the eventual unification of financial, social, and commercial legislation; but its implementation was already encountering national resistance which proved insurmountable, largely because there was no independent centre of decision. Moreover, the two economies, both exporters of agricultural produce, were competitive rather than complementary; and the addition of Benelux to the scheme, which was then given the absurd name 'Fritalux', did nothing to help.

These experiments were not without value, however – provided they taught us a lesson. They made it easier for me to persuade the champions of mere co-operation that inter-governmental systems, already weakened by the compromises built into them, were quickly paralysed by the rule that all decisions must be unanimous. I had already learned this from my experience at the League of Nations; but apparently no one remembered the vetos that had blocked all our efforts to find peaceful solutions to the conflicts set off by Japan, Italy, and Germany. The United Nations Organization had the same inbuilt flaw, and so had the Council of Europe. More and more people were clearly irritated by the impossibility, in these circumstances, of carrying through any bold initiatives; but everyone seemed resigned to the veto as if it were a law of Nature. The international assemblies gave themselves the appearance of democratic bodies, publicly expressing their peoples' will: what was less obvious was that even their unanimous resolutions were nullified, behind their backs, by a Committee or Council of Government representatives, any one of whom could prevent all the others from acting as they wished. At the Council of Europe in Strasbourg that summer, spectacular resolutions had been passed amid great acclaim. 'The aim and goal of the Council of Europe,' said one of them, 'is the creation of a European political authority with limited functions but real powers.' This text was proposed by a British Labour Party delegate, R. W. G. Mackay. It was sent to the Committee of Ministers, and there disappeared without trace.

In December, Paul Reynaud proposed to the Council of Europe's Consultative Assembly the idea of a Public Authority for European steel. I congratuated him, but he answered:

'To tell you the truth, it's already no longer an "authority". To get the text voted, that word had to be removed. Now it's to be an "organization" answerable to Governments: its task will be to suggest general guidelines.'

'Will it have the power of decision?'

'No. But it won't even see the light of day. The Committee of Ministers will bury it.'

'Well,' I said, 'it was a good idea. But that was certainly not the right way or the right place.'

Paul Reynaud was not the only one to explore this so-called 'functionalist' approach, which was more pragmatic and more concrete than the draft constitutions championed by ardent federalists. André Philip, Edouard Bonnefous, and Robert Boothby used all their eloquence to call for the internationalization of Europe's heavy industries, and in particular coal and steel. But nothing they said could make the idea become fact. I paid little attention to such proposals – not because I thought that their authors were not talking sense, but because I was less concerned to make a technical choice than to invent new political methods and to hit on the right moment for changing the way people thought. The union of Europe would never lack content: but where was the will and the opportunity to initiate it? For the moment, I still saw no clear way ahead.

IV

Germany moves

Looking back on this mid-century period, one can hardly fail to be struck by the extraordinary ferment in men's minds about the idea of European unity. The political parties and militant movements dealt with it in their manifestoes; statesmen discussed it in their speeches; articles were devoted to it in the press. The London *Times* and *The*

Economist published admirable editorials worthy of Jay's, Madison's, and Hamilton's *Federalist Papers*. Re-reading all this, one has the feeling that so rich a current of thought could hardly fail to bring about European unity on the broadest front. And, indeed, the vocabulary and arguments still used on the subject today were already current then. But they had nothing to do with action. In Zurich in 1946, Winston Churchill had called for the rapid establishment of a United States of Europe – but the Council of Europe was what he had had in mind. In Geneva in 1929, Aristide Briand had proposed 'a federal link' between the peoples of Europe – but he had added that it should not affect the sovereign rights of nations. No matter: public opinion was convinced that magic spells had been pronounced, and it could not understand why reality resisted them so stubbornly. In 1949, people were still refining on the spells themselves, and I found it hard to take much interest. At No 18 rue de Martignac we were all far removed from these debates, and neither Hirsch nor Uri remembers our having taken account of pious 'functionalist' hopes.

We were very much concerned, nevertheless, about the real situation. This, far from bringing us nearer to European union, was every day making the prospect more remote. France disagreed with her allies about the German question, and French foreign policy was returning to the habits of the past. After having had to give up her plans for dismembering Germany, France had concentrated on the Saar and the Ruhr. As in 1919, the Saar was now once more incorporated in the French economy, and was governed by Gilbert Grandval, the French High Commissioner, in proconsular style; while the coal and steel resources of the Ruhr had been administered since April by the International Ruhr Authority, on which France's representative was the intelligent and fair-minded Alain Poher. Germany, however, refused to be represented on the Authority alongside the Allies: already she was fighting to secure equality.

'I should agree to an authority that supervised the mining and industrial areas of Germany, France, Belgium, and Luxembourg,' Adenauer declared a few weeks after his election as Chancellor. When in December he finally agreed to the International Ruhr Authority, it was because the so-called 'Petersberg' agreement of November 24, 1949, had begun to give Germany some international recognition as a power in her own right.

Much as France still needed German coal, four years after the end of the war this was no longer enough to justify a system of indefinite domination. No one imagined that the system could go on for ever, but no one was willing to endorse a decision to end it – a decision towards which we were gradually being impelled by pressure from our British and American allies and by the changing situation in Germany herself. In the circumstances, all that France could do was to stiffen her resistance, since the removal of controls over the German economy would have meant renewed uncertainty about our vital supplies of coal, and especially of coke, and would thereby have made our steel industry very much weaker than its powerful German rival. So long as we remained locked into the postwar situation, in fact, a kind of crazy logic would make us repeat all the errors of the past. All I knew was that the situation had to be changed: but French politics made that impossible. Adenauer was so much aware of this that he modified his demands in order to avoid causing trouble in Paris for Robert Schuman, the French Foreign Minister, whose attitude he knew very well. But the friendship between the two men was soon put to the test by the pressure to which both were subjected by the opposition at home. Every step towards reconciliation caused an outcry in the German Bundestag as in the French National Assembly.

Misunderstanding took on overtones of tragedy in January 1950, when France intensified her efforts to have the Saar politically annexed from Germany. When Schuman paid his first visit to Bonn, he found the atmosphere glacial. On his return, he learned that Adenauer had declared: 'In Germany, the idea of European unification is now seriously compromised.' For Schuman, a sensitive man who had made it his highest ambition to reconcile the two nations, this was the beginning of a period of deep perplexity.

'What can we do?' he asked his friends.

He knew my feelings.

'Peace can be founded only on equality,' I told him. 'We failed in 1919 because we introduced discrimination and a sense of superiority. Now we are beginning to make the same mistakes again.'

Schuman very much agreed with me, and we easily understood each other. I liked his simplicity and common sense, and I respected his transparent honesty and strength of spirit. The French people clearly sensed it too, and they trusted him. It was important for him to realize this and to overcome his modesty in order to make his mark with the public as he did with his colleagues, gently but firmly. He was to play a crucial role in the great changes that our foreign policy was going to have to undergo, and I took care to keep in touch with him, both in person and through his *directeur de cabinet*, Bernard Clappier, for whom like Schuman I had both admiration and friendship.

'If I find myself occupying this position,' Schuman had told the National Assembly in November 1949, 'it is not because I have sought it, but doubtless because someone from France's Eastern frontier was needed to try to achieve peaceful co-existence between two countries which have so often been at each other's throats.'

There was no trace of pride in this high ambition, and no intolerance in Schuman's tenacious faith. He was very different in character from Adenauer, who was pursuing the same aim on the far side of the Rhine. Adenauer had no hesitation about what had to be done. 'A Federal Chancellor,' he declared, 'must be at once a good German and a good European.' I knew him only from his powerful public statements, intended alternately to warn and to win over the occupying powers. His intransigence was that of a great patriot, but he was also a very skilled politician: he stood up to his Socialist opponents, but also used them to press the Allies for greater understanding. At that time, however, he had not yet acquired the international fame that the sincerity of his statements and the scope of his proposals already deserved.

In March 1950, in an interview with the American newspaperman Kingsbury Smith of the International News Service, Adenauer suggested a complete union between France and Germany, with a merger of their economies, their Parliaments, and their citizenship. This proposal, which openly drew on the British offer to France in 1940, was not well received in France. The situation was not the same, and the historical allusion was felt to be out of place. Indeed, there was little reaction at all, and I do not recall having paid much attention to it myself, since I did not believe that at that time Europe could be built at a stroke. In London in 1940, we had had only a few days, then only a few hours, to take action and reverse the drift towards defeatism that had already begun in Bordeaux. A sudden shock might have been able to weld together the threatened alliance and fuse the two countries' destinies, for better or for worse. In 1950, where was the Alliance, and where was the immediate danger? For the French, the danger was still Germany and her uncertain future. A total alliance with Germany, therefore, on Germany's own initiative, seemed 'unthinkable'. 'Adenauer wants to build Europe around Germany and for Germany,' wrote the MRP newspaper L'Aube. I disagreed: but I saw very clearly that Adenauer's proposals were not what was needed at the time.

Basically, however, I shared Adenauer's views. 'Undoubtedly,' he declared, 'if the French and the Germans sat down around the same table, in the same building, to work together and assume joint responsibilities, a great step forward would have been taken. The psychological repercussions would be immense. France's desire for security would be satisfied, and the revival of German nationalism would be prevented.' That put the problem very clearly: but the method of solving it was missing; and without a method no one could contribute to a solution. Experience had taught me that one cannot act in general terms, starting from a vague concept, but that anything becomes possible as soon as one can concentrate on one precise point which leads on to everything else. Sitting down around the same table was the right image; but it was only an image. Assuming joint responsibilities was indeed the aim; but to discuss it without providing the means was no more than speech-making. Yet in Adenauer's mind there was one practical preoccupation – the fate of the Ruhr and the Saar. He wanted to sublimate national rivalry over these coal and steel resources by uniting Germany and France. This idea of a prior global union, intended to envelop and remove a particular difficulty, was not in my view realistic. On the contrary, it seemed to me, we should start with the difficulty itself, using it as a lever to initiate a more general solution. Unity would gradually be created by the momentum of a first achievement. Our efforts must therefore be concentrated on the very point about which disagreements had come to a head.

It was natural that in 1950 Adenauer should seek to avoid the precise difficulty with France that was caused by the status of the Saar. It was equally natural that Schuman should cling to the policy of controlling Germany, since this was the only policy which the French Parliament would support. Both were following the logic of their official positions. The Governments of our countries, now as in the past, are called upon to defend a certain conception of the national interest. This conception is the result of a number of influences, among which the most conservative carry the greatest weight. However far-sighted they may be, Governments always find it difficult, and very often impossible, to change the existing state of affairs which it is their duty to administer. In their hearts they may wish to do so; but they have to account for their actions to Parliament, and they are held back by their officials, who want to keep everything just so. All this is very natural. If Governments and civil services were always ready to change the existing order of things from one moment to the next, the result would be continual revolution and incessant disorder. I knew from experience that change can only come from outside, under the pressure of necessity, although not necessarily by violent means. Statesmen are concerned to do good, and above all to extricate themselves from awkward corners; but they do not always have either the taste or the time for using their imagination. They are open to creative ideas, and anyone who knows how to present such ideas has a good chance of having them accepted.

I was not surprised to hear Robert Schuman say at that time: 'We must doubtless envisage some transfer of sovereignty, but not yet.' It was his answer to Adenauer, who was offering to Europe the sovereignty that his own country had not yet recovered. To me, it mattered little whether these attitudes were sincere or not: they would bring no concrete results. Like the Chorus of some Greek tragedy, General de Gaulle added his eloquent commentary:

> If one were not constrained to look at matters coolly, one would be dazzled by the prospect of what could be achieved by a combination of German and French strength, the latter embracing also Africa. . . . Altogether, it would mean giving modern economic, social, strategic, and cultural shape to the work of the Emperor Charlemagne.

But if in fact we had to look at matters coolly, and to reject the dream of a 'Carolingian' Europe totally and immediately integrated, was this any reason for making no effort at all? I thought not. The state of Europe was an additional danger in a world once more gravely threatened: the cold war was becoming an intolerable fact of life for hundreds of millions of people. Relations between France and Germany could no longer be treated in general terms or with a sense of fatalism. I was convinced that the time had come to act.

Chapter 12

A BOLD, CONSTRUCTIVE ACT (1949-1950)

I
Deadlock

I cannot explain the source of that conviction which, at important moments in my life, suddenly calls a halt to my reflections and turns them into a decision. Other people see it as a sense of timing. But I never ask myself whether it is necessary to do this or that: necessity itself forces me to do something which, once I see it clearly, is no longer a matter of choice. To see it clearly I have to concentrate – which I can do only in isolation, on long solitary walks. Since I left Cognac, I have always arranged my affairs so as to wake up each morning in the country, at a good distance from the town where I work. I get up early and walk for miles by myself. When I leave the house, I take with me all the previous day's thoughts and worries. But when I have walked for half an hour or an hour, they begin to fade away, and I gradually start to notice things around me, the flowers or the leaves on the trees. At that moment, I know that nothing can disturb me. I let my thoughts find their own level. I never force myself to think about a given subject – subjects come to me naturally because I always follow the same line of thought, or rather, I follow only one at a time. André Horré, who with his wife Amélie looked after our house – I should say, our successive houses, in Britain, the United States, France, and Luxembourg – for more than thirty years, understood me very well.

'It's simple,' he said: 'Monsieur puts his idea in front of him, talks to it, and then decides.'

André used to see me come back at about 10.00 a.m., change, and go to the office, where I faced complex problems further complicated by people's attitudes towards them, and was able to attack them with energy renewed by contact with Nature. For me, walking has always been a form of intellectual as well as physical exercise: it helps me to reach conclusions. Afterwards, things are different: I come back to the world of action, implementation – and routine. In the spring of 1950, routine had become wearisome. Even the woods of Montfort-l'Amaury, near my home, seemed stifling. I left for the mountains.

Every year, I like if I can to take long trips in the Alps. This time it was in Switzerland, at Roseland, that I arranged to meet my guide to the Huez range. How many miles we covered in two weeks, going from one overnight lodge to another, I have forgotten; but the course of my thoughts is still there before me, traced in the notes that I made every evening. I can read in them the anxiety that weighed on Europe five years after the war: the fear that if we did nothing we should soon face war again. Germany would not be its instigator this time, but its prize. So Germany must cease to be a potential prize, and instead become a link. At that moment, only France could take the initiative. What could be done to link France and Germany, and implant a common interest between them, before it was too late? That was the question I turned over and over in my mind in the silent concentration of the day's march. When I returned to Paris at the beginning of April, I still had no perfect answer: but I did have so full an account of the reasons for acting, and so clear an idea of the direction in which to move, that from my point of view the time of uncertainty was over. It only remained to choose the machinery and seek the opportunity.

My account of the reasons for acting covered several pages. Not many people read them at the time, because action followed very rapidly and overtook the analysis. But the analysis that guided me then is still of interest today, because it helps to explain why matters took the course they did. It shows how precarious world peace then was, and how limited was the scope for any attempt to avoid catastrophe. The very first words sound a note of alarm which has since been forgotten, now that Europe has so long been at peace. Five years after the end of World War II, however, it echoed the very real anxiety that men and women had once again come to feel:

> Whichever way we turn, in the present world situation we see nothing but deadlock – whether it be the increasing acceptance of a war that is thought to be inevitable, the problem of Germany, the continuation of France's recovery, the organization of Europe, or the place of France in Europe and the world.

'A war that is thought to be inevitable'. Today, it is hard to recall the atmosphere of 1950, whose fears were not confirmed by events. But co-existence between the blocs was still precarious, and the East–West dialogue had no rules except those of force. In Berlin, the West had just won a trial of strength after nearly a year's blockade by the East: the American airlift of supplies to the city, using fantastic military resources, had led the Soviet Union to lift the blockade in May 1949. But there were certainly going to be two Germanies, each incorporated in a separate strategic zone. Adenauer's Germany was covered by the newly-formed Atlantic Alliance; and there was active concern to secure a German contribution to the defence of the West. Russia had just acquired the atomic bomb. How far would she now go? The advice which more and more people of influence were giving seemed superficially sound: 'Leave Europe out of these confrontations'. But this neutralist doctrine never became more than an intellectual argument. I pursued it at home with Hubert Beuve-Méry, editor-in-chief of *Le Monde*. I respected his deep sincerity, and we have always remained friends: but I disagreed with him then.

'It is precisely because the countries of Western Europe play no part in the great decisions of the world,' I said, 'that we face the instability from which you're trying to shield us. And, far from backing out, it's vital that we once more play an active part in settling these problems, because they concern the West as a whole.'

No matter; men's minds were confused, and I was disquieted to see developing in Europe, to say nothing of other danger-spots in the world, the climate of the 'cold war'.

The greatest danger, in my eyes, was not so much men's ambitions or the accumulation of arms, but a very specific disorientation among governments and peoples, which itself required specific psychological remedies:

Men's minds are becoming focused on an object at once simple and dangerous – the cold war.

All proposals and all actions are interpreted by public opinion as a contribution to the cold war.

The cold war, whose essential objective is to make the opponent give way, is the first phase of real war.

This prospect creates among leaders that rigidity of mind which is characteristic of the pursuit of a single object. The search for solutions to problems ceases. Such rigidity of aims and attitudes on both sides will lead inevitably to a confrontation: the logic of this way of looking at things is inescapable. And this confrontation will end in war.

In effect, we are at war already.

War was in men's minds, and it had to be opposed by imagination. I remembered that sentence in Roosevelt's first Inaugural Address, on

March 4, 1933, which had so much struck the American nation: 'The only thing we have to fear is fear itself.' In 1950, fear would engender paralysis, and paralysis would lead to disaster. It was vital to break the deadlock.

> The course of events must be altered. To do this, men's attitudes must be changed. Words are not enough. Only immediate action on an essential point can change the present static situation. This action must be radical, real, immediate, and dramatic; it must change things and make a reality of the hopes which people are on the point of giving up.

In Europe, the danger was still Germany – not, this time, because she might initiate something, but because other countries were treating her as the stake in their power games. The Americans, I thought, would try to integrate the new Federal Republic in the Western political and military system. The Russians would oppose that by every means at their command; and at the same time French neuroses would be made worse. It was on the subject of Germany that we needed a salutary shock:

> The German situation is rapidly turning into a cancer that will be danger-ous to peace in the near future, and immediately to France, unless its development is directed towards hope for the Germans and collabora-tion with free peoples. . . .
>   We must not try to solve the German problem in its present context. We must change the context by transforming the basic facts.

It was at that time, undoubtedly, and on that precise problem, that I realized the full possibilities of an approach which had long been familiar to me, and which I had applied empirically in trying to over-come difficulties of all kinds. I had come to see that it was often useless to make a frontal attack on problems, since they have not arisen by themselves, but are the product of circumstances. Only by modifying the circumstances – 'lateral thinking' – can one disperse the difficulties that they create. So, instead of wearing myself out on the hard core of resistance, I had become accustomed to seeking out and trying to change whatever element in its environment was causing the block. Sometimes it was quite a minor point, and very often a matter of psychology. The problem of Germany, vast and complex though it was, could surely be approached in this same way. It would certainly not be solved until we had changed the conditions that made the future of the Germans so uncertain and disquieting, for their neighbours as for themselves. From the German point of view, those conditions included the humiliation of being subject to indefinite Allied control;

from the French point of view, there was the fear of a Germany ultimately freed from any control at all. These two elements were by no means the only ones on the world scene at that time; but they were enough to block any constructive evolution in Europe.

The situation was tangled. What we had to do was find a thread to pull so as to unravel some of the knots and gradually sort everything out. But where was that thread to be found? In the confused state of Franco-German relations, the neurosis of the vanquished seemed to be shifting to the victor: France was beginning to feel inferior again as she realized that attempts to limit Germany's dynamism were bound to fail.

> France's continued recovery will come to a halt unless we rapidly solve the problem of German industrial production and its competitive capacity.
>
> The basis of the superiority which French industrialists traditionally recognize in Germany is her ability to produce steel at a price that France cannot match. From this they conclude that the whole of French production is similarly handicapped.
>
> Already, Germany is seeking to increase her production from eleven to fourteen million metric tons. We shall refuse, but the Americans will insist. Finally, we shall state our reservations, but we shall give in. At the same time, French production is levelling off or even falling.
>
> Merely to state these facts makes it unnecessary to describe what the results will be: Germany expanding; German dumping on export markets; a call for the protection of French industry; an end to trade liberalization; the re-establishment of prewar cartels; perhaps, Eastward outlets for German expansion, a prelude to political agreements; and France back in the old rut of limited, protected production.

From my vantage-point at the Planning Commissariat, I could clearly detect the first signs of such a retreat on the part of France. The international timetable was increasingly crowded. On May 10, 1950, Robert Schuman was due in London, to meet his colleagues Ernest Bevin and Dean Acheson in order to discuss the future of Germany and the raising of her production quotas. Schuman had no constructive proposals to take with him, although he had pondered deeply and consulted many people. Myself, I was beginning to see more clearly. Action would have to be taken, I realized, where misunderstandings were most tangible, and where past errors were most likely to be repeated. If only the French could lose their fear of German industrial domination, then the greatest obstacle to a united Europe would be removed. A solution which would put French industry on the same footing as German industry, while freeing the latter from the discrimination born of defeat — that would restore the economic and political preconditions for the mutual understanding so vital to Europe as a whole. It could, in fact, become the germ of European unity.

Quite naturally, the plans I had discussed in 1943 with Etienne Hirsch and René Mayer now came back to my mind. At the time, they had been intellectual blueprints, traced over wartime maps whose frontiers were due to be redrawn. Now, I rediscovered them – or rather, reinvented them in response to the needs of the hour. To apply them to the new peacetime map of political Europe was another matter. German sovereignty had just been re-established. Could it now be called in question again, even partially? Quite early on, the Allies had renounced the idea of dismembering occupied Germany into a number of small States: then, they had decided to annex no territory, including the Saar; now, finally, they were even preparing to give up inter-nationalizing the resources of the Ruhr. All successive attempts to keep Germany in check, mainly at French instigation, had come to nothing, because they had been based on the rights of conquest and temporary superiority – notions from the past which happily were no longer taken for granted. But if the problem of sovereignty were approached with no desire to dominate or take revenge – if on the contrary the victors and the vanquished agreed to exercise joint sovereignty over part of their joint resources – then, a solid link would be forged between them, the way would be wide open for further collective action, and a great example would be given to the other nations of Europe.

The joint resources of France and Germany lay essentially in their coal and steel, distributed unevenly but in complementary fashion over a triangular area artificially divided by historical frontiers. With the industrial revolution, which had coincided with the rise of doctrinal nationalism, these frontiers had become barriers to trade and then lines of confrontation. Neither country now felt secure unless it commanded all the resources – i.e., all the area. Their rival claims were decided by war, which solved the problem only for a time – the time to prepare for revenge. Coal and steel were at once the key to economic power and the raw materials for forging weapons of war. This double role gave them immense symbolic significance, now largely forgotten, but comparable at the time to that of nuclear energy today. To pool them across frontiers would reduce their malign prestige and turn them instead into a guarantee of peace.

By now I was sufficiently convinced to be sure of convincing others. But whom, and when? On the question of timing, the May 10 meeting in London seemed to me the opportunity to seize. But a meeting of that sort would not be the right place to make the proposal I had in mind, which itself would obviate the need for such talks among the three occupying powers. To achieve that result, a totally new situation must be created: the Franco-German problem must become a European problem. I wrote:

> At the present moment, Europe can be brought to birth only by France. Only France is in a position to speak and act.

To my mind, this was a simple statement of fact, not the proclamation of an historic privilege.

> But if France fails to speak and act now, what will happen?
> A group will form around the United States, but in order to wage the cold war with greater zeal. The obvious reason is that the countries of Europe are afraid and are seeking help. Britain will draw ever closer to the United States; Germany will develop rapidly, and we shall not be able to prevent her being armed. France will be trapped once more in her old Malthusianism, and this will inevitably lead to her eclipse.

I was not yet trying to decide who should speak in the name of France, or on what occasion. What mattered was to know beforehand exactly what should be said. Proposing to place several countries' coal and steel under a joint sovereign authority was no more than an idea. It had to be given concrete form; and there I had no experience to fall back on – except the negative experience of international co-operation, whose institutions were incapable of decision-making. Their ineffectiveness told me what to avoid. But what form should be given to a decision-making authority common to Germany and France? History offered no precedent; as yet, I was groping, and I needed advice. Yet at the same time I wanted to keep the idea as secret as possible. At that point, as luck would have it, there came to my office at No 18 rue de Martignac a young professor of law, Paul Reuter, whom I had not previously met. I think we were seeking his opinion on French anti-trust legislation, which to my mind needed tightening up. Reuter was a man from Eastern France, solid and unexcitable; he used his brilliant powers of reasoning to master concrete problems in politics and law. He taught law at the University of Aix-la-Chapelle, but came regularly to Paris to deal with practical problems at the Quai d'Orsay in his capacity as legal adviser to the French Foreign Office. I saw at once that he was both professionally and personally concerned about Franco-German relations. Could international law abolish the conflicts whose most constant victims had been frontier-dwellers like Reuter himself?

I expounded some of my ideas to him; and he reacted with such intelligence and enthusiasm that I asked him to come back again on the following Saturday, April 15. That day, I explained the essentials of my plan for a coal–steel pool, and I asked him to reflect overnight about the form of institution required to administer these joint resources. Next day, Reuter, Hirsch, and I met at my country home. It was there, on that Sunday, that we drafted the first version of what was to become the French Declaration of May 9, 1950. At a distance of more than twenty-five years, I can no longer distinguish which of us contributed what to the text we dictated to my faithful secretary Mme Miguez. I can only say that, without Hirsch and Reuter, it would not so quickly have assumed the final form that made it the European Community's true founding document. I had a clear view of our goal: they supplied the means of attaining it through the interplay of economics and institutions, for which in a very short time they invented new structures on a European scale.

World peace can be safeguarded only by creative efforts which match the dangers that threaten it.

The contribution that an organized and living Europe can make to civilization is indispensable to the maintenance of peace.

This introduction survived through all the successive versions of the text. For the rest, the days that followed produced many variations, between the lines of which it would be possible to follow the way our thoughts progressed. But it was all there in embryo already:

Europe must be organized on a federal basis. A Franco-German union is an essential element in it, and the French Government has decided to act to this end. . . . Obstacles accumulated from the past make it impossible to achieve immediately the close association which the French Government has taken as its aim. But already the establishment of common bases for economic development must be the first stage in building Franco-German union. *The French Government proposes to place the whole of Franco-German coal and steel production under an international Authority open to the participation of the other countries of Europe.*

The aims and methods of the European Community were now set. Later improvements concerned only the style and the machinery. What strikes me, re-reading this text, is the clarity of its design, which became somewhat less sharp in the final version. In this one, Franco-German union was the central concern. If it could not be achieved at once, this was because of 'accumulated obstacles'. A start must be made by 'the establishment of common bases for economic development', first in coal and steel, then in other fields. For a time, undoubtedly, I thought that the first step towards a European federation would be union between these two countries only, and that the others would join later. Finally, that evening, I wrote in on this first version that the Authority would be 'open to the participation of the other countries of Europe'. That morning, this had not been the decisive point; and one always has to go back to the beginning of things to understand their meaning.

On the powers of the new Authority, the main guidelines had been drawn up, and they were to prove durable. Thanks to Hirsch, the foundations were solid. To place the production and distribution of coal and steel on a common basis, to ensure that they were sold on identical terms, to level up social conditions, and continually to improve production –

> – these aims call for complex institutions and measures of broad scope. Competitive conditions of production in the two countries must be equalized – taxation, transport, social security and other labour costs. . . . Production quotas will have to be fixed, and financial machinery set up to compensate for price differences, together with a retraining and re-employment fund.

The main headings of the European Treaties were already there in outline. Paul Reuter sketched the institutional machinery:

> The above principles and essential commitments will be the subject of a Treaty to be signed by the two countries. The Authority which is to administer the whole enterprise will be based on equal Franco-German representation, and its President will be chosen by agreement between the two parties.

Although not yet fully explicit, this was the first juridical statement of the principle of equality between France and Germany, which was to be the decisive step towards a more hopeful future. And the text ended with a few lines which summarized its overall aim:

> This proposal has an essential political objective: to make a breach in the ramparts of national sovereignty which will be narrow enough to secure consent, but deep enough to open the way towards the unity that is essential to peace.

Why this sentence is missing from subsequent versions, and why others later appeared, only to be replaced by those that today are found in the history-books – this is a matter of balance between form and content in a series of texts worked out over several days. Between Sunday April 16 and Saturday May 6 there were nine different versions. Whether this is few or many I cannot judge: in these matters I have only one rule, which is to work as long as is necessary, starting again a hundred times, if a hundred attempts are needed for a satisfactory result, or only nine times, as in the present case. Those who have worked with me over the years will say that the average is more like fifteen; and they themselves would often have been content with fewer. The proof, they argue, is that we often come back to the first version, which then turns out to be the best. But what is the point of this arithmetic of effort? How can one be sure that the first version is the best, except by comparing it with what one believes to be better still? How easy everything would be if intuition or luck led straight to the exact formulation of a thought that presented itself fully formed. At the very least, intuition and luck need to be tested – and the test is to re-read them after a good night's sleep, or subject them to fresh scrutiny by someone else.

It was Pierre Uri who looked at the text with fresh eyes on the following morning, Monday April 17. I had decided to ask him, and him alone, to work over our initial draft. His imagination and his crisp style proved invaluable. He read the text with that astonishing capacity for concentration that wrinkles his whole face; then he said simply:

'This puts many problems in perspective.'

That was the point. It was less a question of solving problems, which are mostly in the nature of things, than of putting them in a more rational and human perspective, and making use of them to serve the cause of international peace. In this, Uri played an outstanding part. With his help, the draft became more orderly, and the institutional system stronger: the 'international Authority' became the High Authority. In the fourth version, the High Authority was described as 'supranational'; but I disliked the word, and always have. What mattered was the task it implied, which was much better described by the following sentence in the next version of the text:

The High Authority's decisions shall be immediately binding in France, Germany and the other member countries.

Such power required safeguards, and the idea of a means of appeal was introduced, without further details. Having made his contribution, Paul Reuter returned to Aix and his professorial chair. We kept in touch by telephone, and I hoped that he might come back to work out the Treaty with us. He never did, and I do not know why. But in any case Paul Reuter was one of the inventors of the High Authority, and of the name as well as the institution itself.

Uri, for his part, lent coherence to the economic aspects of the plan, and gradually brought into focus the notion of a 'common market', an area without customs barriers and without national discrimination, but with rules to preserve the common interest. He also introduced the idea of transitional measures. The whole project gave an impression of strong organization combined with liberal principles. In this there was no contradiction:

> Gradually, conditions will emerge which will of themselves ensure the most rational distribution of production at the highest level of productivity.

We could go no further in our technical proposals, because no experts were to be let into the secret; and in any case we were short of time. The essential elements were all in the 104 lines of text we now had, to which further days' work brought only minor modifications. In fact, it was all summed up in the following sentence:

> *By the pooling of basic production and the establishment of a new High Authority whose decisions will be binding on France, Germany, and the countries that join them, this proposal will lay the first concrete foundations of the European Federation which is indispensable to the maintenance of peace.*

I asked for this passage in our text to be underlined, because it described at one and the same time the method, the means, and the objective, which henceforth were indissolubly linked. The last word was the most important: peace.

II

Solution

'The French Government proposes. . . .' But the Government still had to see the proposal and adopt it as its own. I had to find someone who had the power, and the courage to use it to trigger off so great a change. Robert Schuman seemed to me the ideal man to do so; but owing to a misunderstanding I did not approach him first. What happened was this. I had had a long conversation with Bernard Clappier on the day before Reuter had first come to see me. I had spoken in general terms about my ideas, which had interested him greatly.

'M. Schuman,' he said, 'is looking for an initiative that he can propose in London on May 10. I have the feeling that this has been his one great preoccupation since the Big Three met in New York last September. I was there when Acheson said, with Bevin's agreement: "We fully concur in entrusting our French colleague with formulating our common policy on Germany." The deadline's approaching, and no one seems able to advise him on what to do.'

'Well,' I said: 'I have some ideas.'

I thought that Clappier was going to call me back after having spoken to his Minister. But a combination of circumstances gave him no time to do so; and on Friday, April 28, thinking that Schuman was not interested, I decided to send the plan to Georges Bidault, the Prime Minister, under whose aegis the Planning Commissariat worked.

That very same day, only a few moments after I had had the dossier taken round to Pierre-Louis Falaize, Bidault's *directeur de cabinet*, Clappier got in touch with me again, apologizing for his long silence.

'Here's the proposal,' I said. 'I've just sent it to Bidault.'

Clappier read the text, and quickly made up for lost time.

'It's excellent,' he said. 'May I show it to M. Schuman?'

I gave him a copy, and he took it straight to the Gare de l'Est, where Schuman was about to take the train for Metz, to spend the weekend as usual in the solitude of his country house at Scy-Chazelles. Clappier found him already sitting in his compartment.

'Could you read this paper of Monnet's?' he asked. 'It's important.'

On Monday morning, Clappier was back at the Gare de l'Est to meet the incoming train. No sooner had Schuman got off than he said:

'I've read the proposal. I'll use it.'

Those few words were enough. The idea had entered the political arena: it had become the business of the authorities, and their dangerous responsibility. It is the privilege of statesmen to decide what is in the general interest. Since I could not exercise that privilege in my own right, I naturally had to help those who could.

Schuman and Clappier, then, joined the conspiracy. Bidault and Falaize did not, and for good reason: they had not taken the time to read the letter in which I had suggested that we meet next day to discuss 'the enclosed proposal, designed to transform the general situation, which is growing worse every day.' The meeting did not take place – although I read in *Le Monde* of Tuesday May 2 that I had been received by the Prime Minister. The comedy of errors was not over: on Wednesday, after the Cabinet meeting at which Schuman made a veiled allusion to a forthcoming French initiative, I was summoned to the Prime

Minister's office at the Matignon palace, where Bidault received me in a furious rage. He had a copy of the proposal in his hand.

'Schuman's just shown me this paper,' he said. 'It appears that you're the author. I should have appreciated your telling me first.'

'I did,' I said, 'I wrote to you on Friday.'

He looked for the letter: it was on his desk. Had he read it? In his memoirs he affirms that he had, and I believe him. Probably the plan clashed with his own concern at that time, which was to set up an Atlantic High Council. What might have happened to the project if Bidault had taken it over, and what might have happened to Europe, are questions that others have tried to answer. Myself, I have never wondered what consequences might have followed something which has not occurred: that seems to me an utterly barren speculation. The fact is that there was no Bidault Plan, but a Schuman Plan.

Clappier helped us put the finishing touches to the text, which on Saturday May 6 assumed its final shape with the addition of some further sentences:

> By making herself for more than twenty years the champion of a united Europe, France has had as her essential objective the maintenance of peace. Europe was not built, and we had war.

This was a homage to Aristide Briand, but also a farewell to rhetoric.

> Europe will not be built all at once, or as a single whole: it will be built by concrete achievements which first create *de facto* solidarity.

This was the fundamental choice of a method for continual material and psychological integration. It seems slow and unspectacular; yet it has worked without a break for more than 25 years, and no one has been able to suggest any other way of making the Community progress.

'Now we must stop,' I said; and I wrote 'Definitive text, Saturday 3.00 p.m.' From that moment on, it was all a matter of tactics. Soon afterwards, I went into Schuman's office with René Mayer, now the Minister of Justice. He at once became an enthusiastic champion of the proposal, in which he saw the traces of our wartime talks in Algiers about the need to build a peaceful Europe. It was at Mayer's request that we added a sentence which at the time was thought to be purely formal, but which later revealed its full implications:

> Europe will be able, with increased resources, to pursue the realization of one of her essential tasks, the development of the African continent.

Meanwhile, I had the documents taken to René Pleven, Minister of

Overseas Affairs. He was their only other recipient. In all, only nine people were in the know.

How and when to disclose the secret we discussed on Sunday. Pleven, now fully informed and committed, advised us on how to proceed. At the end of the morning I met Schuman and Clappier again. They had thought it advisable to bring in Alexandre Parodi, who was now Secretary-General at the Ministry of Foreign Affairs. Thereby, the Ministry was officially informed, but also pledged to silence. We were determined, in fact, to mount the whole operation outside diplomatic channels, and not to use ambassadors. In particular, the personal contact with Adenauer that Schuman wanted to establish was to be made by a member of his personal *cabinet*, who was to go to Bonn at the very moment when the decision was due to be taken. It remained to be decided when that should be. There was no longer much choice, since a decision of this importance required the consent of the whole Government. Yet we could not wait until Wednesday, the normal day for French Cabinet meetings, for this was when the Conference was due to start in London, and Schuman had to go there with a plan for Germany in his hands. Pleven and Mayer arranged for the Cabinet to meet on Tuesday morning instead of Wednesday. Until then, there had to be total secrecy. There was – but with one exception.

This was the result of a curious coincidence. Dean Acheson, the US Secretary of State, had decided not to go to London direct, but to come via Paris in order to confer quietly with Schuman, whom he greatly respected. It would have been inconceivable to let the two men talk intimately about everything except the one subject which in two days' time was to be all-important. Courtesy and honesty obliged us to take Acheson into our confidence, and we never regretted having done so. The description in his memoirs of that Sunday, May 7, in Paris is characteristically lively, witty, and amiable. He admits that he failed to realize the significance of the Schuman Plan when it was first described to him through an interpreter. He suspected it of being a sort of huge coal and steel cartel, the nostalgic dream of European industrialists and a capital sin for Americans, who respected the laws of competition and free trade. The lawyer and the politician in Acheson instinctively recoiled, and I had to come and calm his fears.*

I knew Acheson well. He had often come to our house in Washington and greatly appreciated Amélie's French cooking. Every morning, he could be seen walking to the office with Felix Frankfurter. With their

* Dean Acheson, *Present at the Creation* (London, Hamish Hamilton, 1969), pp. 382–4.

two bowler hats, the two friends were the incarnation of Law and the Constitution. They were both good company, quizzical and full of warmth. Acheson could be urbane and even flippant; but his powerful intelligence was anchored in firm principles. I have described the part he played in the birth of the Marshall Plan; and I had no doubt that he would realize the political importance of the Schuman Plan. With David Bruce in attendance, he very quickly did; and from then on we had two chance accomplices who were also very powerful allies. However, the fleeting contretemps set me thinking: I saw that the nature of the plan for a coal and steel pool might be misunderstood. So I at once asked Uri to prepare an answer to the objection; and he drafted a note to be distributed at the same time as the proposal itself. He wrote:

> The proposed organization is in every respect the very opposite of a cartel – in its aims, its methods, and its leadership.

The full proof was convincing; but there would have to be great vigilance, and strict legal rules – a real European anti-trust law – not only to disarm suspicion but also to prevent the formation of cartel.

Monday May 8 was the eve of battle, but to all appearances it was a normal day at the French Foreign Office and at No 18 rue de Martignac, where we deliberately carried on as if nothing were in the air. That evening, Clappier told me that, as planned, a friend of Robert Schuman's, a magistrate from Lorraine by the name of Michlich, had left for Bonn, where he was to be met by Herbert Blankenhorn, head of the Federal Chancellor's private staff. How he reached the Chancellery on Tuesday morning, unbeknown to any French official and even to the French High Commissioner in Germany, André François-Poncet, only that discreet diplomat could describe. All I know is what I have read in Adenauer's memoirs:

> That morning I was still unaware that the day would bring about a decisive change in the development of Europe.
>
> While the Federal Cabinet was in session, news came that an envoy from French Foreign Minister Schuman had an important message for me. Ministerialdirektor Blankenhorn received the gentleman, who gave him two letters from Schuman to myself. Their content, he said, was exceptionally urgent: they must be put before me right away. The French gentleman, whose name I do not know, told Blankenhorn that the French Cabinet was at that very moment meeting to discuss the content of the letters. . . . Blankenhorn brought the letters to me in the Cabinet meeting.

One of them was a personal, handwritten message from Robert Schuman. . . .

In his personal letter to me, Schuman wrote that the aim of his proposal was not economic but highly political. There was still a fear in France that when Germany had recovered she would attack France. It could also be imagined that in Germany, on the other hand, there was a corresponding desire for greater security. Rearmament would have to begin by increasing coal, iron, and steel production. If an organization such as Schuman envisaged were set up, enabling both countries to discern the first signs of any such rearmament, this new possibility would bring great relief to France. . . .

I immediately informed Robert Schuman that I agreed to his proposal with all my heart.*

The French Cabinet was indeed meeting, in the Elysée Palace, and Clappier still remembers his long wait in a nearby office. He was in touch with us at No 18 rue de Martignac via the interministerial telephone. Midday came and went, and the Cabinet had reached the end of its agenda; but still Schuman had not spoken. He could not make a move until he had Adenauer's full agreement, which he had no reason to doubt but still had to receive. The long silence was agony to us: was everything going to hinge on a matter of minutes? At last, just as the Cabinet meeting ended, Michlich's call came through to Clappier, and everyone sat down again. Exactly what Schuman said to his colleagues is a Cabinet secret, but I have reason to believe that it was even more elliptical and less audible than usual. No one cast doubt on the desirability of the proposal he was taking to London, which was strongly supported by Pleven and Mayer, even if most members of the Cabinet learned its precise terms only from the next day's press. When the Cabinet meeting was over, Clappier called me.

'That's it,' he said. 'We can go ahead.'

To 'go ahead', as we saw it, meant to make public that evening, in spectacular fashion, the project so discreetly unveiled that morning. At once, French and foreign newspapermen were asked to come to the Foreign Office at the Quai d'Orsay at 6.00 p.m.; and the Salon de l'Horloge there was turned into a press room. In our haste, we forgot to invite the photographers and radio reporters – with the result that Schuman had to go through a reconstruction of the scene some months later to record it for posterity. The afternoon before the press con-

* Konrad Adenauer, *Erinnerungen*, Vol. I (1945–53), pp. 314–15.

ference was taken up with receiving the ambassadors of European countries and briefing them on the proposal which their Governments were going to read on the agency wires even before the ambassadorial telegrams were ready to send. When Schuman came into the Salon de l'Horloge, more than two hundred newspapermen were waiting. I was there too, with Silvia, Hirsch, Uri, and my young assistant François Fontaine. I am not at all sure that Schuman's dull, hesitant voice immediately convinced them that they were witnessing a profound transformation of international politics, even though the tone of the preamble left no room for doubt:

It is no longer a time for vain words, but for a bold, constructive act.

France has acted, and the consequences of her action may be immense. We hope they will.

She has acted essentially in the cause of peace. For peace to have a real chance, there first must be a Europe.

In fact, this was a conclusion rather than a preamble; and I at once set about persuading the men from the leading newspapers that it was right. They were still uncertain about the significance of the proposal, whose technical aspects at first sight masked its political meaning. I knew that they would write about it as an industrial arrangement, a coal and steel pool – which was true enough. But it was also about Europe and peace. Roger Massip of *Le Figaro*, Charles Ronsac of *Franc-Tireur*, Jacques Gascuel of *France-Soir*, and Harold Callender of the *New York Times*, among others, had no doubts: their articles hailed the event for what it was. In Germany, meanwhile, Adenauer in his turn was waiting for the announcement of the French proposal in order to tell the newspapermen gathered in Bonn that Germany accepted it:

The proposal that France has just made to us is a generous move. It is a decisive step forward in Franco-German relations. It is not a matter of vague generalizations, but of concrete suggestions based on equal rights.

With his habitual realism, the Federal Chancellor saw the immediate advantage:

Since the production of the Saar will be pooled, one cause of tension between France and Germany will be removed.

It had all been settled in a matter of hours, in public, by two men who by themselves had dared to commit their countries' future. But at that moment, pleased as I was, I knew that the essential task remained to be completed; and I was impatient for only one thing – institutions to give shape to an agreement based on goodwill. Nothing is possible without men: nothing is lasting without institutions.

Robert Schuman, who was in a hurry to catch his train for London, so skilfully evaded the newspapermen's detailed questions about the future of the plan that one of them exclaimed:

'In other words, it's a leap in the dark?'

'That's right,' said Schuman soberly: 'a leap in the dark.'

Few people realized how true the metaphor was. They tended to think that the technical aspects of the plan had been meticulously prepared – why otherwise should it have originated at No 18 rue de Martignac, as people were beginning to realize that it had? That seemed sheer common sense, but it led to many misunderstandings – beginning in London, where on their arrival Schuman and Clappier were bombarded with questions about the powers of the High Authority, the fate of a particular coalfield, or how prices were to be fixed. Unable to answer, they asked me to help them, and I decided to join them on May 14. Meanwhile, they were busy with the Three-power Conference, whose opening was overshadowed by Bevin's resentment against Acheson and Schuman, whom he suspected of having hatched an anti-British plot. Acheson has good-humouredly described the difficult moment when, while he was lunching with Bevin at the Foreign Office on May 9, the French Ambassador René Massigli asked to be received. Bevin 'wondered what was up'. Acheson, pledged to secrecy, said nothing; but he very soon paid for his silence.*

Massigli had come to communicate the French Government's decision, which at that time had still not been officially announced. He had hardly had time to assess it himself, and I think he never assessed its true importance. Bevin made no immediate official response, but he told Massigli in private: 'I think that something has changed between our two countries.' Bevin was a politician of instinct and impulse, aggravated by the disease from which he was soon to die. It so happened that he was alone in London when the shock came: the Prime Minister, Clement Attlee, and his Chancellor of the Exchequer, Sir Stafford Cripps, were both on holiday at different places in France. In the confusion, the young Minister of State at the Foreign Office, Kenneth Younger, was inclined to recommend that Britain accept the French offer. Anthony Eden, then in opposition as Conservative spokesman on foreign affairs, made a speech strongly urging the Government to join, and so did Lord Layton on behalf of the Liberal Party. But already *The Times* recoiled at the word 'federation', and the *Daily Express* wrote: 'It would be the end of Britain's independence.' Attlee, now

* Dean Acheson, *Sketches from Life* (New York, 1959), pp. 38–41.

back in London, spoke in the House of Commons on May 11. He welcomed Franco-German reconciliation, but wished to make a full study of the economic implications. Any further decision was to await my own visit to London.

Acheson, for his part, had lost no time before making a positive declaration, in agreement with President Truman: 'We recognize with sympathy and approval the significant and far-reaching intent of the French initiative.'* Count Carlo Sforza, the Italian Foreign Minister, welcomed it warmly on behalf of his own Government. The three Benelux Governments wanted more technical details, but public opinion impelled them towards rapid acceptance. And in London the three Powers were at last able to agree about Germany. Charles Ronsac cabled:

> Everything is changed. Instead of a negative, cold-war conference, we are going to have a positive conference, an attempt to forge European unity.

The echoes of 'the Schuman bombshell' continued in the world press and caused a sensation in diplomatic circles. But everything now seemed to hinge on the attitude in London, where decisions about Europe had so long been determined. I knew that it would be a hard fight, and I hoped to win it; but in my heart I knew that the essential prize had already been won, irrevocably. Europe was on the move. Whatever the British decided would be their own affair.

As soon as I arrived in London, together with Hirsch and Uri, I as usual got in touch with my old friends. Not all of them were people in the public eye; but like those in New York whom I have already mentioned, many of them were businessmen, lawyers, and newspapermen – people whose work required and enabled them to get to the bottom of things, and whose success depended on their good sense. They included Lord Brand, Lord Kindersley, Arthur Salter, and the editor of *The Economist*, Geoffrey Crowther. Between them, they knew what I needed to know, and a talk with them was enough – afterwards, I could face my political contacts. Crowther was in favour of Britain's joining in the Schuman Plan, and was going to argue the case in his newspaper: but he made no secret of what a battle it would be. Britain had not been conquered or invaded: she felt no need to exorcize history. Her imperial role was not yet at an end, and her experience of general well-being had only just begun. Churchill declared: 'We must be with France.' But he added: 'We must be careful that it does not carry with

* *New York Times*, May 11, 1950.

it a lowering of British wages and standards of life and labour.'*
Attlee could say no less. Plowden, who was my official interlocutor,
asked me more: how would the High Authority be composed, how
would it intervene, what safeguards would there be to prevent its
acting arbitrarily, would it have the right to close down firms, how
would it ensure full employment?

It was clear that the British did not want to commit themselves to
principles, or to a negotiating method, without knowing in advance all
the practical consequences – which in our view were what we should
be negotiating about. Certainly, Hirsch, Uri, and I could give some
answers and collect some suggestions. But the British Government
would not feel at ease unless it received 'a piece of paper'. I promised
Plowden that we would write to him as soon as we returned to Paris,
which we did. To have to do so was useful: it made us clarify some of
our ideas, in particular about parliamentary supervision of the High
Authority. But it soon became clear that this approach was not enough:
we should not be able to avoid the basic issues that Attlee raised in the
House of Commons on June 13:

> It became perfectly clear in the course of informal discussions between M.
> Monnet, Chief Planning Officer of the French Government, and British
> officials, that while the French Government had not worked out how their
> proposal would be applied in practice, their views on the procedure for
> negotiations were definite.†

In this respect, indeed, we were more pragmatic than the British, since
we were proposing a basis and a method for future discussion. Plowden
had the idea of inviting the Permanent Under-Secretaries of the relevant
Ministries to dine with us. At the end of the evening, one of them
sighed:

'Blessed were our fathers, for they knew what to do in all circumstances.'

It was typically British nostalgia. When I met Schuman and Massigli
after the dinner, I said:

'The British will not find their future role by themselves. Only outside pressure will induce them to accept change.'

It was better to speak plainly. Sir Stafford Cripps asked me to come to
his office before leaving London.

'Would you go ahead with Germany and without us?' he inquired.

---

* Speech at Edinburgh, May 18, 1950, in Winston S. Churchill, *In the Balance,
Speeches 1949 and 1950*, ed. R. S. Churchill (London, Cassell, 1951), pp. 271–80.
† *Parliamentary Debates* (Hansard), Fifth Series, Vol. 476, House of Commons,
Session 1950, cols. 35–6.

'My dear friend,' I answered, 'you know how I have felt about Britain for more than thirty years: there is no question about that. I hope with all my heart that you will join in this from the start. But if you don't, we shall go ahead without you. And I'm sure that, because you are realists, you will adjust to the facts when you see that we have succeeded.'

At the same time, Schuman was talking at a luncheon given by the Anglo–French press.

'How many countries are needed to make the plan work?' someone asked.

'If necessary,' he said, 'we shall go ahead with only two.'

The British would have been left in no doubt about his determination if he had not added:

'As regards Great Britain, if there is not 100% participation, there can be association compatible with her structure and her economic ideas.'

This overture was unwise, for experience has taught me that it is not a good thing for the British to obtain special conditions and an exceptional position in their relationships with others, or even for them to cherish such hopes. On the other hand, they are at their best if you firmly offer to work with them on an equal footing. If you stick to your principles, there is every likelihood that the British will sooner or later adapt to the situation and become partners in the full sense of the word.

I realized, then, that haggling would lead nowhere, and that we must simply press ahead. So as soon as I had returned from London I went to see Chancellor Adenauer in Bonn. With me, to act as a link with Schuman, was Bernard Clappier, who was equally devoted to our plan and to his Minister. 'Clappier is solid gold,' Schuman used to say. He had long watched the young man's progress as a civil servant; and when Clappier had been his *directeur de cabinet* at the Finance Ministry for about six months, Schuman invited him to lunch at a small restaurant and took him fully into his confidence. From then on, Clappier was one of the rare people to whom Schuman divulged his innermost thoughts. I, too, found him not only discreet and efficient, but also a man of great intellectual honesty, and totally disinterested. We soon became friends. Arriving in Bonn, I went to see another friend, Jack McCloy, who this time was to be my opposite number in a delicate negotiation where his steady political vision and diplomatic skill were to prove very valuable. At that time he was US High Commissioner in Germany, and Chairman of the Council of the Allied High Commission, where his colleagues were André François-Poncet and the British General Sir Brian Robertson. This Council still had extensive supervisory powers, especially over the foreign relations of the new Federal Republic. It was an unusual situation: I had to ask McCloy's permission to start talks with Adenauer, and those talks presupposed that France and Germany would henceforth act as equals. The Council's decision, therefore, was more than a formality: it was its last act of diplomatic tutelage.

Nor was there anything automatic about that decision. I had to make a long exposé to persuade my hearers. True, McCloy was already in favour of our aims; but he had to take account of the reservations expressed by his British colleague. Robertson declared:

'Germany is under Allied tutelage. Her coal and steel are requisitioned. So the High Commission must be represented at the negotiations.'

That would have run counter to the spirit of the French proposal; and Armand Bérard, assistant to François-Poncet – who was away that day – answered in accordance with the instructions that Clappier had brought to Bonn:

'From the moment we authorize the Federal German Government to negotiate, it must do so as a sovereign power.'

On this, the discussion began to get bogged down; so I said:

'Given the scope of the commitments Germany will be undertaking in the Schuman Plan Treaty, it is vital that no one in future should be able to claim that they were not freely accepted.'

The members of the Council saw that we were making a political point, and they soon relented. I was authorized to begin talks with Adenauer.

That afternoon, we were shown into the Chancellor's office at the Schaumburg palace. I was accompanied by Clappier and Bérard, who this time came in his personal capacity. Adenauer had Blankenhorn with him. I already had some idea of how Adenauer looked, with his rigid figure and impassive face: but now I realized at once that I did not know him. The man before me was not self-assured, but anxious to know what I was going to say, and unable completely to conceal a degree of mistrust. Clearly, he could not believe that we were really proposing full equality; and his attitude was still marked by long years of hard negotiation and wounded pride. Our conversation lasted for an hour and a half. As it progressed, I saw the old man gradually relax and reveal the emotion that he had been holding back.

'We want to put Franco-German relations on an entirely new footing,' I said. 'We want to turn what divided France from Germany – that is, the industries of war – into a common asset, which will also be European. In this way, Europe will rediscover the leading role which she used to play in the world and which she lost because she was divided. Europe's unity will not put an end to her diversity – quite the reverse. That rich diversity will benefit civilization and influence the evolution of powers like America itself.

'The aim of the French proposal, therefore, is essentially political. It even has an aspect which might be called moral. Fundamentally, it has one simple objective, which our Government will try to attain without worrying, in this first phase, about any technical difficulties that may arise.'

I stressed this point because it now seemed to me essential to turn from the problems to the method, and to agree on a certain conception of our common task. My visit to London had convinced me that the French proposal, so clear and simple in its form and spirit, might be totally distorted by an approach that was too scrupulously or too insidiously technical. I saw a similar risk, though for different reasons, in dealing with the Germans, and especially with their industrialists and diplomats.

'The Schuman proposal,' I added, 'has had a profound effect on public opinion. People are no longer prepared to see their hopes disappointed. We must turn as soon as possible from words to deeds. The negotiations must produce a general Treaty setting up the High Authority: then the technicians can get to work. I know from experience that practical problems are never insoluble once they're approached from the starting-point of a great idea.'

Adenauer listened attentively and answered with warmth:

'I too am not a technician, nor entirely a politician either. For me, like you, this project is of the highest importance: it is a matter of morality. We have a moral and not just a technical responsibility to our people, and that makes it incumbent upon us to fulfil this great hope. The German people have enthusiastically welcomed the plan, and we shall not let ourselves be caught up in details. I have waited twenty-five years for a move like this. In accepting it, my Government and my country have no secret hankerings after hegemony. History since 1933 has taught us the folly of such ideas. Germany knows that its fate is bound up with that of Western Europe as a whole.'

We then discussed what should be done next. When Clappier announced that the French Government had decided to put me in charge of negotiating the Treaty, the Chancellor said that he would have to look for what he called 'a German M. Monnet'. He mentioned the names of several businessmen. None of them meant very much to me.

'It would be a mistake,' I said, 'to worry too much about expertise. What counts is a sense of the general interest. In this respect, M. Schuman fully intends to keep a close eye on matters himself; and, if you will allow me to say so, I should advise you to choose a delegate who is directly responsible to you. The last word is always political.'

When we had finished, Adenauer rose to his feet.

'Monsieur Monnet,' he said, 'I regard the implementation of the French proposal as my most important task. If I succeed, I believe that my life will not have been wasted.'

We took our leave. I can say of Adenauer what he said in his memoirs about me: 'After that, we were friends for life.'*

My visit to Bonn ended with an official communiqué announcing the agreement. Referring to it in the House of Commons shortly afterwards, the Prime Minister, Clement Attlee, declared:

> This fact naturally determined the course of the subsequent exchanges of views between the two Governments and made difficult the achievement of His Majesty's Government's desire to play an active part in the discussion of the French proposal, but without commitment to the acceptance of its principles in advance.†

There could be no clearer summary of what underlay the confused diplomatic exchanges which began when I returned to Paris and continued until June 3, 1950. It took ten days, eleven notes, and four thousand words to exhaust all the diplomats' debating points. The British and French White Papers on the subject make it perfectly clear that this was trench warfare over one particular issue: whether the method for negotiating the Schuman Plan was itself negotiable or not.‡ To put it another way, could anyone sit down at the negotiating table in order to question the very principle of establishing a High Authority? This was more than the purely formal question that it seemed. To treat it as a merely procedural point, and to compromise over it, would have completely undermined the methods and principles from which

---

* Adenauer, *op. cit.*, p. 323.
† *Parliamentary Debates, loc. cit.*, col. 36.
‡ *Anglo-French Discussions regarding French proposals for the Western European Coal, Iron and Steel Industries, May–June, 1950* (HMSO, Cmd. 7970), henceforth cited as 'Cmd. 7970'; *Documents relatifs au projet français de mise en commun des productions de charbon et d'acier et à l'institution d'une Haute Autorité nouvelle* (*La Documentation française*, No. 1.339, 13 juin 1950, Textes diplomatiques XCIV).

the unification of Europe was to derive, and still derives, its dynamic force. On this point I remained firm from beginning to end.

On May 25, 1950, the French Government sent a Memorandum to London proposing a draft communiqué which had already been accepted by Germany, and which was sent simultaneously to the Belgians, the Dutch, the Italians, and the Luxembourgers. It read:

> The Governments of ... are resolved to carry out a common action aiming at peace, European solidarity, and economic and social progress by pooling their coal and steel production and by the institution of a new High Authority whose decisions will bind ... and the countries which may adhere to it in the future.
>
> Negotiations on the basis of the principles and essential undertakings contained in the French proposals of 9th May last will open on a date which will be proposed almost at once by the French Government, with a view to working out the terms of a treaty which will be submitted for ratification to the respective Parliaments.*

This message crossed with a first British Note which rejected in advance the idea of an international conference, and suggested instead that France and Germany should open direct bilateral talks, in which the British wished to take part from the beginning, in the hope of obtaining a clearer picture of how the system would work in detail.† Next day came a further and more precise British Note:

> His Majesty's Government have received the French Government's Memorandum....
>
> It should ... be realized that if the French Government intend to insist on a commitment to pool resources and set up an authority with certain sovereign powers as a prior condition to joining in the talks, His Majesty's Government would reluctantly be unable to accept such a condition. His Majesty's Government would greatly regret such an outcome.

The British Note rejected the 'commitment' and suggested that those who wished should perhaps participate in the discussions 'on a different basis'. That, in fact, summed up the whole debate – and the whole British attitude too.‡

This fundamental divergence abated only after many years, as the European Community proved its success. But why then did we exchange so many notes before we accepted it? The reason, I think, is that I never despaired of convincing the British, while the diplomats on either side each hoped to win. There was something extraordinary about this negotiation by telegram. At one end, in Paris, were Clappier, Uri, Hirsch, and myself; at the other, Kenneth Younger, alone with the

* Cmd. 7970, pp. 7–8.   † *Ibid.*, pp. 6–7.   ‡ *Ibid.*, p. 8.

staff of the Foreign Office while Bevin was away ill. No messenger crossed the Channel; no ambassador or semi-official envoy played any part in the prolonged bout. On Whit Sunday, May 28, we drafted a long despatch to deal with Britain's anxieties: in effect, it was the 'piece of paper' they had been asking for. But I took care to stipulate that the aim was indeed a 'partial fusion of sovereignty'. As for the word 'commitment', I made it clear that this referred only to a certain method and a certain line of inquiry, not to once-and-for-all agreement to become subject to the High Authority.*

It was on this grammatical point, nevertheless, that the British fought the last round. On May 31, they answered:

> After the most careful study of the French Memorandum, it remains the view of His Majesty's Government that to subscribe to the terms of the draft communiqué ... would involve entering into an advance commitment to pool coal and steel resources and to set up an authority, with certain supreme powers, before there had been full opportunity of considering how these important and far-reaching principles would work in practice.†

There followed a proposed addition to the communiqué which would have given the British a special role in the negotiations. This was the result of an attempt at compromise suggested by Schuman and immediately followed up by Massigli and Younger. I was resolved not to consider it.

'Those countries that have already accepted, and Germany in particular,' I said, 'will obviously respond by asking for a special position themselves. That is the opposite of what we want, which is to eliminate all discrimination and put everyone on an equal footing.'

In some haste, Hirsch and I wrote a note to the French Government to make sure that there was no mistake:

> To accept British participation on these terms – i.e., in a special capacity – would be to resign oneself in advance to the replacement of the French proposal by something that would merely travesty it. Soon, if that happened, there would be no common rules and no independent High Authority, but only some kind of OEEC. In the end, a time would come when France would have to take the responsibility of breaking off the negotiations and incurring the blame.

We had to make an end of it. Next day, we proposed to all the Governments concerned a new draft communiqué. In the hope of being conciliatory, this no longer spoke of 'the principles and essential commitments' of the Proposal of May 9; but the establishment of the

---

* Cmd. 7970, pp. 9–11.   † *Ibid.*, p. 11.

High Authority had become an 'immediate objective'. We asked for an answer by 8.oo p.m. on June 2.* There was no more to be said. All that followed were attempts at self-justification aimed at public opinion. 'There is still a difference of approach between the two Governments,' wrote the British, once more analysing the texts.† Finally, it was agreed that each side would keep the other informed, 'to enable the French Government,' we wrote, 'to take into account to the greatest possible extent the point of view of the British Government, so that the latter may find it possible to join or to associate themselves with the common effort at the time when they judge it to be possible.'‡ On June 3, 1950, six Governments published the joint communiqué which opened the way to European unity.§ The British Embassy in Paris hailed the event in its own manner:

> There are precedents of international organizations set up with fanfares of trumpets which encounter only difficulties and disappointments when the time comes to put them into practice.

In his reference to 'trumpets', the British Ambassador Sir Oliver Harvey spoke more truly than he knew. Like the trumpets at Jericho, ours had shaken the majestic ramparts of British self-confidence. In the press, in the House of Commons, and inside the political parties, a passionate debate was about to begin.

That debate contained in embryo all the many successive attitudes that Britain was to take *vis-à-vis* the European problem during the twenty-five years leading up to the referendum of 1975, when the question was settled once and for all. It revealed in the pure state, free from later controversies about the economic costs of the Common Market, the way in which the British saw themselves and their national destiny. The greatest revelation was a document from the National Executive Committee of the British Labour Party, published by some mischance on June 13, 1950 – the very day when Attlee was reporting to the House of Commons on the failure of the preliminary talks. Its title was *European Unity*. It was the work of a group led by Hugh Dalton, Minister of Town and Country Planning, but since it was subtitled 'A statement by the National Executive Committee of the British Labour Party', it implicated Attlee and five of his Ministers, members of the National Executive themselves. It declared:

> The European peoples do not want a supra-national authority to impose agreements. They need an international machinery to carry out agree-

* *Ibid.*, p. 12.   † *Ibid.*, p. 13.   ‡ Cmd. 7970, p. 15.   § *Ibid.*, p. 14.

ments which are reached without compulsion.*

The rejection of common rules, and in particular majority rule in relations between peoples, was clearly affirmed; and so were two fundamental principles of British policy at that time. First, no change in the relations between Britain and continental Western Europe must diminish Britain's role as nerve-centre of the Commonwealth and banker to the Sterling Area. Secondly, there could be no delegation of power to a supranational authority which might interfere with Britain's Socialist experiment. The pamphlet also contained the following tell-tale words:

> In every respect except distance we in Britain are closer to our kinsmen in Australia and New Zealand on the far side of the world, than we are to Europe. We are closer in language and in origins, in social habits and institutions, in political outlook and in economic interest.†

Attlee tried to dissociate himself somewhat from his party's manifesto, but it had a profound psychological effect in Europe and the United States. Continental Socialists were openly dismayed, because British membership was a guarantee which they would willingly have made a precondition to accepting the Schuman Plan, had the Labour Party not adopted this wholly intransigent attitude. The French and Belgian Socialists declared themselves 'deeply shocked'. Finally, the British Conservatives led by Churchill and Eden gave up the notion of exploiting the subject against their political opponents, and the debate was cut short. Neither Party wanted any High Authority. I had confirmation of this when I saw the counter-proposals that Harold Macmillan made to the Council of Europe in Strasbourg on August 8. In these, the High Authority was to be no more than a committee of representatives from the coal and steel industries, with powers proportional to the production of their respective countries; there was also to be a Council of Europe Ministerial Committee with the right of veto. Macmillan sent me his proposal with a friendly covering-note. This gave me the opportunity to react against so profound a misunderstanding, which I knew would delay British membership, necessary as that was. In a long letter in English, which went the rounds in Strasbourg, I wrote:

* *European Unity: A statement by the National Executive Committee of the British Labour Party* (Transport House, London, May 1950), p. 6.
† *European Unity*, op. cit. p. 4.

The Schuman proposals are revolutionary or they are nothing. . . . Co-operation between nations, while essential, cannot alone meet our problem. What must be sought is a fusion of the interests of the European peoples and not merely another effort to maintain an equilibrium of those in-terests through additional machinery for negotiation. . . .

The Schuman proposals provide a basis for the building of a new Europe through the concrete achievement of a supranational regime within a limited but controlling area of economic effort. . . . The in-dispensable first principle of these proposals is the abnegation of sovereign-ty in a limited but decisive field and . . ., in my view, any plan which does not involve this indispensable first principle can make no useful contri-bution to the solution of the grave problems that face us.

Later, Macmillan came round to this point of view. In the meantime, I wanted him not to create too much confusion. I added:

I know the British people well enough to be confident that they will never oppose a progressive measure for the benefit of all Europe even though their special problems may for the moment prevent their joining fully in its achievement.

In reality, these 'special problems', real or imaginary, present or past – the problems of the Commonwealth, sterling, or the Socialist experiment – did not wholly explain the attitude of the British.

I had in fact sensed a deeper and less articulate worry on their part, of which I had confirmation in a letter that Félix Gaillard wrote me from Strasbourg while the Council of Europe was in session:

Members of the Labour Party are opposed to the Schuman Plan because they are defeatist about continental Europe, which they have deliberately written off in case of war – something they regard as inevitable and very near at hand. . . .

The Conservatives are more or less of the same opinion.

It is important to realize what the atmosphere was like in that summer of 1950. As we shall see, it was pervaded by fear – the cold war in the heart of Europe, the Korean War in Asia. And the same fear led to contrasting reactions: unity on the continent, isolationism in Britain. In some notes I made at the time, I wrote:

Britain has no confidence that France and the other countries of Europe have the ability or even the will effectively to resist a possible Russian invasion. . . .

Britain believes that in this conflict continental Europe will be occupied but that she herself, with America, will be able to resist and finally conquer. She therefore does not wish to let her domestic life or the development of her resources be influenced by any views other than her own, and certainly not by continental views.

If this, as I suspected, was really what the British felt in their heart of hearts, we had no hope of convincing them for a long time to come. Besides, we ourselves had already plunged into action.

Chapter 13

THE SCHUMAN PLAN CONFERENCE (1950)

I

Invention

The six countries that had accepted the Schuman Plan were to open their conference in Paris on June 20, 1950. The public expected great things of it, but some people approached it with disquiet. Not unnaturally, interest groups in the various countries felt particularly threatened: in their eyes, the plan was bound to work to the advantage of their neighbours, not themselves. It was our task to point out that these mutually contradictory fears cancelled each other out. Most alarmed of all were the steelmakers, whose corporate bodies, accustomed as they were to secret agreements, campaigned against this new High Authority, which would deal with problems in the light of day. Privately, however, they were less unequivocal. Hirsch, who knew them well, had not gone ahead without taking some soundings; and even before May 9 he had on his own initiative been in touch with one of the wise leading lights of the French steel industry, with whom he was on terms of trust.

'There's no choice,' he had been told: 'for us, it's either that or extinction.'

Obviously, we could not quote this remark, or the assurances which we had had in private from members of the French National Coal Board; we had to let the industrialists claim that we had taken decisions over their heads. The truth was that we were not prepared to negotiate with private interest groups about a venture of such great public importance. As it was, the Governments were bombarded with complaints, but public opinion gave them the will and the strength to resist.

The attitude of the trade unions, in particular, was impeccable. Although the CGT at once denounced the plan as 'infringing national sovereignty', Force Ouvrière, led by Léon Jouhaux, and the CFTC, under Gaston Teissier, approved it in principle. At its conference in Düsseldorf on May 23, the International Confederation of Free Trade Unions gave the plan its support and expressed its desire to take part. These positive reactions contrasted with the prudence of the Socialist political parties. In France, under the leadership of Guy Mollet, the gap between them and the unions was gradually narrowed; but in Germany it widened, owing to the Socialist leader Kurt Schumacher, whose hostility to Adenauer pushed him to extremes.

'The Germans,' he said, 'are in the process of accepting Occupation for another fifty years.'

He made much of the alarmist slogan of 'the four Ks' – *Kapitalismus, Klerikalismus, Konservatismus, Kartelle*. The Chancellor riposted just as vigorously:

'Anyone who sabotages or vilifies the Schuman Plan is a bad German.'

But a young Socialist deputy from Berlin was already looking to the future:

'We have long been calling for a true Europeanization of heavy industry,' he declared, 'and we warmly welcome something that brings us closer to that goal. We must do justice to the French proposal.'

The author of these words was beginning to make his name. It was Willy Brandt.

I followed closely the anxieties expressed by the old Belgian coal industry, the young Italian steel industry, and the ambitious Dutch planners. None of their particular problems seemed to me insoluble. On the contrary, I was certain that they would all be carried forward by the new European impetus; but I knew how hard it would be to convince them of that fact. The Netherlands Government, in particular, had written to stipulate that it could always withdraw from the negotiation. This went without saying, but the need to say it suggested that the Dutch would be difficult partners. All the agitation, however, made me optimistic. If so many misgivings had not prevented Governments from taking the first step, it was because that step was political, and because a large majority everywhere was in favour. To ensure that there was no misunderstanding and that the conference took the right course from the start, Adenauer told the German Bundestag on June 13:

Let me make a point of declaring in so many words and in full agreement, not only with the French Government but also with M. Jean

Monnet, that the importance of this project is above all political and not economic.

With this in mind, the Chancellor was still concerned about the choice of his own negotiator. He wrote several letters asking my advice, and he actually sent a first candidate to see me – a capable businessman, but no more. I said as much to Adenauer, who agreed. Then he told me:

'I've heard about a professor from the University of Frankfurt who has the qualities we need.'

It was Walter Hallstein. When I met him shortly afterwards, I took to him at once, and we trusted each other from the first. His cultivated mind and breadth of vision equipped him admirably to understand other people's problems. He was a man of action as well as a scholar, and a great European – as the future was to show. But less obvious in this very private man are his inner qualities, the loyalty and sincerity that struck me at our first meeting. He invests them in what he does rather than in his personal friendships, which are rare. Everyone respects his authority, and the care with which he maintains it. The proof of his ability lies in the success of what he has achieved. His modesty and kindness are less well known; but I have had continual proof of them from that day to this.

Hallstein was not a politician, but he had political vision. Adenauer was a leader and man of affairs, a strong man for whom the analysis of facts was secondary, because what mattered to him was the objective, and then the decision that was needed to attain it. He went straight to conclusions; and in 1950 his conclusion was the same as mine: the need to organize the West. How, by what means – that was not his main concern, but ours; and it was great good fortune that he placed his trust in Hallstein, who was as eager as we were to push ahead and transform the situation by means of the Schuman Plan. Agreement between France and Germany was a political necessity; but in this case necessity was greatly aided by the choice of men. From now on, we could move fast. On June 16, Adenauer wrote to me:

I entirely share your opinion that we should expedite the negotiations as rapidly as possible and, if we can, draw up the Treaty before the summer parliamentary recess. Only in that way can we be certain of making this great idea a reality.

The date of June 20 was the earliest that we could arrange for the opening of a conference that we hoped to conclude by August, in order to profit from the general psychological momentum. Public opinion was counting on the rapid success of a project whose political importance it had perceived from the start. The European press was on our side, and although nationalists and conservatives everywhere were hostile to the plan, it was easy for us to turn this to our advantage by arguing that we embodied the desire for change that our peoples shared. Yet at the same time we had to outpace the opposition, which was mustering powerful resources against the plan. That was why, like Adenauer and Schuman, I believed that the agreement setting up the High Authority must be very rapidly signed and ratified. Once that institution was in place, the breakthrough would have been made, and it would be time for the experts and the inevitable difficulties: the political step would have been taken.

Many people argued that this was a gamble, and one that we should lose. But I have never thought in terms of gambles. When anyone has settled on the objective to be attained, he must act without forming hypotheses about the risks of failure. Until you have tried, you can never tell whether a task is impossible or not. The method we had in mind then was right; and while I cannot claim that it would be the best in any circumstances, I can say that at the time I was convinced that progress towards a united Europe would be easier if we could exclude from the new Treaty the legal and technical formalities that normally burden such agreements. For the Schuman Plan, things did not work out that way; but in the end we made a virtue of our disappointment. We used the long, painstaking negotiations to draw up an entirely novel Treaty, in which future generations will no doubt look for models of how to pool resources and bring nations together. We should waste no time in regretting what never happened, but profit instead from the unexpected circumstances that fate put in our way.

The two weeks preceding the conference saw a remarkable development in people's ideas. To me, that was the proof that, in a creative political venture like the Schuman Plan, what really matters can be achieved at a stroke, even if many months are needed to turn it into a joint achievement. By June 12, we were able to submit to the French Interministerial Council a draft paper describing the role of the independent High Authority and the means of appeal against its decisions. Already there had emerged the notion of an arbiter, and of the Executive's being politically answerable to a parliamentary body. The idea of a motion of censure was quite explicit.

'Thus,' I told the Interministerial Council, 'we shall lay the concrete foundations of a Federation of Europe.'

The Council asked me to go ahead. A week later, this first draft had developed considerably; and by the time the Schuman Plan conference opened, I had on my desk a draft Treaty forty articles long containing in rough but recognizable form the basic structure for the organization of Europe. This text, which enlarged on the Schuman Declaration of May 9 and made it operational, was also the work of the same few people. Their contribution did not stop there: but, important as it was to be later, there is no doubt that this was an exceptionally creative phase. Such a phase in the history of ideas is always brief, and is often hard to distinguish from the later, practical phase which involves great changes for people and things. As we saw it – and as we had said in the Schuman Declaration itself – once the Treaty was signed, this second phase should be handled by the High Authority and the Governments, with the help of the arbiter. But this did not happen, for reasons that will soon emerge.

Monsieur Schuman opened the conference of the Six at 4.00 p.m. on June 20, 1950, in the Salon de l'Horloge at the French Foreign Office. The national delegations were large – larger than I could have wished, overloaded with experts: I had scarcely had time to meet the men who led them. Schuman declared:

> We believe that we cannot afford to fail, to give up without reaching a conclusion. But never before have States undertaken or even envisaged the joint delegation of part of their national sovereignty to an independent supranational body.

He recalled the procedure and method of work we had in mind:

> We shall have to think about the technical details that will be the subject of conventions to be concluded later, but without writing them into the Treaty now. We shall work as a team, and not as a negotiating conference with rigid, pedantic rules.

Announcing the names of the French delegation, which included Clappier, Alphand, Hirsch, Uri, and Desrousseaux, the Director of Mines and Steel, the French Foreign Office spokesman added that a certain number of people who would not take part in the talks would nevertheless be consulted. These would include the chairmen of the major Parliamentary Committees; the President of the Economic Council, Léon Jouhaux of Force Ouvrière; Georges Villiers, President of the French Employers' Organization; the leaders of the coal and steel industries; and the trade unionists Robert Bothereau, also of Force Ouvrière, and Gaston Teissier of the Catholic Workers' Confederation, the CFTC. Hervé Alphand was to maintain liaison between the conference and the British Government. The other national delegations were made up on similar lines. I quickly split them up into working groups, and kept with me only the leading figures. But, first of all, everyone had to be made to realize that this was not just another of those economic conferences in which they were professional and in some cases virtuoso performers. That, I knew, would be the hardest part of my task.

I set about it next day, tirelessly repeating the lesson, irrespective of how impatient my audience became. Experience has taught me that people who think they have understood it right away are no more likely to act accordingly than anyone else, because negotiation is second nature to them: it seems to be an end in itself.

'We are here,' I said, 'to undertake a common task – not to negotiate for our own national advantage, but to seek it in the advantage of all.'

The sixty delegates present were not to know that for more than ten months they would go on hearing me repeat this same lesson, which men trained to defend and advance purely national interests find one of the hardest to learn.

'Only if we eliminate from our debates any particularist feelings shall we reach a solution. In so far as we, gathered here, can change our methods, the attitude of all Europeans will likewise gradually change.'

I therefore asked that the word 'negotiations' should not be used to describe our meetings. Instead, for ourselves as for the public, they should be known as 'the Schuman Plan Conference'. It was on that same day, I think, that I first used the term 'European Community' to describe our objective.

For more than two hours I expounded the French draft, but without distributing the text, so as not to cramp the discussion. I intended to incorporate any important points made by the other delegations:

'All difficulties and all suggestions will be pooled, so that the draft, although originally French, will become a joint work.'

In fact, our working document, drawn up by Hirsch and Uri, was the only text of any substance. The other delegations had come more to ask questions than to make proposals. At this stage, it was normal that the initiative should come from us; but that, in my view, was not a mere matter of chance. I have never sat down to discuss anything without having a draft before me – and I care very little whether it be the first or the only text. It is at least our contribution. If the others accept it because it seems the best, or for any other reason, so much the better. To tell the truth, our suggestions have often been accepted in the absence of any competition. Generally, people come to the table empty-handed, out of either circumspection or sloth. In their hearts, they are pleased to find that a paper has been produced overnight. To produce it means staying up late.

In the course of what I said on June 21, I also went into a new aspect of the High Authority's independence. It should, I argued, have its own revenue, drawn from a levy on coal and steel production, and not depend on government subsidies to finance its administration and its operational work. Its moral and financial credit would make it the best-placed borrower in Europe. By making loans, it could encourage investments that served the general interest, but without wielding coercive power. Other ideas that emerged that day were the Consultative Committee and the name of the parliamentary body, the Common Assembly. Little by little, the whole structure was taking shape. To complete it, two important elements were still to come: the Council of Ministers, on which the small countries were to insist, and the Court of Justice, which we had so far only touched upon. At the same time, our idea of an arbiter and of a two-stage procedure were soon to disappear under pressure from the same small countries, which from the following day onward began to hedge the political plan with a thousand technical precautions.

That next day's meeting, on June 22, began the series of restricted sessions in which the heads of delegation, with one or two advisers, were to steer the conference and deal by themselves with the institutional problems. Here, everyone could speak freely, unchecked by his technical experts and unconstrained by official minutes. My colleagues from the other five countries were men of goodwill, picked from among their countries' most experienced negotiators. Of all of them, Hallstein was certainly the least well known – he had been seen only at a few UNESCO conferences. The others were habitués of international meetings where national representatives bargained with each other. The Belgian, Maximilien Suetens, was an affable and conciliatory senior official. Dirk Spierenburg was the living incarnation of Dutch stubbornness, and a very tough debater. Albert Wehrer, a skilful Luxembourg diplomat, knew very well the interests he had to defend. All three had had experience of a limited customs union, Benelux. The only political figure was Emilio Taviani, a young deputy from the Italian Christian Democrat Party. Except for Hallstein, I had not been consulted on the appointment of my colleagues. Over the months, I came to know them; but what mattered now was to bring them rapidly to look at the problem from the same point of view and tackle it as a common task – an approach that came less than naturally to officials trained to obey their Governments' instructions. I relied on the pressure of hard work, in the enclosed atmosphere of No 18 rue de Martignac, to create a team spirit, not only among the six of us, but also among the experts on the various committees, who were subject to the same régime.

I encouraged them to express their fears in the form of questions. Concerted or not, these all pointed in the same direction, showing the natural bias of men accustomed to negotiating agreements between States or between producers – more or less secret agreements restricting free competition. They found it hard to adjust to the idea that this regulatory role could be entrusted to the High Authority, acting openly and with sovereign power. One by one, the Benelux and Italian delegates asked whether all these important technical questions could not be settled by intergovernmental agreement before the High Authority was set up. This was the very opposite of the spirit and procedure of the Schuman Plan. But it was clear that most of the participants were not yet prepared to give up the guarantees they now enjoyed, even if the High Authority were hedged about with the most elaborate democratic safeguards. For my part, I would certainly not agree to its being tied down or limited in advance; but it was obvious that we should have to write into the Treaty some of the points that would otherwise have figured in the subsequent implementing conventions we had originally planned. My colleagues wanted these technical clauses settled beforehand: I should have liked to deal with them afterwards. In the event, they were to be drawn up simultaneously with the Treaty itself.

In the course of the discussion it became evident that Spierenburg would be the toughest negotiator, and that his Benelux colleagues were relying on him and on his stubborn temperament to limit the power of the new institutions. Two of the objections that he raised that day were to be among the most serious obstacles the conference faced; and while we were able in the end to eliminate one of them, reason and necessity persuaded me to incorporate the other in the Community's basic structure. The first question was: 'What relationship will there be between the Common Assembly of the Schuman Plan and the Consultative Assembly of the Council of Europe? Will it not involve needless reduplication?' I saw the trap, I guessed what was behind it, and I saw where it might lead; but I wasted no time on it then. More urgent and substantial was the second objection: 'The French plan as at present described will revolutionize many things. How will governments react? If we are to carry them with us, they must be given a role in the system and wider powers, even if they are to give up some of their sovereignty.' I took note of this argument, although at the time I was not quite clear as to what it might imply. Originally, I had decided against including any intergovernmental body in the Community's institutions, and I pointed this out. Hallstein, who had so far said little, strongly agreed.

The days that followed were taken up with useful debates about economic problems. Then came the time to bring out our working document, which was to act as a basis for consideration by Governments. A summary of the text was given to the press, and the delegates departed for their respective capitals, to report back and receive further instructions. I was actually hoping that they would do rather more, and tell their Governments all they had seen and heard during these few dramatic days in Paris when Europe had begun to take shape. There was no doubt that the delegates had already been coaxed beyond their official mandates and beyond their own personal positions: they had quickly begun to work together enthusiastically, as a team.

As the meeting broke up, I said:

> It's true that the venture we are engaged on raises very many questions. But most of them would arise in any case, and would find their own solutions, in disorder and to everyone's disadvantage. If we do nothing, fate will deal with our present difficulties, in spite of ourselves. The Schuman Plan has not created these problems: it has merely exposed them to the light of day.

I could say no more: I could only hope that my five colleagues were convinced, and that they in their turn would be convincing. We decided to meet again on July 3. In the text that was given to the press, I was careful to include the following stipulation:

> The withdrawal of a State which has committed itself to the Community should be possible only if all the others agree to such withdrawal and to the conditions in which it takes place. This rule in itself sums up the fundamental transformation which the French proposal seeks to achieve. Over and above coal and steel, it is laying the foundations of a European federation. In a federation, no State can secede by its own unilateral decision. Similarly, there can be no Community except among nations which commit themselves to it with no limit in time and no looking back.

After that, no one could any longer doubt our ambition and our determination.

II

Construction

When the conference resumed a week later, national positions had hardened, and I realized that the task would be difficult, because the men around me were now equipped with new instructions. Yet for the most part these instructions were defensive: they accepted the principle of having the High Authority. How independent it would be – that was the question, and that was where conflict might arise. Suetens fired the first shot.

'My Government,' he said, 'is not prepared to give the High Authority excessive powers. That would make it an object of fear; and besides, no such powers are needed to achieve our aims. These can be attained more simply, by prior agreement among the States concerned. Furthermore, we do not agree that the supervisory body should be a Parliament recruited from among the national Parliaments, since only they have the political responsibility. On the contrary, the supervisory body should be the Ministers, who effectively exercise power.'

Wehrer, the Luxembourger, seemed more concerned to establish a means of appeal based on the notion of a country's 'vital interests' – a notion open to all sorts of interpretations, as the future was to show. Spierenburg took up the same argument.

'Why,' he asked, 'should these means of appeal not consist of a majority decision – perhaps a two-thirds majority – taken by a committee of Ministers from the countries concerned? This would give the Governments back their proper role. They, after all, are responsible for their countries' general policies.'

Spierenburg always spoke with passion, in excellent French, and his words came in a rush at moments of tension, which he himself created.

'Besides,' he said, 'let me make myself quite clear: this is a point on which I see no possibility of compromise.'

Hirsch then asked him a question.

'In the system you propose,' he inquired, 'would the two-thirds vote of the committee of Ministers be to validate or to invalidate decisions by the High Authority?'

'To validate them,' Spierenburg answered. The Benelux countries were clearly thinking in terms of a blocking minority.

It was now Hallstein's turn to speak.

'The German Government,' he declared, 'reaffirms that the importance of the Schuman Plan is above all political. In this context, economic problems, substantial as they may be, are secondary: solutions to them will always be found. That is why the German delegation appeals urgently to all members of this conference to subordinate their economic interests to this great political goal. The war that has just broken out in Korea gives Europe yet another reason for uniting, for the peace of the world is under threat. This said, we do not underestimate the economic problems, and I shall return to them in greater detail later on. But the safeguards you seek will depend on the quality of the men who are chosen to run the Community, and on respect for the principles to be laid down in the preamble and articles of the Treaty – including in particular the principle of equality. The Assembly and the Court will see to that.'

This firm and dignified statement confirmed that France and Germany still saw eye to eye. That was the crux of the matter, and I was able to continue my work of persuasion. My first target, I remember, was Taviani. When he asked for the Italian steel industry to be put on a par with those of other countries before the High Authority started work, I answered:

'I agree that competitive conditions should be made equal. But let us get out of the habit of talking about the Italian steel industry, the French steel industry, and so on, because soon there will be only a European steel industry. That is the whole purpose of the Schuman Plan.'

There was a constant risk that this would be forgotten. Turning to Spierenburg, I reminded him that intergovernmental co-operation had never led anywhere:

'I realize,' I said, 'that there may be serious concern about the radical change which the French proposal represents. But remember that we are here to build a European Community. The supranational Authority is not merely the best means for solving economic problems: it is also the first move towards a federation.'

Our starting-points were different: there was no disguising the fact. But it seemed to me undesirable to make them public before we had worked to bring them together. Spierenburg disagreed. I realized that I had to play for time, and get my colleagues used to discussing problems of national sovereignty without flinching from the thought. It seemed better to fall back on a practical approach: so we set up five technical working groups. The group dealing with the economic problems of establishing a 'common market' for coal and steel set to work at once. Its task was the most extensive, and it made good progress. I have to say that Hirsch, who was its Chairman, found himself in his element. The methods of the French Planning Commissariat were readily adaptable both to European problems and to the Europeans involved. Overnight, the six countries' experts, industrialists, trade union leaders, and civil servants became integrated into a team. For reasons both practical and symbolic, it had its headquarters at No 18 rue de Martignac, which in its day had been chosen and arranged for the purpose of continual consultation. Now, the same process began again – a small group, using the experience of those best qualified and most directly concerned with the field it was exploring. That was how we had drawn up the Modernization Plan for France. But the exchange of experience had not been limited to the first, creative phase: it had continued into day-to-day action and become in a sense institutionalized. Now we had to work out a new method, transposing into the organization of Europe the principle underlying the Modernization Commissions, and running a complex entity with a small team very precisely aware of what existed and what was needed in every field. I knew from experience the working habits of many peoples here and there in the world: I had worked with men of several different nationalities. But I had seldom had contact with the Germans and the Dutch; and I had a lot to learn about their style of thinking and their legal approach. The problem, however, was not to adapt to their psychology or to ask them to think like me: it was to induce them to put the common interest above purely national concerns. For that, I had to rely on the intelligence and good-will that exist in every man worth his salt, and which reveal themselves as soon as one has established trust.

To establish trust is more straightforward than is often thought: straightforwardness, indeed, is the secret of how it is done. If some delegates had arrived full of suspicion, they gradually found that we had nothing to hide. We demonstrated to them, day after day, that all our intentions were set out in the Declaration of May 9, and that all one needed was to read that. Our working document, in fact, was a faithful reflection of the Schuman Declaration, and no arbitrary or dictatorial intent could be read into the notion of the High Authority. If Hallstein sometimes warned us against *dirigisme*, this was mainly to appease Ludwig Erhard, the German Minister of Economic Affairs, a dogmatic 'liberal' economist, who kept a close watch on our work. Hallstein had understood, as had several others, that we were not planning to substitute the High Authority for private enterprise, but seeking to make possible real competition throughout a vast market, from which producers, workers, and consumers would all gain. It was not unrealistic to hope that a proper balance of interests would often be reached automatically; but it would not have been wise to imagine that it would last without intervention by an independent High Authority. The problem was to limit such intervention to what was strictly necessary, to codify it, and to make it publicly accountable.

We tried to reassure everyone by showing that this open approach was itself the most effective safeguard. One of the essential features of the High Authority's work would be the information which it would have the right to collect and the duty to publish. In this way, in contrast to the traditional practice of industries jealous of their secrets, all concerned would be able to take their decisions in full awareness of the facts, and purchasers in particular would know how prices were arrived at. Publicity of this kind, together with the public debates of the Consultative Committee and the Common Assembly, as well as the verdicts of the Court, would make the new institutions as open to scrutiny as a house of glass. But too much light undoubtedly blinded men who had been brought up in the shadowy corridors of power. Their innermost security lay in their power to say No, which is the privilege of national sovereignty: No to change, No to the uncertainty of unprecedented innovations. I saw that it would take time to achieve among us the atmosphere that the Community ought to have, and I completely abandoned the idea of settling matters all at once. What counted was to prevent the constitutional debate getting bogged down, and to get to the heart of things before the summer recess.

I spent a whole week convincing Suetens and Spierenburg that, while Franco-German reconciliation was the means to the Schuman Plan's goal, which was peace, this would not be achieved at the expense of the smaller nations. Schuman, through other channels, persuaded the Governments that their negotiators in Paris were not in the desperate position of being the sole defenders of national independence. No one was threatened. Despite all my arguments, I think I failed to alter the basic convictions of my two colleagues; but it was enough if they came to see that my own views were both sincere and unequivocally straightforward. This greatly affected the way they behaved. To expect more of people is unwise: the art of persuasion has its limits. In this respect, I have often been credited with more power than I possess. Montagu Norman apparently said of me: 'He's not a banker – he's a conjuror', which suggests someone almost magically adroit. About banking, he certainly knew more than I did, and more than anyone;

but what he failed to understand was the power of simple ideas expressed plainly and unvaryingly, over and over again. That at least disarms suspicion, which is the main source of misunderstandings.

Mutual understanding is always difficult; but once suspicion has been eliminated, a major obstacle is removed. Between men of different nations and different upbringing this is the first step to take: but one must commit oneself wholeheartedly, or else it would be only a recipe or trick. I am not proposing recipes: I have none to offer. People act or fail to act, naturally, according to whether they are all of a piece or a medley of conflicting elements. I am sure to disappoint any-one who is looking for more elaborate lessons in the art of per-suasion. I will only add that, when I have failed, it was less often because people were naturally narrow-minded than because their minds were deliberately closed. This was the case with many senior civil servants, handicapped by loyalty to their national system. I first en-countered the phenomenon in London in 1916. I had wanted to see Grimpré, the Director of Merchant Marine in Paris, who was opposed to our plan for an Allied shipping pool.

'Come and see us,' I said; 'then I can explain.'

'I do not intend to come,' was the reply: 'I do not wish to be influenced.'

Thirty-five years later, I heard the Director of European Affairs at the French Foreign Office, François Seydoux, say very sadly:

'Don't try to persuade me: you know that my job is to defend national sovereignty.'

His frankness was that of a sensitive and intelligent man, but it nevertheless revealed the insurmountable barrier dividing my own wish to persuade from the conservative reflex of so many people set in their old patterns of thought.

There was more than one such person at the Schuman Plan con-ference; but they were all assembled to put into practice the Declaration of May 9 – that is, to provide for the delegation of sovereignty. This was no longer the subject of dispute: it was now the point of departure. In this situation, which the British had refused to share, the Benelux representatives felt ill at ease; but since we were all shut in together, there was nothing for it but to agree. It was obvious that those who were hesitant had the furthest distance to make up; so, as far as possible, I forestalled their anxieties, at the risk of sometimes disquieting Hallstein, who vigorously championed the supranational cause. On July 12, the Heads of Delegation met together once more.

'I have to admit,' I said, 'that there was a gap in our original draft, which Spierenburg and Suetens have suggested ways of filling. We can now distinguish two types of problem: those which the Treaty, by a collective decision of our national Parliaments, will expressly entrust to the High Authority; and those which spill over into the responsibility of Governments, and in which Governments should be empowered to intervene, provided that they act collectively. In such circumstances, well defined in advance, the High Authority and the Governments could hold joint meetings. We have just made a great step forward.'

We had: the Council of Ministers of the European Community had just been born.

But Spierenburg wanted to press home his advantage.

'The Ministers ought to be able to give the High Authority political directives,' he said.

As always, his tone was quick and sharp, very like his appearance. Hallstein's calm firmness was in marked contrast. In his quiet, pleasant voice, he broke in to stem Spierenburg's offensive:

'In the eyes of my Government,' he declared, 'the High Authority is the keystone of the European Community.'

The atmosphere was tense: one could not help feeling that a single word might halt the building of Europe. Everything had still to be decided, and the solid structure that exists today was then still dependent on the shifting lines of force that linked or divided six very different men. The fear of failure and the need for union were pulling in opposite directions. I had no doubt that anxiety to agree would prove the more powerful; but I know that nothing in this world can be taken for granted, even by the most strong-willed – and there is no doubt that at that time the smallest distraction, the slightest weakness, would permanently have changed the nature of the European Community. We had to halt the debate about principles and set before everyone a structure in which he would find his own ideas given practical shape. To inaugurate this new phase, which would be that of the lawyers, I had asked Schuman to come and sum up the conclusions of our work.

He slipped almost unnoticed into the room, to join the conference whose chairman he had been since the very first day, after which he had not reappeared. Sitting down at the head of the table, he apologized for being 'an intruder'. Then he quietly expressed his firm conviction that the High Authority must be independent.

'But independence has never meant irresponsibility,' he said; 'and in your work you have achieved a balance between national and

Community power which to my mind is a remarkable system of democratic safeguards. That system now exists: it no longer has to be invented.'

From that moment on, indeed, the system had acquired its definitive form: a supranational authority, a council of national Ministers, parliamentary and judicial control. But it took further meetings to prevent the definition of powers from limiting the High Authority's scope.

I was neither surprised nor displeased to see these obstacles accumulating: they proved that we were approaching the heart of the problem. The progress of change can be measured by the vehemence with which it is resisted; and what many people still did not realize was the ineluctable nature of the process in which they were now engaged. We were coming to a time when the complexity of the problems, the multiplicity of the suggestions made, and even the strength of the criticisms we faced, could only advance matters further – so long as we kept our objective in view. That objective remained so clear in my eyes that I was in no danger of being upset by arguments between the experts we set to work. I had asked Paul Reuter to come back to Paris, and he kept a committee of legal experts in session to sort out the points of agreement and turn them into a memorandum of understanding. This enabled us to consolidate what we had agreed on, without making it depend on other questions that were still undecided, as traditional negotiators might well have done. What we had already settled, as it appeared in a memorandum dated August 5, 1950, was the institutional structure of the future European Coal and Steel Community: the High Authority, the Common Assembly, the Special Council of Ministers, and the Court of Justice. The terminology itself was now fixed. In this way, by writing down in black and white what was beginning to be lost in verbal confusion, we astonished everyone with a coherent structure which discouraged quibbles. Not only had the High Authority emerged unscathed from the ordeal, but the very constraints which had sought to limit its independence only emphasized the federal nature of the institutional system which it headed. One last offensive soon petered out.

'We do not accept the expression "merger of sovereignty",' said the Belgian representative. ' "A certain delegation of sovereignty" would be enough.'

'That argument's over,' I said. ' "Merger" is the word.'

The method that had proved its worth on institutional questions gave fresh impetus to the economic debate which had so laboriously begun.

Hirsch and Uri drew up a balance-sheet of the progress so far made: it was considerable, and in their hands it emerged as an integrated whole. The 'common market' had become a well-defined concept, and the only questions remaining were the means and timetable whereby it was to be set up.

It was still less than two months since the opening of the conference, and already the essentials of the new structure had been worked out. But what struck me most forcibly was the rapid change in the attitude of my colleagues. Day after day I could see the cohesive effect of the Community idea, which was working on men's minds long before it assumed practical form. Although all the delegates retained their well-marked national characteristics, they were now working together on the same quest. So much had their viewpoints converged during the past few weeks that they now and then asked one of their number to speak on behalf of the whole group. These weeks, it was true, had been intensive, cooped up at No 18 rue de Martignac, which was ill-adapted for international conferences – it had no interpretation facilities – but which was very well suited to informal meetings and talks. I have already described the advantages of our tiny dining-room, reached by an awkward flight of stairs. There, we were sure of not being disturbed, and it was there that friendship grew up among the heads of delegation, who soon formed a united group, resolved to interpret their national instructions in ways that would assist the common effort. Material surroundings have an effect on people's attitudes. When people from other countries came to see me to find out how to produce a national plan, I often said to them: 'Above all, have a dining-room.' In the dining-room at No 18 rue de Martignac, many problems were very simply solved.

The delegates dispersed for the summer vacation carrying with them the memorandum which the French delegation had prepared. This, like a searchlight in the mist, revealed a structural whole where most people had hitherto seen only vague shapes. Yet we had avoided special pleading, and we had distorted nothing that had been said. Confusion might persist in men's minds, but there was order now in reality. It only had to be clearly described; and in this respect both Reuter and Uri knew their business. I was about to leave Paris when I heard about Macmillan's Strasbourg proposal, which I described in the previous chapter. On August 15, 1950, I wrote to Robert Schuman:

> Some telephone calls from Strasbourg have confirmed my belief that the utmost confusion reigns there, and that we risk seeing the Consultative Assembly pass a Resolution which will interfere with, and perhaps

endanger, the success of all our efforts. The British are waging a skilful campaign to sabotage our plan.

What disturbed me most was the uncertainty I observed in many European statesmen who were perplexed by these British moves. 'Can we afford to let slip this last chance of enlisting Great Britain?' they asked each other. One of them was the French Socialist leader, Guy Mollet, whom I found greatly unnerved. 'We are heading for a European schism,' he kept saying. In reality, he was thinking mainly of the split between the British Labour Party and his own SFIO, as well as of those within the SFIO itself. He had been on the alert since the end of July, when a foreign policy debate in the French National Assembly had revealed a hostile movement within his own party, led by Daniel Mayer and Paul Ramadier. I realized that the British phantom must be exorcized once and for all, and I set about it by giving the maximum publicity to my letter to Harold Macmillan. In Strasbourg, that debate came to an end. But our efforts were already now haunted by a grim apparition elsewhere.

Chapter 14

TWO TREATIES (1951)

I

Defence: a single army

Since May 9, 1950, we had been grappling with history, halting the drift of events by an act of will. By joining forces with Germany, by pledging ourselves to face the future together, and by pooling the industries that fed the military arsenals, we thought we had removed all possibility of armed conflict in Europe and defused the detonator of world war. But history was to have its revenge, and in its own fashion, unexpectedly. The first shock reached us only a few days after the opening of the Schuman Plan conference. George Ball has described it in his excellent book *The Discipline of Power*:

> On Sunday, June 25, 1950, I had gone to Monnet's thatched-roof country house sixty kilometers from Paris for a day of work in connection with the Schuman negotiations. Three or four Europeans from other delegations had assembled during the course of the afternoon, when someone brought the word that the North Korean Army had invaded South Korea. Monnet was, I recall, quick to see the implications. The Americans, he was sure, would not permit the Communists to get away with a naked aggression of this kind, since it could mean the beginning of the erosion of the lines drawn with such difficulty during the postwar years. Yet an American intervention would not only jeopardize the Schuman Plan, it would create serious problems for European unity. It might well stir up an atmosphere of panic in Europe while increasing American insistence on a larger role for Germany in the defense of the West.
>
> This last point was of special importance.*

It was indeed the most delicate point, and one which it had been agreed never to broach in the course of our talks. French diplomats had obstinately denied that it was real. Robert Schuman himself had even

* George W. Ball, *The Discipline of Power* (Boston, 1968), p. 49.

solemnly told the French National Assembly, during the ratification debate on the North Atlantic Treaty just one year earlier:

> Germany is unarmed and will remain unarmed. . . . It is unthinkable that she should be allowed to join the Atlantic Pact as a nation empowered to defend or help defend other nations.

With World War II only five years behind us, the mere mention of a German army was enough to horrify Europeans, including the vast majority of the German people themselves. The Soviets, clearly, would not tolerate the re-establishment of a German army, despite the fact that they had begun to build up in Eastern Germany a para-military force of so-called *Bereitschaften*, a potential threat which Adenauer had already denounced. Which side was more afraid of the other it was impossible to say, so thoroughly were people's minds conditioned by the cold war. It was precisely in order to eradicate this obsession and the climate of rivalry and mistrust in which it grew that I had proposed, in my April memorandum, to change the course of events by means of 'radical, real, immediate, and dramatic' action. That action had begun; it was succeeding; and all Germany's energies were bent towards peaceful and constructive ends. But if the West were to mobilize against a Communist challenge, those energies would certainly be enlisted into a war effort which America could not sustain alone.

Good fortune had given Germany a Chancellor profoundly committed to peace, a man who had suffered from his compatriots' military violence and who now declared:

'My country has lost blood enough: it does not want to rearm.'

This historic opportunity might now be missed, before the European Community had taken shape. True, the question of a German contribution to the defence of the West had been raised now and then by the leaders of the Alliance. Their argument ran as follows: because Germany is the main potential prize in the cold war, it is reasonable to ask her to defend herself. We argued the opposite: that Germany should cease to be a potential prize, and so no longer be discussed in military terms. Adenauer had long been looking for another way out – taking the bull by the horns and proposing a European army. In December 1949 he had declared:

> Even if the Allies asked for a German contribution to the defence of Europe, I should refuse to reconstitute the *Wehrmacht*.

But he had immediately added:

> The very most that I could imagine would be a German contingent in the

337

army of a European Federation, under European command.

At the time, given French opposition, his words were academic; then came the Schuman Plan, which made them irrelevant. The Korean War suddenly put them back in the centre of the debate.

It was not long, in fact, before my fears were confirmed. On July 22, John J. McCloy, US High Commissioner in Germany, declared that it was 'very difficult to deny the Germans the right and the means to defend their soil.'* It was a way of telling the United States Congress that America would not have to defend the European front alone, and of telling European statesmen that she would soon be unable to defend two fronts at a time. Adenauer did not see it that way.

'The fate of the world,' he told McCloy, 'will not be decided in Korea, but in the heart of Europe. I am convinced that Stalin has the same plan for Europe as for Korea. What is happening there is a dress-rehearsal for what is in store for us here.'

His anxiety was profound and genuine. In August, he resigned himself to asking permission to levy a police force of 150,000 men. Simultaneously, in Strasbourg, Winston Churchill proposed a European army under the control of a European Minister of Defence. The French and British Governments, for their part, did nothing. Once again, we were in an impasse.

Sheer necessity has several times involved me in military matters, for which I have neither aptitude nor inclination. In 1914, and again between 1938 and 1945, I saw our freedom and our conception of humanity threatened by primeval lust for power, and in both cases I saw the finest men and the bravest efforts thwarted by disunity. Aggression not only divides people into two camps: it also divides the efforts made in either camp, because fear encourages selfishness. In 1950, despite the bitter lessons of the past, self-protective reactions to the return of violence encouraged purely nationalist attitudes which set us back several years and threatened the constructive efforts that had barely begun. I could not allow this new crisis to develop unchecked; but for the time being I was uncertain what to do. I had never believed that we should tackle the problem of Europe via defence. Although this would no doubt be one task for the future federation, it seemed to me by no means the most powerful or compelling motive for unity. But if circumstances were to accelerate or reverse the course of events – well, then, that would be another matter.

* Royal Institute of International Affairs, *Survey of International Affairs 1949–50* (London, 1953), p. 159; *New York Times*, July 23, 1950.

In August 1950 the rapid Communist advance in Korea was becoming an emergency, and it was to be feared that any day the Americans might make hasty moves in the direction of German rearmament or a widening of the war in the East. I had at last gone on vacation, to our small house on the Ile de Ré where I spend part of every summer. I have no real taste for the seaside – I much prefer the mountains, where I feel fully alive; but I have never been able to persuade my whole family to share my enjoyment of long upland walks. Silvia had grown very attached to the island, with its white houses bathed in a light that has always attracted painters. She brings back images of a changing sky that live on in the pictures she paints at Houjarray through the rest of the year. The children go to the beach. I take walks in the country-side, through charming villages miraculously unspoiled; and I talk with the people of the island. That summer, I remember, two young soldiers on leave were discussing the world situation on the terrace of a café.

'With the Schuman Plan,' said one of them, 'one thing is certain: we shall no longer have to go to war.'

It was vital not to disappoint such hopes. Yet even on the Ile de Ré, peace seemed precarious. Fighting had continued there until the very end of World War II, and the concrete pill-boxes on the island seemed indestructible. Soon, perhaps, we should hear news that the German Army was to be revived. That summer, I found no relief in my favourite walks.

René Pleven was now Prime Minister of France: he had replaced Georges Bidault on July 11, 1950. He was a friend of mine; he was now in power; and the French Government still held the key to Europe. It was to Pleven in person that I had to express my anxiety: I knew that he would take it seriously. At the end of August, I wrote him a long letter:

My dear René,

I am writing to you from the peace and quiet of the Charente, where everything moves slowly. I am very much afraid that this is not the case with our political affairs. Events are moving rapidly, too rapidly – things are crystallizing, and without having taken deliberate decisions we are being drawn into a fatal situation. No new political strategy has been worked out, in fact, since the notions of 'cold war' and 'containment' came into being three years ago: we have been living with them ever since. When these ideas originally took shape, their aim was the maintenance of peace. But their practical application has led to a series of reactions to particular events, each occurring in isolation, each adding to those that went before, without any overall view of where we are heading. Now, we find ourselves confronted with the need to achieve a 'cold victory' over the enemy and to prepare for war.

I went on to express my doubts about the West's costly efforts to 'contain' by force the rise of Communism in South-East Asia. Then, returning to my constant preoccupation, I wrote:

> The critical position of the French Army in Indochina, and the cost of this war, which prevents France playing any part in the defence of Europe, make us increasingly dependent on our American allies, and may lead us into a war which we have not sought but which might well destroy us. Drift is no solution; nor is the tempting but absurd illusion of neutrality; nor is capitulation. New, powerful, and constructive ideas are needed to ensure the defence of Europe, the development of our society, and the re-establishment of peace in the East. The United States would be prepared to listen to France if she expressed such ideas in the form of a positive and practical plan.

Fundamentally, we were in the same psychological state as in the spring, facing the same vacuum that the Schuman Plan had filled. I went on:

> The drift towards the inevitable continues. The Schuman Plan, even before it took practical shape, proved that it was in line with the forces of change. Everything that tends to create a broader community of peoples . . . and to transform old-fashioned capitalism into a means of sharing among citizens the fruits of their collective effort . . . will be enthusiastically received.

Rarely in the course of my life have I so clearly seen the signs of change as during that mid-century year. As always, change had already affected events before it had affected our thinking. It had taken several years for the West to learn the lessons of the greatest civil war in history. In 1950, Europeans were beginning to look at their past with sufficient detachment and at their future with sufficient confidence to hanker after new forms of mutual relations. With the Schuman Plan, these hankerings had turned into reality: peace had seemed possible, and the cold war had receded. And yet now, here we were, facing it again from a different angle. Once again there was talk of an arms race, and above all of returning to the former aggressor the weapons he had seemed glad to lay down. I heard ordinary people asking: 'Are we going to have to go through it all over again?' It was very tempting to turn in on ourselves and look after our own selfish interest. That was why, in this time of danger, I spared no effort to convince our country's rulers that our only hope of salvation lay in continuing and accelerating the process of change we had begun.

At the beginning of September 1950, the Schuman Plan conference resumed work in Paris, and the various working groups made good progress along the lines laid down in our memorandum of August 10. During September, a further memorandum was drawn up – a fresh landmark, summarizing what we had already agreed. Experience showed that these papers were like successively closer photographs of the same landscape, with the details growing clearer each time. But each one was an overall view, a coherent whole, no part of which could be challenged without dislocating all the rest. There was a steady line of progression from the Schuman Declaration of May 9, 1950, through the first working document of June 20 and its successive new versions, right up to the draft Treaty, which the lawyers were now beginning to draw up, article by article. I knew, however, that serious problems remained – we were pushing them along in front of us, so to speak – and I now turned my attention to the critical provisions for dealing with mergers and cartels. Even so, my main concern at that time was not so much with Paris as with New York, where the Foreign Ministers were gathering on September 15, on the occasion of a United Nations meeting.

I went to see Schuman before he left for the United States.

'You won't prevent German rearmament coming up early in your talks,' I said. 'So the question of changing Germany's present status is bound to arise. We cannot afford to be caught unprepared. Nothing should be decided in New York outside the context of the Schuman Plan, which has inaugurated a new French policy towards Germany. For if the Germans get what the Schuman Plan offers them, but without the Plan itself, we shall run the risk of their turning their backs on us. If they were rearmed on a national basis, and thereby recovered their freedom of action, they would be able – and tempted – to strike a balance between East and West. They would either regard the Community as a thing of the past, or reduce it to a purely technical arrangement.'

'I'm certain of that,' Schuman answered. 'But the French Government's official line is simple: it maintains that there can be no question of rearming Germany at all. I prefer to believe that the question will not arise. Besides, Jules Moch is going with me, and you can be sure he'll see to that.'

Moch, a Socialist, was France's Minister of Defence. Like some others, he had never forgiven Germany for the crimes committed by the Nazis. He had the systematic mind of an expert, and he tended to be the prisoner of *a priori* theories which in the end had to bow to political reality. I knew that this time his negative attitude would prove untenable. So we had every interest in transforming the situation as a whole.

'France,' I said, 'now has a moral standing which enables her to speak and be listened to as never before, at least for many years past. We must keep the initiative; and to do so, we shall have to remove the controls and restraints on Germany faster than we had planned. But it's up to us to make the proposals.'

Forewarned though he was, Schuman had a shock when he reached New York on September 12. No sooner had he arrived than Dean Acheson told him and Bevin that America would send reinforcements to Europe only when the Europeans themselves had armed sixty divisions – 'ten of which might be German'. It was the first time that the spectre of German soldiers had been revived. Until then, we had thought that Germany's contribution to defence would be purely economic.

'There is no question of raising a *Wehrmacht*,' the Secretary of State added, 'but simply of assigning these units to NATO under the unified command of an American general, probably Eisenhower.'

Even in this form, even with time to adjust, this proposal was unacceptable to the French Foreign Minister, because it lifted a fundamental ban.

'Why on earth are you in such a hurry?' asked Schuman. 'Why not begin by forming your unified command and integrating into it what already exists? There would then be time to bring in the Germans later. Meanwhile, their contribution can remain economic.'

From this side of the Atlantic, indeed, one could not help wondering why the Americans were publicly raising a problem which could have continued to evolve for months without publicity. But the American military saw no point in concealing any longer what had become inevitable: Europe could not really be defended without the full participation of those most directly threatened. Schuman, who had been counting on support from his British colleague, saw Bevin fall in with Acheson's argument. At the Atlantic Council meeting on September 16, he found himself isolated. That same day, I wrote him a letter which I gave to Maurice Couve de Murville, who was leaving for New York:

There seem to be three possible courses to take. To do nothing – but is that possible? To treat Germany on a national basis – but that would stop the Schuman Plan and the building of Europe. Or to integrate

Germany into Europe by means of a broader Schuman Plan, taking the necessary decisions within a European framework.

I myself was determined to work for this third line of action, and if necessary to alter the balance of what was being so laboriously built in Paris. In any case, a Coal and Steel Community could no longer be set up in isolation, ignoring these new circumstances: we were forced to take short cuts. Now, the federation of Europe would have to become an immediate objective. The army, its weapons, and basic production would all have to be placed simultaneously under joint sovereignty. We could no longer wait, as we had once planned, for political Europe to be the culminating point of a gradual process, since its joint defence was inconceivable without a joint political authority from the start.

We had no choice: so I wasted no time thinking about which course I preferred – a pointless question when events are in command. Those events were on a world scale, and it was already impossible to say where the responsibility lay: some historians now think that the Korean War was the result of a misunderstanding. I was looking for a way out; but the French Government was heading into the cul-de-sac of a categorical refusal. One cannot blame statesmen for sticking to their principles; and if necessity had not been so pressing and time so short, I could have understood France's trying to discourage the Allies' plans. But the military machine was on the move, as overwhelming as the responsibilities which it had to bear – and which we had to understand. At a time when General Douglas MacArthur was recovering the initiative in Korea with the aid of fresh troops, the Pentagon was not prepared to strengthen its forces in Europe without a proportionate contribution from European units. The French Army was fighting a difficult war in Indochina; Britain's forces were scattered throughout the world. It was natural to ask Germany to make up the balance: it was equally natural for Europeans to be appalled at the prospect. Caught on the horns of this dilemma, the French Government was playing for time. It sent firm instructions to Schuman, and dismissed his suggestion of exploring a European solution to the problem of German rearmament. A further meeting was arranged for October 28. This gave us one month's respite.

It was little enough time to work out and secure acceptance for so fundamental a change, which touched on the core of national sovereignty and involved the oldest and most effective means yet found for conquering and defending it. Coal and steel had been supreme for only a century: the army, on the other hand, had immemorial traditions. Its symbols were the flag and the uniform: both were regarded as sacred. I knew that it would be asking a great deal of Europeans to try to persuade them to merge these relics of past glory, the souvenirs of victories won and defeats suffered in mutual confrontations. But I liked to think that men and women would be wise enough to realize that the time had come for change in this field too. At all events, the attempt had to be made. I set about it in private, while in public continuing my work as Planning Commissioner and Chairman of the Schuman Plan conference. From this vantage-point, I watched for signs of change on the part of the German delegation. Although Hallstein's attitude, like Adenauer's, remained loyal and constructive, a few symptoms of stiffening resistance caused me concern. The reluctance of the Ruhr industrialists, moreover, was obvious. Dr Robert Lehr, who was generally regarded as their spokesman, quite openly attacked the Schuman Plan. This became serious when we learned a few days later that he had been made Minister of the Interior in the Federal Government, in succession to Gustav Heinemann, who had resigned in protest against the prospect of German rearmament. There was no longer doubt: fresh winds were starting to blow Germany off course.

As time went by the French position weakened, and the Government began to come round to the idea of a compromise. My belief was that we should remain firm in opposing a German national army, however small and well-supervised. Adenauer himself had just repeated to McCloy:

'We are prepared to supply a contingent for a European army. But in saying this, I am giving you formal notice that I will not agree to remilitarize Germany by establishing a national military force.'

Adenauer's attitude was clear and categorical, and it did not change. He would not tolerate the spirit of Prussianism and its incarnation in a German High Command, always ready to dominate his country and lead it into fresh adventures. For France and for Europe this was extraordinarily fortunate. The Chancellor was a great patriot, and he had no hesitation in warning foreign statesmen against re-establishing an independent *Wehrmacht*. To help him in return, we could do no less than propose, in accordance with his own wishes, a European army which would include German military capacity, but without any ambition for conquest and deprived of any purely national initiative. There was no precedent or model for such a European army; and we had only a few days in which to invent it.

In the intervals of the Schuman Plan conference, the same team set to work. Hirsch, Uri, Clappier, and Reuter, joined later by Alphand, tackled the problems of defence with the same intellectual rigour and imaginative power that had helped them master the economy. Once again we kept out the technicians, who always make things more complicated, and always resist change. We had no more need of military experts than we had had of specialists to Europeanize steel. I was not concerned, in fact, with the technical forms that the European Army would take. When the time came, there would be no lack of suggestions and criticism, and ways would always be found to reconcile what was necessary with what would be effective. Essentially it was a political question, and it was at the political level that I had to make my efforts at persuasion. When people find themselves in a new situation, they adapt to it and they change. But so long as they hope that things may stay as they are or be the subject of compromise, they are unwilling to listen to new ideas. The best plans for joint defence would have no chance of being taken seriously by Governments unless I could prove that this was the only way of preventing France being totally isolated at the meeting on October 28. Pleven would be easy to convince; but I knew that in the position he occupied he would be subject to pressures from the other side, and would have to take them into account. If a powerful case were made out, however, he would be strong enough to face a fight and win. I kept in touch with him every day, and sent him notes on our talks in a series of confidential memoranda, in which can be traced the genesis of what came to be called 'the Pleven Plan'.

On October 14, 1950, I wrote:

> If we let events take their course, we shall sooner or later be forced to agree to a compromise solution (priority for France, but a German army made up of small units) which will simply be an illusion. By this indirect means, the German Army will be reborn. Our resistance will have proved futile. We shall lose face, and lose the political initiative. Perhaps the Schuman Plan will be carried out, but in Bonn rather than in Paris.
>
> Our attitude must be extremely firm, and we must resolutely oppose America's present policy. But we have no hope of succeeding unless we give our opposition a positive content inspired by an overall policy for Europe.
>
> I am anxious to bring the Schuman Plan conference to a successful conclusion, and I therefore think I must suggest to you what seems to me the only way out of the impasse, which is to make a positive contribution to solving the German problem.
>
> Before the Defence Committee meets in New York on October 28, the French Government should:
>
> (i) reiterate its implacable opposition, in the interests of Europe and

of peace, to the re-establishment of a German army;

(ii) propose that the solution of the German problem in its military aspect be sought in the same spirit and by the same methods as for coal and steel: the establishment of a European Army with a single High Command, a single organization, unified equipment and financing, and under the control of a single supranational authority (German units would gradually be integrated into this initial nucleus);

(iii) seek guarantees that this solution will not be adopted until after the Schuman Treaty is signed.

This last point was essential. At that time, it has to be remembered, the Schuman Plan conference was in its final phase. If public opinion was no longer following the day-to-day technical work, it was nevertheless awaiting with total confidence a spectacular final result. The hope and enthusiasm that had been aroused little more than four months earlier were still general, and the threats now overshadowing the world were reviving Europeans' instinctive urge towards unity. It would be unthinkable to disappoint these confident expectations; yet the risk of failure could not be ignored. Depending on how it was approached, German rearmament could either halt the European Community or give it fresh life. For the moment, I was concerned to prevent it slowing things down. Two days later, on October 16, I went to see Pleven and Schuman.

'The negative attitude France has taken to German rearmament,' I said, 'has had a double effect. It has made Germany doubt our willingness to co-operate, and it has led her to expect, to our disadvantage, greater favours from the United States. In our conference, I am now running into new difficulties, which under technical pretexts threaten to delay or even prevent a successful conclusion. Yesterday, Hallstein handed me this note, on the changes in the Occupation Statute which ought to follow on from the Schuman Plan.'

Schuman was astonished.

'I've not received any note,' he said.

'It was given to me on a personal basis,' I explained, 'and Hallstein didn't insist on it. But it looks to me like a portent.'

For Pleven and Schuman, this was a further problem to add to the serious worries they already faced. A few days earlier, France had learned of the fall of Cao-Bang, the first major defeat in the Indochina war. General Alphonse Juin had been sent out in a hurry. Clearly, the Government needed to restore its prestige in Europe.

'We must move fast,' said Pleven. 'Parliament resumes tomorrow. There will be a difficult debate on Indochina for the rest of this week.

We shall be attacked by the Right, by the Communists, and even by Mendès-France. On Tuesday, the German problem will be on the agenda; and Jules Moch will have to leave for the New York Conference on the evening of the 25th. We have scarcely a week to draw up our plan for Europe's joint defence.'

'Here it is,' I said: 'I've drafted a Government statement.'

That draft, I need hardly add, was followed by ten further versions. But like the first version of the Schuman Declaration it already contained the germ of what was to come:

> The French Government thought that the achievement of the Schuman Plan for coal and steel would accustom people to the idea of a European Community before the delicate question of joint defence had to be broached. But world events have given us no respite. Therefore, confident in the peaceful destiny of Europe and convinced of the need to give all European peoples a sense of collective security, *the French Government proposes to solve this problem by the same methods and in the same spirit. . . . It proposes the creation, for common defence, of a European Army under the authority of the political institutions of a united Europe.*

As the days went by, the underlying ideas became more precise:

> A European army cannot be established simply by juxtaposing national military units: this would merely mask a coalition of the old type. Tasks which are unavoidably common tasks require common institutions: the Army of a United Europe, made up of men from Europe's various nations, must as far as possible achieve a complete merger of the human and material elements it brings together under a single military and political authority.

The declaration that Pleven made to the French National Assembly on October 24, 1950, spoke for the first time in public of a European Defence Minister responsible to a Council of Ministers and a Common Assembly, with a common European budget. It also contained the following sentence, which was to give rise to one of the lengthiest and most dramatic pieces of exegesis in our time:

> The contingents supplied by the participating States would be incorporated in the European Army *at the level of the smallest possible unit.*

This vagueness concealed growing dissensions within the French Cabinet. Furthermore, Pleven had left out the phrase 'in the same uniform', whose symbolic significance had seemed to us crucial. And it was stipulated that those sections of our army that were stationed overseas would not be integrated. Already, that is, the French proposal

347

contained the contradictions and equivocations which in time were to eat it away. Still, at this price the Government secured its majority. There was tacit approval for a conference to which the Six would be invited together with Great Britain. Nothing was to be done before the Schuman Treaty was signed in a few weeks' time.

So far so good. The Schuman Plan was no longer in danger of being wrecked by the hasty establishment of a national German Army. But the Pleven Plan, as it was now called, could not be merely an expedient or a delaying tactic, as some people hoped, even in France, and as others feared, especially in the United States. I knew that the Plan would have to be fully implemented, and rapidly too. Unfortunately, I was unable to monitor its progress, because of the huge and cumbersome diplomatic machine that was at once superimposed. Before the New York conference resumed work, it waited for the French delegation to present its plan. The response was very cool. General Marshall ignored the French project, and pressed stubbornly ahead with his own plan to recruit German divisions under very strict controls and limitations – no tanks, no navy, no officers above the rank of Colonel, etc. To Adenauer, this American plan seemed even less acceptable than the French proposal, which he already thought implied a desire to discriminate, because it denied to Germany, alone of the participating nations, the right to have an army of her own.

'Do people want us to lose face?' he asked. 'The only information I have comes from the newspapers. It's humiliating to be left in the dark.'

It was urgently necessary, I realized, to remove these misunderstandings; and I invited McCloy, Pleven, and Schuman to spend a full day with me out at Houjarray. McCloy brought with him the contrasting views of Acheson and Adenauer, both of whom trusted him implicitly, as we did ourselves. I knew that he would believe what we had to tell him, and that he in turn would be believed, in both Bonn and Washington, so great was the respect he inspired by his independence and goodwill. We were able to convince him that our intentions were sincere, and he became the champion of the French plan wherever he went, more successfully in the State Department than in the Pentagon, and very effectively with Adenauer. But it was many months before everyone came to recognize that the Pleven Plan was simple and practical, that it had no ulterior motives, and that in fact it was the only possible choice. I was determined not to be dragged into the academic arguments in which the diplomats and military men were soon to be embroiled, so I concentrated on a few essential points. First, that no arrangement, however provisional, should be allowed to create even an embryonic German Army or High Command; secondly, that the first soldier placed under arms in Germany should be a European soldier; and thirdly that no decision should be taken before the Schuman Treaty was signed. I kept a close daily watch on these points, while at the same time speeding up the work of the Schuman Plan conference, which I hoped would soon be complete.

Everything always takes longer than one expects – which is why one must never set time-limits for succeeding. Admittedly, I have often talked in terms of deadlines, and on more than one occasion I have drawn up a timetable for action: because, to work toward the same end with the right priorities, everyone must know his objective and work at the right pace. But on many occasions, too, I have adapted my plans to changing circumstances. A distinction has to be drawn between what depends on one's own will – the objective, the method, and the successive stages – and what depends on circumstances – the opportunity to be seized and the time it takes to carry out one's plans. Any agreement on German rearmament would depend on the implementation of the Pleven Plan, and this in turn would depend on the signing of the Schuman Treaty. On that I was not prepared to compromise. As for dates, I was no longer master of events, however much I hurried things along. Serious differences divided France from her allies in New York, and even within the Schuman Plan conference she was facing resistance from Germany.

I shall not dwell on the long, overlong history of the plan for a European Defence Community (EDC), in which I was not a constant participant. Pleven, then several of his successors as Prime Minister, with Schuman and then Bidault as Foreign Minister, Moch and his successors at the Defence Ministry, and Alphand at every stage – they were responsible for EDC in France, where the greatest difficulties lay. If I played a part in the initial phase, it was to prevent French policy vacillating between rigid opposition and the temptation to compromise under pressure from the United States, backed by almost all her allies. Unrealistic opposition would have led to unacceptable compromises: this was the paradox confronting the French Government, and I helped Pleven to overcome it. At the same time, I had to convince the Americans that they were on the wrong track. Here, I had the support of McCloy and David Bruce, both of whom knew how to influence Acheson. But the greatest difficulty was with General Marshall. In the face of French resistance, he suspended the New York conference, and delayed sending Eisenhower to Europe as Commander-in-Chief. Fortunately for us all, his proposals for the controlled rearmament of Germany were rejected by German public opinion, which was torn between pacifism and resurgent nationalism on both Left and Right.

So matters stood during the autumn and winter of 1950. Committees of experts went on working simultaneously but separately on two alternative hypotheses – an 'Atlantic' German Army, or a European Army – while waiting for the political choice to be made. Verbal quibbles tried to conceal brute fact. Who would recruit the first German soldiers if there was not to be a national War Ministry? At what level would they be integrated into an Allied command? There was a long controversy over the meaning of the phrase 'the smallest possible unit': was it a regiment, a battalion in the French sense, or what the Americans called a 'combat team'? Once again, I saw how difficult it was to get people to talk about the same thing – but also how much simpler everything was if one tackled the difficulty itself, following the time-honoured maxim of Descartes and reducing it to its basic elements. After a great deal of time had been wasted, it was agreed that the European divisions could be made up of basic units, each comprising five to ten thousand men, irrespective of what they were called. I have to add that the same pointless controversy broke out later over the definition of the word 'division', and the Pleven Plan became bogged down in legal quibbles.

II

The economy: common rules

Adenauer's determination not to allow his country to be rearmed except on a footing of equality virtually ruled out any solution other than the European Army. He was prepared to see Germany's sovereignty not fully restored, but only if other European countries agreed that their own should be limited by belonging to the Community. This attitude was logical and worthy of respect; but it did not always make for easy solutions. It had to be realized that Adenauer had his difficulties too. On the German Left, Kurt Schumacher dismissed the Pleven Plan as meaning 'a French Foreign Legion', while on the Right Robert Lehr protested against Germany's becoming 'a nation of mercenaries'. In the last analysis, the Chancellor could explain to both sides that Germany's demand for equality would best be met by European integration; but in the Schuman Plan conference we had to expect that demand to become more insistent. Could we really conclude a Treaty based on equality while maintaining controls over Germany like those of the International Ruhr Authority, which became all the more irksome as they grew less relevant? Adenauer made an issue of the question, and he sent Ludwig Erhard, his Minister of Economic Affairs, to deal with it in Paris.

Like everyone else, I was familiar with Erhard's heavy bulk, and I knew his reputation for stubbornness. But when I met him, I found that he was subtle and highly intelligent – although we did not always agree. The prestige he enjoyed was well deserved: he had shown clear-sighted courage in successfully imposing and carrying out his ideas. He had no reason to doubt the superiority of the so-called 'liberal' economic policies that had worked so well in his own country. He was no nationalist, but the Schuman Plan had no place in his vision of an international economy based on pure free trade. Where we were proposing a code of good conduct, he scented the danger of *dirigisme*; where we were organizing European solidarity, he suspected protectionism.

'We don't understand,' he told me, 'why the Allies insist on decartelizing the industries of the Ruhr; and yet we know that you are making this a precondition of the plan. It's as if you were deliberately trying to put German industry in an inferior competitive position *vis-à-vis* its partners. And above all it's against the spirit of the Schuman Plan itself to go on legislating in our country as if there were no German Government.'

The problem was to break up excessive concentrations in the coal and steel industries of the Ruhr, where the *Konzerne* or trusts, which had underlain the military power of the former *Reich*, were quite naturally being rebuilt. The Americans had been the first to tackle the problem, many months earlier. Their economic and political philosophy would not tolerate either the practice or the apparatus of domination, at home or abroad. They insisted that the German coal-selling organization, the *Deutsche Kohl-Verkaufsgesellschaft* (DKV) should lose its monopoly, and that the steel industries should no longer own the coalmines. This apparently technical measure, which interested the labour unions very little and the general public not at all, in fact touched on the very foundations of Germany's strength in Europe. There could be no return to equilibrium on the continent if the Ruhr magnates were in a position to manage, to their own advantage, the main source of the coal that was needed both by their own industry and by that of their neighbours. Uncertainty would once more prevail in France if the Ruhr mine-owners once more began to control our steel production by regulating the supply of coke; and this could lead only to subordination or conflict. The cartels, acting in concert, had already made the most of this situation: but the public would find the results unacceptable. McCloy, more than anyone else, had become the advocate of de-cartelization. He had with him a young Harvard professor, Robert Bowie, who was said to be the leading expert on US anti-trust legislation, which the Americans applied as rigorously as morality itself.

Talks in Bonn on the subject dragged out, because the German industrialists believed that time was on their side. Meanwhile, in Paris, the conclusion of the Treaty depended on a general agreement on anti-trust rules, which we had to draw up in accordance with the Schuman Declaration of May 9.

I sent Hirsch to see Adenauer. The Chancellor listened to the message I had sent him.

'Tell Monsieur Monnet,' he answered simply, 'that this problem is now solved.'

In his mind, I am sure that it was. In reality, we still had to wait.

For three months now the Treaty had been lying on my desk – one hundred Articles, but two of them subject to reservations that were holding everything up. The text was essentially the work of Uri and an eminent French jurist, Maurice Lagrange. Good fortune had been with us once again, when at the beginning of the autumn I had asked Alexandre Parodi to suggest a member of the *Conseil d'Etat* who could draft an agreement rigorous enough to last fifty years and serve as a model for future European treaties. His choice had fallen on this modest and austere litigation counsellor, who found himself abruptly transferred from his legal labyrinth to the hubbub of No 18 rue de Martignac. He was a tall, upright man with a pale, bony face, one of those eminent but anonymous men of law who for centuries have quietly held France together. He came into my office, and I said to him:

'Monsieur Lagrange, you are going to draw up the Treaty.'

'Monsieur le Président,' he replied calmly, 'I don't know what it's about, but I shall do my very best.'

With that, he set to work. His contribution was invaluable. Afterwards, as Advocate-General at the Community's Court of Justice, he began building up that corpus of European law which today is applied by the courts of all the member States.

On March 14, 1951, the Allied decartelization plan finally secured Adenauer's agreement, and Hallstein at once accepted the two Treaty Articles that were still in dispute. They had been drafted by Robert

17. President Kennedy receiving Jean Monnet, the French statesman and architect of the Common Market, at the White House, 1962
(© Keystone)

18. Dwight D. Eisenhower, Mamie, David, Monnet at Houjarray, 1962 *(France-Soir)*

19. Monnet and George Ball, Freedom Award of 1962 (United Press International)

20. Monnet and John Foster Dulles

21. Robert Schuman, Franz Etzel, Etienne Hirsch, and Jean Monnet in Luxembourg, May 9, 1963 (Photo by Pol Aschman)

22. Monnet and Lyndon B. Johnson, signed photo, 1963

23. Monnet and David Bruce

24. Monnet and Paul-Henri Spaak

25. Monnet and Willy Brandt in Bonn, 1969 (Press & Information Service, Bonn)

26. Portrait by Karsh (© Karsh, Ottawa)

27. Monnet and James Reston, signed photo, 1975 (Photo by Sally Reston)

28. Monnet and Henry Kissinger, the Grenville Clark Prize, 1975

29. Monnet in front of his home in Houjarray (Photo by Henri Cartier-Bresson, Magnum)

30. Recent portrait of Monnet

Bowie, with meticulous care. For Europe, they were a fundamental innovation: the extensive anti-trust legislation now applied by the European Community essentially derives from those few lines in the Schuman Treaty. I have no regrets about having fought for them for four months at a stretch. Bowie, having completed his task in Europe, returned to the United States, where his reputation steadily grew; later, he became an influential White House adviser on European affairs. Finally, on March 19, 1951, the Treaty establishing the European Coal and Steel Community (ECSC) was initialled in Paris. It only remained for Ministers from the six countries to reach agreement on a few delicate words still left blank, and sign the master copy of the Treaty.

The words left blank concerned a political problem – the relative weight of the member countries in the future Community's institutions. For more than a year, the representatives of Luxembourg in the Schuman Plan conference had been debating on an equal footing with those of Italy, whose population was a hundred times as great, while the Dutch delegates had argued against those of France and Germany, whose combined steel production was twenty times that of the Netherlands. This was the natural result of the unanimity rule which governs international relations when there is no Community structure. The great difficulty, we knew, would be to induce six countries of very different size to abandon the unanimity rule in favour of a new system in which, to everyone's advantage, the idea of the common interest would replace that of the national interest – or rather, the national interests of six separate countries.

It was too much to ask most people to imagine something that had never yet existed, and to take it on trust. The right to say No was the large countries' guarantee in their dealings with each other, and the smaller countries' safeguard against the large. The signature of the Schuman Treaty would be their last chance fully to exercise that negative right. Afterwards, they would enter an unknown world where the veto would be the exception and the rule of the majority would be law. But what majority? Four of the six countries – Italy and the three Benelux countries – accounted for only a quarter of the Community's coal and steel production. It would not have been reasonable for them to be able to hold back France and Germany – which was what would happen if every country enjoyed one vote. That is why we proposed a system of weighted voting, to ensure that no decision could be imposed either by the combined power of France and Germany or by that of the other four. For the Common Assembly, we suggested that each of the three large countries should have eighteen seats, with a similar number for Benelux as a whole.

The Ministerial conference was due to meet on April 12, 1951. A week earlier, I went to Bonn to make sure that the positions of France and Germany would be essentially the same, and that they would resist the offensive that the Benelux countries seemed likely to mount. I knew that the Germans planned to propose that each country's weight in the institutions be proportional to its coal and steel production. This criterion, which gave the Germans too great an advantage, would involve discrimination in reverse, which was certainly not the intention of the Schuman Declaration of May 9, 1950. It was sure to be rejected by all Germany's partners, and I believed that Adenauer would not want to fight on those grounds. When he received me in Bonn on April 4, 1951, I began by saying:

'I have been authorized to propose to you that relations between France and Germany in the European Community be based on the principle of equality in the Council, the Assembly, and all existing or future European institutions, whether France be a member on her own or with the French Union of overseas dependencies, and whether Germany be the Federal Republic or a future reunified State. Let me add that this is how I have always envisaged the offer of union which was the starting-point of the present Treaty; and I think I am right in saying that this is how you envisaged it from the moment we first met. The spirit of discrimination has been the cause of the world's greatest ills, and the Community is an attempt to overcome it.'

Adenauer answered:

'You know how much I am attached to equality of rights for my country in the future, and how much I deplore the attempts at domination in which it has been involved in the past. I am happy to pledge my full support for your proposal. I cannot conceive of a Community based on anything but complete equality. This being so, I hereby withdraw any suggestion of an economic weighting system that may have been made by our representatives.'

This highly important political agreement had the virtue of being clear and simple. It had needed courage for the French Government to propose it, at a time when German rearmament threatened to transform the balance of power in the West, and when many people in the Federal Republic had not given up hope of reunification with the East. I did not speculate about who would benefit most from it: all I knew was that equality was the psychological prerequisite for peace in Europe. The rule of equality had the advantage of being automatic: it could not lend itself to calculation, bargaining, or conflicting interpretations. It obviated all temptation to play with the balance of power within the Community institutions, since it had an ethical basis that ruled out such manoeuvres. And its immediate advantage was that it gave the Ministerial conference every chance of success.

The signing of the Schuman Treaty gave Adenauer his first opportunity for an official trip abroad. It was also the first visit to Paris made by a German Government since World War II. For fear of hostile demonstrations, exceptional security measures were laid on. No Minister came to meet the Chancellor at the airport: I went to welcome him instead, with some of my colleagues. Our small procession of cars drove back to Paris at headlong speed: that day, there was more danger of an accident than of an attack. The most violent opposition came from the Communists, who had been against any form of West European organization ever since the USSR had rejected the Marshall Plan. Their campaign against the Schuman and Pleven Plans coincided with those of conservative groups, who were opposed to the slightest change in the country's economic structure or its arrangements for defence. From now on, it was easy to see, Right-wing and Left-wing nationalism would tacitly join forces to sabotage the European Treaties – if they were given the time. For many people, Germany still seemed the immediate danger, and it was easy for them to cast doubt on her conversion to democratic ways. Even those who were immune from this fear could not ignore the severe warnings issued by the Soviets every time the Federal Republic recovered a little more sovereignty. The prospect of war seemed to loom at the end of this escalation of words and, quite naturally, neutralism began to gain ground in France. The result was that all those who, for various reasons, wanted Germany to remain subordinate regarded Adenauer as a powerful adversary. That was why the Government was by no means anxious to give him a State reception.

The Chancellor was not a man to stand on ceremony. At the same time, however, he greatly valued the quiet tokens of appreciation he received from friends and strangers in Paris. He took the long view, and while he wanted to hasten his country's recovery, he knew that it must be done gradually, step by step. For him, the signing of the Schuman Treaty was the point of departure on a political course which he had deliberately chosen and which he never sought to abandon – however great the temptation to take short cuts to total independence and purely national power, and however powerful the external threats and internal pressures. He too had to confront the conservatives of Left and Right, the military traditionalists, and the growing attractions of neutrality, which he knew to be false.

In the course of our conversations, I found that he shared my anxiety about the psychological effects of the new cold war, which was dividing public opinion as Europe seemed to be turning into a pawn in the Soviet-American power struggle. He was more alarmed than I was by the violence of Moscow's repeated diplomatic notes. They threatened, he thought, to disconcert many French and German politicians, and above all many diplomats from either country who might be nostalgic for an alliance with the East. Adenauer therefore reacted very sharply to the Soviet notes, and demanded firmer support from the United States. For my part, I advised him not to dwell on these polemics, but to break out of the vicious circle by affirming our determination to go our own way.

'I know what responsibilities you bear,' I told both Adenauer and Pleven. 'But we shall be submerged if we stay on the defensive. Our position ought not to be a reaction to American demands or an attitude of fear *vis-à-vis* Moscow, but a constructive policy, one which might have been adopted in any case, without reference to the Americans or the Russians: that is, the construction of Europe.'

On many occasions in my life, I have had to say much the same thing. It can be summed up in a sentence: 'We must succeed in what we are doing, not base our actions on what other people think of us or what they would like us to do.' To my mind, there is nothing selfish in this: quite the reverse. The best contribution one can make to civilization is to allow men to develop their potential within communities freely chosen and built. But, to achieve this, one must concentrate on the objective and not expect anything of others, except that they may rally round when they see that one's determination is firm as a rock. With the Coal and Steel Community, this was to be put to the test.

The Treaty was signed on April 18, 1951, in the Salon de l'Horloge at the Quai d'Orsay, where the Schuman Declaration had been made almost a year before. One of my trusted colleagues on the French Planning Commissariat, André Lamy, a man of great tenacity and enterprise, had prepared a surprise for us. He handed to the signatories a copy of the Treaty which he had had printed by the French Stationery Office on Dutch vellum in German ink; it was bound in Belgian parchment with Italian silk ribbons and Luxembourg glue.

The text of the Treaty deserved so fine a setting: it was beautifully written, in a strict and limpid style which has inspired the constituent documents of the developing Community for more than twenty-five years. These sentences from the Preamble, which in the name of three Sovereigns and three Presidents took up where the Schuman Declaration left off, will long retain their significance for the peoples of Europe:

> CONSIDERING that world peace can be safeguarded only by creative efforts commensurate with the dangers that threaten it,
> CONVINCED that the contribution which an organized and vital Europe can make to civilization is indispensable to the maintenance of peaceful relations,
> RECOGNIZING that Europe can be built only through practical achievements which first create *de facto* solidarity, and through the establishment of common bases for economic development,
> ANXIOUS to help, by expanding their basic production, to raise the standard of living and further the works of peace,
> RESOLVED to substitute for age-old rivalries the merging of their essential interests; to create, by establishing an economic community, the basis for a broader and deeper community among peoples long divided by bloody conflicts; and to lay the foundations for institutions which will give direction to a destiny henceforward shared,
> HAVE DECIDED to create a European Coal and Steel Community.

They had decided, but the six Parliaments had yet to ratify the Treaty. We were to need more patience still.

The conference on the European Army had been at work in Paris since February 1951. Britain had not joined it, and the Netherlands were hesitant. Curiously enough, the military men reached agreement fairly easily on the complex organization of an integrated command. Their profession equipped them to solve the supply and logistic problems raised by the Pleven Plan. But the politicians continually confused matters by disputes about the level of integration – not the level which would be most effective, but that which public opinion would accept. If it was proposed to integrate small national divisions in large European divisons, the French objected on account of the word 'division'. I could understand why people thought it dangerous to make the basic national units large enough to be almost autonomous: in this case, if circumstances changed, a Germany Army could quickly be revived. But the small units that were acceptable to France threatened to lack the necessary cohesion. In reality, when the will was there, agreement was reached on an effective unit – a small division or large combat team, depending on which terminology was used. I had long urged Alphand to accept this compromise. At the end of July he did so, and put an end to the stalemate that had bedevilled the conference for four months.

By then, to tell the truth, many things had changed. If the French delegation had been able to become more flexible, it was because the June elections had shifted the political centre of gravity: the Socialists no longer had a place in the Government, and Jules Moch's stubborn resistance was removed. The new Assembly would no doubt throw up new and serious difficulties, since both the Gaullists and the Communists had increased their strength; but Pleven, once more Prime Minister after the four-month premiership of Henri Queuille, now had a brief moment of respite in which to further his Plan. Another obstacle, too, was now removed: United States policy *vis-à-vis* the European Defence Community had undergone a total transformation. How this happened, at a time when it was least expected, is explained by a luncheon I had in Paris with Eisenhower at the end of June.

The Commander-in-Chief of NATO forces obviously had a prime interest in seeing Germany contribute as rapidly as possible to the defence of Europe; and with the Pleven Plan negotiations going so slowly, he reacted like everyone else in the Pentagon: for him, the quickest solution was the best. But now he had settled in Europe, in Paris; and he realized very well that things were not so simple as they seemed in Washington. He had a number of contacts, and confided in such well-informed people as Bruce and McCloy, who were ardent supporters of European integration. Their reasoning was the same as mine: we were all concerned for the maintenance of peace. And there was not, as knowing people often claimed, an American way of preserving peace, a German way, or a French way. Any speculation about the supposed ulterior motives of those who were working for the same cause in Europe seemed to me beside the point. On the other hand, I could see why those responsible for the defence of the West should continue to study all hypotheses so long as the fate of the European Army hung in the balance. By the beginning of the summer, the Americans were ready to make substantial concessions to Germany's demands, which were legitimate as a bid for equal rights, but unacceptable to European public opinion. It was at that time, by arrangement with McCloy and Bruce, that I had a long talk with Eisenhower and some of his colleagues at the Hotel Waldorf-Astoria where they were staying in Paris.

Eisenhower's Chief of Staff, General Alfred Gruenther, was also with us; and so, if I remember rightly, was Averell Harriman. Over luncheon, I argued that Europe would become responsible and strong only if it were united.

'Without unity,' I said, 'everyone will go on seeking power for himself – and Germany will be tempted to seek it in an agreement with the East. Even at best, that would mean neutrality, which would be a blow to all Europe's morale. The strength of the West does not depend on how many divisions it has, but on its unity and common will. To rush into raising a few German divisions on a national basis, at the cost of reviving enmity between our peoples, would be catastrophic for the very security of Europe that such a step would be intended to ensure. If, on the other hand, you give France, Germany, and their neighbours common resources to exploit and defend, then Europe will recover the will to resist.'

This explanation of the Community greatly interested Eisenhower, and his outgoing temperament made him see its constructive side.

'To sum it up,' he said, 'what you're proposing is that the French and the Germans should wear the same uniform. That's more a human problem than a military one.'

'You're right,' I said: 'it's in that order that problems come up in Europe. What we have to do first of all is make people aware that they're facing the future together.'

I felt that Gruenther was growing impatient with the turn the conversation had taken.

'We can go on talking in general terms,' he said; 'but for us the real question is whether we're going to have divisions of ten thousand men or fifteen thousand. . . .'

Eisenhower broke in:

'You're a typical technician: you only see the part you're interested in – you don't look at the problem as a whole. The strength of the divisions is one aspect of things, but the real problem's a human one. What Monnet's proposing is to organize relations between people, and I'm all for it.'

Eisenhower's political sense overrode his military instincts when it came to defending the peace; and no doubt because people sensed that in him, his prestige at home went on growing.

If 'Ike' said something, that was it. And a few days after our talk he made an important speech in London, in the presence of Winston Churchill, then still Leader of the Opposition. In it, he committed himself unequivocally to supporting European unity. I was glad to find in his words some echoes of what we had said:

> Europe cannot attain the towering material stature possible to its peoples' skills and spirit so long as it is divided by patchwork territorial fences.

They foster localized instead of common interest. They pyramid every cost with middlemen, tariffs, taxes, and overheads. Barred, absolutely, are the efficient division of labor and resources and the easy flow of trade. In the political fields, these barriers promote mistrust and suspicion. They serve vested interests at the expense of peoples and prevent truly concerted action for Europe's own and obvious good. . . .

True security never rests upon the shoulders of men denied a decent present and the hope of a better future.

But with unity achieved, Europe could build adequate security and, at the same time, continue the march of human betterment that has characterized Western civilization. . . . The establishment of a workable European federation would go far to create confidence among people everywhere that Europe was doing its full and vital share. . . .*

This speech made a stir, and Eisenhower at once went into action, using all his influence on the Pentagon and the Department of State. As soon as Adenauer no longer had to choose between two negotiations, one with the Americans and the other with the Europeans, things moved fast. All he asked was that his country be given security and equality as soon as possible. If the European Community gave him guarantees as great as those offered by the Pentagon, and above all if Acheson, Schuman, and McCloy were all now in agreement, he obviously preferred the European solution. Without further ado, he appointed one of his close associates, Theodor Blank, to head the German delegation at the Paris EDC conference. Blank was a man of energy and conviction. He had to make sure that there was no discrimination against German troops in the European Army, and at the same time that it put an end to the constraints of the occupation régime. Alphand, for his part, was under instructions to ensure that the first German recruited should be a European soldier under European command. Everyone had an interest in settling matters quickly; but, as always, even when the way has been cleared, the machine moves forward only with difficulty if it has been overloaded with technical problems. It took almost a whole year more, and at least five major international conferences, in Washington, Ottawa, Rome, Lisbon, and Paris, to agree on a text which simply put into practice the principles of the Pleven Plan which had been accepted in the summer of 1951.

And yet those who drafted the Treaty had not had to invent very

* Dwight D. Eisenhower, Speech at the English-Speaking Union, London, July 3, 1951, in Department of State *Bulletin*, Washington, July 30, 1951; reprinted in Roberto Ducci and Bino Olivi (eds.) *L'Europa incompiuta* (Padua, Cedam, 1970), pp. 201–6.

much, because they contented themselves with transposing to the European Army the machinery of the Schuman Plan. Except for the executive, the institutions were to be the same. There were certainly good reasons why the common organization for defence had to be compatible with that for the economy, and strengthen its embryonic federal structure. In both fields, the men who would have to take the decisions would have to be subject to democratic control and to a supreme court; they would also have to work in tandem with the Governments of the member States. It was therefore reasonable that they should work within the same institutional system. But if it was important to listen to reason, it was also important to resist the temptations of mere symmetry. Where the tasks differed – and defence cannot be conducted in the same way as a common market for coal and steel – new methods were needed; and I was sorry that there was no one there to invent them as we had done, day by day, at the Schuman Plan conference. As an outside observer, I saw that the negotiations were overloading the Pleven Plan with a mass of details that made it cumbersome and forbidding. But we could not keep an eye on everything; and besides, from September 1951 onwards, I had a further absorbing mission to fulfil in addition to my work as French Planning Commissioner.

For many months, efforts to share out defence costs among the members of the Atlantic Alliance had mainly been considered from a military point of view – and the political world had been wholly absorbed by the question of German rearmament. But those responsible for public finance had their eyes on more immediate concerns, and in every country they saw the military budget as a heavy burden on the economy and a threat to domestic peace. The British, who were determined to lighten the burden, and the French, who had an army in Indochina, were particularly unwilling to respond to American requests for a bigger contribution from Europe. The problem became acute at the Ottawa meeting of the Atlantic Council in mid-September 1951. How were we to reconcile the requirements of defence with our countries' need for economic and social equilibrium? It was neither the first nor the last time that the question arose; but in 1951 it was a real and understandable worry for hard-headed administrators like René Mayer, the French Minister of Finance, and Hugh Gaitskell, the British Chancellor of the Exchequer. So 'Three Wise Men' were appointed to size up the situation – Averell Harriman, Plowden, and myself.

I had known Harriman for many years, but we had never before worked together. During the war, he had been Roosevelt's special envoy and later Ambassador to Stalin, and fifteen years before that he had negotiated with Trotsky. As a man of affairs, he enjoyed both respect and influence in the Kremlin. His fine mind matched his distinguished appearance: he was a remarkably able negotiator. Like many American diplomats at his level, he approached problems as a statesman – he had in fact had a career in politics – and as one of the 'Three Wise Men' he joined in our search for an equitable solution without following the demands of the American military, which turned out to be too ambitious. It was a good idea to seek recommendations from three civilians: in this way, political and social necessities dictated our conclusion – which was that the targets should be revised and the structure of the Alliance reorganized. Its main features, we thought, should be Supreme Headquarters, Allied Powers, Europe (SHAPE) and the integrated NATO command. It took no less than six months' work to bring together all the data that led to this conclusion. In March 1952 it was approved by the NATO Ministers at their meeting in Lisbon. Hirsch undertook the greater part of the work involved in compiling our monumental inventory. My task was to ensure that Europe's contribution to the defence of the West was seen as a common effort. Once that was completed, I could once more concentrate on helping to secure the ratification of the Coal and Steel Community Treaty.

Personally, I do not believe that democratic control really requires the ritual and pace of parliamentary procedure to be as slow as they are; but the fact that more than a year elapsed between the signing of the ECSC Treaty and the final vote at least shows that the debate was thorough, and that it was not, as was alleged, a technocratic conspiracy. Dozens of committees, in eleven upper and lower houses of Parliament, closely scrutinized the text of the Treaty. It was discussed publicly for days and nights on end, amid passionate controversy in the press. All in all, the debates vindicated the Community countries' parliamentary systems: they bore witness to the scruples of men who were called upon to delegate part of that very national sovereignty which was their own *raison d'être*. A few of them defended private interests; some others championed bygone principles: but their ardour served to illustrate aspects of the Treaty hitherto obscure. And even if most of the fears expressed proved to be vain, the debate enabled everyone to commit himself with his eyes open. Today, of course, it is easy to be detached about a battle which was not fought on the ground I should have preferred – the common future of Europeans – and in which I myself did not escape attack. Nationalistic arguments and corporatist special pleading played too big a part in the discussion: but how could it be otherwise in assemblies elected primarily to protect their citizens against risks? Few Members of Parliament were capable of declaring that the greatest risk of all would be to do nothing and change nothing.

The Netherlands, so hesitant at the start, were the first to ratify, in October 1951. The country had reconciled itself to the absence of the British, and was fully aware of how much they would lose by isolating themselves from the Community. In the Netherlands, as in Belgium and Luxembourg, only the Communists voted against. In Belgium, the debate was close-fought: the Socialists, who were anxious about miners' jobs, abstained in the Senate, although Paul-Henri Spaak was able to rally some of them in the Chamber. The Italian Parliament took its time. The advantages of creating a Coal and Steel Community were not clearly perceived in Italy, although special clauses in her favour had been written into the Treaty, and her interests as a consumer were obvious enough. Ideology carried the day, and in June 1952 the Right wing found itself voting No in alliance with the Communists and Socialists. In Germany, ratification was achieved after a long and difficult parliamentary process which began in July 1951 with a first reading in the *Bundestag*. The Socialist Opposition, always very violent, proved unable to block the project; but it forced the Government to be attentive to its own Right wing. While the second and third readings were in progress, Adenauer was still negotiating with the Allies on de-cartelization, the Saar, and an equal status within the European Army. On both fronts, internal and external, he fought with extraordinary vitality and brutal candour.

It was piquant to look at some of the arguments advanced by German industrialists and Socialists, which were a mirror image of the fears expressed by their counterparts in France. The Schuman Plan, they thought, would handicap the industries of the Ruhr. The High Authority would restrict investment in the steel industry, and costs would be higher at home than in France. Finally, no guarantee had been secured for the Saar. These equal and opposite worries, however, by no means cancelled each other out: on the contrary, European employers made common cause against the plan, and the Communists too sang the same tune everywhere. But the Socialists of the French SFIO and those of the German SPD did not see eye to eye. The violent intransigence of Schumacher, who demanded independence for Germany more loudly than anyone, had nothing in common with the misgivings of those French Socialists like Paul Ramadier, Robert

Lacoste, and their followers, who on this subject differed from Guy Mollet. However, what seemed to me then and later the most encouraging sign was the positive attitude adopted by the leaders of the great German trade union federation, the *Deutscher Gewerkschaftsbund* or DGB. Some of its members had affinities with the Social-Democrat Party, but these were not so close as to make them share its doctrinal excesses; and this seemed to me one of the great opportunities for the Schuman Plan and for the future of European unity. Finally Adenauer was able to persuade Schumacher to let the debate continue calmly, and on January 11, 1952, the Treaty was ratified by a majority of ninety, compared with a normal Government majority of thirty votes. Although the ratification process was still not completed, in Germany and elsewhere, for me this date marked the victory of the Schuman Plan and the hopes it represented. I sent Adenauer a telegram: 'The Community is born: long live Europe.'

The debate in the French National Assembly did not begin until December 6, 1951. Work in committee had been long and thorough; and in the meantime the opponents of the project had been preparing their ammunition. The steelmakers, who had been taken aback by the signing of the Treaty, sent their lobbyists to haunt the corridors of Parliament, and tried in every way to influence the press. I myself made immense efforts to persuade people, and I found a ready hearing among those same men who had never ceased to support the Modernization Plan – Socialists, Radicals, Popular Republicans, and Moderates. Together, they made up a parliamentary majority: only in appearance was it precarious. If one looks at these men's achievements, the continuity is striking, in major matters at least – the modernization of France, the foundations of a united Europe, and the beginnings of decolonization. It was in matters of daily administration, which also requires continuity, that the Government's chronic instability became hard to bear. This worried me, and at that time I was studying possible remedies. A young professor from Bordeaux, Maurice Duverger, who had written some remarkable articles in *Le Monde* about the Modernization Plan and the Schuman Plan, worked with me on a plan for constitutional reform which we thought would remove the temptation for Parliament to overthrow Governments with such unconcern. When I left No 18 rue de Martignac shortly afterwards, this project stayed in my files. Whether it would have been enough to give the men of talent and goodwill who led the Fourth Republic the strength to overcome their ordeals, or even to avoid them, I am now inclined to doubt. At that time I had not experienced the working of institutions, or thought about them, as much as I have today.

I followed the debates in the National Assembly at the Palais Bourbon, and was astonished at the skill with which Pleven, Schuman, and René Mayer, each in his own way, avoided the adjournment motions, previous questions, and other procedural traps set for them day and night by their opponents at both extremes. I heard Florimond Bonte declare on behalf of the Communist Party:

'This is a vast plan to deport workers, who are looked on as cattle or mere merchandise to be sold abroad.'

Then Gaston Palewski, a Gaullist, prophesied that:

'All customs barriers will fall, and the whole French market, from Strasbourg to Brazzaville in the Congo, will be inundated by the dynamism of German industry.'

And finally, Jacques Soustelle, another Gaullist spokesman, declared:

'Sovereignty cannot be delegated: nor can responsibility.'

But the most shrewdly-aimed blows were delivered by two remarkable debaters, Pierre Cot on the extreme Left and Pierre André on the extreme Right. Both of them spoke with mellifluous eloquence, feigning immense politeness towards the Government.

'I should like,' said Pierre Cot, 'to pay tribute to the generosity of your dream. I respect it, even if I do not support it. But as well as dreams, there are realities to be considered. Those realities are the nations. One cannot force the hand of history.'

This was a man who proclaimed himself progressive. His audience was attentive, but unconvinced. More to be feared was Pierre André, in whose constituency the steelmakers' word was law. His role was to sow doubt among the majority by claiming that France was ill-prepared for the risks of competition; then, on the pretext of obtaining further safeguards, to adjourn the debate until times improved. André returned to this theme until he was ready to drop. Finally, Pleven floored him with a vote of confidence, in which Paul Reynaud rallied some of the Moderates. The Chamber of Deputies ratified the Treaty on December 13, 1951, by 377 votes to 233. The Communists, the Gaullists, and a few Independents voted against.

But the battle was not yet won. The opponents of the Treaty were preparing to repeat the same tactics in the Senate. To secure the vote in the Chamber, the Government had had to undertake other commitments, in particular the canalization of the Moselle. Would it now be forced into making further concessions, perhaps even compromising the essentials of the plan? Prepared by violent press campaigns, the attack was launched on March 25, 1952, by Michel Debré, a young

Senator from Indre-et-Loire. That day, the political world discovered that it would have to reckon with this passionate and skilful defender of the French nation. He invoked a thousand imaginary dangers, the better to rescue France: he begged that she be not left defenceless before a neighbouring people capable of the worst:

'You must realize that nation's lust for power, its lack of respect for freedom, its political instability and, I would add, its total failure to learn the lessons of the past. . . . In the interests of Germany itself, Europe must not become a German Europe!'

Debré's gloomy prophecies scarcely troubled the Senate, which had little taste for excess. Speaking of the Schuman Plan's institutions, he went on:

'You think you have set up an authority. You have not. It is a mere show, a marionette theatre. Behind it are the puppet-masters, the strongest and most determined of men. They will have their way. And let me say what I believe, at the risk of being called nationalistic: here, France is neither determined nor strong.'

From the Government front bench, Félix Gaillard shouted:

'But you're preaching defeatism!'

It was true – because in Debré's eyes France could not be herself again until she was ruled by General de Gaulle.

From the beginning, de Gaulle had condemned the Schuman Plan.

'We're offered a mish-mash of coal and steel, without knowing where we're heading, under some sort of cabal,' he declared in Metz on May 19, 1950. After that, however, he scarcely spoke of the project: the European Army became the main target for his attacks. He left it to his followers to criticize what for him was no more than a bad technical agreement with no prospects, a vision dreamed up by technocrats in quest of irresponsible power. When the process spread to defence, he was outraged, and his reaction was much sharper:

'Here is a crafty scheme for a so-called "European" Army which threatens to put a legal end to France's sovereignty. It would make our Army disappear in a hybrid creation under the deliberately misleading label of "Europe". But since Europe does not exist as a responsible sovereign entity – because no one has done what is needed to create it – this force will be entrusted to the American "chief".'

De Gaulle's whole argument was based on the premise that nothing European could be undertaken so long as Europe was not a political reality. But at the same time he affirmed that the only political reality was the nation-state. What then was this 'Europe' that he was calling for with so much obvious sincerity? 'A vast confederation of States', about whose geographical limits and internal links he was wholly vague, and which belonged to the hazy world of 'co-operation' and 'association'. All that was clear was his wish to include Germany, harnessed by an agreement giving France the dominant role, especially as regards defence. The whole system, finally, was to be validated by referendum.

De Gaulle's idea was tempting, and it looked ambitious; but on closer inspection it fell short of the plans for a Community which it proposed to replace. It made no provision for the pooling of sovereignty, for independent institutions, or for equal rights. Above all, it had no intention or prospect of assuming concrete form within a reasonable time. Everything about it was conditional, because nothing could be done before 'France was herself again'. She had ceased to be herself, in de Gaulle's eyes, under the present régime. This prerequisite of 'national recovery' was to be invoked in the debate in order to postpone any European project; and since nothing could be done for the present, why not construct grandiose plans for the distant future? Our approach was very different. We believed in starting with limited achievements, establishing *de facto* solidarity, from which a federation would gradually emerge. I have never believed that one fine day Europe would be created by some great political mutation, and I thought it wrong to consult the peoples of Europe about the structure of a Community of which they had no practical experience.

It was another matter, however, to ensure that in their limited field the new institutions were thoroughly democratic; and in this direction there was still progress to be made. In the Schuman Plan, the Common Assembly was to supervise the High Authority, and if necessary to censure it. This same Assembly would serve EDC, which gave it the same power over the Defence Commissariat. Now, a new provision had been added, Article 38. This stipulated that the Assembly should be elected by universal suffrage within a federal system which it was to start planning as soon as it took office. In this way, the pragmatic method we had adopted would also lead to a federation validated by the people's vote; but that federation would be the culmination of an existing economic and political reality, already put to the test – whereas that proposed by de Gaulle would have to invent and test everything itself. In the abstract, one could debate the merits of the two alternatives. Ours was already real: it was bringing together men and practical matters; for nearly a year it had embodied the hopes of millions of Europeans. There was no longer any choice. Given the urgency of making progress, I found it hard to see why a Europe still to be thought out was being proposed in place of the Europe already being built. Military integration, it was true, forced us to go further and faster politically than we had originally proposed in the Schuman Plan. But Article 38 was the response to this need: it was the germ of the federal institutions that would soon be needed to discharge the responsibilities of a shared economy and joint defence – the unification, that is, of the six countries' most vital concerns.

The final vote on the ECSC Treaty came on April 1, 1952. It was carried by a large majority; but there could be no doubt now that the concerted nationalism of Left and Right would form a constant barrier to Europe's progress. In the great battles to come, this opposition would be swelled by conservative elements from among the Radicals and Moderates, and by those whom weakness of character or political calculation inclined towards neutrality. Already in February the Government had faced a difficult debate about the future of the European Army project, and the new Prime Minister, Edgar Faure, had carried the day only by deploying all the resources of his eloquence. When his opponents tried to lay down preconditions, he answered with a quotation from the philosopher William James: 'First continue, then begin.' Little as I like paradoxes, I must confess that this one suited the occasion. We had to continue along our chosen path and take the new steps that everyone wanted, just as soon as our progress allowed. In default of full British membership, however, the Government had to promise to undertake no commitment before securing American and British guarantees for EDC. Those guarantees were already implicit in the Atlantic Alliance; but to have them reaffirmed, in each case, was no easy task. It was in the nature of things that the United States and Britain would come to Europe's aid if she were once more under threat. It was America's intention to leave her troops in Germany, and formal agreements added nothing to that fact. But the French authorities needed written promises, and we obtained them at the same time as the EDC was signed in Paris on May 27, 1952, in the presence of Eden and Acheson, by the same men who one year earlier had signed the Treaty establishing the ECSC.

By then, Antoine Pinay had been Prime Minister for nearly three months. I had not met him when he took over the Government; but Hirsch, who had worked with him on the Modernization Plan, described him to me as all France was to come to know him: a small, ordinary-looking man, of determined common sense and very great goodwill. 'He'll astonish people,' I was told. I personally was far from astonished to find such very human qualities in a Head of Government, particularly the ability to listen and then decide. My relationship with Pinay was always straightforward and constructive; it was based, I think, on mutual esteem. But someone else had certainly recognized Pinay's unostentatious qualities, and had surprised everyone by making an obscure Minister the Premier of France. This was the French President, Vincent Auriol, a warm-hearted man of whom I was fond. In my work on the Modernization Plan, I knew I could count on his advice and his full support; but already in 1950 I realized that the Schuman Plan left him perplexed. Although he did nothing to prevent it, he never gave it his active backing; and when EDC took shape, he fought that with the powerful weapons of his influence behind the scenes. For him, as for many of his compatriots, mistrust of Germany seemed the surest form of patriotism. He knew how determined I was, and he never reproached me: we simply avoided discussing the subject, which was already a bone of contention among politicians, and then among more and more Frenchmen generally, as the politicians prepared and recruited them for the decisive battles.

Those battles still lay ahead. Schuman was in no hurry to lay the Bill before Parliament, and none of his colleagues encouraged him to do so during the ten further months he spent at the French Foreign Office. True, we all had a more urgent duty – to get the ECSC off to a good start. There were still a few crucial decisions that required the agreement of Governments. On July 23, 1952, the Six at last met in Paris. On their agenda were political Europe, and the choice of the men, the official languages, and a site for the institutions. Once again, Konrad Adenauer, Alcide de Gasperi, Paul Van Zeeland, Dirk Stikker, and Joseph Bech were welcomed by Robert Schuman. Once again, and for the last time as regards coal and steel, they met as national Ministers, each still enjoying the power to block any decision he disliked. The discussion about the site for the institutions was a last, derisory parade of the right of veto. It began on Tuesday morning and ended at dawn on Thursday, with an equivocal arrangement which only time and the force of circumstances were to confirm. How the High Authority ended after eighteen hours haggling is an unedifying tale.

I had no preference for one place in Europe rather than another: all that mattered to me was that it should be the site of all the institutions and that it should become a European territory, the embryo of an eventual Federal District. There was nothing Utopian about this proposal: the Community would probably have grown up in a different atmosphere if the Governments had been sensible enough to found a capital city for it, isolating it from national rivalry and national influence. But in July 1952 everyone had his own choice to propose. France, backed by Italy, pleaded for Strasbourg; Belgium for Liége, the Netherlands for The Hague. When at the last moment Schuman proposed the idea of Saarbrücken, I imagine that he thought it would solve several problems at once. All it did was add yet another. Adenauer was surprised at this attempt to overcome the difficulties of the Saar by 'Europeanizing' them, and he showed his displeasure. Although the proposal satisfied two of my wishes – for a European district and a single site – I thought it unwise, because I had been long enough familiar with the Saar dispute to know that it could not be resolved by political artifice. De Gasperi came to Schuman's aid, and proposed that the question be adjourned until September, pending Franco-German agreement on the Saar. The prospect of a fresh delay seemed to me intolerable, and I told the Ministers:

'The ECSC has waited long enough: believe the experts.'

The competition for the capital began again, and only fatigue brought it to an end. At three in the morning, we were in both Strasbourg and Turin. I then declared that in this case the Ministers must no longer count on my accepting the offer of the Presidency which the six Governments had made. In the ensuing confusion, I remember a revealing remark of Van Zeeland's:

'It's late, we're all tired, and so I'll speak frankly. . . .'

Brussels had been proposed: he was against it – for electoral reasons, since his mandate was limited to Liége. Paris or the Paris area, which tempted some people, was rejected by Schuman: Pierre Pflimlin, the Mayor of Strasbourg, would have been up in arms. Then we heard the voice of Joseph Bech, who until then had seemed half-asleep:

'I propose that work begin right away in Luxembourg: that will give us time to reflect.'

Everyone was relieved; and that is how the ECSC acquired its 'provisional' headquarters in a small town which became a European crossroads. The meeting ended after a decision on the four official languages – Dutch, French, German, and Italian. The main point on the agenda – political Europe – had been forgotten. Debate on it was to be resumed in September.

That night gave us the final proof – if we still needed it – that a Europe of sovereign States was incapable, despite its leaders' goodwill, of reaching the sensible decisions that were needed for the common good. It would be quite another matter, however, once the power of decision was entrusted to institutions serving the general interest and applying the will of the majority in a system of common rules. As we left the French Foreign Office on the Quai d'Orsay, the sun was coming up. I said to François Fontaine:

'Now we have a few hours to rest and a few months to succeed. After that –'

'After that,' said Fontaine, smiling, 'we shall face great difficulties, and we shall use them to make further progress. That's it, isn't it?'

'It is indeed,' I said. 'You've understood what Europe's all about.'

Chapter 15

THE EUROPEAN COMMUNITY AT WORK
(1952-1955)

I
Pioneers in coal and steel

On the morning of August 10, 1952, Europe came to Luxembourg. The Grand Duchy's leisurely and picturesque capital city was unprepared for so motley an influx of foreigners, impatient to start work. Within a few days, old administrative offices were vacated to accommodate our new institutions, whose multinational staff came from Bonn, Paris, Rome, Brussels, and The Hague, like waves of invaders from another world. In their wake, a crowd of statesmen, diplomats, and newspapermen arrived for the inaugural ceremonies. The Luxembourgers were flattered by this sudden interest, which gave their country prestige and promised well for the tourist season. They hardly suspected that these day trippers would shortly return, to set up embassies, press agencies, and professional liaison bureaux, or that the small team which had been invited to camp for a while in Luxembourg would soon multiply until it filled their houses and crowded their streets. The more traditionalist among them came to regret Joseph Bech's diplomatic victory, whose results gradually altered the balance of their small national community. From our point of view, the inconveniences of being in Luxembourg were soon overcome, and I found some advantages in the isolation I had once feared. The Grand Duchy was peaceful and beautiful, and in our work we were subject to no local pressures. If communications were not easy, we should simply have to try harder to make our voice heard in the great capitals and secure the attention of all Europeans.

To tell the truth, I had not made any plans for a large-scale and lasting establishment, because I still hoped then – as I do even today – that the European institutions would eventually be located in an independent 'District'; and in any case I was determined to keep the High Authority's staff as small as possible. I know from experience that on matters like these one always has to make concessions; but at least it was worthwhile telling everyone what my position was, and warning them that only powerful arguments would make me change my mind. Only in practice should we discover what the ideal complement would be, and it was best to begin with the few people who had helped to draft the Treaty. This first nucleus could be enlarged by co-optation when we saw what jobs had to be done. But the High Authority ought to remain a nucleus and confine itself to organizing and stimulating the work of others. For the rest, it could rely on the national civil services and on its own powers over the firms, whether for obtaining information before reaching a decision or for seeing that its decisions were carried out. The French Modernization Plan had proved that authority could best be exercised by small teams. People collaborate willingly when they see that you are not trying to supplant them or take their place. A few hundred European civil servants would be enough to set thousands of national experts to work, and to make the powerful machinery of firms and Governments serve the aims of the Treaty. It was on this model, at least, that I was going to try to frame the first Community institutions.

That August morning in Luxembourg there were barely thirty of us to represent the High Authority before hundreds of witnesses, most of them special correspondents whom the world's major newspapers had sent to attend the official inauguration. Many of my new colleagues were strangers, and they met each other at the same time as they met the press. Several of them were new to me too; and, except for Spierenburg and Wehrer, I knew little about them. On the main point, however, I was already reassured. In the course of a weekend among friends in the Westerwald, Hallstein – who was now German Under-Secretary of State for Foreign Affairs – had introduced me to Franz Etzel, whom Adenauer had proposed as the High Authority's Vice-President. True, I had never had any anxiety about Adenauer's choice, because I knew that he gave Franco-German friendship priority over everything else. Even so, luck was needed to turn this political idea into practical reality. And I was quick to recognize, behind the massive appearance of my new partner, tall and stiff like the popular idea of a typical Prussian, a man of great goodwill. Etzel had been brought up in the Rhineland, and he was already convinced that agreement between us was essential to the success of our work. Subsequently, he came to see me several times in Paris, with the result that we already had a number of ideas in common when we came to sit down at the same table with our new colleagues.

Among the latter I already knew Léon Daum, whom the French

Government had proposed as the second Frenchman on the team. Pinay's high opinion of him was already a good augury, and I was in no way worried by the fact that he was a leading light of the steel industry, which was still suspicious of the High Authority. It was not to make the Community serve his former interests that 'Monsieur Daum', as we always called him, had given up his position at the head of some of France's biggest firms. He was a man of honour, and he had carefully read the Treaty before committing himself. The oath of total independence which he took with us that August 10 was to be his watchword. Lest there be any mistake about it, he always had the Treaty to hand on his desk.

'Read this little book,' he told steelmakers who came to visit him: 'it's very interesting.'

His moral stature enhanced the High Authority's internal cohesion and external prestige. I was present when he first met Paul Finet, the Belgian trade unionist whom we had co-opted, in accordance with the Treaty, to complete our nine-man team. A former metalworker who had become President of the International Confederation of Free Trade Unions (ICFTU), Finet had the same youthful enthusiasm as Daum, the former mining engineer who had become President of the *Forges et Aciéries de la Marine*. Both showed the same team spirit, and I knew that they would be completely loyal. Finet had undoubted influence over workpeople: he had won it by his ability, and maintained it by his gifts as a speaker. With him, the new practice of co-optation had begun well.

In addition to Etzel, the Bonn Government had also proposed Heinz Potthoff, a trade unionist from the DGB, who had been Germany's representative on the International Ruhr Authority. This choice of a Social-Democrat balanced that of Etzel, who was an influential member of the Christian Democrat Party and Chairman of the Economic Affairs Committee in the *Bundestag*. Discreetly but effectively, Potthoff kept useful channels open, leaving Etzel the forefront of the stage. Equally discreet, but this time by inclination and as if disdainful of practical action, was Enzo Giacchero, who was a brilliant analyst and orator. He had been badly wounded in the war; but this had not prevented his fighting in the Resistance. All his enthusiasm went to federalist ideals: the rest left him smilingly indifferent.

Of all my colleagues, only Albert Coppé seemed to present a problem. A former Belgian Minister, he had been a professor of economics; and his economic ideas were so *laissez-faire* that, to listen to him, one might well have wondered whether he was not opposed to all the principles of the Community that it was his duty to apply. In reality he learned fast, and he was quick to recognize, very candidly, that his first suspicions had been unfounded. Although he had come to defend the interests of his country, which thought itself threatened by the weight of its larger neighbours, he became one of the most ardent champions of the Treaty and of majority voting.

'Even my family,' he said one day, 'wouldn't work if we applied the veto.'

With seven children, Coppé spoke from experience.

At the inaugural ceremony in the Luxembourg Town Hall I made a first speech, and in the name of all my colleagues gave the following solemn pledge:

'We shall carry out our tasks in full independence, in the general interest of the Community. In fulfilling our duties, we shall neither solicit nor accept instructions from any Government or any other body, and we shall refrain from any action incompatible with the supranational character of our tasks. We have noted the member States' pledge to respect this supranational character and not try to influence us in our work.'

The ceremonies over, the visitors caught their trains. We were left alone to start on an unprecedented task. As usual, the lights of the little town went out early. Only the windows of the High Authority building in the Place de Metz remained lighted, long into the night. It was another new habit, that of Europe's pioneers, for whom there was to be no further rest.

I had taken with me to Luxembourg Pierre Uri, Jacques Van Helmont, François Fontaine, and André Lamy. I had left the French Modernization Plan in good hands: Hirsch succeeded me as Planning Commissioner, keeping with him Vergeot, Ripert and, for some time, Rabier. We were glad to join forces again with some of those who had negotiated the Treaty and who had agreed to start work with us: Richard Hamburger, the Dutch legal expert, a fund of plain good sense and a source of valuable advice; Cesare Balladore-Pallieri, a capable and conscientious Italian civil servant with a great organizing gift; Rolf Wagenfuhr, economic adviser to the German trade unions, with an ever-growing reputation; François Vinck, a Belgian coal expert, full of dynamism and earthy common sense; Tony Rollmann, a Luxembourg steel expert of international renown. As a team, they were glad to work with Uri, whose inventive mind and warm heart everyone had come to know. On the very first day, the High Authority set these men the task of forming its organization and preparing the most urgent steps: its own job was to debate and decide together. To do so, it needed a secretariat to co-ordinate and execute its decisions; and for this task we recruited a young diplomat who had distinguished himself on the Dutch delegation at the Schuman Plan conference. His name was Max Kohnstamm.

Really exceptional qualities were required to interpret and give shape to the thoughts and wishes of a collegiate body made up of nine men from six different countries, speaking four different languages – not to mention their differences of character and upbringing. I had never dared to hope that we should find a single person capable of fulfilling this role, which was really a task for the European of the future – or rather, which recalled the European of the Renaissance. Kohnstamm was able to understand the French, the Germans, and the British in their own languages, as well as his compatriots in theirs; he was also familiar with their literature and their press. The misunderstandings to which we were liable owing to ignorance of each other's customs held no pitfalls for him: he was an invaluable intermediary. Everyone was impressed by his great open-mindedness and his deep moral qualities. I found in him a colleague and a friend, unshakeably and permanently loyal.

It was with this small team that we were to tackle the most urgent tasks: drawing up a balance-sheet of the Community's coal and steel output, making our first outside contacts, and helping to establish the other institutions within the time-limits set by the Treaty. On every one of these points, the approach we adopted would commit us for the future; so from the first we had to consider very carefully our decisions' long-term effect. To draw up our comprehensive balance-sheet, we had to call in as many national experts as we could. Three hundred of them came within a few weeks – while we had no more than ten people of our own to extract from them the information which Uri put in his masterly report. We were strongly tempted to keep with us the best of the national experts; but we were wise enough to let them go. They would come back as soon as they were needed. Within a matter of months, in fact, these countless comings and goings had made Luxembourg a busy international centre, so that we were simultaneously able to enjoy the peace and quiet of a small principality, surrounded by magnificent pine-forests, and to benefit from continual contact with the far corners of Europe. Our day trippers went away with the feeling that they had seen pioneers at work, and when they returned home they helped to spread the word.

Their repeated and consistent travellers' tales fed the legend that a new race of men was emerging in the Luxembourg institutions, as if in a laboratory; and this not unnaturally worried those who suspected us of being a technocracy cut off from national life and exerting broad, uncontrolled powers. There was no doubt that something new and powerful was taking shape within our team: it was a European attitude, the fruit of working together and above all of having to reach a common conclusion after long discussion and widespread consultations. This European attitude challenged old habits of thought; but if it prevailed, it was certainly not by virtue of technocratic authority. That we did not possess; and the European Commission of today is protected from technocracy by the very nature of its power – the power to propose and consult rather than to decide. The influence of which Luxembourg was the centre derived from the force of example which enthusiastic men from six countries, all talking in the same terms, exerted on their compatriots. Among these men, everything was simple: the only difficulty lay in the problems they tackled and solved. There were no language barriers or psychological obstacles that the Community did not immediately overcome. The experiment had never been tried before; so how could Europeans divided by frontiers have been expected to feel their solidarity and look ahead to unity? But now the proof existed; and among our visitors, many reporters and academics came from afar to examine it.

Interest was not confined to the Community countries themselves: the British were not slow to share it. The day after our arrival in Luxembourg, I received a message from London:

> Her Majesty's Government welcome the establishment yesterday of the High Authority of the European Coal and Steel Community. . . . Her Majesty's Government have on several occasions made clear their support of the purposes of this Community and their intention to establish the closest possible association with it as soon as the High Authority is created. . . . Her Majesty's Government are ready at any time to begin conversations with the President of the High Authority concerning their relationship with it.

I replied immediately:

> It is a matter of particular satisfaction to me that the first message of welcome the Community has received should come from the British Government. I am certain that a close association can quickly be established. . . .

Ten days later I was in London, where in the absence of Anthony Eden I had talks with Plowden and Sir Roger Makins, Deputy Under-Secretary at the Foreign Office*. Makins welcomed me with the words:

'Now that you are a fact, we shall deal with you.'

* Later Lord Sherfield.

It had taken less than two years for the prediction I had made to Sir Stafford Cripps to come true. The British were looking at a Europe which existed, and they were moving towards it. A UK Delegation was ready to leave for Luxembourg, led by Sir Cecil Weir, a Scot with white hair and a mischievous smile, very down-to-earth but also very dignified. Britain could not have made a better choice, or one more agreeable to me. Sir Cecil had a great reputation, and his appointment showed that the Government took us seriously. Moreover, by sending so experienced a man, and one who had undertaken important international assignments after a successful career in industry, Britain was opening the way to further developments which it was up to us to encourage.

I had not yet made up my mind about what those developments should be. In a letter to me on August 29, Eden wrote:

> The task of the Delegation will be to lay the foundations for an intimate and enduring association between the Community and the United Kingdom.

The British do not use words lightly, and 'an intimate and enduring association' meant a serious commitment, whose content would be arrived at empirically, as is the British way. I was ready for the most liberal amount of empiricism in this new situation, where we ourselves had yet to fathom what the real problems were.

'You will be there to observe how we operate from day to day,' I told the British. 'Nothing will be hidden from you. In so far as you face the same problems, we shall together seek the forms of relationship and agreement that will best enable them to be solved in our common interest. If we find those forms, if we work according to the same rules, then our Community will develop in harmony with Britain; and one day this experiment, itself born of action, will reveal possibilities for deeper union.'

The day when the British were to join us was still far off; but my immediate concern was that the doors of our institutions should be open from the start, so that misunderstandings and suspicions could be dissipated rather than deepened. To tell the truth, I already wanted more than just a close relationship. A minimum of rules was needed so that, even if our work were limited to the exchange of information, it would involve mutual obligations. The British, that is, were welcome to go into our problems in so far as they were willing to expound their own. Sir Cecil Weir and I hit on the formula of a Joint Committee, in which for two years his very able assistants – James Marjoribanks, Elizabeth Ackroyd, and Derek Ezra – met experts from the ECSC. Eventually, we concluded a formal Association Agreement with the United Kingdom. True, it was limited; but it went as far as the British were then willing to go in committing themselves to Europe.

Our link with America was of a different kind: we had always had common interests, and on a plane which enabled our new relationship to assume a more general and more political form. On the very day we began work, I received the following message from Acheson:

> It is the intention of the United States to give the Coal and Steel Community the strong support that its importance to the political and economic unification of Europe warrants. As appropriate under the Treaty, the United States will now deal with the Community on coal and steel matters.

This official move, which was followed by many others, recognized the High Authority as an entity in international law. And when we received William Draper, the United States' Special Representative in Europe, a few hours after Sir Cecil Weir's arrival in Luxembourg, there was no further doubt that the Community was a sovereign body. Draper was accompanied by Tomlinson, whom he accredited as US Chief Representative. In my speech of welcome I told them:

'I cannot help recalling that historic occasion when the nations of Europe welcomed the first Ambassadors from America, and thereby gave strong support to the nascent United States. In those years, when the thirteen States of your continent were forming the United States of America, they needed friends to help them overcome the immense difficulties they faced. To succeed in what we have undertaken, we too need friends. . . .'

Some months later, our friendship was still further strengthened. When Eisenhower was elected President, he appointed Foster Dulles as his Secretary of State, and both of them asked David Bruce to serve once more in Europe. On February 19, 1953, Dulles cabled me:

> I have tried unsuccessfully to telephone you to inform you that David Bruce is today being appointed as US Representative to the Coal and Steel Community and US observer to the European Defence Community Interim Committee. This appointment is of course indicative of the great importance which the President and the US Government attach to these movements in Europe to develop a unified six-nation Community. I know that you will be as pleased as we are that Bruce has agreed to serve in the above capacity.

Previously, Dulles had wanted to see our progress for himself, and on his first trip to Europe his Flying Fortress had landed in Luxembourg. He had come to see with his own eyes these new beginnings in the Old

World. Before he left, on a freezing night in February 1953, he talked to us with inspiring faith about the enterprise we had launched. He grew so eloquent that he broke off with a smile and said:

'You must think I'm preaching a sermon! But if I'm preaching, it's from your own Bible. All I'm doing is paraphrasing the Preamble of your Treaty.'

It was true: he knew every word of it; and above all he recognized in it the tradition which the Founding Fathers had enshrined in the US Constitution, and which was so vividly alive in his heart.

We no longer had to win our new-found sovereignty: it had been acknowledged; but to maintain it we had to exercise it. First, we had to complete the Community by setting up the other Institutions – the Council of Ministers, the Assembly, and the Court of Justice: this was part of the High Authority's task. According to the Treaty, I had to convoke the Assembly one month after our own assumption of office. Seemingly, this was simple: the six countries' Parliaments had appointed their delegates, the date was fixed, and the place – Strasbourg – had been settled by the Ministers in July. But this last decision was heavy with ambiguity. We had scarcely been in office a few weeks before we were drawn into a conflict with the Council of Europe; and the dispute was more than merely formal: what was at stake was the independence of the Community itself. The Council of Europe saw the convocation of our Assembly as an opportunity to put into practice the so-called 'Eden Plan' launched a few months earlier, about which there had been much indecisive talk. Like the ill-fated Macmillan Plan of 1950, this was an attempt to water the Community down by including it in the Council of Europe. The latter had a Secretary-General, Camille Paris, who was not without authority: he had tailored his appointment to fit his own ambitions. He thought he was in a position to do battle and – with or without Government backing, I cannot tell – he pushed ahead very boldly, claiming that he and his staff should act as the Secretariat for the meetings of the new Community Assembly. I had little difficulty in convincing my colleagues on the High Authority that this offer of technical assistance was merely a pretext for the Council of Europe to take over our parliamentary and ministerial institutions. We therefore decided to ask the Secretaries-General of the six national Parliaments to organize this first session, at which the Assembly itself would decide on its own administrative structure. It so happened that the Secretary-General of the French National Assembly, Emile Blamont, enjoyed great influence in these professional circles. We asked him to organize a meeting of his colleagues, which he did with remarkable efficiency and speed. He was a brilliant administrator – and no less obstinate than Camille Paris. In case the dispute was not settled in time, he sought out another meeting-place in Strasbourg – since the session had to take place there; and by prodigious feats of improvisation, he arranged alternative quarters at the Chamber of Commerce.

As was to be expected, once we had made plain our determination to meet elsewhere if necessary, the Council of Europe's assembly-chamber was offered to us unconditionally. That was on September 5, 1952, and the Community's Assembly was due to meet on September 10. It was in everyone's interest that it should do so in the vast semi-circular Robertsau – where it continued to hold its sessions for more than twenty years. Blamont reassembled the arrangements as efficiently as he had dis-mantled them; and on the prescribed day the Assembly was able to begin its sovereign debates. With that, the 'Eden Plan' ceased to exist. The political nature of the six-nation Community had just been clearly established, moreover, by the Council of Ministers, which had held its first meeting on the previous day in Luxembourg.

Alphabetical order of the countries' names in French gave Germany the chair at this inaugural meeting of the Council. Adenauer was there, with Hallstein; around the table were Van Zeeland, Schuman, de Gasperi, Bech, and Stikker. Adenauer explained how he saw the role of the Council: it has never been better explained, indeed, than at that first meeting:

'The Council stands at the crossroads of two kinds of sovereignty, national and supranational. . . . While it must safeguard the national interests of the member States, it must not regard this as its paramount task. Its paramount task is to promote the interests of the Community; and, unless it does so, the Community will not develop. That is why the Council will leave the Community's supranational institution – the High Authority – a great degree of freedom to develop. In certain circum-stances, the Council will have to create that freedom. . . .'

That was indeed the nature – and the reality – of the Council of the first European Community. In my reply, I was still more precise:

'The Council's task is to arrive at a common view, not to seek a com-promise between national interests. In the area covered by the Treaty, you will find yourselves associated in the exercise of the new sovereignty that will characterize the Community.'

We were to prove that this genuinely federal balance of institutions was healthy and productive. But was it necessary to go further, at once, towards political union? Since the appearance of the EDC project, many people thought so; and they were looking for an opportunity to make Europe take the next decisive step. One of them was Alcide de Gasperi. He was a distinguished and discriminating man, whose selfless decisions and profound unity of purpose with Adenauer and Schuman were respected in his own country and throughout Europe. He looked austere, but on closer acquaintance revealed both sensitivity and warmth. He had realized that if Italy was to play a role in Europe equal to that of the more industrialized states, the political process implicit in the first European Treaties must be speeded up. The European Defence Community, moreover, involved such great responsibilities that it called for a Government capable of taking the supreme decisions in the name of all Europeans. This was the argument de Gasperi never tired of repeating:

'The European Army is not an end in itself: it is the instrument of a patriotic foreign policy. But European patriotism can develop only in a federal Europe.'

It was to reach this goal as rapidly as possible that he had had Article 38 included in the EDC Treaty, providing for its Assembly to be elected by universal suffrage and called upon to work out a federal constitution, based on the separation of powers and endowed with a two-chamber Parliament. But the Treaty seemed unlikely to be ratified for some time; so de Gasperi secured Schuman's backing for the idea that this task be entrusted to the ECSC Assembly as soon as it was set up.

The Six Ministers accepted this plan at the meeting in Luxembourg on September 10, 1952. The new Assembly was given six months to perform its new task. Next day, in Strasbourg, it asked its best-qualified members to form the so-called *ad hoc* Constitutional Committee. There was indeed no lack of eminent men in this first Parliament of Europe. Heinrich von Brentano and Paul-Henri Spaak vied with each other for the Presidency. Some months earlier, Spaak had caused a stir in this very chamber by resigning from the chairmanship of the Council of Europe's Consultative Assembly, which he had denounced as ineffective. He knew that the ECSC Assembly, on the other hand, would be a forum worthy of his European convictions and his great oratorical gifts. He was elected; and although the ballot was secret it was already obvious that the Assembly's members had voted according to their political affinities, not by nationality. When I rose to begin the first political speech I had ever made, I found myself facing men long experienced in the parliamentary traditions of their own countries, but all kindred spirits and alike, too, in their deep attachment to democracy: Willi Birkelbach, Gerhard Kreyssig, Erich Ollenhauer, Herbert Wehner, Alain Poher, Pierre-Henri Teitgen, Maurice Faure, Pierre Wigny,

Fernand Dehousse, Théo Lefèvre, Marinus Van der Goes Van Naters, Lodovico Benvenuti, and many more. They had a great deal to teach me about the underlying realities of European politics – which did not yet include a full awareness of Europe. From me they were to learn patience, and the method whereby a common awareness could gradually be formed.

One thing surprised me. These men had just met for the first time in a completely novel institution which had still to draw up its own rules and take the measure of its tasks and its resources; yet already they were looking ahead to a new, vaster, and more distant enterprise. They were ardent spirits, and they would work well. I was no less ardent: I too believed that we must build a federal Europe. But at this very moment, when they had just assumed corporate existence and thereby, as it were, made the High Authority politically responsible, I was concerned exclusively with laying solid foundations for this first enterprise, which would later make possible all the rest. I knew that the road to European unity would be long, and that we should have to pass many milestones, each marking concrete but necessarily partial progress. I wished every success to the *ad hoc* Committee, where I knew that leading jurists like Dehousse and Teitgen, who were also considerable orators, would do remarkable work; but I followed it only from a distance. Nothing lasting would be achieved unless the High Authority exercised its power of decision and the Common Assembly its right of democratic control; and this would take longer than the six months the constitutionalists had for their work. To tell the truth, I thought that it was more important to be an 'institutionalist' – in the sense of being vigilant about the institutions already set up by the ECSC Treaty.

'Our common supranational institutions,' I told the Assembly, 'are still weak and fragile. Our duty is to respect and develop them, and to give them the strength to resist the temptation to temporize. Since these institutions were set up, the Europe we want to bequeath to our children has begun to be a living reality.'

In the end, what I had to make clear to these men, still fresh from their national Parliaments, was simple: but it would be a long time before they felt it in their bones. Europe, that is, would be built by the same process as each of our national States – by establishing among nations a new relationship comparable to that which exists among the citizens of any democratic country: equality, organized by common institutions. In Europe, this process had barely begun. It would be slow and difficult. I had no doubts about my audience's goodwill. But in conclusion I reminded the Assembly:

'The union of Europe cannot be based on goodwill alone. Rules are needed. The tragic events we have lived through and are still witnessing may have made us wiser. But men pass away; others will take our place. We cannot bequeath them our personal experience. That will die with us. But we can leave them institutions. The life of institutions is longer than that of men: if they are well built, they can accumulate and hand on the wisdom of succeeding generations.'

Some of our common rules were laid down in the Treaty; but others we should have to agree on in the course of our daily work. The Treaty's rules had the sanction of law, under the authority of the Court which was soon set up. Its President was a very eminent Italian jurist, Massimo Pilotti, a wise old man who gave the Court great prestige. Advocate-General Maurice Lagrange, who had as it were conceived the Court of Justice, gave it solidity and strength. And Jacques Rueff, with his fellow-Judges, helped to establish a new form of jurisprudence, in which law and economic reality balanced each other in full conformity with the letter and spirit of the Treaty. Throughout the Community, I have never known a ruling of the Court to be challenged or ignored. This exemplary institution still performs its duties, in the calm of Luxembourg, discreetly but firmly, like the men who have served it over the years. Later, Robert Lecourt was appointed President. Rarely have Governments made a better unanimous choice.

As for the rules that guided our daily work in the High Authority, they had no sanction other than success or failure. They had to be invented out of nothing: we had to build up an organization where nationalities would mingle, and one language would be as good as another. The lessons I had learned from international organizations taught me above all what errors to avoid. I had found that there was usually an irresistible tendency to set up an administration with all the features of a national civil service – which already existed elsewhere. This, combined with the desire to achieve balance between the nationals of all the member States, often led to a proliferation of staff and to internal divisions which hindered the flow of ideas. The only experience I cared to copy, in fact, was that of the League of Nations Secretariat in the days before I left it. But would it be possible to borrow from so mighty a machine only its small, powerful motor? I wanted at least to try. In the first few months, therefore, we recruited very sparingly. I personally interviewed all the candidates; I consulted my colleagues about them; and I took decisions, I must confess, only after much hesitation. Every organism has its own natural rate of growth. To preserve its character, ours had to absorb new elements slowly. And there was good reason to be exacting in our demands. People came to the High Authority because it was an inspiring venture: but it would remain so only if those we recruited were up to the mark. Little by little, our first nucleus expanded. On the recommendation of Lagrange, I took on a young Master of Requests in the French Council of State, Michel Gaudet, to give proper legal form to our legislative acts. But could their form be separated from their content? Almost without realizing it, I was adding to our machine a constant regulating element, whose paramount importance I had underestimated before. Thanks to Gaudet and his German counterpart, Robert Kravelicki, the Treaty became a permanent element in our institutions and decisions; and if its presence was sometimes a burden, it also contributed clarity and strength. Working devotedly together, Gaudet and Kravelicki greatly assisted the organic development of European law.

If the High Authority was to become a source of new wealth for firms and workers in coal and steel, it had to have an overall financial policy. Under the Treaty it enjoyed a large revenue, drawn from a levy on production; but this, I thought, could be increased if it were regarded as security against which the Community could raise public and private international loans. Who would have the imagination and skill to develop such a policy? At the French Planning Commissariat, I had already had occasion to appreciate the lively practical intelligence of Jean Guyot, a young *Inspecteur des finances* who seemed to me to have the makings of a great financier. I gave him his opportunity: he gave us ours. I have no regrets about having obeyed my instincts and given him so great a responsibility at the age of only thirty-one. He fulfilled it with that superb ability which he himself never completely trusted: no doubt it was because he curbed his natural facility and ambition that I had so high an opinion of him. He remained one of my most faithful and reliable colleagues.

Then came those indomitable young men who were to be the pioneers in our European administration, an élite corps that was a match for any difficulties: Edmund Wellenstein, Fernand Spaak, Winrich Behr, Jacques-René Rabier, Antoine Chastenet. Each bore the marks of his national upbringing, but all were equally dedicated to the common task. Its urgency encouraged teamwork: busy people have no taste for in-fighting. To be on the safe side, we did not divide our work between the coal and steel sectors, but dealt with both in a single Market Directorate, headed by François Vinck, Hermann Dehnen, and Tony Rollmann, all acting as one. In the transport department, two equally experienced rail specialists, Werner Klaer and Roger Hutter, one German and the other

French, sat opposite each other in the same office. They recognized and confessed the ways in which, in their national rail systems, they had both manipulated freight-rates to distort free competition. Together, in the closest collaboration, they now spent months undoing a skein of national discrimination. Gradually, all levels of our administration were permeated by this new spirit. Since we worked in four languages, our staff was swelled by translators and interpreters. While the normal working language was French, I could talk with the German Vice-President, Franz Etzel, only in English or through our constant interpreter, the admirable Ursula Wenmackers.

Fräulein Wenmackers, who met a tragically early death in a road accident, was as talented as she was devoted. She was a witness to every moment of the efforts that Etzel and I made to examine together and jointly solve the problems which might, if we were not careful, once more divide Germany from France. From the very first day, I decided that my door would always be open to my colleagues, and I saw to it that Etzel was almost always with me. I never received any important visitors without inviting him in, and I took no decision without consulting him. I left him no time to nurture suspicions, and in all circumstances treated him as an equal. He was a man who understood and appreciated an attitude of trust, provided that it was sincere. Today, it is hard to remember or imagine how much Germany then needed reassurance. Through Etzel's rapidly growing influence, the German Government discovered a new kind of relationship between peoples – the simplest and most fruitful: that of open doors and frank discussion.

I by no means underestimated the importance of the decisions we were taking together for the market in coal; but above all I knew that our example, which was followed by our colleagues, would have a significance far wider and longer-lived than the ECSC itself. If we succeeded in proving that men from different countries could follow the same text, work on the same problem with the same data, and eliminate all ulterior motives and mutual suspicions, then we should have helped to change the course of international relations. So we had to succeed; and each of us felt this so profoundly that the team trained in Luxembourg acquired a great force of example, which affected people's way of thinking in the broader areas of politics, the civil service, the universities, the trade unions, and business circles, wherever the Community's influence reached. Starting from there, many other changes would become possible. But should we be able to overcome the first obstacles, and open the common market for coal and steel?

For coal, the necessary conditions were met; and six months after we had begun work, as the Treaty required, I was able to announce over the radio:

'Since this morning, February 10, 1953, there has no longer been Belgian, Dutch, French, German, Italian, or Luxembourg coal, but only European coal, flowing freely among our six countries as if they were one.'

The fact that everyone could now obtain coal from the supplier of his choice and at the best price, throughout the Community, marked the end of an epoch in which everything had been organized otherwise, to restrict consumers' free choice and discriminate among them according to their nationality or their membership of this or that group. In retrospect, it is hard to realize the effect of such a change, because the new situation now seems so normal that one can hardly imagine the absurd system it replaced. The Europe of sovereign States abounded in absurd regulations which were legitimate in a context of national rivalry. No higher law or authority could have abolished them, except that of force. The only effective remedy was to change the context, to create a broader form of sovereignty in which the object of rivalry was shared in common. That done, the absurd rules collapsed, virtually of their own accord. This is what happened in the ECSC. And if in the Europe of the Common Market today many absurd national rules still remain, they are all fated to disappear by the same process of attrition, as the delegation of sovereignty to common institutions proceeds.

The common market for steel was due to open a month later than that for coal. The deadline was approaching when, one day, Uri asked to see me urgently.

'We're going to face a major crisis,' he said. 'The Germans are starting up a great campaign about turnover taxes. They want to challenge the whole present system, which is based on taxing a product in the country where it's consumed.'

'Give me an example,' I said.

'Well, German steel in Germany pays 5%. When it's exported to France, it's exempted from the 5%, but it pays our tax – which is 25%. In the opposite direction, it's the other way round. In reality, if one goes into it deeply, there's not all that much difference; and what difference there is reflects the disparity in exchange rates. But the Germans look as if they're being discriminated against, and they're beginning to shout about it.'

I realized that we were heading for serious difficulties. The Germans would be exasperated if they felt, rightly or wrongly, that they were the victims of injustice.

'Did they raise the question during the negotiations ?' I asked.

'Never,' said Uri. 'No one saw any problem – probably because there isn't one.'

'That may be so, but it looks as if there is. Since there's to be a common market, there will no longer be any imports or exports between the countries inside it; so only the tax of the country of origin ought to be paid. At any rate, that's what the Germans will say.'

That, in fact, was the argument that Etzel put to his colleagues on the High Authority shortly afterwards. No one was able to persuade him that, until taxes were harmonized or the common market was extended to all goods, differences would continue and would justify corrective measures. Etzel had convinced himself by a completely different set of arguments, based on the principle of non-discrimination; but the upshot would have been to give German steel an immense tax advantage in Europe. He was patently sincere, and his views were shared by part of German public opinion, which became greatly incensed. Late one evening, we thought we had convinced him; but the next morning he had changed his mind again, and what he said was massively supported by Germany's industry, trade unions, and press. The High Authority and the Council of Ministers saw dramatic scenes. In the circumstances, we could not think of opening the common market in steel, except by outvoting Etzel and Potthoff. We were empowered to do so, since the High Authority's decisions could be taken by majority vote. But I had made it a rule that no important decision should be reached in conditions of conflict. To force through a decision without having convinced those of my colleagues who were most directly concerned would not in my view have been a victory, but a defeat. We had to continue our efforts at persuasion, and try one form of argument after another. Meanwhile, I decided to impose a two months' delay on the common market for steel.

Perhaps economic theory was not sufficiently developed at that time to formulate clearly what everyone felt as a matter of common sense, and what under the name of 'harmonization' has become current practice in the Common Market today. We were still moving forward in the labyrinth which several generations had built between contrasting and rival national systems. Our task was to blaze the trail by removing physical and mental barriers. The tax question was forcing the High Authority to develop its ideas more rapidly, and I knew that the Community would be changed by it – for better or for worse. I proposed consulting the best authorities on the subject. Jan Tinbergen's was the name that everyone thought of; we also recruited an Italian, a Belgian, and an Englishman.* All four were quite outside the present dispute. After an inquiry in depth, in which all parties were able to state their case, and which had further fruitful consequences, our independent advisers reached the same conclusion as the majority of members of the High Authority. Although still not wholly convinced, Etzel and Potthoff withdrew their objections, and the crisis subsided as quickly as it had arisen. The question was never raised again.

I have recalled this forgotten technical affair in some detail because it was the Community's first big test, and because the experience was not lost on us. I realized at that time that the rule of majority voting was the best way of reaching unanimous agreement, because it led towards decisions, and the prospect could bring those in the minority to see reason. But reason also required that the majority should not use its power to impose its views, or at least should not do so without exhaustive discussion. The role of the Community institutions is to reach decisions; but it is also, and above all, to organize the discussion and carry it far enough for everyone to understand and respect the other side's point of view, even if it be rejected at the end of the day. Some years afterward, when Etzel had become German Finance Minister, he talked to me about our first dispute, which for a time had made him wonder whether my colleagues and I were acting in good faith.

'I was wrong,' he said. 'Everything proves that, because in the Common Market today it's Germany that's reforming her tax system. But at that time we were not prepared to go to the root of the problem, and we couldn't resist the chance of gaining an overwhelming advantage.'

An overwhelming advantage was the temptation that nature, circumstances, good fortune, or war had always previously offered one State or another in its relations with the rest. The Community that we were building removed such chance temptations by correcting natural inequalities and re-establishing competitive conditions that were fair to everyone. This was the aim of the rules which the Treaty's signatories had accepted and which the institutions were called upon to apply. But to change attitudes I was relying as much on the spirit of the rules as on their legal force; or rather, I knew that men who are placed in new practical circumstances, or subjected to a new set of obligations, adapt their behaviour and become different. If the new context is better, they themselves become better: that is the whole rationale of the European

* F. di Fenizio from Padua, Léon Dupriez from Louvain, and W. B. Reddaway from Cambridge; they were assisted by six experts, one from each Community country.

Community, and the process of civilization itself. The difficulties that Europeans still encounter every day in their relations with each other should not mislead us: those difficulties are now internal problems, similar to those which we normally solve, within our countries, by discussion and freely agreed decisions. Like all political systems, the Community cannot prevent problems arising; but it offers a framework and a means for solving them peacefully. This is a fundamental change by comparison with the past – the very recent past.

In February 1953 the Germans may for a time have dreamed of flooding Europe with their steel. They changed their minds as soon as it became clear that this would not be playing the game. At any time of serious crisis, the same thing happens: when a member of the Community sees that it is likely to be isolated, it knows that work together will have to go on; and its own self-interest requires that agreement be reached. The fact is that everyone's self-interest is involved in the common interest. In the present instance, the High Authority had fulfilled its role: it had made a proposal, held long consultations, and then reached a decision. The common market for steel was opened on April 1, and there was no disruption: instead, there was a balanced increase in trade, and cyclical downturns no longer spelt disaster for the less favoured industries. The common market tempered the effect of crises which it could not altogether avoid; and above all the Community protected workpeople by means of reconversion and retraining funds, financed from its own resources. Those resources, which also assisted investment for modernizing industry – both directly and by guaranteeing loans – came from the European tax that we were empowered to levy on coal and steel production. This was the institutions' guarantee of independence. If the High Authority made a bold beginning, this was partly on account of its financial autonomy.

The High Authority's wealth was also Europe's, in that the levy could act as security for large-scale loans. I knew that we could offer American capital first-class guarantees, better than those of the separate member States. But it took time.

Jean Guyot brilliantly conducted the negotiation which led in April 1954 to the signing of a loan agreement between the High Authority and the US Government, for $100m. at the low interest-rate of 3.7%. At that time, no Government could have obtained such favourable terms. Our credit was now well-established, and we could already think of borrowing on the private capital market. However, the most difficult part of our task still remained. This was to persuade industry to invest, and to use for the purpose the High Authority's exceptionally advantageous loans. The same power which reassured our American creditors still disquieted European steelmakers.

The trade unions, however, took a much more positive attitude toward the High Authority's power and resources. Except for the Communists, all the major labour unions saw the advantages they could derive from the proper implementation of the ECSC Treaty – advantages for workers in coal and steel, who now enjoyed guaranteed employment and were no longer at the mercy of much-needed technological change. In the past, modernization had too often been achieved at the cost of unemployment, and too often delayed by fear of social disruption. It meant closing firms that were clearly not competitive and moving some centres of production. But what would happen to workers in those firms? How would those who moved to expanding areas be resettled? The ECSC had not created these problems: it had revealed them; but at the same time it provided means of solving them, by financing retraining and resettlement for those hit by technological unemployment, by rehousing them where necessary, and by helping to modernize uncompetitive industries. All this, which today seems commonplace, was then a bold experiment, which everyone watched with passionate interest, because it was clearly the key to future economic and social progress.

In fact, we ventured further in this direction than ever before or since, and the ECSC's retraining, resettlement, and housing programmes remain models of their kind. But the trade unions were also looking ahead. They saw in the Community's development the promise of less costly and more abundant production, with the assurance that lower prices would not be achieved at the expense of wages. This Treaty pledge, they felt sure, could not be limited to coal and steel, but must become a general rule. The clearest-sighted among them realized that the High Authority offered them a powerful means of action, in that it made public data which had previously been disguised or only patchily perceived. Our statistical inquiries at European level produced surprising revelations in the most obvious fields. Walter Freitag, the President of the DGB, told me:

'Our members didn't even know the state of wages in Germany. Now, they can compare them with wages in France, Belgium, and so on.'

The trade union victories and the general levelling-up that have taken place since then in Common Market Europe would have been impossible without such comparative data.

The to-ing and fro-ing of people and information around the High

Authority also enabled the labour unions to get to know each other and recognize their common interests. Very soon, the Free and Christian trade unions each established in Luxembourg their own very active liaison bureaux, and they took great advantage of our invitation to look over our shoulders at what we were doing. In the Consultative Committee, they were self-assured enough to deal as equals with the producers; and if the Committee never became an arena of confrontation, it was because men who previously had always been on opposite sides were now sitting round the table together, facing problems which they all found novel and which now for the first time were common to them all. This proved once again that major psychological changes, which some seek through violent revolution, can be achieved very peacefully if men's minds can be directed towards the point where their interests converge. That point always exists: but it takes trouble to find it.

We took a great deal of trouble, in fact, to keep to the deadlines we had imposed on ourselves. One by one, the barriers were removed and the prophecies of doom were confounded. Production and trade increased; and steel prices, resisting cyclical pressure, rose far less rapidly than elsewhere in the world. The Italian steel industry flourished beyond all expectations, while the Belgian coalmines overcame their previous backwardness with help from their more advanced competitors. Producers, with a general picture of the Community's needs before them, were able to invest wisely; and consumers, now at last publicly informed of the real price situation, could choose where to purchase their supplies. But the success of the ECSC went far beyond these material achievements. It meant that frontier barriers were definitively on the way out, that sovereignty could be delegated, and that common institutions worked well. This proof remained valid even when the inevitable difficulties arose. It was more valid still in later economic crises, which the Common Market overcame better than its separate member States could have done. Above all, it was now clear that the ECSC method was indeed the way to establish the greatest solidarity among peoples. I spelled out the lesson before the Common Assembly:

'We can never sufficiently emphasize that the six Community countries are the fore-runners of a broader united Europe, whose bounds are set only by those who have not yet joined. Our Community is not a coal and steel producers' association: it is the beginning of Europe.'

The beginning of Europe was a political conception; but, even more, it was a moral idea. Europeans had gradually lost the ability to live together and combine their creative strength. There seemed to be decline in their contribution to progress and to the civilization which they themselves had created – doubtless because in a changing world they no longer had institutions capable of leading them ahead. National institutions had proved that they were ill-adapted to this task. The new Community institutions, it seemed to me, were the only vehicle through which Europeans could once more deploy the exceptional qualities they had displayed in times past; and I did my best to make my listeners in the Assembly share this view:

'A long time ago, I was struck by an observation made by the Swiss philosopher Henri-Frédéric Amiel: "Each man's experience starts again from the beginning. Only institutions grow wiser: they accumulate collective experience; and, owing to this experience and this wisdom, men subject to the same rules will not see their own nature changing, but their behaviour gradually transformed." If justification were needed for our common institutions, that is it. When I think that Frenchmen, Germans, Belgians, Dutchmen, Italians, and Luxembourgers are obeying the same rules and, by doing so, are now seeing their common problems in the same light; when I reflect that this will fundamentally change their behaviour one to another – then I tell myself that definitive progress is being made in relations among the countries and peoples of Europe.'

II

A great test and a new beginning

'Only institutions grow wiser: they accumulate collective experience.' This process needs time for contact with reality to take effect. But in a limited field, among a group of men united for a common purpose and working hard together, I saw how quickly things could move. I was sure that the lessons we were learning day after day from our difficulties and our successes would spread far beyond the circle of the ECSC, which itself was growing ever wider. Gradually, other tasks and other people would become subject to the same common rules and institutions – or perhaps to new institutions: it was too early to say. What seemed most important to me was that our experience should gradually spread by osmosis; and for this process I should have preferred not to set time-limits. But we had been taken by surprise: external events had suddenly speeded up the unification of Europe. Scarcely had the Schuman Plan seen the light of day than a new situation had suddenly arisen which, left to itself, might have wrecked the whole project. To this situation, the only constructive response had seemed to be to pool our armed forces and our nations' basic strength. We had managed to work out how to do so on the same model as our existing Plan, within the same institutional framework, thereby remaining faithful to the method described in the original Schuman Declaration of May 9, 1950: 'Europe will not be built all at once, or as a single whole: it will be built by concrete achievements which first create *de facto* solidarity.'

Yet, as we have seen, the European Defence Community project, 'concrete' and *'de facto'* as it undoubtedly was, forced the pace towards 'a single whole'. By its very nature it implied common political responsibilities, and its own founding document – its constitution, as it were – provided for simultaneous steps towards a full federal structure. The Constitutional Committee which had begun work in the autumn of 1952 had managed, by dint of extraordinary efforts, to complete its task within the time-limit laid down. The men who had devoted six months of their lives to this carefully balanced project were on a par with history's great constitution-makers; and if fate was against them, the importance of what they achieved is nevertheless worthy of respect. Nothing that has been conscientiously made in this way is ever useless: for, by working together, everyone acquires better knowledge of his partners and their problems, and he passes it on to others in his turn. Many of the elements in this first plan for a European Political Community were to reappear in later efforts. One such plan, one day, will exactly fit the bill. The text submitted to the six Governments on March 10, 1953, will then be seen to have been a first model for all the rest.

Re-reading that text, I am struck by how ambitious it is – but also by its wisdom. Some people remember it as a supranational monstrosity. Yet it called for no further delegation of sovereignty by the member States in any field beyond EDC and the ECSC. A common foreign policy was to be achieved by co-ordinating those of the member States, and the general Common Market was to be established by successive agreements. If the constitution-makers were perhaps too cautious on these points, they were insufficiently so when they imagined that European unity would *begin* with the establishment of a federal political system. Yet this, although premature, was good of its kind. It included a Peoples' Chamber to be elected by direct universal suffrage, and a Senate, to be elected by the national Parliaments; a five-member European Executive Council responsible before the two Chambers, with its President elected by the Senate; a Council of national Ministers, to act as a link between the European Executive and the member Governments, as in the ECSC; and, finally, a Court of Justice.

The proposed system thus recognized the reality of the member States, and provided a link between them and the developing Community. It was a step in the right direction; but it proposed to go too fast, without waiting for the force of necessity to make it seem natural in the eyes of Europeans. That was why I was in no way surprised at the reaction it provoked in Georges Bidault. Speaking for the Council of Ministers, he told the Strasbourg Assembly in his most cutting tone:

'Let us beware, if I may say so, of believing that everything is possible to the pure in heart. Honesty obliges us to recognize that the enterprise is a vast one, and not without difficulty. Men who are destined, by their irreproachable attachment to ancient traditions, to make heard the voice of the earth and of the dead are troubled by an enterprise which they fear may finally efface our fatherlands. . . .'

All that was hardly encouraging; and when I heard Bidault invoking History, I knew that the project was doomed:

'It is my pleasure, Gentlemen, to render you the homage that Queen Elizabeth the First addressed to the founders of an Empire; "Hail to the seekers after adventure".'

Coming from Bidault, that was a message of farewell.

Three months previously, in fact, the French Government had undergone a change. René Mayer had replaced Pinay as Prime Minister; and to form his Cabinet he had had to take account of the Gaullist deputies' demands. Although the apparent reasons for successive French Government crises were internal political disputes, the real differences emerged in the great debate about European integration. For four years, Robert Schuman had given Europe a certain continuity through his uninterrupted tenure of the Foreign Office. Everyone knew that his convictions were unshakeable; and his political position was still very strong. But if the premiership of a noted 'European' had to be paid for by a simple exchange of portfolios, bringing Bidault back to the Foreign Office, was this a case of political slippage and a genuine cause for alarm? No close observer could be under any illusion. The nationalists had made the first breach in a front that had held against them since May 1950. French foreign policy was once more going to vacillate. Schuman had an intimate knowledge of Germany, which had made him approach things frankly. Bidault, on the other hand, looked on Germany through the eyes of an historian. Both had fought against Nazi domination; but each had reacted differently to it. Bidault remained insecure. The Europe he wanted was a French Europe: on this point he differed little from the Gaullists. I once heard him say:

'Make Europe without destroying France.'

The formula was impeccable, and I might have agreed with it – except that in his mind it meant refusing any further delegation of sovereignty.

For more than a year, the dispute about EDC had underlain all political attitudes in France, in the parties, in Parliament, and in the Government itself. The EDC Treaty, signed in May 1952, was not put before the French National Assembly until January 1953. Pleven, Pinay, and Schuman played for time, and I have never really understood what they were hoping would happen. One thing is certain: they gained nothing by waiting, because in 1953 the opponents of the Defence Community joined the majority and entered the Government. From then on, with safeguard protocols and special preambles to the Treaty, one concession led to another. The result was to nullify part of the Treaty and above all to cast doubt on France's determination. Disquiet became more acute when the crucial National Assembly committees appointed as their *rapporteurs* Jules Moch and General Marie-Pierre Koenig, both confirmed opponents of EDC. De Gaulle, for his part, announced:

'With or without protocols, the Treaty is totally unacceptable.'

Yet the French Government had to go to a great deal of trouble to persuade its partners to accept the protocols. It was in this atmosphere that the German *Bundestag* ratified the Treaty on March 19, 1953. Thereupon, once more, it stopped dead. No sooner had René Mayer shown that he intended to push ahead with EDC than its opponents joined forces against him, and he had to resign. His successor, Joseph Laniel, was careful to do nothing: he lasted until the fall of Diên Biên Phû. I myself have sometimes been reproached for not doing more to prevent things becoming bogged down. But I was far from Paris and fully occupied in bringing to fruition an enterprise which everyone saw as the advance-guard of European unification. If I had spread my efforts, at the risk of compromising the growth of the ECSC, should I have been able at least to put some new life into EDC, which was already a prey to pressures and preconditions? I do not know the answer. But I do know that to work for the success of the ECSC was my first duty, and my only duty if a choice had to be made.

Many writers have wondered whether the EDC Treaty would have had any chance of securing a majority in the French Parliament in 1953. I am surprised that some of them, including some of those best qualified, think that it would. I have no wish to quarrel with their opinion, but I cannot share it – for the simple reason that I find it impossible to put a question in those terms. To wonder what might have happened if matters had gone otherwise is an exercise of which I am incapable. To rewrite history on the basis of hypotheses which were not fulfilled is not only a vain effort: in my view, it makes no sense. I have scarcely ever been known to seek out who or what was responsible for things that have happened, and still less for things that have not happened. If successive French Governments never thought the time was ripe for submitting the EDC Treaty to Parliament, who can say that they were well or badly informed? What is certain is that the time finally chosen was wrong. Thrown into consternation by the drama of the war in Indochina, the French were temporarily unable to look clearly at their future. Pierre Mendès-France, who seemed to very many people a man of destiny, was not prepared to face and solve several problems at a time. Among the priorities which he chose, or which events imposed upon him, Europe had no place.

He and I exchanged several personal letters during the last days of August, 1954, just before the EDC debate in the Chamber. On both sides, they reveal great anguish, the feeling that we were heading rapidly towards an accident; and my reproaches, like Mendès-France's debates with his conscience, were all in vain.

For France, the EDC dispute was a painful parting of the ways. The forces of the past and those of the future tore the country apart; and in the confused debate it was the former that prevailed. But the decision was reached democratically, so it has to be accepted. Is there any point, therefore, in criticizing those who had not fully enlightened the public about the true choice that faced France's representatives – a European Army or a German army? I am not accusing anyone in particular: no one was master of events when the moment of truth came. In fact, the currents of opinion that clashed so tumultuously in August 1954 were long-established; they were also to be long-lived. The clash was merely a little sharper than many others in the Community's history. Many people saw it as a cataclysm; but although I was very disappointed, I did not believe that the French National Assembly's rejection of EDC marked the end of Europe. Once again, I had to explain to my friends that the only true defeats are those that one accepts. We had underestimated the strength of the nationalist current; and perhaps it was salutary to have taken its measure at the flood. We now needed time to build more solidly.

Whatever the opponents of EDC may have said, or some people may have believed, by rejecting integration they were not preventing German rearmament. The negative vote of August 30, 1954, put the clock back four years, to that same season in 1950 when the re-establishment of a German army had seemed inevitable. The collapse of the patiently-built structure in which we had hoped to merge Germany's military contribution with those of other countries meant that a German army was now free to develop autonomously. Now, Adenauer's great political wisdom was the only protection against the danger we had sought to avoid. Until the last moment, he had beseeched his partners not to allow the restoration of a German national High Command. The French Parliament's decision affected him deeply; but he at once reacted as a statesman: the crisis had to be overcome, and an interim solution had to be found which would safeguard the building of Europe. It was British diplomacy that found the solution: by blocking her own policy, France had lost the initiative to Anthony Eden. As British Foreign Secretary, and soon to be Prime Minister, Eden saw the opportunity to act as arbiter on the continent, and substitute for the European Army a policy of co-operation. The resultant Paris Agreements setting up Western European Union made it possible for Germany to join a traditional military alliance between national armies financed by national budgets and run by national High Commands. That was the reality: the rest was no more than a feeble co-ordinating structure doomed to a vegetative existence.

The failure of EDC created a vacuum, but it in no way changed the nature of things. A coalition had been formed in France between opponents of the very principle of integration and advocates of a neutrality who found it hard to evolve a positive policy; and both had joined in temporary alliance with war veterans who refused to forgive and forget. Now, this negative coalition dissolved. But the need to build Europe remained; and repeated overtures from Moscow, to which some people now wished to subordinate the further integration of the West, were no good reason for changing course. I had long been convinced that, *vis-à-vis* the Russians, the only reasonable attitude was to organize ourselves without speculating about their secret intentions or their possible response. To remain divided, waiting for them to make a global arrangement with our ancient nations, would be to pursue an illusion. On the contrary, the Russians would surely adapt to a new situation which they had no means of preventing; they might even recognize that it gave them greater security. A Germany integrated into a peaceful organization of the West might, after all, appear to them the lesser of two evils. Adenauer was the first to agree with this analysis, and it was very fortunate that at a time of such deep confusion he did not seek greater freedom of action for his country. The Paris Agreements gave him back all the sovereignty he sought, and opened the door into NATO. He was wise enough to renounce atomic weapons, and he was still ready to pay whatever price was needed to bind Germany and France together in a West European federation.

Once more, there was something to be done; but someone had to take the initiative, and most of the men in a position to take decisions were paralysed by mistrust. I recognized the same impasse that had faced us four years earlier. But difficulties have this advantage: they can be used as a lever. I have never forgotten the words which Jacques Benoist-Méchin quotes in his fine biography of Ibn Saud. A Western visitor had asked him for the secret of his success. Ibn Saud replied:

'God appeared to me when I was a young man, and said something which has guided my actions throughout my life. He told me: "For me, everything is a means – even obstacles".'

The obstacle in Europe's path, in 1954, was political resistance – in the last resort, the difficulty of taking decisions. It had to be tackled head on, to persuade those who held sovereign power to delegate a part of it. I pondered on how to ensure that political forces everywhere ceased to act as a brake and became instead the motor of European unity. The first prerequisite was that I should be free to act as I saw fit. I therefore decided to resign from the Presidency of the High Authority.

According to the Treaty, my term of office as President was due to expire on February 20, 1955, two years after the opening of the common market for coal; but it would be fitting, I thought, to announce my decision three months before that date. Nothing prevented my mandate's being prolonged; but in order to facilitate the search for a successor, I wanted it to be known in advance that I was not seeking re-appointment as President, and that I was also giving up my ordinary membership of the High Authority, which still had two years to run after the expiry of my presidential term of office. On November 9, 1954, I called a meeting of my colleagues and made the following statement:

'In order to be able to take part with complete freedom of action and speech in the achievement of European unity, which must be practical and real, I shall resign on February 10 next year, at the end of my term of office as President of the ECSC High Authority. What is being achieved in our six countries for coal and steel must be continued until it culminates in the United States of Europe. The institutions of the European Coal and Steel Community are so far the only European institutions to which the Parliaments of our countries have agreed to transfer sovereignty and delegate powers of decision.

'Our countries have become too small for the present-day world, for the scale of modern technology and of America and Russia today, or China and India tomorrow. The union of European peoples in the

United States of Europe is the way to raise their standard of living and preserve peace. It is the great hope and opportunity of our time.

'If we work without delay and without rest, we shall make it the reality of tomorrow.'

I informed the Governments of my decision at the same time; and I told the Common Assembly at Strasbourg:

'It is for Parliaments and Governments to decide on the transfer of new powers to the European institutions. The impulse must therefore come from without. I shall be able to join in the efforts of all those who are working to continue and enlarge what has been begun.'

To enlarge what had been begun – or in other words to delegate more power without reviving still smouldering disputes – that was the difficulty; and I discussed it on more than one occasion with Paul-Henri Spaak against the background of the Ardennes, white with winter snow. The High Authority existed: it was well-established: it still had its job to do. At that time, it seemed to us wiser to remain within the ECSC framework, perhaps enlarging it, but in any case not departing from a model which had proved its worth and become an accepted feature of the scene. So the path of further progress seemed obvious: it was directly to extend the activities of the High Authority in those areas where we were beginning to feel hemmed in. Those we had in mind were transport and energy. But, on examination, the problem of atomic energy seemed big enough to require a structure of its own.

The atom, in fact, was a new and major problem which for Europeans was an object of both fear and hope. Their fear was the fear of nuclear weapons, which were ceasing to be the monopoly of three technologically advanced powers – the United States, the USSR, and Great Britain – and would soon be within the reach of the Community countries. While those responsible for French defence were strongly tempted to enter the race, nuclear weapons would remain forbidden to the Germans. This made it impossible to embark on any common venture in nuclear defence. At the same time, however, the dissemination of nuclear technology was closely linked to hopes of its peaceful development. In August 1953, the US Senate had modified the MacMahon Act, passed shortly after World War II, which had imposed the death penalty for communicating American nuclear know-how to any foreign power, even in peacetime. This gave our countries the possibility of obtaining information which had hitherto been secret, and thereby catching up with the development of atomic energy for industrial use. European scientists and technologists were urging their Governments to press ahead. The prospect of fresh national rivalry in this new and apparently limitless field alarmed me; but equally, that of a vast common enterprise attracted me, provided that a careful distinction were maintained between civil and military ends. The reports from our experts left no room for doubt: nuclear energy could replace all other forms of energy by the end of the century – and for centuries to come.

To approach our atomic future separately, when with great effort we were pooling ancient resources that past generations had fragmented, would have been insane. If there was one field in which the method of the Schuman Plan ought to be applied fully and successfully, it was surely this prodigious new technology, which so far was virgin territory. It warranted the establishment of a specialized institution, which I saw as a new High Authority for the peaceful development of atomic energy, and whose tasks I now set out to define. It was Louis Armand who was to baptize it, some three months later, when he lent it his enthusiastic support and the power of his inventive genius. The name he chose was 'Euratom'.

The pooling of so many basic resources and activities would involve far broader harmonization and unification, affecting the fundamental elements of the economy, of finance, and of social policy in the countries concerned. To use technical terminology, integration could no longer be purely 'vertical': it must now begin to be 'horizontal'. I therefore foresaw the gradual formation of a customs union, leading eventually to full economic integration. This seemed to me reasonable and altogether within our reach. It did not imply an institutional revolution: the member States would not have had the courage to undertake one only a few months after a failure that had made them ultra-cautious. They would simply be asked to persuade their Parliaments to extend the range of the High Authority's mandate and to set up a new Authority for atomic power. For the rest, the Council and the Assembly would remain the same – the latter being elected, after an experimental period, by universal suffrage, which would give it greater authority to invent and propose to Governments the further steps that were in prospect – unless Governments could take the initiative themselves. Finally, I saw in all this an opportunity to associate Great Britain more closely with the new venture.

I had Spaak's agreement on the proposal, which was already drafted in the form of a declaration. He made every effort to convince his Benelux colleagues, in particular Johan Willem Beyen, the Dutch Foreign Minister, who on his side was pressing for full economic union. But the Belgians were not prepared to put fresh pressure on France, and they proceeded with caution. We were concerned only to decide who should make the declaration and when. The date of February 10, 1955, when my term of office expired, was approaching, and a conference of Foreign Ministers was convened to appoint my successor. Would Benelux seize this opportunity? Or should I have the declaration made, once I had recovered my independence, by a group of men representing the political parties and trade unions? Already, I was taking steps to assemble such a group. This latter solution, it seemed to me, would best meet the need to give a new impetus to European affairs; and I was firmly resolved to establish a new framework for democratic action which would help or oblige Governments to face their responsibilities. Events forced me to delay the announcement and launching of this plan, to which I was later to devote twenty years of my life. The fall of Mendès-France's Government in early February made it impossible to hold the meeting of Ministers and appoint my successor.

Already, in fact, I had said goodbye to my colleagues and staff on the High Authority. In everyone's mind, one period had ended. For them, in their Luxembourg citadel, another was beginning – as it was for me, in the battle outside. The Paris apartment which was to become the headquarters of the Action Committee for the United States of Europe was ready to receive the furniture from our house at Bricherhof on the outskirts of Luxembourg, already packed up. I remember coming home from a walk with Silvia one winter evening to find the house brightly lit and surrounded by cars. My colleagues on the High Authority were waiting for me with their retinue of advisers. At first, I thought it was an improvised farewell party; but they had an embarrassed air which puzzled me. Finally, Etzel pushed forward Michel Gaudet, who made the following statement:

'*Monsieur le Président*, your legal service has the duty to inform you that you cannot leave your post. We have gone through the Treaty over and over again, and it is clear that you remain President in office for as long as your successor has not been appointed.'

We halted our removal, and I stayed in Luxembourg for five more long months. Everyone had a reason for not hurrying to convene the Ministers of Foreign Affairs, the most valid being that a further political change in France now made possible a fresh European initiative which needed careful preparation.

The idea that Governments might make a proposal now seemed more realistic, and Spaak suggested to his five colleagues that they take as a working basis the draft declaration on which he and I had agreed. At first, he had little success. Pinay, Minister of Foreign Affairs in the new French Government headed by Edgar Faure, was afraid to reopen the European debate which had so recently been closed. The Germans, contrary to my first expectations, were not enthusiastic about the idea of an atomic Community on the model of the ECSC. Uri, I must say, had long predicted this attitude.

'Men like Erhard,' he explained, 'will not see any advantage in setting up a new supranational organization of the Six for an industry in which they can negotiate for technology from Britain, America, and Norway, instead of from their Community partners, who at present have little or none. On the other hand, if you propose to them making general the integration already begun, by forming a six-nation Common Market for all goods, then they will see the point of establishing an atomic Community in the same general framework.'

I soon had proof that this was so; and Uri's explanations played a large part in converting me to the idea of the general Common Market, which had at first seemed rather vague. Finally, Spaak reached an agreement with Beyen, who was delighted to see new scope for his own ideas. Under the name of the 'Memorandum from the Benelux Countries to the six ECSC Countries', Spaak drafted a four-page proposal, which his *directeur de cabinet* Robert Rothschild sent me on May 6, 1955, with the simple message 'Herewith your child'. It contained, in fact, the essentials of our draft declaration. If the words 'United States of Europe' were no longer included, the notion of an 'Economic Community' was nevertheless more sharply defined; and a procedure was proposed. The Treaties were to be prepared simultaneously, by a conference comprising the Six, the ECSC, and the British Government.

I was in agreement with these proposals, which in some respects went further and faster than my own. In fact, the situation was now more favourable. In the interval, France had ratified the Paris Agreements – and if the vote did not involve major commitments, it at least had the virtue of being a decision. The long period of uncertainty was over. Everyone was haunted by the thought that it would be disastrous for a new attempt to fail. Some therefore counselled prudence, but others on the contrary were encouraged to ask more from France: she would hesitate, they thought, to say No a second time. These speculations continued throughout the 'relaunching of Europe', which began when a conference of the six Foreign Ministers was convened to meet at Messina on June 1, 1955. The result could only be a compromise between boldness and timidity; but the essential, in my view, was that the conference should give a mandate to someone to do something along the lines that we had already embarked on with the Schuman Plan five years earlier. Afterwards, it would be up to us to see that his mandate was as broadly as possible fulfilled.

At Messina, the Ministers took the Benelux Memorandum as the basis for their agreement: they had no time to do more than slightly weaken its form. On the other hand, they inaugurated a working procedure which was to prove very practical and fruitful: a committee of delegates and Government experts was to prepare a report to Ministers under the chairmanship of a ranking statesman. The Ministers would then give instructions with a view to drafting the Treaties. One detail was important: the High Authority, now under the Presidency of René Mayer, was to assist the committee. Finally, Great Britain was to be invited to take part. This was a satisfactory result: once again, the method was inseparable from the objective, and no less important. When the Ministers came to discuss who should preside over the committee, Spaak's personality made him the obvious choice; and when the High Authority was asked for its advice, it gave of its whole experience. Uri, Paul Delouvrier (who had succeeded Guyot), Spierenburg, and others did their utmost to infuse the spirit of Luxembourg into the meetings, which took place in Brussels. The experts' report on which the Treaties were based was essentially the work of Uri – as Spaak himself always acknowledged. It is nonetheless a fact that the political credit for this vital document is due to that outstanding Belgian statesman, who laboured so well in the cause of Europe.

Chapter 16

THE ACTION COMMITTEE FOR THE
UNITED STATES OF EUROPE (1955-1975)

I

A new political force

So, in the early summer of 1955, I found myself a private citizen once more after sixteen years of uninterrupted public service. In my successive posts, I had never in fact had the feeling that I was pursuing a career or that I belonged to a hierarchy, whether French, British, American, or European. At the same time, if I had held official mandates, I had always taken great care about how they were drawn up. And if I had had administrative staff, I had either limited its size or dealt only with that part of it which was directly relevant to what I had to do. What I sought from my colleagues was fidelity rather than obedience. Whether I myself have ever obeyed anyone, I could not say: I know no other rule than that of being convinced and convincing others. No one has ever succeeded in making me do anything which I did not think desirable and useful, and in this sense I have never served a master – but I in turn have rarely obliged anyone to act against his will. No good ever comes of that: it is better to hand the task over to somebody else, or to perform it oneself. When I left the High Authority, Léon Daum reminded me that I had lost a bet. Early on, I had said to him:

'If one day there are more than two hundred of us, we shall have failed.'

'Now we're six times as many,' said Daum, 'and we're succeeding.'

I was less certain, at that point; which was why I thought it reasonable, and not presumptuous, to tell my colleagues:

'I think I can be of more use to you outside.'

They doubted whether I could, without the help of a large administration. Only Giacchero drew the right conclusion.

'We're a citadel under siege,' he said. 'The most fearless among us is making a sortie.'

It was important for there to be no mistake: my resignation was not a sign of discouragement, but the beginning of a new battle; and although I had taken the decision by myself, I had no intention of fighting alone. To face one's responsibilities when the objective is to unite Europe means recruiting others – politicians or labour leaders – who are prepared to join in the task. Through them one can influence the men and women whose future they affect by their political or trade union activities and their administrative or economic decisions. So there had to be a great deal of thinking and consultation before setting up a new force aimed at changing both attitudes and things.

For me, the phase of thinking was already over. Now, I was determined to bring together the organized forces I had seen at work when I was French Planning Commissioner, and later at the High Authority – the political parties and trade unions. With their help, I had been able to effect some very radical changes; without them – or worse, against them – I could have done nothing. Both had helped me enormously in the conception and execution of the French Modernization Plan; they had backed the Governments in their efforts to set up the Schuman Plan; and they had played an essential role in making the Community work. But they had also proved that their opposition could be insuperable. The British Labour Party had led the campaign against Britain's membership of the Community; a coalition of parties in the French Parliament had blocked the development of Europe through EDC. Recent events had proved that it was unsafe to bank on the decline or division of nationalist forces. In any case, I refrained from any speculation about tactical alliances. European integration was a new idea which often disconcerted party strategists, because reactions to it cut across traditional party lines. Both the majority and the opposition were divided on many of our proposals, and I had to make the same suggestions to both of them.

I wondered for a time whether I should go further and recruit producers' organizations and militant 'European' groups. But experience had taught me that they were not always effective, and that they sometimes lacked a sense of the general interest. The 'European' militants were sincere, but they had no power; while the employers' organizations had large resources, but used them in the interests of the private enterprises on whose behalf they operated. Only the political parties and the trade unions had both the strength and the element of disinterest that were needed for the building of Europe. Political parties, by their very nature, have to take an overall view. Trade unions are interested in practical matters and alive to change. So it was to these two types of body that I confined my approach, using as intermediaries men whose ability and goodwill I had come to know in the Common Assembly, in the Consultative Committee, and in the course of other contacts in the various Community countries. But it was clearly understood that these men would not merely agree to join forces in their personal capacity: they would represent and commit their organizations. The body they were to join I now gave a name: The Action Committee for the United States of Europe.

Everyone I approached in the six countries encouraged me to go ahead; but nothing struck me more forcibly than my encounter with the leaders of the German trade unions at the end of December 1954. We met at their request, in Luxembourg, where they had invited me to come discreetly to the Hotel Kons. Walter Freitag, President of the DGB, was there; so were Heinrich Imig, from the miners' federation, and Heinrich Straeter of the metalworkers.

'We are convinced,' said Freitag, 'that Europe is the workers' opportunity, and essential to peace. But we are worried, and we don't know what to do. You have announced that you wish to continue your action from the outside. We have seen you at work at the High Authority for the last two years, and we trust you, because you do what you say and you say what you do. Go on building Europe, and we'll follow you.'

I was moved and encouraged by these words, coming from a man who in his own country represented an organized labour movement six million strong, and who was speaking in the presence of, and in agreement with, the leaders of the two great Ruhr trade unions. I explained to them how I saw the Committee I had in mind, and I asked Freitag:

'Would you agree to join the Committee on behalf of the German trade-union federation?'

'Yes,' he answered: 'I can tell you that the DGB will join.'

'But what if your Social-Democrat friends go on following a different policy?' I said. 'Won't that cause you problems?'

'No problem,' said Freitag. 'We'll go ahead with you in any case.'

This willingness to commit themselves, and to act independently of political parties, was characteristic of the great German trade union leaders, who played a leading role in their country's democratic development. From that day onward, I had no firmer or more faithful supporters. Their massive backing, I felt sure, would make the SPD leaders think very hard about their own position.

'A federal authority of the mind' is what the French journalist and politician Jean-Jacques Servan-Schreiber once called the Action Committee. The phrase is striking; but I think that it would have been more accurate to speak of the moral influence the Committee exerted on the established authorities in each country. I was not trying to acquire or exercise political power in competition with the normal powers of Governments. But the problem was precisely to persuade Governments to transfer more and more of their powers to common institutions. For that purpose, constant outside pressure had to be brought to bear on them. In a democratic country, this was surely the role of the political parties and trade unions. But they in turn had to be welded into a single European force. I thought I had some title to try to do that; but I knew how precarious anyone's authority is if he wields it only in his own name. People do not willingly follow an individual: even if they are unaware of it, the prestige they respect in him is that of the organized power or legitimate authority for which he stands. Forgetting this, many people have found themselves isolated and powerless. I remembered a dinner party at Churchill's house at the end of the war. He was now only Leader of the Opposition, but he more than filled that role. Someone at the table referred to the immense personal authority he had exerted on men and events during the darkest hours. To everyone's surprise, Churchill interrupted, flushed with indignation.

'Just remember this,' he said: 'everything I did I was able to do because I was Leader of the Conservative Party.'

His experience had given him good reason to believe that; and while some people saw the incident as a striking lesson in modesty, it seemed to me a lesson in democratic legitimacy. Authority in our countries has a collective basis, and its source is always free elections. I knew that my personal influence would not long survive my resignation from the High Authority, where I had been the nominee of six Governments and answerable to a parliamentary Assembly. I should not be able to recover influence by myself, but only through elected statesmen and trade unionists who trusted me. This was the new form of authority I wanted to establish in Europe: the collective authority of the whole Action Committee. It would be maintained only by constant initiative and action, to stimulate which would be my particular task. It would be for the members, and the organizations they represented, to take political decisions and reach political conclusions. Their objective was what the Committee's title proclaimed: the United States of Europe; and the first steps, dictated by immediate events, were the rapid ratification of the Treaties and the establishment of the new Communities. After that, we should see.

I appeared to be alone and without resources to organize the numerous forces on which I was counting. But that was merely how it seemed. In reality, I felt myself supported by men of goodwill who were merely waiting to be given the prospect of common action towards which they would direct their parties and their unions. And to respond to their expectations I had no need of vast resources. An office, a telephone, and a secretary would be enough. I had them, and more. When one is bent on action, and that alone, one is not long left in need; and I had no lack of loyal supporters. Jacques Van Helmont, seconded from the High Authority, came to help me set up and run the Action Committee: then two young Englishmen, François Duchêne and Richard Mayne, to whom I shall return later.

Small as it was, this headquarters staff was a source of tireless stimulus, and we organized it as a multiplier of ideas. In establishing and maintaining the innumerable contacts I needed throughout Europe, I was fortunate enough to be helped by Max Kohnstamm, who had the priceless ability to communicate across the barriers of political frontiers, linguistic differences, and national habits. But what I appreciated even more was the proof of friendship he gave me by coming to share the risks of my venture. He left a promising career to help run the Action Committee, whose Vice-President he was from beginning to end.

I knew that I should be able to count on a great deal of voluntary help. The Committee could call on the ablest advisers of their generation, men like Marjolin, Uri, Robert Triffin the American economist, and Guido Carli the Italian banker. They were ready to give us the full benefit of their experience because they saw the Committee as a means of more rapidly applying the ideas that each of them was urging in his own particular sphere. All those ideas involved change, and for that very reason they ran into opposition from the civil service. At a given moment, they needed to be taken up by decision-makers, at political level; and that was the Action Committee's whole aim. Its authority depended both on the quality of its proposals and on their likelihood of being accepted; and these were closely linked. I had to show, as rapidly as possible, that the Action Committee's machinery was well in control of the two dynamic processes that I wanted to bring together in Europe – proposals and decisions. But the Committee had no precedents to guide it. I had to convince its founders and members one by one.

During the second half of 1955, I travelled throughout the Community to recruit the six countries' political and trade union leaders. For me, this was a very rewarding experience, and I should like many others to do the same. But unless they were forced, as I was, by the need for action, would anyone take the trouble to pay individual attention to all the various strands that make up the political life of Europe? Many of the people I visited already knew each other because they belonged to an international party or trade union organization; but none of them knew all the others. The Socialists of the north and the Christian Democrats of the south had never had occasion or inclination to meet. The Strasbourg assemblies brought some of them together – always the same ones – in polite confrontations. But immense distances separated the headquarters of many political parties, within countries as much as from one country to another. Foreign policy sometimes forged temporary coalitions – we had seen them in the case of EDC; but the true demarcation lines were those of internal politics. In France and Belgium, the Socialists and Christian Democrats might well share the same European aims; but their mutual relations were dominated by the dispute over Church schools. This was the kind of thing that had to be changed. The trade unions had established European headquarters organizations when the ECSC began, and in the coal and steel industries they had become aware of the interests they had in common: but the main part of their work was within national frontiers, and it was there that I had to go and meet, one after another, the powerful, modest men to whom millions of working people had entrusted their interests. That those interests were common interests, irrespective of frontiers, was for most of them no more than an abstract idea. They were waiting to be shown that Europe was a living reality, not just a diplomatic affair that had nothing to do with their concerns.

To know and respect those concerns took much time and patience, as it did to discern the different currents within the political parties. I had to be careful of people's susceptibilities, and make no mistake about who really held the power. Then I had to persuade these men, who were normally on opposite sides, to come and sit down together around the same table somewhere in Europe. I am not saying that everything was easy; but I met no insuperable obstacles. I should add that I approached neither the Communist parties nor the Communist-led trade unions, who were opposed to any form of European unity, nor – for the same reason – the Gaullist Members of Parliament, who had long declared their hostility to the very idea of integration. But I did see the leaders of twenty major parties, representing 70% of the six countries' voters, and trade union leaders who represented 14m. workers. I spoke to all of them in the same way, and they all showed the same trust in me. They had taken the time to think and consult, and I put no pressure on them personally: they had to represent their organizations as a whole. This led to serious internal debates which were an important contribution in themselves.

On July 25, 1955, I was in Bonn, where in the *Bundestag* offices I met Ollenhauer and Wehner, who were then respectively President and Vice-President of the German Social-Democratic Party (SPD). I had known them well in the Strasbourg Assembly. I had not forgotten that their party had voted against EDC; but since Ollenhauer had taken over from Schumacher it was at least possible to talk. The fact that they had agreed to sit in the Community's Parliament showed that they wanted to have some influence on the building of Europe. I watched their hesitation. Visibly, they found it difficult to quell the suspicion that behind our altruistic words there might still be un-avowed national interests which would one day come to the fore. In their questioning of our action I sensed concern rather than hostility, and I did my best to reassure them, relying to a large extent on the proof that lay before their eyes. Ollenhauer I found sensitive and receptive; but behind him stood Wehner, whose character I found hard to fathom. Although he deliberately held himself back, the power of this second-in-command, formerly a Communist, could not be ignored. He was a real force of nature: his essentially German appearance and his sudden furies or enthusiasms left me perplexed; yet at the same time I sensed in him something deeply human, ever searching for ways to prevent a return to brute force. He had fled from Nazi Germany, and he would always fight against tyranny. That was why the Community attracted him, and why he was exacting in his demands on it. That, too, was why we soon understood one another. The solid friendship that grew up between us enabled us together to face many years that were difficult for Europe.

That day, I still detected in Ollenhauer and Wehner a lingering mis-trust which I could well understand. True, we no longer faced the problem of the Germany Army: that had been wrapped up in the ambiguity of the Paris Agreements, under which Bonn had renounced nuclear arms. But the Social Democrats might well suspect that this renunciation, which they believed to be essential to the establishment of peace, might be challenged through the new atomic Community which I was proposing as one of the Action Committee's objectives. I explained to them at length that, on the contrary, only by integrating Europe's nuclear industries should we be able to guarantee that they were confined to strictly civilian use. Once reassured on this point, how could they refuse what an inexhaustible source of energy promised to give mankind? They listened attentively. They knew that their trade-union friends in the DGB had already expressed their confidence in me. The conversation ended inconclusively. Later that day, Wehner telephoned me: 'Could you come back and see me? I have a message for you.'

We met again in his office.

'We'll go along with you,' he said. 'Ollenhauer thanks you for having made the offer at this precise moment.'

Apparently, I had given him the opportunity to abandon a policy inherited from the past, and to start again on new and more constructive lines.

From that July day onward, the German Social Democrats were firm supporters of the Community which at the start they had so violently opposed. Germany's European commitment, which Socialist hostility had made more and more uncertain as Adenauer's party grew weary in office, was now assured. In France, Guy Mollet was delighted at the change, which he had long hoped for, and which removed an obstacle to co-operation between the Socialist parties on the European continent. During the summer, I saw other Socialist leaders: J. A. W. Burger in The Hague, Max Buset in Brussels, Jean Fohrmann in Luxembourg, Matteo Matteotti in Rome. All promised their help. The Christian Democrats – Amintore Fanfani, Kurt Kiesinger, Théo Lefèvre, C. P. M. Romme, Robert Lecourt – and all the Liberal leaders, also agreed with the Committee's aims. None of them, of course, committed himself without the agreement of his colleagues in the party leadership. But I wanted more: I wanted them to be mandated, so that the discussion and decisions would involve the party itself. I proceeded in the same way with the trade unions; and after many contacts, many comings and goings, and many explanations, I managed to secure the agreement of Auguste Cool and André Renard in Belgium, Robert Bothereau and Maurice Bouladoux in France, Giulio Pastore in Italy, H. Ooosterhuis in the Netherlands, and so on. None of them could be unaware of what the Committee sought to achieve, and so none of them was surprised when at the beginning of October they received the following letter:

I have the honour to ask you to participate in the establishment of the

Action Committee for the United States of Europe.

The personalities who participate in the establishment of this Committee will each ask his organization to join. It is understood that the political and labour organizations joining the Committee will be represented by the delegate whom they themselves choose for this purpose.

The Committee will ensure unity of action by the member organizations in order to attain by concrete achievements the United States of Europe.

At first, by the Committee's intervention and that of the organizations grouped within it, its action will consist in demonstrating to Governments, Parliaments, and public opinion their determination to see that the Messina resolution of June 2 becomes a veritable step toward the United States of Europe. . . .

To achieve these objectives, it is necessary to put aside all specious solutions. Mere co-operation between Governments will not suffice. It is indispensable for States to delegate certain of their powers to European federal institutions mandated by all the participating countries as a whole. At the same time the close association of Great Britain with these new achievements must be assured. . . .

On October 13, 1955, I was able publicly to announce that all the recipients of the letter had accepted, and that the Action Committee for the United States of Europe had been formed. That day, Guy Mollet declared:

'The French Socialist Party has unanimously authorized me to join the Committee. . . . This puts an end, once and for all, to the dissensions that arose at the time of EDC. Realization of this fact transcends the boundaries of the Socialist parties themselves. Today, European integration is once more common ground.'

He added, very significantly:

'This is the first time that the trade unions of all our countries have agreed to take part, alongside the parties, in joint political action.'

He might have added something else: that it was also the first time that so many people had joined together to pursue common goals in foreign policy, irrespective of their differences over domestic policy. Announced simultaneously in the capitals of the six Community countries, the establishment of the Committee was hailed by the press as an important political event, in particular because the German Social Democrats had joined. A disquieting split, which had weakened the Socialist front in Europe and cast doubt on the future of Germany, was now healed. The psychological effects of the EDC dispute would now gradually disappear. Finally, people were impressed by this joint show of determination on the part of men who normally had little in common. Those in favour of European unity, who as the opinion polls showed were a majority in the six countries, had new cause for encouragement. But one thing was clear: what we had established was not another European Movement or a federalist political party; it was a new means of action, determined and optimistic, but still as yet untried. That same day, speaking to the British on BBC radio, I said:

'Don't forget the Action Committee for the United States of Europe. You'll be hearing from us again.'

I was not promising sensations, but initiatives publicly explained and followed by action on the part of democratic organizatons throughout Europe. Except through those organizations, the Committee would have no means of action or influence. Free from any subordination to Governments, it would have to operate with the minimum of resources needed to maintain the tiny secretariat that I set up in Avenue Foch in Paris, in the apartment where Silvia's brother let me have two rooms. Essentially, the Committee's resources came from its member organizations' subscriptions. It was vital for the headquarters team to remain small, and I kept its budget to a minimum.

The budget was clear: anyone could read it. I wanted my action to be clear too. Everyone, whatever his relative importance in his own country or in Europe, would have to be kept informed of what I was doing, and consulted before decisions were reached. Given the distances involved, and the multifarious commitments of these busy men, it was a major operation to secure agreement on a proposal, and still more to fix the date for a full meeting of the Committee. I spent a great deal of time on this; but time spent on adjusting ideas and expressions, and even on settling dates, was far from wasted. It maintained an uninterrupted flow of information among men who themselves were always on the move in Europe to hear and mould the opinions of their federations, their trade-union members, or their constituents. It was essential that our meetings be carefully prepared and that there should be a very well-developed consensus by the time the thirty-odd members of the Committee gathered for one or two days in one of the capitals. In so brief a meeting, all we could hope to do was put the finishing touches to a text whose essentials were already agreed. The first text, like those that followed it, was prepared at No 83 Avenue Foch with the help of Kohnstamm and, because the subject required it, the leading experts on nuclear questions. I no longer remember how many versions we wrote between October and December 1955. All I can say is that there were as many as were needed – that is, a large number, to take account of the many acute observations I collected on my travels to the capitals, and in the manifold correspondence and telephone calls by which we were inundated in Paris.

The same process took place once or twice every year. In all, there were eighteen meetings, in which a total of more than 120 people took part, keeping our small team constantly at a stretch. The adoption and publication of our texts in the form of resolutions, at our plenary sessions, were widely commented on in the press. They were vital, in that they steered and accelerated the Governments' European policies; but they were only the visible part of the Committee's work. Unseen by outside observers, it had a daily influence on its huge network of members. Our group included more than thirty leaders from six countries – and then, when the British parties joined in 1968, from seven. They represented twenty major democratic political parties, and the ten most powerful non-Communist trade-union federations. When they all shared the same conviction and worked towards the same goal, they wielded considerable moral power. Perhaps only the idea of a peaceful community of peoples could have inspired such a gathering, the genuine harbinger of that European political leadership which in the future will guide our different democracies as one. For this leadership to emerge, the great rival political groupings will one day have to undertake just such a patient joint apprenticeship in the realities of Europe, and once more forget, as the members of our Committee forgot, their partisan domestic disputes. The history of the Action Committee, indeed, is one of open-mindedness and friendship.

Observers were always astonished to see men who fought bitterly for power in their own countries meeting several times a year in Europe around the same table, signing the same texts, and championing them with the same constancy before their Parliaments and their trade-union congresses. At home, they might pass from Opposition to Government or vice-versa: in the Action Committee, their attitude remained unaltered by the change. They might be made Minister, President, or Chancellor: their place on the Committee was still reserved for them, and they occupied it whenever they wished. Several of them, and among them the most eminent – Guy Mollet, Willy Brandt, Kurt Kiesinger, Pietro Nenni, Helmut Schmidt – took advantage of that opportunity. When they did so, they set aside their official titles and refused to exploit for political ends the temporary advantage of their national rank. The leaders of the Opposition, likewise, avoided embarrassing their political opponents. And this consensus was achieved, not at a low level of compromise, but on commitments to act publicly and change the course of events. What looked exceptional from outside was normal within the Committee, because we met with the specific aim of agreeing and reaching joint decisions.

True, by virtue of joining the Committee, everyone had agreed in advance on the general objective. But the understanding that prevailed there was not due only to the convergence of our ideas. Our working habits were just as important in encouraging unity. When a statesman of goodwill is no longer under public scrutiny – when he can be sure that his words will not be published and that the opponent with whom he is now co-operating will not quote them against him later – then, he asks nothing better than to contribute to the common cause. His positive nature encourages agreement. I have no recollection of any personal conflicts or party tensions inside the Committee. By the time it met, on each occasion, Kohnstamm and I had already done our best to reconcile divergent opinions, by a series of explanations that sometimes took many months. To help us, we had our power of persuasion; but above all we had an asset whose power is little realized: sincerity. We put our cards on the table, and everyone could be sure that we were talking to him in the same terms as to everyone else. It may not always be wise to tell everything to everyone: but it is essential to tell everyone the same thing. That is the only way to win trust; and without trust I have never obtained anything – indeed, I have never tried.

And there was more uniting us than that: there was also friendship. It was not there at the start, and it could not be a prerequisite for the Committee's success. But gradually it grew, and it became a great source of supplementary strength. Twenty years of meeting together and fighting side-by-side creates a firm personal bond among the most diverse of men. What that bond has contributed to the maintenance and progress of European union can be appreciated only by those who have felt its strength at times when decision was difficult. Many people have borne witness to it, publicly and in private. The testimony of Willy Brandt, Edward Heath, Herbert Wehner, Walter Scheel, and Mariano Rumor, among others, should be enough to remove any doubts, if I had ever had them, about the usefulness of what the Action Committee achieved.

Its practical work began in January 1956, and it continued for twenty years. Some of its results can be appreciated today; others will be easier to judge in the future. But as I look back on that long period, I see it as a single whole – the most continuous and tenacious effort in my life; and that, heaven knows, has not been lacking in continuity. It was circumstances that led me into a form of stubborn action whose length I had not foreseen but whose difficulty I had never under-estimated. I have always believed that Europe would be built through crises, and that it would be the sum of their solutions. But the solutions had to be proposed and applied. With the benefit of hindsight, I personally doubt whether such results would have been secured without the European political authority of the Action Committee for the United States of Europe.

II

Euratom and the Common Market

The Action Committee held its first meeting on January 18, 1956, at the Institut Branting in Paris, a few yards from the rue de Martignac house where ten years earlier, almost to the day, I had launched the French Modernization Plan. Since then, many things had changed in the world and in Europe; but in France government instability was still rife. After Edgar Faure had dissolved the National Assembly in December, fresh elections had thrown up a Centre-Left majority which gave Guy Mollet the Premiership. For some months, Pierre Mendès-France was in his Government. But what mattered most was that the Foreign Minister was Christian Pineau, with Maurice Faure as his Secretary of State. Both, like Mollet himself, were convinced of the need to build Europe rapidly. Pineau, an idealistic Socialist and war-time deportee, was anxious to tie Germany into a peaceful community; Maurice Faure, an exceptionally talented young Radical, was soon to reveal remarkable gifts as a negotiator. The Mollet Government had the good fortune to survive longer than any other in the Fourth Republic, which enabled it to succeed in one great venture – the conclusion of the Rome Treaties – and to start on another – decolonization, which owed a great deal to the courage of Gaston Defferre. The Government's senior civil-service team was exceptionally well-chosen: Robert Marjolin was working with Pineau; Georges Vedel and Jean François-Poncet were with Maurice Faure; while Mollet himself had with him an outstanding young graduate of the Ecole Normale Supérieure who had proved his worth on the Constitutional Committee of the Community Assembly. His name was Emile Noël. At the Matignon Palace, he was a very valuable link. Since then, with a tenacity as great as his modesty, he has worked untiringly as Secretary-General of the European

417

Commission to make the Community's institutions both supple and strong.

In Brussels, Félix Gaillard headed the French delegation at the conference set up by the Messina meeting and chaired by Paul-Henri Spaak. This conjunction of outstanding men, all equally convinced, was a great new opportunity for Europe. It had to be seized, and rapidly: once again, pressure had to be applied on a limited but decisive point. The text on which I now knew our Committee would unanimously agree called on the Governments to set up Euratom without delay:

> Action is urgently needed if Europe is not to let her opportunity pass by.
>
> An atomic industry producing atomic energy will inevitably be able to produce bombs. For that reason the political aspects and the economic aspects of atomic energy are inseparable. The European Community must develop atomic energy exclusively for peaceful purposes. This choice requires a watertight system of control. It opens the way to general control on a world-wide scale. . . .
>
> In order that the necessary measures may be taken rapidly, we have agreed to submit the attached declaration for Parliamentary approval in Belgium, France, Germany, Italy, Luxembourg, and the Netherlands, and to invite our Governments to conclude without delay a Treaty conforming to the rules set forth therein.

The declaration that followed called for the establishment of a Community on the model of the ECSC. The Commission which was to be its executive body was to be the sole owner of nuclear fuels, whether imported or home-produced, and to monitor their use from beginning to end. The Commission was to have the sole right to negotiate and conclude agreements with non-member countries; it was also to be responsible for the security rules. This plan was in accordance with the work being done by the experts in Brussels. But while there was no doubt about the combined imaginative powers of Armand and Uri – the genius of the engineer combined with that of the economist – it was still essential to repeat the two requirements that have guaranteed progress in Europe: institutions and deadlines. The best of plans remain nugatory unless they are given the means to reach decisions, and a time-table for what has to be done. The intergovernmental conference needed to be pushed along by political will if it was to take the step about which Europe had hesitated since 1950 – the delegation of sovereignty. Would Governments have given the conference its mandate if Parliaments had not strongly urged them on? And would Parliaments have taken the initiative if the members of the Action

Committee had not pledged themselves to put a joint resolution before them without delay?

That day, in the baroque setting of the Institut Branting, the first practical embodiment of the relaunching of Europe publicly stated its position on the only project which could then secure the agreement of Europeans. Around the table were some thirty men, all trusted by their parties or trade unions, and some of them holding office in their countries' Governments. They included Guy Mollet, Amintore Fanfani, Giovanni Malagodi, Ugo La Malfa, Théo Lefèvre, Max Buset, C. P. M. Romme, J. A. W. Burger, Erich Ollenhauer, Herbert Wehner, Hans Furler, Maurice Faure, René Pleven, Robert Bothereau, Auguste Cool, and Walter Freitag. All agreed with the Action Committee's aim:

> The development of atomic energy for peaceful uses opens the prospect of a new industrial revolution and the possibility of a profound change in living and working conditions.
>
> Together, our countries are capable of themselves developing a nuclear industry. They form the only region in the world that can attain the same level as the great world Powers. Yet separately they will not be able to overcome their time-lag which is a consequence of European disunity.

If the Euratom project was unanimously agreed on by the Committee, this was because it benefited from the convergence of two complementary lines of thought. The French saw it as guaranteeing greater independence in energy, through a joint effort; for the Germans, it was a way to enter the atomic age, but for peaceful purposes only. For Ollenhauer's friends, this proviso was the express condition of any agreement and very largely the justification of their presence on the Committee. I agreed with them that it was essential for the ownership and control of fissile materials to be vested in Euratom. For the majority of French people, an atomic energy Community was a clear and distinct idea – while that of an economic Community remained nebulous. For some Germans, on the other hand, the Common Market was the only dynamic element in the relaunching of Europe, but one for which they would have to pay the price of Euratom and its dirigiste approach. So we had no choice: the spearhead for the unification of Europe would have to be the peaceful atom. The Common Market would follow naturally, which is why we postponed discussing it until a later session. In Brussels, the Spaak Committee was working on both projects at the same time and the same pace; but I myself thought that the creation of Euratom should be speeded up. We took every step to ensure that our Resolution was debated and voted on by the six Parliaments. By July, it was done. On this occasion, the French National Assembly was the scene of an extraordinary event: at the Government's request, Louis Armand and the atomic expert Francis Perrin gave evidence; and there is no likelihood of the Parliament's forgetting its two guests' brilliant speeches, which initiated a new and fruitful, if rare, parliamentary tradition.

It was during this debate that I heard Guy Mollet make a statement which was to hang heavily on the future of Europe.

'Euratom,' he said, 'will not stand in the way of a possible French decision to build nuclear weapons.'

On this point the French Socialists disagreed with their German colleagues. This made the latter even more exacting; and in October, Ollenhauer wrote to Heinrich von Brentano, the German Foreign Minister:

> My party, for security reasons, regards it as absolutely essential that there should be watertight control of the uses to which fissile materials are put, through their being owned by Euratom. The establishment of Euratom, which my party and I consider to be urgently necessary, would cease to enjoy our support if it were not to be based on the watertight control demanded by the Monnet Committee's Resolution.

But the Bonn Government was divided. Strauss and Erhard delayed the Brussels talks on Euratom in the hope of negotiating bilateral agreements with the United States – a hope that proved vain when Strauss visited Washington. Only then was Adenauer able to impose on his Ministers and on German industry his own views about the ownership and control of fissile materials. At the beginning of November, he came to Paris to reach an agreement with Guy Mollet. Agreement was all the more urgent in that, some months earlier, President Eisenhower had decided to offer Europe twenty tons of uranium 235 for peaceful industrial use. Only the rapid establishment of Euratom would enable us to preserve the new Community's independence by substituting purely European controls for the international control which would otherwise be required as the counterpart of the American offer. The whole battle would be difficult; but it was my belief that we must undertake it so that Europe could become aware of its identity and affirm its sovereignty.

During the summer, a very significant event occurred. On July 26, 1956, Gamal Abdel Nasser, the Egyptian President, announced:

'From today, the Suez Canal Company no longer exists. The Canal is ours from now onward – all ours.'

From that moment on, the whole world trading system was at the mercy of one of its vital arteries being cut off, and our oil imports were under constant threat. On September 19, the Action Committee met in Paris and passed the following Resolution:

> The energy supplies of Western Europe determine the progress or decadence of our countries. . . .
>
> Today, Western Europe imports a fifth of the energy it uses. In ten years' time, imports will have to supply one-third of its needs. The greater part of these imports consists of Middle Eastern oil.
>
> Such dependence results in insecurity and permanent risks of conflict. Between industrial and under-developed countries it hinders the collaboration which is indispensable for freeing the disinherited masses of the world from their misery. The possibility of bringing pressure to bear on Western Europe by means of Middle Eastern oil hinders the development of peaceful relations between East and West. . . .
>
> But together, by developing and uniting their resources, our countries can produce atomic energy in time and in sufficient quantities to keep their oil and coal imports within reasonable limits.

At the time, this warning was noted; but then it was forgotten for fifteen years. Men take great decisions only when crisis stares them in the face. The Suez crisis first revealed a situation which was dangerous for world stability. More than any argument, the paralysis which struck transport in Europe made public opinion aware of how vulnerable all our industrialized countries were, and how much they needed to act together. The Committee therefore called on Governments rapidly to conclude the Euratom Treaty and to secure its ratification before the end of the year. But because circumstances were on our side, we had to go further: we had to anticipate events and bring together all those concerned by setting them practical objectives. Experience had taught me that this was one way of mobilizing immense latent capacities, which go into action only when they are offered a point of convergence which is both ambitious and realistic. This had been the case with maritime transport in the 1914 war, with the Victory Program in 1942, and with the French Modernization Plan in 1946. Scattered, hesitant efforts take on new meaning and vigour when they are integrated into an overall plan. The conquest of a new form of energy could be a great collective enterprise on the part of Europeans who were determined to live better and live independently. But they had to be given a precise goal, and be shown the steps whereby it could be attained. So the Committee proposed that the Foreign Ministers should ask three eminent experts to report to them on these points.

The following month, the Ministers appointed what we had called the 'Three Wise Men' – Armand, Etzel, and an Italian nuclear specialist, Francesco Giordani. They spent six months on their inquiry, which took them to the United States, Canada, and Great Britain. Their eventual report was remarkably clear and tight-packed: it can still be read with profit more than twenty years later. Indeed, events rapidly confirmed the purpose of their mission. The Franco-British Suez expedition of November 5, Bulganin's ensuing threats, and Eisenhower's disavowal of Franco-British action, left a divided Europe all too well aware of how humiliatingly precarious its economic and political situation was. The era of far-flung adventures, when problems were solved by force, would soon be over for good. Soon, Europeans would know no prestige, independence, or progress unless they were united in a collective effort. Armand suggested that we erect a statue to Nasser, the federator of Europe. It was a joke. The federator was not any named individual, but always that same multifarious abstract force that operates on everyone: necessity.

Necessity also drove on the Brussels negotiators, working away at the Château de Val Duchesse on the outskirts of the city to draw up the Treaties, step by step. The Spaak Report had greatly simplified matters. Uri's pen had tidied up the catalogue of desiderata compiled at Messina and turned it into two major projects, the Common Market and Euratom. They were linked, as it were, by the contrasting interests which each of them involved. The French allowed themselves to be coaxed towards the Common Market, which they feared was full of traps. But they were tempted by Euratom – which many Germans, on the other hand, regarded as a threat to place their industry under tutelage. For these reasons – which in the end proved illusory – the two negotiations were being conducted in parallel; and I realized that the two Treaties would also have to be simultaneously signed. Euratom would have to await agreement on the Common Market, which the French wanted to be hedged about with exceptions in their favour. There could be no doubt about either the ability or the goodwill of Maurice Faure and Marjolin; but all France lacked self-confidence. As in the ECSC, she had an exaggerated idea of the disparity in competitive conditions, and in particular of the social-security burden of which she thought herself the victim. The state of the franc was certainly worrying; but the protective measures France was demanding seemed exorbitant. Only her requests to include agriculture and overseas dependencies proved in the end well-founded. Every problem bristled with technical difficulties; but by the beginning of 1957 all that was lacking was the political will to succeed.

Would the opportunity be lost? That was my worry; and I shared it with members of the Committee, whose role was to prove decisive.

'Several times,' I told them, 'we have all seen that a two-week delay in a Ministerial conference can mean a two-month delay in negotiations. The same is true of ratification.'

What was more, we faced a looming deadline: on July 6 the German *Bundestag* was due to go into recess until the September election. Every day lost would strengthen the SPD members' temptation to harden their opposition and, at the very least, abstain. It was my constant concern, therefore, to give Mollet and Adenauer not a moment's respite; to keep up the pressure on their Ministers Maurice Faure and Hallstein; and to call on the influence of Noël, Etzel, and many others. Faced with a clear duty and a deadline set by the calendar, they would not shirk their responsibilities. They would need courage; but lack of courage is not the commonest failing of statesmen: obstacles arouse their fighting spirit. Even so, the obstacles have to be made clear and unavoidable; those who face them have to be shown that by temporizing they risk losing everything, including power. The example of EDC was still fresh in men's minds; and the lesson would not be lost on them.

In Brussels, the experts were still busy drafting meticulous texts, a blend of caution and audacity. Both, as their authors wished, were to prove very effective, according to where the emphasis was placed. Myself, I never bothered to speculate on whether the new Community Treaties might have been improved. I think that they embodied as much as was possible at that time and that stage in men's thinking – at any rate, I could only place my trust in the most able and convinced Europeans of their generation. The work they did may have disappointed the hopes of the federalists; but its balanced structure has withstood all subsequent trials. Its keystone is the constant dialogue it establishes between national institutions and common institutions, whose objectives are linked. Neither has any option but to advance towards the immense horizons that now lie open to Europe.

The dialogue between national and Community institutions, which is inseparable from the decision-making process, is the very essence of the Community's life. It is this that makes it unique among modern political systems. If experience has shown that too little power of decision was initially transferred to European level, it is up to the men of today to do what those of yesterday dared not propose to their hesitant Members of Parliament. In 1957, Spaak could not have been more adroit, Uri more imaginative, or Hallstein and Maurice Faure more courageous. Above all, moreover, Adenauer and Mollet had to exert their authority. They did so manfully, and by February 1957 all was ready. France was to enter the Common Market together with her overseas dependencies; the ownership of fissile materials was to be vested in Euratom. The problem of the Saar was settled once and for all. The Treaties were signed in Rome on March 25, 1957.

Even so, we still had to win a race against time. Meeting at the beginning of May, the Action Committee called on Governments to secure the Treaties' ratification before the summer break. The parliamentary committees set to work, and once again I appealed to Emile Blamont's ingenuity to speed up the process in his discreet and masterly way. On June 22, I was in Bonn with Kohnstamm. Ollenhauer was still hesitating about what was in the best interests of the SPD.

'Perhaps it would be better to postpone the debate until after the election,' he said. 'We should prefer the French to commit themselves first.'

'That would be a terrible mistake,' I said. 'The institutions must be set up by the beginning of 1958. Soon, it will be too late.'

I foresaw a danger that the German Social Democrats might abstain.

'The French Socialists,' I added, 'are about to vote unanimously in favour of a European Treaty for the first time. France and Germany must ratify the Treaties more or less simultaneously.'

'Very well,' said Ollenhauer. 'We'll commit ourselves too.'

It took great courage for him to do that. On July 5, he persuaded his party to vote with the Christian-Democrat CDU, the 'German Party', and some of the Liberals. That date marked an epoch in the history of Europe. The brooding menace of a split in West Germany receded: the whole nation had abandoned its overlong indecision and opted for its links with the West. Franco-German reconciliation was now firmly sealed.

A few days later, the French National Assembly began its debate, on the basis of two excellent reports. That by Alain Savary, on the Common Market, reached a firm conclusion:

> The choice is not between the Community and the *status quo*, but between the Community and solitude.

The rapporteur on Euratom was Pierre July. He had in his hand the prophetic report of the Three Wise Men, which confirmed with the aid of statistics the prospects already outlined by the Action Committee. The Wise Men declared:

> Europe's dependence on the Middle East is bound to increase. . . . As the

quantity of oil imported from the Middle East increases, there will be a corresponding increase in the political temptation to interfere with the flow of oil from that region. A future stoppage could be an economic calamity for Europe. Excessive dependence of our highly industrialized countries on an unstable region might even lead to serious political trouble throughout the world. It is essential that oil should be a commodity and not a political weapon.

The European economy must be protected against an interruption of oil supplies, by finding alternative sources of energy to limit the further rise in oil imports.

The Wise Men's foresight underlines the heavy responsibility borne by those who, disdaining a warning whose value we can appreciate today, were then already preparing to stunt the growth of Euratom.

The Assembly debate was serious and dispassionate, and the vote was more favourable than had been expected. There were few defaulters among the Independent Peasants, who were looking forward to the outlets that the Common Market would offer French agriculture. Mendès-France voted against, but that did not surprise me. In an earlier debate I had heard him say:

'France must not be the victim of a Treaty. A democrat may abdicate by giving in to an internal dictatorship, but also by delegating his powers to an external authority. A genuine Europe can only be built on the recovery of France.'

Mendès-France was followed by some Radicals; and the Gaullists, responding to an appeal from Raymond Triboulet, voted 'against the Europe of Jean Monnet'. With the Communists and the Poujadists, the opposition amassed only 239 votes. The European majority had 342.

Attention now focused on Rome, where the parliamentary debate began at the very end of the session. On July 30, the Chamber of Deputies voted for the Treaties by 311 votes against 144, with 54 abstentions. The majority consisted of the Christian Democrats, the Liberals, the Republicans, and the Saragat Socialists. The Nenni Socialists, who at that time were not members of the Action Committee, voted for Euratom but abstained on the Common Market. Now, it was only a question of months before the other countries ratified the Treaties. The Belgian Chamber approved them on November 19 by 174 votes against 4, and the Luxembourg Chamber on November 26 by 46 votes against 3. In the Netherlands, by large majorities, the Second Chamber of the States-General in October, then in December the First Chamber, completed the ratification process. In all six countries, the Senates confirmed the votes of the Assemblies: the Treaties thus

secured a broad democratic consensus. All the political parties represented on the Action Committee voted in accordance with their pledge.
We were to renew that pledge in order to turn the texts into reality.

I next applied myself, with varying results but consistent energy,
to trying to solve a number of problems which in my view were vital
if the new Communities were to make a good start. The first of these
was the choice of people. We had not fought and won so great a battle
in order to place the institutions in unreliable hands. In appearance,
those institutions were economic and technical, but their objectives
were political. I wrote to Adenauer and I saw Gaillard, who by now had
become French Prime Minister, to make sure that they would nominate
men who were competent and determined to act, beginning with the
Presidents – something which in my experience cannot always be taken
for granted, and to which I have many times had to pay close attention
to avoid facile or complaisant choices. This time, wisdom prevailed,
and we had no difficulty in agreeing on the names of Hallstein and
Armand. This established the prestige of the Common Market and
Euratom from the start; and it was confirmed by the appointment of
Marjolin, Jean Rey, and Sicco Mansholt.

On the second of my problems I was less fortunate. Once again, I
tried to persuade people to share my conviction that the whole adminis-
stration of the Communities ought to be brought together in a single
place, and that this place should be given European status. In 1952,
as has been seen, I had not succeeded in preventing the ECSC
institutions being split between Luxembourg and Strasbourg; and the
practical inconvenience was considerable. It would be even greater if
the new institutions were set up somewhere else again; and so fragmented an appearance would certainly damage the Community's
prestige. Indeed, the time seemed to have come to give it the scope
and status that it would derive from having a capital of its own, rooted
in the soil just as Europe was rooted in history, but new and unique.
This would not only be convenient: it would also be a symbol of
unity.

In November, the members of the Action Committee pledged themselves to intervene with their respective Governments to persuade them
to take the following decisions:

(1) The grouping in the same place of the Institutions of the Coal and
    Steel Community, the Common Market, and Euratom;
(2) The setting-up of the headquarters of the Institutions in a 'European
    District', administered by the common Institutions;
(3) The choice of a site easily accessible to all.

The Committee offered no suggestions about where that site should be, and I myself refrained not only from expressing a preference, but also from having one. That would have been the certain way to weaken the position of principle that I continually championed. Unfortunately, however, I could not prevent others thinking in terms of local interest and suspecting me of putting forward candidates of my own. In January 1958, the affair became inextricably confused: the Ministers agreed on the principle of a single site, but disagreed about where it should be. In their disappointment, the Belgian members of the Action Committee took offence, and absented themselves for some months. But there was nothing I could do, if Luxembourg insisted both on keeping the ECSC and on not 'losing its soul' in the words of Joseph Bech, who was afraid of a second European invasion. In the end, the new institutions were set up in Brussels. From that moment on, dispersion was inevitable, and the repeated appeals of the Action Committee, like those of the parliamentary Assembly, could make no headway against the *fait accompli*. Personally, I have no regrets about having spent so long championing the cause of a European District. When the builders return, they will find the plans still waiting, and have only to choose the site.

When one undertakes any action, one must not speculate about whether it will succeed – that is something I no longer consider once I have made up my mind. By then, the debate is over: it has led to a conviction and to action, which for me are inseparably linked. When Gaillard, remembering the stabilization efforts we had made together ten years earlier, consulted me in December 1957 about how to remedy France's financial imbalance, starting with her external deficit, I had long talks with Wilfrid Baumgartner of the Bank of France, Marjolin, and Pierre-Paul Schweitzer, Director of the Treasury. They led to the conclusion that what was needed was a considerable effort, coupled with immediate aid from international monetary institutions and from the Government of the United States. That was the prerequisite for France's recovery, on which would depend her ability to face the opening of the Common Market. Gaillard and his Finance Minister Pierre Pflimlin were clear-headed and courageous: in a situation where public confidence had already evaporated, no one could have done better than they. They had inherited inflation, a flight from the franc, and a long-standing balance-of-payments deficit which could not be allowed to go on. They had to be helped to put paid to the threat that hung over France, and hence over Europe. So I agreed to go to the United States in January 1958 to negotiate immediate aid, but not before the Government had launched an austerity plan for France, without which my efforts would certainly have failed. It was a difficult and extremely complex assignment, and I put a great deal into it. But while it led to the unhoped-for loan of more than $600m., it did not prevent the collapse of the Fourth Republic some months later in the face of a different threat. It at least saved the subsequent régime a disastrous day of reckoning, and gave a breathing-space in which confidence could be restored.

Announcing the result of my mission in Washington on January 30, I said to the Americans:

'I want to underline this fundamental point: henceforth, no Frenchman, no German or Italian or Belgian or Dutchman or Luxembourger welcomed here in Washington will come simply as a representative of his own country. Each will become more and more what he has been hitherto only in a cultural sense – a European.'

If I thus ceaselessly returned to my main objective, it was because the nature of the problems no longer made it possible to confine them to a national context. Europe was not something imaginary: as successive crises would gradually make apparent, it was now the scale on which economic phenomena occurred. For the time being, France was the first to be affected; but it was not too soon to look ahead to regulatory machinery at European level. In March 1958 I wrote to Gaillard:

> The objective would be to establish a European financial and money market, with a European Bank and Reserve Fund, using jointly a part of national reserves, with free convertibility of European currencies, free movement of capital among the Community countries, and the development of a common financial policy.

There are no premature ideas: there are only opportunities for which one must learn to wait. The idea of a European Reserve Fund was endorsed by the Heads of State and Government at their 1972 'summit' meeting, after fourteen years of Action Committee resolutions which stubbornly went on calling for it to be studied, and putting forward plans. Those plans, worked out by Marjolin, Uri, Delouvrier, and Robert Triffin, attracted the attention of the responsible authorities, who could delay matters but not finally ignore necessity. In 1961, Pierre Drouin of *Le Monde*, a penetrating observer, wrote:

> Experience has proved that most of the ideas launched by the Action Committee, although they may sometimes take a long time to make their way, eventually end up, in one form or another, in the realm of reality.

This instance was typical of many others which the Action Committee dealt with in its early years, with the aim of erecting milestones along the road which the Community would sooner or later follow, either of its own accord or under pressure from Governments.

The Community had begun well; but France, after having contributed so much to its beginnings, was now caught up in a national drama which the authorities could not avert. In a few days, the events which revolutionized Algeria spread to Paris, sweeping away a régime already weakened and constitutionally incapable of either avoiding or surviving serious crises. Resignation had been the habitual response of Governments in the face of difficulties and trials of strength. The chance of escaping burdensome responsibilities, together with the permanent danger of being outvoted by an Assembly which ran no risk of dissolution, had made governmental instability a political way of life. Crises had become the most natural and simple way of dealing with problems that demanded courage: it was a case of solving them by default. That is why, when de Gaulle assumed power in June 1958 and proposed to establish by referendum a Constitution that would guarantee the stability of the executive, I saw in it great benefits for our country – as a means not only of solving the Algerian problem that divided France, but also of pursuing the forward-looking ventures on which we were engaged both internally and in foreign policy.

The Fourth Republic had been badly shaken by the loss of Indochina, and it had not been able to withstand the threats of secession in North Africa. But it nevertheless deserved credit for exceptional successes, both in modernizing France and in opening her horizons to the outside world. Those successes had to be consolidated, and in the referendum of September 9, 1958, on the new Constitution I decided to vote Yes. I gave the reasons for my decision in an article published by *Le Monde* at the beginning of the referendum campaign:

> The Third Republic fell, after the defeat of 1940, at the end of a period in which France, already drained by the First World War, was showing many signs of old age: the population was decreasing, producers were seeking security in State protection, and production was stagnant. The French people had lost confidence in their future.
>
> The political bankruptcy of the Fourth Republic, on the other hand, finds France in full renaissance. Her youthfulness is shown by the increase in the population, and by the industrial and agricultural revolution she is undergoing, catching up at last with other modern nations. Producers are looking to expansion for their future. This break with the past

also includes the reconciliation of France and Germany and the beginnings of a united Europe, in which France and the French people will find new horizons.

When he votes, every citizen must make up his own mind whether he will be speeding up or retarding this process of adjustment to the modern world.

To safeguard our future, we must now put an end to the Algerian crisis and ensure governmental stability and authority. These two imperatives are linked.

I went on to explain at length how the new Constitution would guarantee the continuity of the Government's work. Some years later, the Constitution was further modified to include the election of the President of the Republic by universal suffrage. Once again, I voted in favour of a step which would give the executive greater legitimacy and also facilitate the decisions required for the unification of Europe. For sovereignty to be delegated, authority must be well-established.

The sensible and courageous monetary measures taken at the end of 1958 gave France back her self-confidence, and she took in her stride the first tariff cuts on the way to the full Common Market. The credit for this must go to General de Gaulle and to Antoine Pinay, whom he had chosen as Minister of Finance, with Jacques Rueff as his adviser. What was more, it became apparent that the fears aroused by the opening of the Common Market had been exaggerated. In November 1959, the Action Committee called on Governments to speed up progress through the stages set by the Treaty:

> Already, on different sides, one hears demands that the transition period of the Common Market be shortened from twelve to six years, and that practical effect be given to the essential provisions of the Common Market Treaty which in general terms call for the establishment of a common economic policy in various fields.

Since it was possible to go faster, it was necessary to do so – not merely to hasten the increase of trade among our six countries and improve their standard of living, but also to arrive as soon as possible at a point when the Community would be ready to be enlarged and to share its prosperity with other countries in Europe and Africa. This would also bring closer the time when a political Europe could be built. These two objectives were now to become the chief concerns of the Action Committee and the main focus of my own work.

Chapter 17

POLITICAL UNION (1960-1962)

I

Towards confederation

> At the moment, however urgent political union may be, and however great the progress already made, it does not seem possible to by-pass the requisite stages. The political union of tomorrow will depend on making the economic union effective in the everyday activities of industry, agriculture, and government.

These empirical views were expressed by the Action Committee in October 1958. They echoed the wise principles embodied in the Schuman Declaration of May 9, 1950. While the Common Market was not yet fully open, and its common policies remained to be worked out, ought we to follow those who were urging an immediate move to the federal stage? I thought not, and the members of the Committee agreed with me that we must continue along the path so laboriously charted and now so broadly opening out:

> Little by little the work of the Community will be felt, and the already distinguishable bonds of common interest will be strengthened. Then the everyday realities themselves will make it possible to form the political union which is the goal of our Community, and to establish the United States of Europe.

Even today, that statement has lost none of its significance; and if at times we have forgotten it, events have sooner or later brought us back to it. Does this mean that we must await the slow growth of *de facto* solidarity, and simply rely on it to develop automatically? Certainly not; nor is that what the 1958 text says. *The everyday realities will make it possible to form the political union.* The idea is clear: political Europe will be created by human effort, when the time comes, on the basis of reality. The story of how we came on several occasions to believe that

431

the time was in fact ripe is a tale of many misunderstandings, but also of much goodwill. If Europe has been pulled in many different directions by people with contrasting ideas of her destiny, I regard that as a great waste of time and effort, but no denial of the need to unite. It was simply that ideas and methods differed; and, as always, reality had the last word. Today, I believe, reality is having the last word again – and it closely resembles the first, written in 1950. What it spells is the delegation of sovereignty and the joint exercise of the new and larger sovereignty thus created. I cannot see that in twenty-five years anything else has been invented as a means of uniting Europe, despite all the temptations to desert that path.

For me, there has been only one path: only its length remains unknown. The unification of Europe, like all peaceful revolutions, takes time – time to persuade people, time to change men's minds, time to adjust to the need for major transformations. But sometimes, circumstances hasten the process, and new opportunities suddenly arise. Must they be missed simply because they were not expected so soon? The question arose in 1950, when we were abruptly faced with the prospect of German rearmament. We seized the opportunity to try a new step forward on the basis of what otherwise might have been a setback for the process of integration that had barely begun. As has been seen, we failed. The European Defence Community project was no doubt premature; but it came to grief largely because it was allowed to drag on. In 1960, a further surprise opportunity arose, when at a press conference on September 5 General de Gaulle made the following proposal:

'To ensure regular co-operation in Western Europe is something that France considers desirable, possible, and practicable in the political field, the economic field, the cultural field, and the field of defence.'

The system he advocated included 'regular organized concertation by the Governments responsible', specialized bodies subordinate to Governments, an Assembly of delegates from the national Parliaments, and finally 'a vast European referendum'.

This system was open to criticism in a number of respects. But I had fewer doubts about its value than about the state of mind of its author. Certainly, de Gaulle had not abandoned his customary ideas:

'What are the realities in Europe? What are the pillars on which it can be built? In truth, they are the States . . ., the only entities that have the right to command and the authority to act. . . .'

Nor was I surprised to hear him make ironical references to 'certain more or less extra-national bodies'. What mattered, in my opinion, was that he had taken a political initiative, and given it some solemnity.

Whatever reservations one might have about its content, one could not ignore this fresh relaunching of Europe to which de Gaulle had linked his own prestige. It was up to us to make what we could out of the new situation – which, to tell the truth, was not altogether a surprise to me. Since our wartime days in Algiers, I had maintained friendly contact with Maurice Couve de Murville, who was now de Gaulle's Foreign Minister; and from our recent talks I had sensed that the time was coming for a great European debate. I only hoped that it would not turn into a great dispute.

As early as August 10, 1960, I had forewarned the members of the Action Committee. I wrote to them:

> It is proposed to set up a political authority at the level of Heads of Government of the six Community countries. This in my view would be an important step forward. Hitherto, our Committee has supported the creation of a European economic entity, and has deliberately refrained from taking up a position on the form of a political authority. It is clear that we must have an exchange of views on this important question before deciding on the Committee's attitude.

I must say that the September 5 press conference did not make the task of persuasion I had in mind an easy one, for it contained some disquieting reflections on the Community institutions, which in de Gaulle's 'Europe of the States' would be reduced to co-operative bodies subordinate to Governments. Both the form and the content of the press conference raised hackles in Europe. Nevertheless, I was determined to see the positive side of the change I detected in de Gaulle by comparison with his attitude hitherto.

During his years in opposition, Europe had been one of the constant themes in the press conferences at which he had made his ideas public. Every time, he had conjured up grandiose visions of a Europe formed by juxtaposing sovereign States from the Atlantic to the Urals. The Community of the Six, by comparison, seemed insignificant – and so he refrained from attacking it, leaving that task to his political sympathizers. But as soon as the Community had seemed likely to integrate defence, de Gaulle had attacked, and had also aimed his onslaught at myself. That had been in November 1953, when he had accused me of being 'the Inspirer' – in June 1940 in London, in 1943 in Algiers, and now, of 'a stateless European army,' each time coming up with 'a panacea called "pooling".' I had thought it my duty to answer him publicly, because he was making a mockery of honourable moments in history.

'General de Gaulle's proposals,' I said, 'are based on notions that are out of date. They forget the lessons of our most recent history. They completely ignore what a series of failures has taught us: that it is impossible to solve Europe's problems among States which retain full national sovereignty.'

The title of 'the Inspirer' stuck; but it does not worry me. That dispute went no further, and it was not of a kind to affect our personal relations. They had been good in the past, and for the sake of Europe they could remain so in the future.

Now that de Gaulle was once more invested with responsibilities, moreover, I noticed a marked change in his tone and his ideas. European diplomacy had become active again: meetings of Foreign Ministers and visits by Heads of State succeeded one another throughout 1960. However, mistrust had reappeared since the September press conference, and its shock effect would have to be smoothed away. Relations between de Gaulle and Adenauer, which had become excellent, and between France and Germany, which had remained so, now grew chilly. The Dutch and the Italians sounded out French diplomats, who assured them that there was no question of tampering with the existing Community. For my part, I tried to convince the members of the Action Committee that French overtures might give us an opportunity to set up machinery which could be developed later on. Since I was immobilized by an operation on my knee, Kohnstamm went to see the members of the Committee, while I began the debate by letter. That letter, dated November 22, 1960, put European affairs in their new setting: for, suddenly, they seemed to have assumed world proportions. Several recent events, I recalled, showed that the Common Market had made its appearance on the international scene. Britain had reacted to it by setting up the seven-nation European Free Trade Association with Austria, Denmark, Norway, Portugal, Sweden, and Switzerland; and the United States had crossed the Atlantic, to become a member, with Canada, of the Organization for European Economic Co-operation, now renamed the Organization for Economic Co-operation and Development at the Château de la Muette in Paris. Everywhere, the Six were faced with the intercontinental responsibilities thrust upon them by their own rapid success. The acceleration of the steps provided for in the Rome Treaty had given resounding proof of the Common Market's dynamism. Within the Community, customs duties were being lowered ahead of schedule; around it, the common external tariff was being more rapidly set in place. Both confirmed the Community's identity and called for the establishment of genuinely European economic policies, including the common agricultural policy which the French were eager to see set up.

Three things, in my view, were prerequisites for balanced progress, although they were difficult to achieve simultaneously: to develop the Community, to establish a political structure, and to recruit Great Britain. Many people, with exaggerated logic, saw these as a tangle of contradictions. To me, they were joint necessities. For years, the Action Committee fought to prevent any one of them being sacrificed to the success of the others – to ensure that political progress did not call in question the role of the economic Community or leave out Great Britain, and that British membership was not bought at the expense of what had been achieved already or was anticipated in the future. At any given moment it would have been easier for Governments to negotiate for one of the three possibilities at the cost of another. As will be seen, France would gladly have taken a political step forward if a setback could be inflicted on the Community, while the Netherlands would have given up many of their supranational principles to have Great Britain commit herself to the continent. Myself, I have always been convinced that the unification of Europe cannot be achieved by inter-governmental compromises: such supposedly time-honoured pro-ceedings are never-ending, and they never satisfy anyone. The search for the common interest, on the other hand, by no means excludes taking account of the others' point of view; but it must not turn into haggling. We held fast to our method, which consists in determining first what is good for all the Community countries as a whole, then taking the measure of the particular efforts which each will have to make – but without vainly seeking, as in the past, a meticulous balance of advantage.

To advance on several fronts at once did not necessarily mean doing so at the same speed. What mattered was that movement should be general, for only by deeds would Europe take shape. On November 21, 1960, I wrote to Adenauer:

> I must tell you that my greatest fear today is that we risk halting our pro-gress in the organization of Europe in order to hold long debates about questions which, although important, must not become preconditions for action. Must the question of NATO be settled before we continue the unification of Europe? Must Britain take part in our political discussions? Are General de Gaulle's proposals merely for 'co-operation', and not 'supranational'? It is only by advancing that we shall find the answers to these questions, primarily on the political plane. I believe that some of the suggestions which you have discussed with General de Gaulle may use-fully serve the development of Europe, and that we must act at once to give them practical shape.

This was my personal position, and when I stated it in my letter to the members of the Action Committee on the following day, I asked not for their agreement but for their opinion. Adenauer was wondering what attitude to adopt at the conference of the Six to be held in Paris in a few weeks' time, and for the moment I was anxious to convince him of the need to act without waiting for de Gaulle to give better assurances on Atlantic or European issues. More than that, I believed that before the end of the year Germany would have to show some understanding towards French demands for a common agricultural policy. Did Adenauer feel, as I did, that this might be a fleeting opportunity? I continued:

> I have often told you that your presence as leader of Germany at the same time as de Gaulle is leader of France offers us a possibility of action *today* which may not occur again.

Although events did not confirm my hopes, I have no regrets at having believed at that time, very firmly, that the meeting of minds between two exceptional men, both very experienced, both deeply attached to peace, and both enjoying great authority in their countries, could be the chance to give the Community new impetus through the Franco-German agreement on which it was essentially based. I did not mind if that agreement took on a solemn and special form, provided that it strengthened the union of Europe. The time had come, I thought, to sketch the outlines of what that union might involve. I wrote to Adenauer:

> I believe that it is a useful suggestion that the Heads of Government should meet as frequently and regularly as possible to discuss our six countries' common policy, and that there should be meetings of Foreign Ministers and also of Ministers of Education and Defence.
>
> For the time being, in the present situation and for these new political questions, I think that co-operation is a necessary stage. It will be a step forward, above all if the whole European system – the integrated Community and the organizations for co-operation, different as they are – be included in a single whole, a *European confederation*.

I knew that not all members of the Action Committee would agree with this approach, and that it would upset those who would have liked the political project to be more ambitious. Had I not accustomed them to the idea that co-operation was not enough, and that our aim was a federation? Most of them wanted the European Assembly to be elected by direct universal suffrage, and de Gaulle was opposed to that. He spoke of holding a referendum; and this, which was forbidden by some national constitutions, revived unhappy memories. Finally, de Gaulle's proposal seemed to many people to be seeking substitutes for what they regarded as the very basis of Western security: the Atlantic Alliance. Ludwig Rosenberg, by now President of the German Trade Union Federation, told me about their doubts:

'If it's only a regular conference of Ministers, then we must give up the term "confederation" and not mislead people. It's sometimes better to admit that nothing can be done than to give the impression of having achieved something which in reality is no more than a name, without the desired content.'

I could understand this attitude: I should have reacted in the same way myself if I had not felt that it was once more time to be pragmatic and use a fleeting conjunction of circumstances to transform the psychological context. I explained to the members of the Committee:

I have no doubt, for my part, that a confederation will one day lead to a federation. But, for the moment, is it possible to go further? I cannot say that it is. Meanwhile, the confederation would have the very great advantage of assuring public opinion in our countries that they have joined an entity which is not only economic but political, and that they are therefore part of something bigger than any of their countries alone.

That it was not possible to go further for the time being I knew from a most reliable source. As early as July, 1960, in my talks with Couve de Murville, I had suggested a form of confederation whose executive organ would be a Supreme Council of Heads of Government, and which in a number of cases would take decisions in the same way as the Community institutions. It was only when I received confirmation that the French Government ruled this out that I resigned myself to a less ambitious first step, without however abandoning the idea of further steps once we were launched on the dynamic process for which Europe was now prepared. Those who thought we must wait for better times misunderstood the situation of Germany in 1960, the political uncertainties, and the impatience of public opinion. Adenauer was in a hurry to bind his nation to the West, and he understood the sense of my letter. He answered:

You are the Trusty Eckart of the European idea.

I confess that I had to consult an encylopaedia. Trusty Eckhart, I discovered, was the hero of German legend whose name was regarded as synonymous with 'ever faithful servant'.

The process had begun; and if its impetus was soon exhausted, if the history of these attempts at European political union is a long series of disappointments, I am uncertain where to lay the blame. General de Gaulle himself assumed a great deal of it, by adopting attitudes which aroused misunderstanding and resentment both among France's neighbours and in France. But the public disputes alone were not enough to explain the failure: they merely prolonged it in the form of words. Failure was implicit, from the beginning of the talks, in the way they were undertaken. If any grand design existed, it certainly had no time to take shape: instead, the six countries plunged right away into a defensive quest for reciprocal concessions. De Gaulle made some which were considerable: people wondered at them, not realizing that he would withdraw them as soon as he thought he need no longer appease the smaller countries. For the moment, he had to deal with Joseph Luns, the Dutch Foreign Minister, and his Belgian colleague Pierre Wigny, both of whom suspected him of cherishing ambitions – for France first of all, and then, with Adenauer's connivance, for France and Germany – to dominate the continent. Some of de Gaulle's statements, no doubt, lent credence to such suspicions; but my belief was that it would be a waste of time to look for ulterior motives on either side. Whatever political strategists may say, to act in response to the supposed intentions of your partner is the surest way to fail in your aim. I am not even sure whether Luns and Wigny *had* an aim. What is certain is that no one had aims on the scale of Europe's needs. The confederation itself would not have involved any decision by the six Heads of State to improve on the existing situation. All that it would have meant was asking a committee of senior officials to draw up a catalogue of what was possible at the time.

This was not apparent right away. The Paris conference met at the beginning of February 1961, and set up the Fouchet Committee, named after its French Chairman, Christian Fouchet. Although it was not given a very precise mandate, the mere fact of its having been set up showed on the one hand that de Gaulle had not objected to its discussing the strengthening of the Community institutions, British entry, and co-operation with the United States, and on the other that Luns had not succeeded in making preconditions of these things. So it would still be possible to make progress in these three areas; and I made every effort to do so, following at a distance the labours of the intergovernmental committee. During the first six months of 1961, I made two trips to the United States to talk with my many friends in and around the new Administration headed by President Kennedy, including Acheson, George Ball, McGeorge Bundy, and Arthur Schlesinger. I also had a long talk with the President. I came away with the conviction that

Europe now had an exceptional opportunity at last to establish a relationship of equals with the United States. Then I went to London, where I observed a rapid evolution in the attitude of the Conservative Government. Soon, I felt sure, it would commit itself to the continent. In Brussels, finally, I saw that Walter Hallstein's Commission had consolidated its authority: all that remained was to develop common policies and make a greater contribution to the development of the world's poorer countries. The first steps towards a European currency now also seemed to be practicable.

Amid all the possibilities now open to Europe, political union was an important opportunity, and indeed a necessity; but it was only one of the courses of action that had to be pursued. When our Committee met on July 10, therefore, it surveyed the changes that were taking place in the world and the progress that a united Europe, including Great Britain and in co-operation with the United States, would have to make in order to share in the general movement. On political union, the Committee remained deliberately laconic: the 'summit' conference of the Six was due to take place in Bonn in a week's time, on July 18. The summit promised to be productive, and so it was – to judge by the communiqué, which contained many reassuring statements about the existing Community and the Atlantic Alliance. It spoke of 'the institutional consecration of the task in hand' and of extending the powers of the parliamentary Assembly. Finally, it called for 'the adherence to the European Communities of other European States that are ready to undertake, in all fields, the same obligations and the same responsibilities.' This careful wording went to the heart of the matter. Seen in this light, the mandate which the Heads of State and Government gave the Fouchet Committee was very clear:

> To present proposals on the means which will as soon as possible enable statutory character to be given to the union of their peoples.

Despite this, there was to be no more chequered history than that of the Fouchet Committee, whose members were able and well-intentioned, but subject to ambiguous national directives.

What stubborn force prevented the Heads of Government agreeing on a union of States which could satisfy the modest ambitions of the time, provided that it did nothing to jeopardize past achievements and future hopes? Why did France try to bring back into an intergovernmental framework what had already become a Community? Why did she stifle hopes of future progress? Was it reasonable to suppose that she could go on enjoying the advantages she derived from the European institutions if they were to lose their independence? Would it have been rash to promise to examine further possible steps after three years? I thought not; and that was why, until the very end, I persisted in believing that common sense would prevail. One proviso at least seemed to me obvious: that when the European Council discussed economic questions, it should apply the rules and procedures of the Community Treaties which it was in duty bound to respect. But logic of this kind had no place in the Gaullist plan, which to my eyes remained obscure. Equally, I have never understood why the Dutch and the Belgians barred the way to political progress in Europe when there was still some hope of making it. If they hoped thereby to make British entry easier, their calculation was ill-founded. The British would throw in their lot, as the future was to show, only with a Community that was active and continually developing.

The Fouchet Plan disappeared from the agenda in April 1962, and Adenauer did not make the effort necessary to save it. Clearly, he no longer wished to put pressure on de Gaulle, to whom he left the initiative in European affairs. What mattered to him, in Europe now, was Western solidarity in the face of the East. His confidence in American support had weakened, and he acted as if he had received firm assurances from France regarding Berlin. However, many people in his own party and in the opposition saw matters in a different light, and his political isolation became a serious problem. I still believed, like the stubborn old Chancellor, that we must move quickly to tighten the institutional bonds that would link Germany indissolubly to the West – but to the West as a whole, including Great Britain and in equal partnership with the United States. This plan went further than Adenauer's; but his was its necessary first step – and one which he, in large measure, had achieved and was able, better than anyone, to complete.

Nevertheless, the impetus that statesmen had in all honesty sought to impart to Europe had petered out in misunderstandings, and already the reaction had set in. On May 15, de Gaulle gave a press conference to apportion the blame – and set out his own conception of Europe. There was nothing novel about its content; but its deliberately scornful language came as a shock. It was de Gaulle's contempt which led his MRP Ministers to resign, including men as loyal as Pflimlin, Robert Buron, and Maurice Schumann. The most serious insult was not the word 'Volapük', which with de Gaulle dismissed both Community jargon and any future common language, but his definition of Community Europe and the suspicion he cast on its creators:

'Only the States, in this respect, are valid, legitimate, and capable of achieving it. I repeat that at present there is and can be no Europe other than a Europe of the States – except, of course, for myths, fictions, and pageants. . . .

'A so-called "integrated Europe", which would have no policy, would come to depend on someone outside; and that someone would have a policy of his own. There would perhaps be a federator, but it would not be European. And that, perhaps is what sometimes and in some degree inspires some of the remarks of one or another of the champions of "European integration".'

II

The Committee takes its stand

One word in this impassioned invective remained in my mind: the word 'federator', obviously referring to the United States. This caricature of the great venture that for twelve years had been uniting the peoples of Europe caused great offence everywhere, and the Action Committee wanted to riposte right away. Although it was not the Committee's role to enter into a debate, and still less to exchange polemics with anyone, we felt it necessary to reaffirm our conception of what the European Community was. That it could have been so travestied by a statesman who in the eyes of his people seemed its natural champion meant that we could never do enough to explain the purpose of our action and the progress of the union, which our fellow-citizens were experiencing every day without realizing the fact. Perhaps we had neglected the task of education, against which were mustered all the resources of counter-education. Perhaps we should have to repeat ourselves a thousand times. Perhaps we need to do so even today. . . . Let the Action Committee's declaration of June 26, 1962 speak for itself:

> The prospects open to Europe today are the outcome of the decision of European countries not to treat their economic problems as national ones but as common to them all. To solve these problems, they have adopted a new method of collective action.
>
> After a period of trial and error, this method has developed into a regular interchange between a European body responsible for suggesting solutions to common problems and the Governments of member countries which put the national points of view.

This is a completely new approach. It does not create a central Government. But it does result in Community decisions being taken within the Council of Ministers notably because the proposal of solutions to common difficulties by the independent European body makes it possible, without risk, to give up the unanimity rule. The Parliament and the Court of Justice underline the Community character of the whole.

This new method is the real 'federator' of Europe.

Writing in *Le Monde*, André Fontaine declared:

The Action Committee and its President have declared themselves firmly in favour of the Europe of the possible against the doctrinaires in both camps.

In *Le Figaro*, Walter Lippmann wrote:

This declaration is an important event and a decisive turning-point.

It did in fact cause a widespread stir. It was published on the same day in all six capitals, where the members of the Committee, who had not had time to meet, commented on it in public. For the first time, public opinion was presented with a global approach to the problems that a uniting Europe would have to solve within its own borders and in its relations with the rest of the world. This approach, shared by 'the vast majority of political parties in our six countries as well as the free and Christian trade unions representing ten million workers', was expressed as follows:

Only through the economic and political unification of Europe, including the United Kingdom, and the establishment of a partnership of equals between Europe and the United States can the West be strengthened and the conditions created for peace between East and West.

Although progress in this direction may be slow and fraught with difficulties, it is nevertheless inevitable and the only sure path. The Committee believes that any other course would involve our separate countries in profitless adventures and preserve that spirit of superiority and domination which not so long ago led Europe to the brink of destruction and could now engulf the world.

The very foundations of integration seemed to be challenged by one of our partners. After the failure of simple co-operation among six, it had briefly been tried among three – France, Germany, and Italy. Then Italy dropped out, and we were moving towards a conventional alliance between two countries, France and Germany. And yet, at that very moment, the voices of democratic opinion in Europe were heard to say:

Further headway is now possible and necessary. The points at issue are the accession of the United Kingdom to the European Community and the conclusion of a treaty initiating a political union. . . .

The partnership between America and a united Europe must be a relationship of two separate but equally powerful entities, each bearing its share of common responsibilities in the world.

In the disillusioned atmosphere of 1962, some found this programme surprisingly ambitious. But the failure that had affected everyone so badly was the failure of an intergovernmental conference, not of the Community method. The latter retained its full value as an example; and it remained the objective, even if in the one domain of politics we had to go through a stage of mere co-operation. The year before, Britain had made her first application for membership of the Community, and was negotiating hard with the Six. But there too the method was wrong, and the conference degenerated into haggling – although this in no way qualified the basic need, which sooner or later made agreement inevitable. In the United States, the vision of a strong and united Europe was firmly before the new Democratic administration, which was looking for a reliable partner with which to discuss and share world responsibilities. Many of those to whom I explained these matters called me an optimist.

'I'm not an optimist,' I answered: 'but I am determined.'

I was not alone in my determination, even if for many years I faced adverse circumstances and often, in the eyes of most people, had no reasonable grounds for hope. No member of the Committee came to tell me: 'I'm giving up'; none refused to be associated with the texts in which we reaffirmed our unchanging will and unabated confidence. All of them, in their trade unions and their parties, worked on Parliaments and Governments – sometimes within Governments – to win people over to the few simple ideas required for the organization of Europe. These ideas led to much complicated activity, involved vast material interests, and affected the future of millions; but that was a matter for the public authorities and their officials. It was for statesmen to safeguard the aims to which they had pledged themselves by joining the Action Committee. Each of them did so in his own sphere of influence; but, great as their influence was in our democratic systems, it still had to reckon with the inertia of things and people, and it took time to bear fruit. Resistance is always proportional to the scale of the proposed change; and when it was a question of changing the traditional form of authority, which had always previously been national, the resistance was stronger than ever.

In this struggle to create a new sovereignty by pooling existing national sovereignty, we naturally came up against the authorities and their officials, who were responsible for administering the established order. National civil servants needed very firm instructions if they were to delegate to Community institutions the fields of competence that were in their charge. Even those Governments which were most in favour of the European idea had to do violence to their own feelings and habits in order to give those instructions, which diminished their own power of decision. 'Put yourself in my shoes for a moment,' some Ministers told me, apologetically; but that was not my concern. On the contrary, I had to remain at the point where national interests converged, a position which no one ordinarily seeks. However, I was willingly joined there by imaginative men who had chosen to act politically because they believed that change was essential to the progress of modern society. Together we felt that we had the strength to change the established order of things. I told them:

'When once the ferment of change is introduced into a static system, no one can tell where the process will stop. We must not cease to act, but we must be patient.'

Over the years, I grew to know these men: we became friends. Some were impatient, like Giovanni Malagodi, who goaded the Committee on with remarkable pertinacity. 'We're not going fast enough,' he would say. I could understand how he felt; and I also liked the enthusiasm of Ugo La Malfa, who was always bubbling with ideas. Variety was an Italian characteristic. Mariano Rumor's personality added weight to his wise advice, just as Giuseppe Saragat's moral uprightness made people respond to his conciliatory efforts. The Dutch were scrupulously positive and helpful: I always knew that I could count on their support. From the very first day, Alders, Burger, Romme and others were both loyal and punctilious; Romme's sound judgement, in particular, was universally respected. Other very active contributions to our work came from Théo Lefèvre, a strong and energetic Belgian statesman, and from his compatriots Paul Vanden Boeynants and Leo Tindemans; while Auguste Cool was influential on behalf of the Belgian trade unions. I have already described the role of the first German members – Ollenhauer, Wehner, Freitag, Strater, and Rosenberg; that of Willy Brandt and Helmut Schmidt will be seen later. All these men bore the indelible marks of what they had suffered at the hands of violence and intolerance. Some of them had had to take refuge in exile – Wehner in Sweden, Brandt in Norway, Rosenberg in Britain. It was there that they had first known freedom.

For them, European integration, bringing together the free peoples of continental Europe, was the only hopeful course; and while like all Germans they longed to see their nation reunited, they did not regard this as an alternative to the Community: quite the reverse. But the accession of Great Britain and friendship with the United States seemed to them equally necessary, to strengthen democracy and security in Europe, and give it broader world horizons. On these points, they found me deeply in agreement with them; and the Action Committee, for them, was the political force where their vision of the world was most clearly and effectively expressed. Among the German members, I must also mention the late Heinrich von Brentano, who was a true and loyal friend, and Kurt Birrenbach, to whose work the Committee owes a very great deal. These Christian Democrats were not afraid to show publicly, in the Committee's declarations, their agreement with the Socialists whom they fought so hard on the domestic front. Wehner recalls that in 1956, at my request, he and his Christian-Democrat colleague Kurt Kiesinger made a joint approach to Guy Mollet, demonstrating the bipartisan policy that was to be the Committee's watchword, for the Germans as for everyone else.

The French members included Robert Lecourt, Pflimlin, Pinay, Pleven, Maurice Faure, Gaston Defferre, Guy Mollet, Maurice Bouladoux, Eugène Deschamps, Andre Bergeron, and Robert Bothereau. Later, Michel d'Ornano and Valéry Giscard d'Estaing joined the Committee. The British parties did so in 1968. For political observers, all these men were essential elements in the democratic machinery of Western Europe; and those less well-known to the public were by no means the least influential within their political parties. Rarely have there been so many leading advocates in a single cause – even if, for a number of years, the main role seemed to belong to the prosecution. In France, where the public prosecutors seemed to have the advantage over the defence, it was difficult to realize how much support our neighbours derived from the Action Committee's statements. There was also a tendency to underestimate the resistance of the European institutions – the Common Market, presided over with authority and courage by Hallstein, and Euratom under Etienne Hirsch, who had taken the place of Armand, exhausted by overwork. I was sure that so powerful a network, in the service of forward-looking ideas, would in the long run defeat inertia or nostalgia for the past.

In that month of June 1962 all Europe's political strategists were looking for defensive fallback positions. I took no part in their complex calculations. The time had come for the Community to make progress,

445

internally and externally. Perhaps it would be possible to clear a middle way for political union. At least we had to show clearly that such a middle way existed; and we did so. But it was still more urgent to broaden Europe's horizons on a world scale: and this primarily involved Great Britain:

> The entry of the United Kingdom into the European Community on a basis of equality under the conditions laid down in the Rome Treaty will reinforce the unity of Europe. The union will then comprise 240 million people. It will enable all its members to achieve greater economic growth. The Commonwealth countries, among others, must benefit by this expansion.
>
> Britain's participation in the beginnings of a European political union will increase the influence Europe can exert on the world's affairs. Separately neither the United Kingdom nor our countries could exercise such an influence.

Some months later I received a letter from Wehner:

> The declaration of June 26, 1962, remains for me a political document of immense value. In this year of your life you have given us a great stimulus and you have created movement among men. I want to thank you most particularly.

And he added:

> Of all the people you have to deal with, I am certainly one whom you sometimes find difficult to understand, as much for linguistic reasons as from a political point of view. But I want you to know that you have won in me a grateful friend who is trying to follow where your ideas lead.

The spontaneous testimony of that powerful man, trained in the hardest of schools, was for me a confirmation that we were on the right track.

Chapter 18

GREAT BRITAIN AND THE
EUROPEAN COMMUNITY (1961-1963)

I

·Europe needs Britain

'I remember coming to London in 1950 to persuade you to join the Schuman Plan negotiations. But you felt then, as you feel now, that it was impossible for you to delegate national powers of decision to common institutions.'

This was the reminder that I addressed to the British cotton-makers at their Harrogate congress in October 1957.

'We realized . . . we could not persuade you by words alone. We know you respect facts, not hypotheses.'

That was exactly what I had said to Sir Stafford Cripps seven years earlier. Was the time now coming for us to meet at the rendezvous we had foreseen so long ago? No: the history of nations evolves slowly, except when spurred on by bold acts or bursts of confidence. Great Britain had so far taken only a few cautious steps towards the continent; but the force that was driving her in that direction was that same necessity which was leading the Community to its spectacular achievements. The laws of attraction were being confirmed; and it was certain, now, that the phenomenon could only gather speed. Whether it would take months or years I had no way of knowing. When one is sure of the outcome, one can afford to be patient. I went on:

'The moral for us has been that we had to go ahead. We have done so, and our relations with you have developed naturally from that starting-point. We set up the Coal and Steel Community. When we arrived in Luxembourg, the first telegram I received was from your Government. Two years later, you signed an Agreement of Association with the Community. Why? Because it existed and prospered. Now, we are establishing Euratom and the Common Market. And you have proposed the Free Trade Area. Why? Because these new Communities are becoming a reality.'

Harold Macmillan had proposed the Free Trade Area a year ago. Its aim was to include all the OEEC countries, with the Common Market too. Was it a step forward or a step back? I regarded it above all as a sign of movement. Great Britain had followed the Brussels negotiations for the new Communities from a distance, despite the fact that she had been invited to take part on the same footing as the others. Now, by proposing the Free Trade Area, she had recognized that the new Communities were not the vain notions that she had at first thought. Was she hoping to dissolve them in a broader entity under her own control? Or was she anxious merely to limit their effects and gain a few advantages for herself? I had no time for such questions, although they unduly worried the Six. The best thing they could do, in the face of the British initiative, was to make faster progress themselves. And while the Action Committee welcomed the British proposal in its resolution of October 1956, it took the opportunity to call for the Brussels negotiations on the six-nation Treaties to be rapidly concluded, just as in the following year it urged their swift ratification. The Communities had to exist in themselves and affirm their own identity as distinct from the Free Trade Area project, whose structure remained vague and whose aims were essentially commercial. But the Six could not ignore the problems that they might create. As I said in my Harrogate speech:

'The Six do not want to raise new frontiers between peoples. That would be to deny what they have already done among themselves. The Common Market is outward-looking, not inward-looking. There is nothing magic in the number six. The door has always been open to Great Britain, and it always will be.'

For the time being, what the British wanted was not to enter that door but to surround our Community with a huge network of very diverse tariff relationships. Their negotiator, Reginald Maudling, was a hard bargainer, and during 1958 the atmosphere grew tense. It was one thing to consider the interests of third parties: it was quite another to preserve the unity of the Six. And if Germany and the Benelux countries were infinitely more concerned about the former than France was, everyone was agreed on the latter. In October 1958, the Action Committee issued a warning:

If it is necessary to associate Great Britain and the other countries of Europe with our Community, it is equally essential that this association should respect the integrity of the Community itself.

The Committee certainly included men who by conviction and tradition believed in free trade and in a Europe looking outward to the open sea. Many of them, in times of crisis, showed that their feeling for British democracy had very deep roots. But all of them agreed with me when I affirmed that the only way to develop trade with the rest of the world and tighten our links with Great Britain was to establish on the continent an economic and political entity which would give broad opportunities for trade and exert a powerful force of attraction. To weaken the structure of the Common Market or cast doubt upon its future would on the contrary revive past economic conflicts and attempts at domination. Did anyone want Britain once again to try to dominate Europe from the outside? That was what would happen if we abandoned the rules of the Community to embrace the empiricism of the Free Trade Area.

The problem was most acute in Germany, where the offshore breeze was strong. In January 1969 I had matters out with Ludwig Erhard, the German Minister of Economic Affairs, whose free-trading opinions threatened to steer his country's policy off course.

'The whole thing's very painful,' he said. 'Anyone in Germany who criticizes the protectionist tendencies of the Six is accused of being a bad European, especially by France.'

'There's a fundamental difference,' I said, 'between the Community, which is a way of uniting peoples, and the Free Trade Area, which is simply a commercial arrangement. Our institutions take an overall view and propose common policies; the Free Trade Area project is an attempt to solve particular problems without putting them in the context of collective action. The Community will be enlarged to include Great Britain, but without giving up the principle of integration. If not, the Community will cease to be itself and will be of no further interest to anyone.'

Erhard then made a further remark which showed me how much in two minds he was.

'If I criticize the German constitution,' he said, 'no one tells me I'm a bad German. But if I criticize the Community of the Six in the name of a wider Europe, I'm immediately accused of being a bad European.'

'Germany,' I said, 'is an established country, with its own Constitutional Court, its own Parliament, and its own Government. If you criticize it, that's a serious matter, but it fits into a solid framework. The constitution of the Six, on the other hand, is still fragile and incomplete. By attacking it, you may undermine its foundations and destroy its balance.'

449

Erhard was no nationalist. He had a certain conception of Europe, but it was one which could be influenced. I found him open to arguments in favour of a Community that was both solid and outward-looking.

'No one is more anxious than I am to see the British join the European Community,' I went on. 'But they won't join if we make too many concessions at the start.'

This was not a piece of tactics on my part: it was a firm opinion, which I had formed in the course of many negotiations with the British. In their dealings with others, their national character inclines them to seek a special position which will save them from having to change. That, as has been seen already, was what had been at stake in our very difficult talks on the Schuman Plan in 1950: they had refused to take part in the Paris conference on the same footing and with the same commitments as the other countries. Most of them now agreed that if we had given in there would have been no Schuman Plan at all. 'Now that you are a fact, we shall deal with you': that remark by Sir Roger Makins two years afterward was still fresh in my mind. And why should we adopt a different attitude today, when the success of the Communities was being confirmed? Their success was that of a process of change which would enable our peoples to adapt to the modern world. And although the British were not yet ready for change, did that mean that they would forever reject the process we had thought right for ourselves? I could not accept so static a hypothesis, because it was inconceivable that a great country could stand aside from the course of events. The British themselves would soon understand that, and we had to prepare them and ourselves for the time when they did.

The form the negotiations had taken made a rapprochement impossible. By the time of my conversation with Erhard, no one had any more faith in the Free Trade Area as originally proposed; and London's new proposals for a multilateral association – above all in the spirit in which they were conceived – were no better. Meeting in May 1959, the Action Committee declared:

> The difficulties of this association are considerable, following on the failure of the Free Trade Area. It will be possible to overcome them only if a feeling of trust little by little replaces the hostility born of the polemics around the Free Trade Area, and if the procedures followed in the new negotiation simplify the problems involved instead of increasing them – as has happened hitherto.

But it was to take years to change what is called the 'approach' to these things – which, in my experience, is sometimes more substantial and important than the things themselves. The way in which traditional diplomacy tackles problems tends to perpetuate them by freezing them into adversary positions from the start, like a game of chess. And, as in chess, what would emerge from the complex multilateral negotiations into which Britain was trying to lead Europe would only be the chance result of incalculable individual moves. That confrontation was to last for ten years, until all the players realized that in this new game the essential was for everyone to win together. Already, in my view, the problem of Britain and Europe called for a world approach, and it was not so much a matter of protecting this or that line of production, or perpetuating the Commonwealth preference system, as of organizing relations between the constituent elements of the West.

The civilization of the West needs Britain; and Europe, to continue her unique contribution to that civilization, needs the qualities that reside in the British people. I first went to London in 1905, and since then I have usually been back several times a year. I spent the dark hours of two world wars there. I remember the great days of the City when it was an unrivalled world power. I had admired the stability of the Empire, and I admired the orderly process of decolonization. Over two generations I have seen the role of Great Britain diminish; but I have not witnessed any decline. If I am asked: 'What remains of that astonishing country today?' my answer is: 'The British people'. They have not suddenly stepped aside from history. Passing difficulties may eclipse their contribution; but once the British have surmounted them, the world will see that creative faculties bred over the centuries do not disappear so fast.

Of all the contributions that the British have made to civilization, two seem to me essential: respect for freedom, and the working of democratic institutions. Where would our society be without *habeas corpus* and without Parliaments to counterbalance executive power? It is not simply that the British invented the principle and that we have followed them. It has to be applied in daily life. Here, Britain and the countries of continental Europe have much to learn from each other's democratic practice. The British have a better understanding than the continentals of institutions and how to use them. Continentals tend to believe that problems are solved by men. Undoubtedly, men are important; but without institutions they reach no great and enduring decisions. This the British have long understood. That is why, unlike many people, I had no fear that their accession would upset the working of the Community.

'They want things to work,' I explained; 'and when they see that Europe only works by means of institutions, the British will become the foremost champions of those institutions, and especially of their parliamentary aspect. Continental Europeans have Parliaments too, of course; but no one can say how deeply rooted they are. There was an old man I knew in America who used to say: "You think you understand this in your head, but you will only really understand it when you feel it in your bones." I think the British feel the necessity of parliamentary action: they feel it in their bones.'

I had no illusions about how long this evolution might take, and I would not have ventured to work out a timetable for the necessary process of adjustment. What mattered was to make a start: for nothing would happen so long as the British lacked a view from within. Looking on from outside, they lulled themselves with illusions of grandeur. They had not known the trauma of wartime occupation; they had not been conquered; their system seemed intact. In reality they suffered – paradoxically – from not having had their pride broken and their factories destroyed. The continental Europeans had: at one time or another all of them had been conquered, and they had been obliged to draw up a balance-sheet of their losses, psychological and material, in order to rebuild and to seek a new role. More and more of Britain's leaders were becoming aware of how much her victory had cost her, and they realized that by herself the country would not accept the necessity for change. They had heard Dean Acheson's verdict: 'Britain has lost an Empire and not yet found a role.' They could conclude that the United States was not prepared to offer them a share in its own role: they would find it only by catching up with the Europe that was on the move. By doing so, they would transform Britain's own situation and that of Europe, to which she would bring her resources, her inventiveness, her world-wide view, and her understanding of government. That was a great deal. It was certainly enough to justify a little disturbance in the delicate balance that the Six had established among themselves during the past ten years.

Some were worried in advance lest this disturbance might change the nature of the existing Community. In May 1961 I read that even von Brentano, in his capacity as German Foreign Minister, had publicly suggested seeking some 'middle path' between accession and association. I wrote to him at once:

I am convinced by all the information in my possession, which I believe to be reliable, that we are on the eve of a British decision to enter the Common Market and join in the building of Europe. Furthermore, I am convinced that if the British take this decision, as I confidently expect, they will prove loyal colleagues in the Common Market and in the building of Europe. But – and this is the reason I am writing to you – they will do so on one condition only: that there are no exceptions to the common rules, which might lead to a conflict of interest between Britain and the other members of the Community.

The information I received from my friends in London became more specific, so much so that I thought it necessary to call a meeting of the Action Committee in Paris on July 10, 1961. The aim was both to prepare the political welcome that the parties and trade unions would give to the British application for membership, and to confirm the important conditions that I had stated in my letter to von Brentano:

> Experience shows that the problems which used to separate nations are shared in the Community, and that the decisions arrived at necessarily take account of the special interests of member countries as part of the general interest.
>
> It is therefore possible for the United Kingdom to join the European economic and political union, and this necessarily on the same basis as the present members of the European Economic Community, with the same rights and the same obligations.

That point was crucial. The British are reputed to be difficult partners, and so they are when they negotiate on their own account, in their own way. But they are loyal colleagues when they sit with you on the same side of the table. Then, you can count on them to make things work. That is why it was essential that in joining the Community they should accept all the rules that the Six observed among themselves. Naturally, this stipulation would not prevent Britain's particular problems being dealt with, as had those of Germany and France. Likewise, the method followed to give the British their place would be very important; and on this I made the same very simple proposal that I had tried to have adopted since the beginning of the Schuman Plan: to agree on the objective and negotiate afterwards. To diplomats, this seemed paradoxical: to me it was a matter of logic. An overall settlement is unlikely to be reached by haggling over details. On the contrary, details fall into place, and specific problems are more easily solved, when they are looked at in the framework of a general agreement. 'The technical questions posed by British accession should be solved within the Common Market, using Common Market procedures': that was the approach that seemed to me reasonable. It placed its trust in the wisdom and strength of the existing institutions. And trust was the whole point. In 1950, the British had not trusted either the objective or the method we proposed to them. Would they this time negotiate right to the end with their own weapons, at the risk of never succeeding? Or would they agree to discuss their problems as common problems, using the machinery of the Community, which had been devised for that very purpose? I hoped that they would have learned from experience, and have been convinced by the example which the Brussels institutions had made clear.

On July 30, 1961, I received a messenger from Edward Heath, then Britain's Lord Privy Seal, bringing me news that the United Kingdom was about to announce its request to join the Community. The message read:

> We are sure our decision will be welcome to him. It has of course been a difficult one for the United Kingdom Government. We are very grateful for the efforts which Monsieur Monnet has made to smooth our path and are confident that we can count on his help in overcoming the many difficulties which remain to be solved.

In the answer which I gave the messenger I said:

> I assure you, as you already well know, that I will do all on my part to smooth the way towards Great Britain joining in the efforts, both economic and political, to create the unity of Europe, and particularly to help solving the difficulties in connection with the Common Market.
>
> I do personally hope and I believe it possible and important that the negotiations you mention can be concluded quickly; the great difficulty resided in taking the decision which the UK Government has now taken.

On the following day, Harold Macmillan told the House of Commons:

'After long and earnest consideration, Her Majesty's Government have come to the conclusion that it would be right for the United Kingdom to make a formal application under Article 237 of the Treaty of Rome for negotiations with a view to joining the Community, if satisfactory arrangements can be made to meet the special needs of the United Kingdom, of the Commonwealth, and of the European Free Trade Association.'

I was not too worried by the ambiguity of these words, knowing that Macmillan had to reassure British Members of Parliament. What mattered was that he sincerely wished to succeed; and I was certain that he had not come to this decision without good reasons. One of them, and by no means the least important, was the very clear advice he had received in the United States when he had met President Kennedy in April 1961. Some weeks earlier, I had found the President already convinced, thanks to his Under-Secretary of State for Economic Affairs, George Ball, that Britain ought to join the European Community; and I had written to Adenauer:

> Washington believes that Britain ought to be part of the Common Market and of Europe on the same footing as France and Germany, as a full member and not as an associate. But this, of course, is a decision that Britain must take for herself. What is more, the contacts I have recently had in London convince me that we are close to the moment when Britain's leaders will reach a decision on this question. They are beginning to realize that their 'special relationship' with the United States will not last. We are now in a period of collective decisions and 'large-scale ventures', of which the European Community is the example.

So it was very much more than a tactical manoeuvre on Macmillan's part: it was a deliberate decision to change course and join continental Europe. This choice became even clearer when Macmillan sent Edward Heath to negotiate in Brussels.

Heath was known for his ability and energy, which marked him out for a leading role in the British Conservative Party. I liked him above all for his human qualities and his convictions. On the need for Britain to take part in the building of Europe he had not faltered since his maiden speech in 1950; nor did he in the future. He would try with all his might to succeed; but would he be able – would he know how – to hit on the right method from the start? That was now the only important question I had to tackle. My contribution to the huge and technical negotiations which were about to start, mobilizing hundreds of experts, was precisely to try to ensure that the experts were kept in their place and that the decision was taken at political level. It needed to be taken very soon. On August 1, 1961, I made a statement to the French news agency *Agence France Presse*:

'The negotiations must move rapidly to avoid creating confusion. It is a mistake to think that wide-ranging negotiations are necessary. We must not let ourselves be impressed by the problems of substance: they are not all that difficult to solve. What counts is the decision to tackle questions in a forward-looking and constructive manner rather than in terms of maintaining the past. That is the fundamental decision which the British Government has now taken. That is what is historic.'

That problems of substance were soluble if they were set in their overall context was something I knew from experience; but I still had to convince those now involved. To do so, I had to go into technical

455

questions like trade in Commonwealth agricultural products and raw materials, which appeared to place sizeable obstacles in the way of an economic rapprochement between Britain and the Six. The latter had overcome obstacles just as serious when they had negotiated the Treaties, and above all in four years of applying them. In this work of elucidation, I was assisted by the very same people whom I later saw drawn into the labyrinth of the endless Brussels conference. How was it that the peculiar momentum of international negotiations could overcome men as clear-headed as Heath and his assistants – men like the outstanding Sir Eric Roll, as well as Couve de Murville and Clappier on the French delegation and, from the Commission in its role of general adviser, Hallstein, Jean Rey, and the young Jean-François Deniau, who was to reveal first-class intellectual ability? I never tired of reminding them that the difficulties which were holding them up would cease to do so if they only dared to bypass them now and tackle them together later on, once Britain had joined. Individually, everyone agreed with me; but once they were back at the negotiating table the desire to gain some advantage or defend some vested interest took hold of them all. To clear a path through the technical complications, the Action Committee relied on its Documentation Centre, mainly financed by the Ford Foundation, and on the Centre of European Studies, so remarkably well run by my devoted friend in Lausanne, Professor Henri Rieben. These two institutes produced objective studies leading to simple conclusions, as the greatest experts can when one takes the trouble to have it out with them.

In this task, I was helped by an invaluable colleague, François Duchêne. In 1952, I had noticed some excellent articles on France in the then *Manchester Guardian*, and I had asked if I could see their author. In came a tall young man – almost a boy: he was astonishingly youthful, high-spirited, and imaginative. I liked his subtle and sophisticated mind. He agreed to join the information service of the High Authority, which took him on despite the fact that he was British. Later, he spent three years with the Action Committee, had a brilliant career on *The Economist*, became Director of the International Institute for Strategic Studies in London, and then went on to be a university professor. With him, with his friend and successor Richard Mayne from the High Authority and the Common Market, with Kohnstamm, with Marjolin, with Uri, and many others, we tried for eighteen months to speed up the negotiations, which had not taken the rapid course that would have been possible at the beginning. I made many trips to London and Brussels, during which Heath and I became friends. He took my advice; but no one was any longer in control of events: they had a momentum of their own, and where it was leading was problematical. When the talks sometimes seemed on the point of succeeding – as, for example, on Commonwealth questions – people congratulated themselves on having chosen the harder path. But this only encouraged them to increase their demands, and the whole process became blocked once again.

II

The first veto

Everyone was looking ahead to the outcome: but it was not the same for them all. The Commission thought that it had found a broad area of agreement; the British thought they were on the eve of victory; and the French were thinking of walking out. On December 18, 1962, the Action Committee made one more effort to bring people's minds back to the problem of method. That this recurs so often in the present narrative should be no cause for surprise: recurrent situations make it necessary to recall the same commonsense rules that men continually forget. Hence, incidentally, the need for institutions to establish the framework of rules for action, and substitute an enduring collective memory for fleeting and fragmented individual experience. The Committee declared:

> Owing to the conditions in which the negotiations are taking place, the Governments of the Six and the British Government are tending to confuse the comprehensive view which should govern the negotiations as a whole with the discussion of detailed implementing decisions, important though these may be.
>
> Today, it is no longer a question of compounding national interests, but of considering problems henceforward as common problems, and gradually merging the national interests in a European economic body accepting the same rules and the same institutions, in accordance with the fundamental principles of the European Community.
>
> Since time is today an important factor for the success of the negotiations with Great Britain, these must be rapidly concluded.

But on the very same day, at Nassau in the Bahamas, Macmillan met Kennedy, and they took strategic decisons whose consequences proved very grave. The Skybolt air-to-ground missile project, which had become too costly, was abandoned; and in its place the British obtained American Polaris missiles, carried by submarine. Kennedy made the same offer to the French.

It was very quickly refused. De Gaulle considered that France and Britain had not made the same choice on the vital problem of defence, and that in this field their destiny was now divided. I did not myself go so far as to make a direct link between what was happening at Nassau and what was being planned in Paris. The most one could say was that, in de Gaulle's eyes, two sets of simultaneous events pointed in the same direction. He drew a single conclusion: Britain had no place in Europe. He said so on January 14, 1963, in one of his most resounding press conferences. By its manner no less than its content, it marked a turning-point in relations between France and the other countries of the West. Of Britain, de Gaulle declared:

'It cannot be said that at present she has decided. Will she, one day...? It is possible that one day Britain will change of her own accord, sufficiently to join the European Community, without restrictions or reservations, and without any preference system. In that case the Six would open the door to her, and France would not bar the way. ....'

'One day' meant that it was not for tomorrow: Britain saw herself thrust into the distant reaches of geography and history, as if it were a matter of course. Yet there was nothing in the facts to justify that judgement: the only evidence was in the mind of General de Gaulle, who declared on his own authority that the negotiations had failed. The January 14 press conference shocked world opinion. People could not see how one country could unilaterally decide, at its own chosen moment, to call a halt to multilateral talks that had been in progress for over a year. Had they gone on too long? If in fact they had been bogged down for some time, there was nothing to prevent their succeeding before long. At the very least, the time for a final decision had been close at hand, and anything had been conceivable, barring its cancellation.

My first reaction was to reject the idea that Europe could thus be faced with a *fait accompli*. Nothing is quite an accomplished fact so long as it is not accepted. I told the press:

'I think that, whatever General de Gaulle may have said, the negotiations for British membership of the Common Market could be concluded very rapidly. In fact, Britain has already accepted the Treaty of Rome, and in particular the rules for taking Community decisions. She has asked to enter the Community on the same footing as the present member States, i.e. without special privileges. She has agreed to join with the continent and to apply in full its common external tariff. In the areas that have already been discussed, she has given up all Commonwealth preference. Nor, finally, is she any longer claiming special privileges for British agriculture.

'Almost all the main questions of principle have thus been settled. . . . It would be inconceivable for the negotiations to break down on questions which in the long run are secondary by comparison with the objective, which is the unity of the West.'

But in the days that followed it became clear that France had indeed decided to break the negotiations off; and Couve de Murville told his colleagues so in Brussels on January 28. That day, I made a further statement to *Agence France Presse*:

'The failure of the Brussels negotiations is very serious. It is serious because it would have been possible rapidly to solve the questions that remain between the Six and Great Britain . . ., and because the mutual trust which is indispensable to any collective agreement has been shaken. Instead of a European union including Great Britain, and the establishment of an equal partnership with the United States, both of which are essential to peace between East and West, we face disunion and the dangers it involves.

'At this grave hour, I remember 1954. Then, as now, the unification of Europe was momentarily halted; and yet the need to unite finally broke through all the obstacles.

'So it will be today.'

Hope could not gainsay the depth of the disappointment, and Europe had difficulty healing the wound. Even when people had dismissed it from the forefront of their minds, it remained for many years in their subconscious, and often led them to react with mistrust. For a time, they went to extremes: some tried to block all Community progress, while others thought of going ahead without France. As always, the most difficult thing was to persuade them to take a positive attitude, in which there would be neither victors nor vanquished.

'There is no doubt,' I told my friends, 'that the exclusion of Great Britain has temporarily weakened the Community. But if tomorrow we want to return to the attack and succeed, the Community must go on. And going on, for the Six, means going on together.'

Before long, in fact, not only France but all the member States found that they had an interest in going on together; while Great Britain herself, after the first very sharp reaction, eventually resumed her long march towards Europe. In July 1963 I said to a British newspaperman: 'I know that psychological changes are taking place in Britain today.

They were before the negotiations broke down. Big industrialists were adapting themselves in anticipation of entering the Market. These adaptations are continuing, and I think this process of change will point the way eventually to the re-opening of the question of Britain joining the Market. It must be understood that the Common Market is a process of change – not only economic change, but psychological change as well.'

Unfortunately, psychology had not been the strong point of those who had undertaken a negotiation of traditional type in the hope of solving a problem that was wholly new. This would have to be remembered when the time came to start again. Only experience of life within the Community would change the attitude of the British: that was why no one could say for certain whether or not they were ready to become European. They would become European only inside the Community institutions, where day after day a common view was hammered out. Their great error had been to imagine that they could adapt to this common view from outside, in preliminary negotiations, and even thereby influence it. That was why, without making any excuses for the way in which this first attempt had been halted by veto, I wasted no time trying to apportion blame. The fact that a negotiation had failed in no way removed the necessity to broaden Europe's horizons; and already the Community, with Great Britain, was regarded by the United States as the equal partner that Kennedy hoped to see established in the Western half of Europe. The US President's speech in Philadelphia on July 4, 1962, was in my eyes an historic act, which gave the Community its true dimensions and fully justified our efforts. I shall return to it later.

In February 1963, I wrote to my friends, who had doubts about whether our work could go on:

> This is a time for patience. Nothing is changed, but everything has been delayed. What matters above all is to keep our aim clearly before us, to preserve what we have already won and, as far as possible, to make fresh progress. The aim is to organize peace between East and West. That is the aim of all our efforts. . . . To attain it, we must establish between the civilizations of East and West, with their very different methods of dealing with public affairs, an agreement which requires understanding and acceptance. The Action Committee believes that peaceful co-existence between our way of life and the Communist way of life is possible. To achieve it, we have to acknowledge that the West must seek union among its countries in a common civilization, and not in an out-of-date and impossible system from the Atlantic to the Urals.

We are at present beset by doubts and uncertainties about the course our countries' international policy should take. Nothing in private or public life is as bad as uncertainty. Men need to know the direction to which their Governments are committing them. The time has come to try to clear away the fog that has enveloped us since General de Gaulle's press conference.

It was a time for patience, but not for inaction. If the enlargement of the Community was temporarily delayed, there was no time to lose in organizing the West. When the time came, Britain would resume her natural place in this process, which had to be pursued on the broader front that was now open to us. The repercussions of the Common Market were felt throughout the world – this proved that it was an active force. Britain no longer had the option of opposing that force: she would become part of it. And the United States, which was both attracted and alarmed by the prospect, according to whether it considered the general interest of the West or the particular interests of its own producers, had already taken characteristically energetic steps. My uncertainty, therefore, did not last long. By April 1963 I had made up my mind, and I wrote to my friends:

Until now, the Action Committee has been in favour of taking one step at a time, depending on what is politically possible. This is no longer its view. It believes that overall action has become necessary. There is no longer any need to convince people: the people of Europe are convinced already. Nor is it any longer a matter of overcoming technical obstacles while taking account of present political difficulties. That time has passed. We must complete the organization of Europe and negotiate a treaty between Europe and the United States.

Chapter 19

EUROPE AND THE UNITED STATES (1962-1964)

I

Partnership

The United States and Europe share the same civilization, based on individual freedom, and conduct their public life in accordance with common democratic principles. That is the essential point. History has decisively proved this profound kinship, which in times of danger turns into active solidarity. When the human values that Europe and America share are threatened, the United States intervenes without counting the cost in men or money. But when the sense of kinship gives way to the daily conduct of national affairs, the difference of scale becomes apparent. No one can be blamed for the misunderstandings that ensue. To be the greatest power in the world is a lonely and dangerous business. It involves almost limitless power over others; and, however unfairly, it gives rise to envy and suspicion. It requires the exercise of certain virtues – self-control and generosity. When one is strong, one can afford to be generous; but by trying to impose one's superiority, one loses it. Many Americans are aware of that fact, and they quite naturally shape their policy to take account of it. But I feel easier in my mind when Europeans take the necessary steps to establish equality between themselves and the United States.

After the war, it was pointless to seek equality except through union in Europe – a form of union which would make it possible to act. The Americans recognized in the European Community a force similar to that which they had created two centuries before; and that was why they supported it from the start. Would their support survive our economic successes and political failures? The question was legitimate; but I knew something else about the American people. They respond to what works: deeds are what matter to them, not words. And the choice was ours. If the Europeans acted together in clear determination to solve their own problems and play an active part in tackling the problems that both continents shared, then it would be easy to talk with the Americans. It is not true that they are inclined to dominate: they are ready for any useful discussion and they aim at efficiency. Competition is so much a part of their way of life that they are astonished not to meet it in their partners. The absence of any political initiative from Europe disconcerted them; and when they began to fear that the Common Market might be no more than a regional preference area, they prepared to take up the challenge. That, at least, was the attitude in agricultural and industrial circles, which were very influential in Congress.

I wanted this question to be dealt with before it assumed overtones of conflict. As early as November 1959, I wrote to Adenauer:

> We must realize that there has been a fundamental change in the world economic situation. The American balance of payments has gone into deficit. If this situation grows worse, I need not describe what the results would be for the whole of the West and for ourselves in particular.

It was at that time, as has been seen, that the Action Committee proposed that the problems of the Six and the EFTA Seven, with those of America, should be tackled together because they were insoluble separately. In the years that followed, I went as often as possible to the United States, where a new generation soon came to power with President John F. Kennedy. We had no difficulty in understanding one another, not only through friendship – I knew most of them personally – but also because our ideas were very much the same. The young American Administration was looking at the world with fresh eyes; and I was less concerned about the specific difficulties we had with it – in particular with Orville Freeman, the Secretary for Agriculture – than about the Europeans' own need to explain their plans. In January 1961, in an interview with Robert Kleiman of *U.S. News and World Report*, I said:

'By changing conditions in Europe, the Six have produced a new "ferment of change" in the West. As we can see from American and British reactions to the Common Market, one change brings another. The chain reaction has only begun. We are starting a process of continuous reform which can shape tomorrow's world more lastingly than the principles of revolution so widespread outside the West.'

A few weeks later, I had the opportunity to say much the same thing to President John F. Kennedy.

The President invited me to luncheon at the White House with McGeorge Bundy. We had a long conversation, during which he questioned me very closely. His curiosity and his desire to learn seemed to me one of his most striking characteristics; I already knew of his intelligence and charm. He listened to me, as to all his advisers and visitors: his remarkable receptiveness rapidly gave him a political maturity that was exceptional in so young a man. Those who had been critical of him before they met him soon forgot his youth and saw only his dynamism. I found that his authority was being felt all over Washington, where the atmosphere reminded me of the Roosevelt era. Ideas were discussed everywhere; policies were prepared by public consultations; then came the time for decision, which was the President's job. From the start, Kennedy showed himself to be energetic and courageous. He saw Europe as his affair – his choice of advisers left no doubt of that. On my return, I wrote to Adenauer, who was leaving to meet Kennedy in the United States:

> The President is very straightforward, prudent, and direct. His relations with his colleagues are based on trust. Problems are debated; everyone has his say; but the President has the last word. Talking with him, as I did at length, I came to the conclusion that you would get on well together. He too is a man of action; and, if you will allow me to say so, you share the same youthful spirit.
>
> The men around him have been well chosen. Our friends McCloy and Acheson have very important roles and enjoy great influence, McCloy for disarmament and Acheson for NATO. There are also Douglas Dillon, George Ball – whom you have just seen in Bonn, David Bruce, US Ambassador in London, and Vice-President Lyndon Johnson, who is the expert on domestic affairs and has very great influence in the Senate. A number of other people have also been brought in. Among those you already know are our friends McGeorge Bundy, Robert Bowie, Gene Rostow, Shepard Stone, and Robert Schaetzel.
>
> In the work they have been given – whether Acheson on NATO or McCloy on disarmament – they have all come to the same conclusion: that it is urgently necessary to organize the West – that is, the free world, which essentially comprises continental Europe, Britain, the United States, and Canada. But for all of them it is clear that the central core of this organization of the West is the European Community, at the heart of which is unity between Germany and France.

Everyone in Washington now shares this general view of the world, from the officials in the State Department to the President himself.

Of all American Presidents, Kennedy was certainly the one whose education and upbringing best equipped him to understand the problems of Europe. But this would not have enabled him to reach the heart of the matter so quickly if he had not trusted his very well-informed advisers, and in particular George Ball. It was through him, more than anyone, that the President had come to realize the profound significance of Europe's new institutions and their importance for the stability of this part of the world, which needed to be strengthened before starting up a dialogue with the East. It took only a few hours to convince me that America was ready to welcome a European grand design, and to put our inevitable economic clashes into a broader context on which we could agree. But at the same time it was possible to discern the distant consequences that might result if this overall plan were to fail. The future showed that misunderstanding could arise from even less substantial matters – such as mere doubts about whether the Europeans had the will to go on from the Common Market to political union.

My letter to Adenauer continued:

Co-operation on an equal footing between the United States and a divided, fragmented Europe would be impossible. Equality is possible now only because France and Germany together have begun to build a great European entity with the prospect of becoming a sort of second America.

I became convinced in Washington that without such a prospect the United States, left to itself, would turn back to the particular problems of Asia, Africa, and Latin America. So we must realize that co-operation between the United States and Europe, which is essential to our security, will in the long run be possible only if the European Community is dynamic and shows its understanding of the world-wide problems that concern the Americans. They have ceased to be observers bringing benevolent aid: they have become participants directly interested in the results of the common effort. Henceforward, America will engage with Europe in so far as Europe unites and the European Community makes an effective contribution to solving world problems such as aid to underdeveloped countries and the monetary stability of the West.

Kennedy took the first step towards a rational handling of intercontinental economic problems in January 1962, when he proposed to Congress the establishment of 'an open trade partnership between the United States and the European Community'. The Trade Expansion Act, passed in October 1962, authorized the President to negotiate with

Europe reciprocal tariff cuts of as much as 50% – and more if Britain joined the Community. The biggest and longest trade negotiations the world had ever seen began under the name of the 'Kennedy Round'. Public opinion did not fully realize what was at stake; but so great were the interests involved that no industrialist or farmer could afford to be indifferent. If, as a result, the bargaining was hard, it was nevertheless conducted in accordance with the rules, and on a footing of equality that would have been impossible if the European countries had not presented a solid front and spoken with a single voice. In the person of Jean Rey, a negotiator of great talent who later became a worthy successor to Hallstein, the Commission affirmed its own strength and the unity of the Six. The overall view that was reached during these formidable negotiations gave all parties an understanding of each other's economic systems; and while that did not prevent a hard struggle, it was conducted in an orderly fashion and with the general interest in mind.

A further step was needed. The Europe of the States would not take it spontaneously, so the Action Committee had to point the way. In its declaration of June 26, 1962, the Committee affirmed:

> While the economic unity of Europe is being consolidated and a start made on its political unification, the co-operation that has already grown up between the United States and European countries should gradually be transformed into a partnership between a united Europe and the United States.
>
> The partnership between America and a united Europe must be a relationship of two separate but equally powerful entities, each bearing its share of common responsibilities in the world. . . .
>
> Just as European unity is the result of progress step by step on concrete questions by the countries of Europe, so the new partnership of Europe and America will develop as the outcome of patient and practical efforts to tackle together the problems they have in common.

The United States was not slow to reply. One week later, on the solemn occasion of Independence Day, July 4, 1962, Kennedy took the opportunity to make a speech in Philadelphia which had considerable impact in the world. That speech, which will go down in history as the 'partnership' speech, proposed an equal partnership between 'the new union now emerging in Europe and the old American union founded here 175 years ago'. At that moment, better than in ten years of daily news from Europe, the American people grasped the meaning of the European Community that had been set up by nations which, 'long divided by feuds more bitter than any which existed among the thirteen colonies, are joining together, seeking, as our forefathers sought, to find freedom in diversity and to find strength in unity.' The huge crowd present at this 'Declaration of Interdependence' hailed with enthusiasm its young President's commitment:

'The United States looks on this vast enterprise with hope and admiration. We do not regard a strong and united Europe as a rival but as a partner. To aid its progress has been a basic object of our foreign policy for seventeen years.'

That statement was deeply sincere, and its every word must be read to understand the selfless objective towards which Kennedy was resolved to lead the greatest democracy in the world. He would have done so, or at least he would have spared no effort to do so, in terms which he had fully weighed and around which a programme of practical action was already being organized.

'We believe,' he continued, 'that a united Europe will be capable of playing a greater role in the common defence, of responding more generously to the needs of poorer nations, of joining with the United States and others in lowering trade barriers, resolving problems of currency and commodities, and developing co-ordinated policies in all other economic, diplomatic, and political areas. We see in such a Europe a partner with whom we could deal on a basis of full equality in all the great and burdensome tasks of building and defending a community of free nations.'

One statement of President Kennedy's in the Philadelphia speech did not attract particular attention at the time. But it was a key passage; and when, a few months later, it passed into oblivion for many long years, shadows fell over John F. Kennedy's grand design.

'Europe must first organize itself in its own way, taking its own decisions. When a decision has been reached regarding Great Britain's joining the Common Market, which we hope will be done this summer, then we shall be able to go forward faster.'

The breaking-off of negotiations with London after the French veto of January 1963 deprived Europe of the extra dimension that could have made her the equal partner of the United States. The practical trade problems that remained were dealt with in a fairly balanced way, thanks to the skill and firmness of the European Commission; but defence problems became bogged down in a tiresome argument. It was not always easy for me to persuade the Action Committee to agree on its attitude to the Multilateral Force or MLF – the American proposal for a force of Polaris submarines, with Europeans included in their multinational crews. This affair took up too much of my time;

but I could not evade the real and formidable problems of Europe's defence. Essentially, Europe was protected by the American deterrent, but she was also deeply divided. Britain was integrated in the nuclear system of the Alliance, which was dominated by the United States; France proclaimed her independence; and Germany was excluded from the 'nuclear club'.

So long as Europe had not yet achieved political unity, the Multilateral Force made available by the United States might have made possible the joint use of a deterrent system in which Germany could participate on terms that were honourable to her and reassuring to her partners. This transitional possibility, which would have put Germany on an equal footing with her European allies, greatly attracted the German members of the Action Committee. I could certainly understand that their security needs made them viscerally loyal to the Alliance. The proof of this was given when the Franco-German Treaty of Friendship was concluded in Paris shortly after the breaking-off of the Brussels negotiations in January 1963. The new intimacy between France and Germany alarmed their other Community partners, who suspected the ageing Adenauer of having paid too dearly for hypothetical protection by France. Nor was this all. Both the opposition and the majority parties in Germany, and many Frenchmen too, feared that the new treaty might herald the abandonment of European integration and the weakening of the military alliance with the United States. I myself wondered what de Gaulle's policy was; and without speculating about his ulterior motives – which I have always refused to do – I looked closely at what he was doing.

When I did so, I saw that the Franco-German Treaty sought to promote 'co-operation' in all the fields in question, which cast serious doubt on the future of European integration. I saw that the Treaty lacked any stipulation that Franco-German military strategy would be concerted only within NATO. I heard de Gaulle speak, in a further press conference, of an 'international Aeropagus' to which France could not delegate sovereignty without losing her identity. Meanwhile, we had written a gloss on the Franco–German Treaty, which the parliamentary strategists turned into a Preamble. The *Bundestag* passed it unanimously on April 25. It spoke among other things of 'the maintenance and strengthening of the cohesion of free peoples, and in particular close co-operation between the United States and Europe, common defence within NATO, and the union of Europe including the United Kingdom'. The Preamble and its unanimous approval set things to rights once more. Thus interpreted, the Franco-German

468

Treaty ceased to be an exclusive political alliance and became an administrative vehicle for the Franco-German reconciliation initiated twelve years earlier by the Schuman Plan. It was good that it provided for regular organized meetings of Ministers, civil servants, and young people from the two countries. This could well have been extended throughout the Six, to the benefit of all.

Shaken as it was, Europe took a long time to recover its equilibrium. In Germany, a tired Adenauer, facing opposition within his own party, could not prevent Erhard's rise to power. In Britain, Macmillan left the scene, and the Conservatives continued to lose ground. In Brussels, the European institutions did their best to resume progress. This first great test had shown the strength of the Community machinery. Intergovernmental discord, human ill-temper, and material confusion might slow down its momentum, but they could not stop it. That momentum was a complex phenomenon: everyone had an interest in maintaining it, because it offered him something he could not afford to lose. Self-interest, in moments of crisis, made up for any lack of European team-spirit, and no one any longer thought of withdrawing unilaterally or trying to sabotage the whole affair. Indeed, the spirit of Europe was still alive: it held everything together, even when at governmental level it was no longer visible. It was in the very machinery, ensuring that it worked. Once established, institutions have their own strength, which is greater than the will of men.

Men's minds had to recover their composure before the Action Committee could launch new plans. During 1963, I had no occasion to call a meeting; but no less important than the Committee's plenary sessions were the links we maintained between its members, by going to see them and writing to them throughout this period, which was not a time of waiting. The role of prime mover which France had lost was now taken over by Germany, where Erhard was gradually acquiring a position of power. Gerhard Schroeder, the Foreign Minister, saw to it that the Common Market resumed progress, and he tightened the links between Bonn and Washington, where defence and the MLF had become the main preoccupation. Kennedy came to Berlin to reassure the Germans, and was welcomed enthusiastically wherever he went. At the same time, the Moscow Nuclear Test Ban Treaty which he signed with the Russians showed that all our problems were assuming world proportions, and that Europe risked losing her place – except in the world-wide trade negotiations, which by now were well under way. And Europe meant more than haggling about agriculture, even on a world scale. In some notes I made at the time I wrote:

Recent events, and in particular the nuclear Treaty signed in Moscow, oblige us to look at the unification of Europe in a new light. I believe that we are now facing a situation which must be dealt with globally. I do not believe that people today are sufficiently interested in the unification of Europe as such. They will be, once again, if they understand that the unification of Europe is an essential element in the organization of peace. The unification of Europe including Great Britain, continued negotiations with Russia, and partnership between Europe and the United States – these are three panels of one triptych, and they cannot in my opinion now be treated apart.

This programme may have seemed unrealistic at a time when the Community of the Six was finding it hard to overcome its own difficulties. There was some doubt in Paris about whether the Six would survive, and people were becoming resigned to the idea of a Community of two or three. I knew, too, that in Bonn the old Chancellor was now isolated, and no longer in control of foreign policy: many of his colleagues were tempted to seek a direct agreement with the United States. Certain indications made me suspect that the Americans themselves might no longer believe in Europe, now that it was no longer displaying a common will. All these elements of uncertainty made me determined to continue along the line I was following, before the future grew still darker. When people urged me to think of new ideas, I answered:

'I see none, but that's probably because there are none. We're asking ourselves pointless questions, when in reality the very best thing we can do is continue. There's no alternative policy for France or Germany. There's no longer a world role for Britain. And the United States has only one reliable European ally – Europe.'

I repeated the same thing tirelessly to everyone, in Bonn, London, and Washington. During that 'time for patience' I travelled a great deal.

Continuation and repetition, I realize, are characteristic of this narrative, which is simply the history of a very painstaking creation. Perhaps one day the story will be told in the style of an epic. If it is, I think that the birth of Europe will seem in retrospect a stirring adventure. That may be the truth of tomorrow; but today's truth has the merits of its meticulous patience. One can hardly fail to be struck by the contrast between the meticulousness of the builders of Europe and the grandiloquence of France's policy during the 1960s. That policy was full of spectacular episodes, but they will not be found in these pages. The fact is that the aims which de Gaulle assigned to France's foreign policy from 1963 onward no longer crossed the path of the

Community. Since that is the path we are tracing here, it should be no surprise not to encounter the incidents which gave many Frenchmen the feeling that they alone were living through great days. Their fellow-Europeans, when I went to see them, asked me how France's policy fitted in with the reality of the modern world. They had no illusions about that reality: they measured themselves against it and realized that they were powerless to solve their national problems alone. Their ambitions – and they were no less ambitious than the French – were turned to the future, which each of them knew they could master only if they faced it together. It was not always easy for me to advise them to be patient.

The end of 1963 was marked by a tragedy which affected all feeling men and women in the world. The assassination of John F. Kennedy shattered people's hopes almost before they had arisen. As I say, institutions are more important than men; and America's institutions soon gave impressive proof of that fact. But some men have the power to transform and enrich what institutions pass on to succeeding generations. Kennedy was one such man: he was able to lead his contemporaries by the force of his imagination, and create a consensus through his generosity. I prefer not to speculate on what he might have done with the experience of statesmanship which we saw developing daily before our eyes: I can only marvel at the fact that he left so lasting a memory after so short a career, and that his death left so deep a sense of emptiness. The truest tribute to him that I heard came from a Paris taxi-driver who said to me:

'Monsieur, we have just lost a President.'

My grief that day I cannot describe.

The death of a young and radiant being is distressing in itself. Yet the pain and loss that I felt then were the same as when I had heard seventeen years earlier that Roosevelt had just succumbed to his life-long illness and lifelong effort. We were on a trip in Georgia, I remember; and when Silvia told me the news I exclaimed several times: 'No – it's not possible.' What was not possible was the ending of a great hope. The bearers of hope are never of an age to die. Roosevelt, as I have said, had a universal view of things. Freedom, for him, was indivisible: it did not stop at the frontiers of his country. He had proved that with the last ounce of his strength. Kennedy's strength, so prematurely laid low, was of the same order, and his vision had the same breadth.

I had last seen him in Washington at the beginning of the year. He resented the abrupt breaking-off of the British negotiations, but his understanding of Europe prevented his turning aside from it, as America was tempted to do in the face of our disunion – a temptation to which some of his successors gave way. Since I was about to go to New York to receive the 'Freedom Prize' awarded each year by Freedom House, he sent me the following message:

Dear M. Monnet,

For centuries, emperors, kings, and dictators have sought to impose unity on Europe by force. For better or worse, they have failed. But under your inspiration, Europe has moved closer to unity in less than twenty years than it had done before in a thousand. You and your associates have built with the mortar of reason and the brick of economic and political interest. You are transforming Europe by the power of a constructive idea.

Ever since the war the reconstruction and the knitting together of Europe have been objectives of United States policy, for we have recognized with you that in unity lies strength. And we have also recognized with you that a strong Europe would be good not only for Europeans but for the world. America and Europe, working in full and effective partnership, can find solutions to those urgent problems that confront all mankind in this crucial time.

On November 25, I attended Kennedy's simple and moving funeral.

Less than two weeks later, I found myself once more in the state reception rooms at the White House to receive a last testimony of Kennedy's feelings for Europe. He had decided to confer on me, as on John McCloy and the labour leader George Meany, one of the first Presidential Medals of Freedom. He had planned to give it to me himself on December 6. President Lyndon Johnson performed the ceremony, in the presence of Mrs Kennedy, who watched it quietly from a dark corner of the room. Johnson read to me the text prepared by his predecessor, whose spirit still haunted – but not for long – those rooms where civilization and a sense of greatness had reigned for two short years:

Citizen of France, statesman of the world, he has made persuasion and reason the weapons of statecraft, moving Europe toward unity and the Atlantic nations toward a more effective partnership.

II

Crises and their aftermath

Atlantic partnership did not die with John F. Kennedy. An idea which is in the nature of things is never the creation of one man alone, and his death cannot extinguish it. A relationship of equals between two continents which share the same civilization and enjoy comparable resources has the strength of inevitability: all that is needed is the willpower to grasp it and give it concrete form. And once that relationship has begun to be established, it endures, even if death may seem to have destroyed it along with the willpower that gave it shape. Kennedy's successors in the White House sometimes gave the impression that the grand design was abandoned, and that the United States was succumbing to the temptations of lonely supremacy. Those temptations, if they ever existed, soon faded as far as Europe was concerned; and many Americans came to realize what a mistake it would be not to seek equality, even at the cost of creating large new entities in the world in place of a mosaic of countries doomed to subordination. Equality of this sort can certainly not be achieved overnight; but for me it is less a matter of statistics or legal rights than an order of magnitude and a habit of mind. It has to be anticipated and accepted as a process that nothing can stop, without waiting for precise parity: otherwise, dialogue would never begin.

In 1964, I did not pause to consider whether the America of Lyndon Johnson would be more or less outgoing than that of John F. Kennedy, or whether its obvious military superiority precluded any hope of talking on equal terms. I saw that partnership remained the official policy of the White House, and through the Action Committee I proposed to give it practical form for the first time, by means of a 'Committee of Entente between Europe and the United States' in those fields where Europe had begun to exist. The Action Committee's resolution of June 1, 1964, described the task of the Committee of Entente:

> to prepare joint positions on problems as they call for action, thus making easier the decisions to be taken by the European Institutions and the US Government both in their mutual economic relations and in their respective negotiations with the rest of the world.

The Action Committee tirelessly repeated this proposal; and among the politicians and labour leaders who represented the majority of the democratic forces in our countries I have never encountered the slightest suspicion that a procedure for discussion with the United States might endanger the independence of our countries or of the Community as a whole. Talking has never involved any loss of liberty; on the contrary, talking on the basis of mutual respect is the best guarantee that each party, by explaining its own point of view, can persuade the other to take account of it.

I will not dwell on the obscure reasons which until now have prevented a Committee of Entente's being established. There can be no valid reason for persistently refusing to sit down around the same table to discuss problems of common interest. The misunderstandings which serve as an excuse for our divided countries to avoid a dialogue with the United States are themselves caused by the lack of any procedure for concerting ideas and tackling technical difficulties as they arise. Today, these accumulated misunderstandings may look like a major obstacle in the way of partnership. In that case, it may go down in history as a great opportunity lost. But in reality only those who are reluctant to go forward ever speak of lost opportunities. I am interested only in the opportunities which lie before us, and which it is our duty to seize as soon as they arise. The fundamental reasons that are driving the West towards greater cohesion have lost none of their simplicity and force. Besides, the gap between Europe and America is narrowing: the problems they both face are bringing them closer together. The psychological distance between them remains; but the basic reason for that is mutual ignorance, and the best remedy is a procedure for talking together, such as a Committee of Entente.

To persuade people to talk together is the most one can do to serve the cause of peace. But for this a number of conditions must be fulfilled, all equally important. One is that the talks be conducted in a spirit of equality, and that no one should come to the table with the desire to score off somebody else. That means abandoning the supposed privileges of sovereignty and the sharp weapon of the veto. The second condition is that everyone should talk about the same thing; the third, finally, is that everyone should seek the interest which is common to them all. This method does not come naturally to people who meet to deal with problems that have arisen precisely because of the conflicting interests of nation-States. They have to be induced to understand the method and apply it. Experience has taught me that for this purpose goodwill is not enough, and that a certain moral power has to be imposed on everyone – the power of rules laid down by common institutions which are greater than individuals and are respected by States. Those institutions are designed to promote unity – complete unity where there is likeness, and harmony where differences still exist. The Europeans of the Six had decided to live under the same rules in a Community made possible by their common civilization and similar degree of development. It was obvious from the start that on these grounds Britain should join them without delay. By making common cause, they could recover the role in world affairs which they had lost because they were divided.

What role is that? It has always been the same: to seek the broadest consensus, and to help reduce tension between East and West by creating the conditions for a constant dialogue – but not to try to arbitrate by playing with the balance of power. The countries that are uniting in the Community belong to the same Western civilization whose principles underlie American society; and between these two great entities, so close but so distinct from each other, a deep and constant dialogue is possible, in a framework that can only be democratic. That was and remains the aim of Atlantic partnership, the first machinery for which – a Committee of Entente – the Action Committee proposed more than a decade ago. In the same resolution, our Committee also dealt with relations with the East. They, obviously enough, are no less vital to the peace of the world. But it was clear to me and to all the Committee's members that the form and content of talks between the Community and the countries of Eastern Europe – which, incidentally, refused to recognize our institutions – would necessarily be different from those of our dialogue with the United States. And that would continue to be the case so long as those countries did not conduct their public life according to the principles of freedom, as our democracies did.

None of our countries alone could influence the Soviet Union; nor did I believe that Europe, even if it were united, could reach a lasting agreement with the Soviets unless the United States were involved – any more than an agreement between the United States and the USSR could endure if it ignored Europe. The greatest danger for everyone was that of Germany's undertaking unilateral action in Europe; and in this respect the Community was a guarantee which the USSR was capable of appreciating. But while the Germans had linked their destiny with that of the peoples of Western Europe, they saw their security only in the broader context of Western defence as a whole.

For them, what was known as 'Atlanticism' was not a doctrine but a reflex of self-preservation. I could understand their uneasiness: the German people were more exposed than any other; and I admired the courage of those German statesmen who had discouraged their fellow-citizens from pursuing their dream of reunification by dangerous means. Europe was in the process of bringing about this historic change – Europe, and not some pact between States; but, even so, it could not be isolated from the global context of the defence of the West. This problem gave rise to the most difficult and often the most unrealistic debates that ever men had to face. It ought to have brought them together: yet, so far, it has only driven them apart. But if we failed at that time to find a satisfactory collective solution, one thing remains certain: no national solution has furthered the cause of peace.

Since 1964, years of inaction and verbal confrontation have left in suspense the organization of relations between Europe and the United States. The transatlantic relationships that have been pursued by individual countries may have given some people the impression that America accepted or even welcomed Europe's silence, for reasons of her own. Others may have had the illusion that Europe was not needed for a dialogue with Washington, and that if a European country wanted to wield influence, it could compensate for its lack of size by raising its voice. The truth is that in the absence of any fixed landmarks everyone interpreted in his own way a situation ruled by empiricism, without any regard for the overriding common interest. That interest exists, as was shown by the one instance where a dialogue of equals actually took place. This was the 'Kennedy Round'; and although it was limited to negotiations on international trade, Europe for once spoke with a single voice. That voice was respected; each party took account of the legitimate concerns of the other; and a vast global settlement was reached. Why this method has not been gradually extended to all aspects of the relationship between Europe and the United States, along the lines of the proposed Atlantic partnership, is a complex question: the reasons are various, and not all the blame is on one side. While racial problems, the war in Vietnam, and the quest for détente monopolized the attention of Lyndon Johnson and then Richard Nixon, Europe seemed endlessly to hesitate about strengthening and enlarging the Community. Some were jealous of their independence, but without doing what was needed to make it real: if they showed any inclination to assert themselves, it was always in opposition to the United States and its supposed tendency to dominate others. I myself have never believed that our divergence was deep or lasting. When

476

men learn to master their moods, they will recognize that Europe and America cannot ignore each other's problems, and that to solve them they need each other's help. Separately, they cannot make an effective contribution to world peace. In that respect, too, I realized that we must await the return of wisdom.

Chapter 20

A TIME FOR PATIENCE (1964-1972)

I

Stagnation

The Action Committee did not hold its eleventh meeting until June 1964. Its tenth had been in Paris in December 1962; and now it was meeting for the first time in Bonn. The text of its draft resolutions had been a long time in preparation, and it covered no fewer than twenty pages. It was the fruit of conclusions and agreements that had taken months of thought; and if it continued along the same lines as in previous years, despite recent upsets, this was a proof that the Committee had become a mature institution, able to rise above men's emotions and maintain a steady course. Re-reading that long statement, one can see the scope of Europe and the scale of our ambitions for it. That text amounts to a Message on the State of the Union in the making. The timetable was gradual and the ground to be covered was vast, but the Action Committee made a number of specific proposals. Some had to do with the economic and social development of the Common Market, others with institutional problems, including direct elections to the European Parliament and the extension of its budgetary powers. This proposal was followed by a section on 'The gradual establishment of equal partnership between Europe and the United States' – a relationship to be embodied in a Committee of Entente. There was also a section entitled 'The development by successive agreements of peaceful co-existence between the West and the USSR, settling European problems and in particular reuniting the Germans, at present divided, in the European Community.'

Who today could affirm that this view was Utopian and that the prospect of reuniting the Germans, which ten years ago was still real, is now banished from history? At the very least, if the problem one day arises again, a peaceful solution can be found only within the Community,

478

whose aim is not to make coalitions of States but instead to unite peoples. The Committee declared:

> To deal with this situation by exclusively peaceful means, and to meet the preoccupations of the USSR and the West, an arrangement of true co-existence must gradually be brought about between the USSR on the one hand and Europe and the United States on the other. . . .
>
> It is too early to determine the shape of this future arrangement. But one thing is already clear: if it were to appear that the West were divided, insecurity would dominate the relations between East and West, the prospect of an agreement would vanish, and mistrust and the process of mutual precautions would lead to fresh conflicts.
>
> A conflict involving the use of nuclear weapons would expose the European countries, the United States, and the Soviet Union to such destruction that, as has been remarked, the survivors would envy the dead.

This analysis, it seems to me, has lost none of its significance today. In 1964, at all events, it was the view held by the majority of the political parties and trade unions in the European Community. But the illusion of purely national power was still cherished by the leaders of certain States, despite the fact that America and the USSR were developing forms of relationship between them in which neither Europe nor any European country had a part.

With no political plans and no hope of rapid enlargement, the Community was stagnating. In Britain, where Harold Wilson had become Prime Minister, his narrow parliamentary majority seemed likely to delay the possibility of fresh negotiations. In the United States, President Johnson was preoccupied with internal problems, and seemed to have no interest in Europe as such. Everywhere there was the danger of a return to separate policies and bilateral agreements; and Germany might well be strongly tempted to compete with France in the quest for national advantage. The growing pressure for *ad hoc* arrangements made it necessary to reaffirm, while there was still time, the overall view that the Action Committee had taken in Bonn. In that view, the Common Market was the solid foundation, but no more than the foundation, of a broader vision of peaceful relations between the great entities in the world. To promote and complete the text of our resolution, I travelled extensively in the Community countries. In the French weekly *l'Express*, Marc Ullmann added up how many journeys I made in the early months of 1965: six to Bonn, four to Brussels, four to Rome, two to The Hague, and one to Luxembourg. He wrote:

479

At this rate, at least, misunderstandings are avoided: when a text is made public, one can be certain that it reflects the collective will of all Europe's political forces.

In a situation of deadlock, our 1965 text reaffirmed what was needed if further progress was to be made. What was unique about that resolution, however, was the place in which it was discussed and the day on which it was adopted. It was in Berlin, on May 8, 1965, in the presence of Chancellor Ludwig Erhard and Mayor Willy Brandt, that I told the Berlin Senate:

'Today, May 8, is the twentieth anniversary of the end of the war in Europe. It was from Berlin that Hitler launched his attempt at hegemony. It was in Berlin that it crumbled, amid the ruins of the old Europe.

'On May 9, 1950, France, in the person of M. Robert Schuman, proposed to Germany that both turn their backs on past conflicts and build their future together, alongside other democratic European countries. . . .

'The Action Committee for the United States of Europe is meeting in Berlin today to mark our unequivocal solidarity with you . . .'

Erhard's reply was of great political significance for Europe. He declared:

'The German people has learned to its cost that a policy of power inspired by extreme nationalist feelings is destined to fail, because an attempt at hegemony on the part of any one European nation arouses all the others against it. We are fully conscious of the fact that Europe cannot be German, French, or Russian, but must aim at union and reconciliation.'

Everywhere in Europe, that twentieth anniversary was being celebrated with loud martial demonstrations and speeches vilifying Germany's crimes. Very close to us, on the far side of the Berlin Wall, huge East German military parades contrasted with the atmosphere of our meeting, calmly looking forward to the future.

'Your brotherly feelings do you credit,' the Chancellor said to me. During our morning session, Silvia visited the Wall. On one of the watch-towers, she saw a woman weeping as she looked over into East Berlin. Silvia went up to her and asked what was wrong.

'Oh, Madame,' she answered, 'my whole family is over there.'

Later in the day, attending a reception for the Action Committee given in the Senate, Silvia met the same woman, who told her:

'I've come here, Madame, because I put all my hopes on Europe. Only Europe can bring us together again.'

That day, I believe – and as much by our presence as by the resolutions we passed – the European idea took root a little more deeply among the German people, and became more tangible to world opinion, which certainly made widespread comment. Far from issuing a challenge to the East, the Berlin resolution proposed 'the organization of consultations between the West – the United States and a uniting Europe – on the one hand, and the Soviet Union and the other countries of Eastern Europe on the other'. I should even have liked, in this case too, to speak of a Committee of Entente. The idea lay ahead of us at the end of the road. But to reach it we should have to make progress along that road, and the most urgent stretch of it was the unification of Europe. On this stretch, an accident was close at hand.

In the Action Committee's Berlin resolution, one paragraph which had been accepted without difficulty had approved the Brussels Commission's recent proposals to give the Community its own resources, levied mainly from the common external tariff, and mainly intended to finance the common agricultural policy. Hitherto, the Community's expenditure had been covered by contributions from the member States. The Brussels proposals were based on the Rome treaty and on existing regulations, and Hallstein was not the man to forgo a right which would make this Commission more independent. Nor could he have failed to realize that the European Parliament in turn would seize the opportunity to ask for an increase in its budgetary powers, which would deprive the Council of National Ministers of its right to the last word. All that was perfectly legitimate. But everyone knew that the simple application of the Treaty's provisions in this way would accentuate the federal character of the Community, and shift in the direction of the Brussels institutions the centre of gravity which certain Governments – and in particular the French Government – kept jealously in national hands. The majority of the Commission, convinced of its legal rights, was impatient with the diplomats' warnings:

'De Gaulle will never accept it –'

'We shall see,' was the reply.

We were indeed to see whether one man could resist the normal working-out of the institutional process – whether, and for how long. To tell the truth, the proposals were a challenge only to those who had never accepted the spirit of the Treaties, and who applied to the letter only those provisions that suited their book. French interests were involved in the machinery which favoured French agriculture; and it so happened that the momentum of that machinery involved a further transfer of national sovereignty to the Community domain. Hallstein,

Mansholt, and others believed that the French Government would agree to that transfer as the price of Europe's financing French farm exports. They also believed that the French, because of their intellectual training, could not resist the logic of the argument. Marjolin warned them:

'For de Gaulle your logic is a trap, and he'll smash it.'

I myself did not think it worthwhile pushing this technical affair to the point of conflict, and I thought that those concerned would stop short, as before, at some arrangement enabling modest progress to be made. But a personal factor intervened.

I fear nothing so much as personal problems which distort a debate. The French had decided to have no more dealings with Hallstein; and it mattered little what the technical problem might be: all that counted, in their eyes, were the intentions and attitudes of the Commission's President, who was anxious to increase his institution's power and prestige. Minute protocol pretensions in Brussels were regarded as outrageous in Paris; and the French Government's irritation knew no bounds when it appeared that Hallstein might escape a little from the financial tutelage of the States. The process required to reach a decision on this point was well under way; but agreement had to be unanimous. When the time came, de Gaulle made a clean break. The executant of his decree was Couve de Murville, who at midnight on June 30, 1965, at the close of France's chairmanship of the Council of Ministers, terminated the meeting with the announcement that it had failed to agree. The disagreement was real, and Couve was legally in the right. But he was morally in the wrong from the moment when he refused to continue the debate.

For more than six months, France virtually withdrew from the Brussels institutions, where except for routine necessities her representatives ceased to appear. This so-called 'empty chair policy' broke the Community's unwritten rule; but there seemed to be no way out of it, although it was damaging to both Europe and France. At first, I thought that it was a fit of ill-temper, and I had several discussions with Couve de Murville, with whom I had always been able to talk sense. But this time I could not get to the bottom of his thoughts, except when we spoke of the Commission, which he deeply disliked. It seemed that no solution of the economic problems and no resumption of talks among the Six would be possible unless the Commission were overhauled, in both its methods and its personnel. And behind all this could be glimpsed the desire to prevent majority voting becoming normal practice in the Community from January 1966 onward, as the

Treaty laid down. I suspected that this was a goal on which de Gaulle was irrevocably bent, and I warned Couve against adopting attitudes which would only aggravate our partners' already powerful distrust of France, whom they suspected of wanting to destroy the organization of Europe.

'The German elections next year,' I said, 'may produce a Grand Coalition between Christian Democrats and Socialists. The Germans are in a position to take initiatives. Make no mistake: you will not succeed in detaching Germany from either Britain or America. But you may encourage the conclusion of a military agreement between Germany and the United States.'

For Europe, this hypothesis would have been dramatic; and at the time, unless the Community made progress, it had every prospect of being fulfilled. I had expressed this fear to de Gaulle in a private conversation a few months earlier. I used to see him in this way on those rare occasions when I thought an exchange of views might be useful; and he always greeted me as cordially as at our very earliest meetings. The conversation was always very straightforward, and we never tried to agree on conclusions: each of us simply expressed his own point of view. This is never unfruitful if it is honestly done.

Couve seemed uncertain about how to resuscitate the Common Market, whose stagnation was beginning to worry French farmers and industrialists. Our five partners had firmly closed ranks, in a defensive spirit; and although they could make no progress without France, she herself was involved in an extremely risky diplomatic gamble. The risk to de Gaulle became very serious with the approach of the Presidential election in December 1965, and I thought that a settlement might be reached before that date. I advised Hallstein to re-examine his proposals, at whatever cost: there is no humiliation in adapting to an obstacle, because obstacles are never our masters. The Commission reacted sensibly; but France did not. De Gaulle remained obstinately scornful, although he was not really in a position of strength. In September, he denounced what he called 'a mostly foreign technocracy destined to trample on democracy in France', and confirmed his refusal to countenance majority voting in Community decisions, due at the turn of the year. In October, his five partners appealed to him to resume his place in the Community institutions; but he made no reply. On December 5, however, in the first round of the French Presidential election, he failed to secure an overall majority and was forced into a run-off. European public opinion played a decisive role in this result, which was widely regarded as a warning. Before the vote, I had announced my own choice in the following terms:

'Like many French people, I voted Yes in the referendum on the Constitution in 1958, Yes to the election of the President of the Republic by universal suffrage, and Yes in the referendum on Algeria.

'On December 5, I shall not vote for General de Gaulle.

'We can no longer have any illusions: the policy practised, explained in the press conference of September 9, and confirmed by France's persistent absence from Brussels, is leading us down the outdated path of nationalism and inevitably encouraging nationalism in other countries, and in particular in Germany.

'For the French people, the future is Europe. General de Gaulle has explained to us that he wants to reduce the collective action of France and her neighbours to relations between Governments. Experience shows us that such relations are necessarily precarious, and all the more so if they are constantly called in question by threats to break them off. To win the allegiance and the efforts of a rejuvenated France, the French people of today and tomorrow need a President in their own image and with modern ideas.'

I went on to say that I should vote for Jean Lecanuet, whose courage and sincerity I admired. At the run-off in the second round of the election, I announced that I was transferring my vote to François Mitterrand, who was now de Gaulle's sole competitor. As the single candidate of the Left, Mitterrand had come out in favour of 'a Europe built by the process already begun in the economic and technical fields, a Europe which will be the decisive factor in peaceful co-existence between East and West.' When de Gaulle was re-elected, with 54·5% of the votes, Couve de Murville resumed negotiations with France's partners. I advised everyone to accept the broadest compromise that would leave the Treaties intact. It mattered little if at the next meeting of the Six, in January 1966 in Luxembourg, France insisted on making a unilateral declaration reserving the right to go on saying No. The only victim of that ambiguous accommodation was the Commission under Hallstein – although its continuance in office until 1967 was assured. After more than six months' paralysis, progress began again. If de Gaulle had sought to demonstrate that the Community would not work without France, he had done so: but who had ever doubted that? If his aim had been to freeze the Community's institutional development and prevent any further transfers of sovereignty, he had gained nothing but a little time, which for the Europeans was so much time wasted. What de Gaulle denied them in 1965 they have since acquired as a matter of course. I draw no further conclusions from those very instructive events. That is how things happened; and when all is said and done, they worked out well enough.

It was still a time for patience, and I had plenty of time to pursue my reflections to the point where I could turn them into action, which would then depend on circumstances. Circumstances, I was now convinced, would remain unfavourable so long as de Gaulle ruled France and based French foreign policy on his own ideas, which dated from another age. I had long believed that he would come to realize that European union, about which he spoke with such conviction, required a gradual delegation of sovereignty to a common authority. Would he not see that his ambitions for his country, and his passionate desire for independence, could not be fulfilled by France alone? If he wanted to play the historic role he felt to be his vocation, Europe was of a size to be its vehicle – if he did what was needed for Europe to exist. But it became clear that the passage of time had not changed him, and that co-operation between sovereign States, as in the past, remained the basis of his European policy, with everyone drinking from his own glass, as he put it, and taking whatever decisions he might think best for his country. How, in these circumstances, could one maintain genuine national independence or even build an independent Europe? I saw no way out of this contradiction. The upshot was a France more and more isolated in a climate of suspicion, with precarious coalitions being formed to achieve superiority or fend off supposed threats. That, at least, would be the result if we returned to the 'concert of Europe' – a Europe of mutually mistrustful sovereign States.

The only guarantee against such a relapse was the Common Market, with its institutions, its rules, and its promise of economic, social, and political progress. It had to be strengthened, step by step. German loyalty to the Community was the only safeguard against the disintegration of the West. The accession of Great Britain was the only hope of Europe's becoming big enough to make herself felt in the world and start a dialogue of equals with the United States and the USSR. The Action Committee was prepared to fight for years, if need be, to see that these conditions were fulfilled. My mind was made up: I should have no further questions to ask until these solid foundations had been laid. In fact, between 1966 and 1973, in six separate sessions, the Action Committee hammered away at the same basic resolutions, which little by little began to work their way into reality. During those years, the political context changed under the impact of unexpected events and the slow pressure of generations born since the war. What had been inconceivable for their fathers came to seem natural to their children; what had been impossible to minds nurtured by the past became easy for more up-to-date spirits. But it was essential that at the end of this process the will to build Europe should still be alive and the plans for doing so should be ready. Unceasingly, the Action Committee made sure that they were.

I remember that while I was preparing for this new phase in our persevering effort, I felt the need to define for myself the principles that had always guided me in my day-to-day work. I have kept the notes I made at that time, during the summer break in 1966; and I think that they are more expressive in their immediacy than a longer, more elaborate credo would be:

August 18
Liberty means civilization.
Civilization means rules+institutions.
And all that because the essential objective of all our efforts is to develop mankind, not to proclaim a fatherland, big or small.

1. It is a privilege to be born (humanity).
2. It is a privilege to be born into our civilization.
3. Are we to confine these privileges within the national barriers and laws that protect us?
4. Or are we going to try to extend privilege to others?
5. We must maintain our civilization, which is so much ahead of the rest of the world.
6. We must organize our civilization and our collective action for the sake of peace.
7. We must organize the collective action of our civilization. How can that be done? Only by uniting in collective action Europe and America, which together have the greatest resources in the world, which share the same civilization, and which conduct their public affairs in the same democratic manner.
8. This organization, while seeking a state of co-existence with the East, will create a new order in the world and at the same time make possible the necessary and unconditional aid and support that our civilization, which must be preserved, will bring to the rest of the world. Together they can do it; separately, they will oppose each other.
9. At their origin, at birth, people are the same. Later, drawn into a framework of rules, everyone wants to preserve the privileges he has acquired. The national framework supports this fleeting vision. We are unaware of the extraordinary privilege we enjoy. We must extend it to others. How can it be done? Only by freedom on the one hand and collective effort on the other, so as gradually to enable the under-developed countries to share in our privileges. How can that be done without uniting, pooling our resources, etc.?

August 22

Nations were forged by successive additions. Brittany, Burgundy, etc., were provinces, and centralizing kings brought them together in a unit – France – by arms or by treaty: the *Comté* of Nice, Savoy. All these changes, from 'provincial' into 'national', corresponded to the conditions prevailing at the time. The force of adaptation, which led the provinces of France to make France, still continues.

We are convinced that our epoch will have to see the creation of vast entities such as the United States and the USSR, and that between them there must be established co-operation and collective action by means of organization (that is what we mean by the organization of peace).

It cannot all be done at once: it is gradually that we shall achieve this organization. But already it is essential to make a start. It is not a question of solving political problems which, as in the past, divide the forces that seek domination or superiority. It is a question of inducing civilization to make fresh progress, by beginning to change the form of the relationship between countries and applying the principle of equality between peoples and between countries. People no longer want their future to depend on the skill or ambition of their Governments. They do not want ephemeral solutions, and, for that reason, they want there to be established in our countries an organization, a procedure, that will make possible collective discussion and decision.

These reflections were not the subject-matter for a book but the basis of my daily action. The most practical men with whom I have worked also needed such guidance to believe in what they were doing and never become discouraged. With all of them – political leaders, trade unionists newspapermen – I liked to sit around the fire and talk about our underlying motives. I had found that if those motives became obscure, to them or to myself, our ability to act successfully suffered. That is why we had to work to keep them alive, like the flames in the hearth we stared at as we tried to see our way through the problems. Many were the intimate talks I had, and many were the friendships that grew deeper, as I tried to impart my own feeling of hope to men who often wearied of waiting for Europe to emerge from winter. The first sign of spring came in March 1967, when Harold Wilson, after consultations on the continent, seemed to be getting ready to renew Britain's request for membership of the Common Market. On March 16, 1967, on behalf of the Action Committee, I was able to tell the press:

'The members of the Committee declare themselves unanimously in favour of Britain's entry into the European Economic Community as it is today, with the same rights and the same obligations as the six countries which are already members.'

Those who backed this declaration included two new and influential members of the Committee – Pietro Nenni, President of the united Italian Socialist Party and Vice-Premier of Italy, and the new German Minister of Foreign Affairs, Willy Brandt. Britain had to be coaxed out of her hesitations. A correspondent of *The Times* of London asked me whether an application from her would be successful. I replied:

'She cannot expect to have an answer as to whether her application is successful before she puts the question clearly.'

This Wilson finally did on May 11, after securing the agreement of a large majority in the British House of Commons. But as early as May 16, de Gaulle held a press conference and declared that Britain, which was an island, bound to her Commonwealth and the USA, and weighed down by her sterling balances, could not join the Common Market, which he defined as a sort of prodigy. All one could do, he said, was work out some form of association, or wait. . . . This time, even the usefulness of discussion was being denied! When *Agence France Presse* asked for my opinion, I declared:

'In what kind of society are we living if the Six are to reject without debate the request of a great democratic country, massively backed by its elected representatives, to join in the building of Europe? General de Gaulle, in his press conference, presented the obstacles to Great Britain's entry into the Common Market as if they were virtually insuperable. The British Government considers that they can be overcome. Only negotiations, conducted in good faith and with a will to succeed, will make it possible to decide. What matters is that the discussion between London and the Six should begin.'

This persistent attitude on the part of France led to further uncertainty and discouragement. Many people thought that the time would never come for Britain to join the Community, and that all that could be hoped for were trading arrangements, perhaps even without France. I thought the opposite; and I was glad to find this optimism shared by George Brown, the British Foreign Minister. Stout and not very tall, he sometimes behaved in ways that disconcerted traditionalist diplomatic circles; but he had a lively intelligence and great enthusiasm. He gave of himself both at home and on the continent to ensure that the door of the Common Market remained open to Britain. In January 1967, he and Wilson had toured the capitals of the Six. On January 23, they had stopped in Strasbourg to address the Council of Europe. That day, I heard Wilson declare:

'We are determined to act because the creation of a bigger and more powerful Economic Community is as much in the interests of Europe as a whole as in our own interests.'

What struck me most was to see in the Assembly, which gave Wilson a standing ovation, the British Leader of the Opposition, Sir Alec Douglas-Home. It confirmed by the force of example that we were right to want Great Britain in the democratic institutions of Europe. I proposed to the Action Committee that a resolution be put to each of our national Parliaments calling for the negotiations to be pursued. Its text provided only for full British membership, and ruled out any form of association. On June 15, 1967, in Brussels, the Action Committee met for the thirteenth time. Among those present were Brandt, Schmidt, Nenni, Rumor, Pinay, and Pleven. The Committee passed the resolution, and the members agreed to submit it to the vote in their national Parliaments. On October 13, I attended the session of the German *Bundestag* at which it was debated. Chancellor Kurt Kiesinger left his seat to join me in the gallery, and the German deputies voted unanimously for the resolution. It was a deeply reassuring sign. De Gaulle's opposition, which he reiterated on November 29, might block the negotiations; but it could not dismiss the problem or change the minds of the vast majority of Europeans. The resolution was passed by the Luxembourg, Belgian, Dutch, and Italian Parliaments. Britain no longer need feel isolated. Her accession was inexorably inscribed on the agenda of international politics.

II

The context changes

Then came spring 1968 and the explosion in France of student riots like those that had begun in the United States before spreading to Europe. Our old society, with its antiquated university structure, at first put up little resistance. Concern for justice made the young intellectuals turn towards the workers. Too much social inequality still stemmed from the differing levels of education to which some had access through the accident of birth. But it became clear that these inequities would not be removed merely by idealistic demonstrations. The student revolt and the demands of wage-earners coincided only briefly. While they did, France's institutions were under threat; but French workers still had a sense of discipline, and they parted from the students, who now found themselves isolated. Yet the cause for which they had fought still remained: it was the cause of humanity. And I believe that we have still not adequately responded, either before or after that salutary warning.

In fact, the crisis was implicit in the disparities and inequalities which had been revealed three years earlier by a group of international experts in a report prepared at the instigation of the Action Committee. This was a comparative study of education in Europe, the United States, and the USSR: it was known as the Poignant Report after its author, Raymond Poignant, a Master of Requests in the Council of State. He was a man with a high sense of duty; to reach his position, he himself had had to surmount the barriers between different forms of education. He knew from experience what a problem it was for most young people to continue their studies beyond the level to which the vast majority were limited, and he was able to reveal how much valuable potential went unused through lack of educational opportunities. Already in 1959 I had raised this problem when speaking to the Community's free trade unions:

'The unification of Europe which we are achieving together will only fully bear fruit if our countries put an end to the waste of their young people's intelligence by making access to higher education genuinely democratic. The majority of people ought to be able to enter higher education: it should not be the preserve of a minority.'

The figures revealed by the Poignant Report showed how seriously the Community was lagging behind. For a population of about the same size, Russia had three times as many students as Europe, and the United States five times as many. Whatever progress might have been made in the meantime, the 1968 explosion was caused not by an over-large student population, but by an over-rigid society still marked by injustice.

That society had another weakness: its great complexity. The more sophisticated a structure is, the more vulnerable it is to unforeseen accidents. In 1968, I realized more clearly than ever that the democratic institutions under which we live had become precision instruments, whose economic, social, and political operation depended on trust. This was a phenomenon common to all the countries of the West; and trust – or the damage that was done to it – went well beyond national frontiers. This could be seen in the extent of the international youth protest movement; it was soon to be seen again in the spread of international monetary chaos. Such widespread interdependence called for a general strengthening of solidarity among those European countries which had the same form and degree of civilization. Solidarity had begun with the economic Community: it had to be strengthened and extended until the common institutions were more broadly based and every nation was enriched with the complementary qualities of the others. In isolation, our countries were now very vulnerable to the waves of violence that were sweeping the world: none could protect itself alone. On my visits to Bonn, I found the Germans very much alive to this danger, whose shock-waves had reached them first. They had watched with anxiety its spectacular impact on French society: in Paris, they had seen the main pillar of European policy shaken.

I found Chancellor Kiesinger in a hesitant mood. Tall and youthful-looking, he had more charm than strength, and more skill than vigour. He had a clear view of the problems, but he was not resolute in action. He thought as I did that Britain must be brought in to strengthen Europe's democratic stability; but he was not prepared to stand up to de Gaulle. Both men, in fact, were marked by their wartime experience: it weighed upon how they behaved. In equal and opposite situations, as it were, they had both lived through the drama of France and Germany, and it forever flawed their imagination. The future belonged to a new generation whose dreams we no longer knew. All we could do was hand on to them the solid legacy of a democratic Europe. I left Bonn in July 1968 with the feeling that Germany's growing strength would do nothing to influence France's shaken will-power, so long as men like Kiesinger and de Gaulle remained in power. I went on to London. I met Wilson at No 10 Downing Street, and received from him a veritable lesson in political strategy, an art in which he delighted. He had seen at once the advantage he could gain from the British Labour Party's joining the Action Committee alongside the other British political parties. He had worked out what would be the reactions in his own party; and for the moment the balance seemed favourable. Rarely had I seen him so determined and so pleased to commit himself to Europe. I even hoped that the British trade unions would join the Committee together with the Labour Party, to which they were closely linked; but there the pockets of resistance which later proved so hard to overcome had already formed, and neither Wilson's influence nor pressing appeals from Rosenberg on behalf of the German unions had any effect.

I was very greatly helped in my London talks by Wilson's private secretary, a young diplomat who embodied the finest qualities of the British civil service. His name was Michael Palliser; later, as Sir Michael Palliser, he was to be Permanent Under-Secretary at the Foreign and Commonwealth Office. He enjoyed the esteem of both Labour and the Conservatives, and had excellent contacts on the continent. Thanks to his ability and his European convictions, he never ceased to exert a favourable influence on the Community's development. In Paris, Wilson had appointed as Ambassador Sir Christopher Soames, a Conservative whose European spirit and breadth of mind were to be better known still when he became Vice-President of the Brussels Commission after Britain joined. In London, the Community's loyal and skilful Chief Representative, Georges Berthoin, played a very positive role; while Duchêne and Mayne continued the patient work of explanation in their articles and books.

When I left London that summer, I had secured the agreement of all three of Britain's main political parties. On September 26, 1968, I wrote to Wilson as Leader of the Labour Party, to Anthony Barber, then Leader of the Conservatives, and to the Liberal Leader Jeremy Thorpe:

> The political parties and trade unions which make up the Action Committee, representing two-thirds of the electorate and of organized trade unionists in the six European Community countries, are unanimously convinced that Britain must be a full member of the Community with the same rights and the same obligations as the present six member countries.
>
> They are determined to pave the way for British entry into the European Community as soon as possible. They believe that it is important to develop a European point of view, common to the Six and to Great Britain, in preparation for the day when British entry will be possible.

Wilson replied at once:

> The aims of the Action Committee are in close conformity with those to which the Labour Party subscribes. Our Party believes that European political, economic, and technological integration is essential if Europe is to fulfil her great potential and make a unique contribution to secure and maintain world peace.
>
> The work already undertaken by the distinguished members of your Committee has been most impressive. The Labour Party is honoured to be asked to join in this work and I am pleased to accept your invitation for the Labour Party to join the Action Committee for the United States of Europe as a full member.

Wilson went on to announce that the Party's National Executive Committee had nominated George Brown, Walter Padley, and Michael Stewart to represent it on the Action Committee. The choice maintained a subtle balance, but one thing had to be noted: the unequivocal tone of Wilson's letter and his use of the word 'integration', the strength of which surprised everyone. Then came Barber's answer. He recalled that the negotiations had been broken off in 1963 against the wishes of the Conservative Government, and continued:

> We shall value membership of your Action Committee, whose work is well known to us, as a means of discussing how progress can be made towards the development of greater European unity.

He went on to announce an impressive list of representatives: Reginald Maudling, Sir Alex Douglas-Home, and Selwyn Lloyd. Finally, I received a warmly-worded answer from Jeremy Thorpe, who himself was to represent the Liberals.

We then decided to commission studies on the problems of British membership from independent experts whose authority was universally recognized: Guido Carli, Governor of the Bank of Italy, on monetary questions; Lord Plowden, together with Karl Winnacker of Hoechst industries, on technology; Edgard Pisani on agriculture; and Walter Hallstein on institutions. Meeting in Brussels on July 15, 1969, the Action Committee heard their conclusions, the substance of which was that the problems could be solved. And at the same time, the political obstacles were in the process of being removed.

General de Gaulle's decision to leave office in April 1969 after the failure of an unnecessary referendum was a wise and noble act. Nothing, save his own wish, could have forced him to retire. It appears that he chose to do so while he was still clear-headed and in command of his strength. He left France with solid institutions; and he had been able to legitimize by universal suffrage, for himself and for his successors, an authority which he owed to circumstances. Those circumstances, which were due to the shock of decolonization, had helped him to gain power eleven years earlier; then he had mastered them to re-establish French unity, which for a time had been threatened. We owed him that. But as I saw him depart my thoughts returned to the man of 1940. Never had he been so great as in his rejection of defeat and his call to resist. History would record that he had given the French people back their dignity, that he had restored them to their past greatness. I had hoped that he might see that greatness, to be permanent, required a profound transformation, transcending national boundaries. But I had to accept the facts: he believed that Europe would be built around France, and he could not imagine delegating sovereignty. A community of peoples without common rules and institutions, and without equality – it was an illusion. I could understand the disenchantment that de Gaulle showed towards the end of his life, when he looked at that part of his work which he had failed to complete on a scale that was worthy of his destiny. If he had failed to build the Europe that he sought, he had at least not managed to prevent the development of a Europe in which he did not believe. When Georges Pompidou came to the Elysée palace as President in succession to de Gaulle, he coolly assessed his inheritance.

I hardly knew Pompidou. I had met him only once, at dinner with the Gaullist Minister Gaston Palewski; and I never came to know him well. Neither of us really wanted to explore deeply together problems which we approached from different angles. I was concerned with Europe's place in the world, while his preoccupation was with France's place in the Common Market. His pragmatism led him to see the Economic Community as an opening for the French economy. Indeed, he seemed to see it as a necessity – just as he regarded Great Britain's accession as inevitable. On these points we could agree; but our agreement was reached discreetly, through intermediaries who remained in the background – his personal assistants, the great initiates of the Elysée palace's inner mysteries. One of them was Michel Jobert. He was never more effective than in the shadow of Pompidou, trying to promote European affairs, which he saw as a source of further power for the President of the Republic, ill at ease as he was among the other Heads of State. On technical questions, Jean-René Bernard was the most capable and loyal of contacts, with whom I established a relationship of enduring trust. Through him, Pompidou knew what I thought, and so was able to follow my advice or not, as he saw fit. More could not be asked of men conditioned by years of secrecy and jealously-guarded sovereign power. And yet the initiative for a further step forward could come only from France, and therefore from them.

A note of pragmatism now quite naturally marked our relations with our European partners; and if this made the problems themselves no simpler, it at least restored them to their true proportions. In October 1969, Brandt was elected Chancellor of Germany. I was delighted, because I was sure that he would introduce into European politics an element of boldness and generosity. He and Pompidou were not alike in character, but they refrained from making an issue of the fact. The 'summit' conference which they proposed to hold in December was their first opportunity to make their mark as European statesmen. Each vied with the other to show his European spirit, and Brandt won on points. His proposals went a long way, and caught everyone up in their impetus. They also came from a long way back: several of the ideas we had worked out together in the Action Committee were now given their chance to succeed. I had reminded Brandt of them in a letter on the day after his election as Chancellor:

> The summit meeting is soon due. It will afford the opportunity to take a broad view of Europe's needs and to make fundamental and practical progress in uniting European peoples. The transformation of the Common Market into an economic and monetary union, the beginnings of political union, and negotiations with Britain – all are possible, on one condition: that an initiative from you changes the climate from peevish haggling about points of detail to a positive collective effort to solve the problems that are common to us all.

What I was suggesting included action in the monetary field; and it went further than the proposals made by the European Commission at the instigation of Raymond Barre. Brilliant and sound as that great economist's ideas were and are, he had to respect the political possibilities of the time. And the currency was still regarded as an almost magical expression and weapon of national sovereignty.

Once again it had to be demonstrated – as it will for years to come – that national sovereignty withers when entrapped in the forms of the past. For it to be effective, in an expanding world, it needs to be transferred to larger spheres, where it can be merged with the sovereignty of others who are subject to the same pressures. In the process, no one loses: on the contrary, all gain new strength. My letter to Brandt went on:

> As for the limited pooling of national sovereignty that such a monetary organization would require, it becomes clearer every day that this would be a great deal more modest than the blind and total abandonment of sovereignty which is involved today in the continuing drift towards a dollar zone, and the continuing and uncontrollable financing of the deficits run up by the so-called reserve currency countries – the United States and Britain, either through our own central bank issues or through their merchant banks and the Eurodollar market.

This same phenomenon of losing national sovereignty by trying to protect it too jealously is not confined to the monetary field. It runs through the whole history of European countries in the past twenty years, delaying and jeopardizing the collective action needed to make them genuinely independent. Brandt took the point; and he persuaded the Hague summit to adopt the plan for economic and monetary union, with a European Reserve Fund, as the Action Committee had proposed.

The December 1969 summit removed other obstacles to progress. It was agreed to resume negotiations with Great Britain. The road that led to the Treaty of Accession, signed in January 1972, was a long one, and the biggest difficulty now lay with the British, victims of disappointment and wounded pride. We had done everything we could to leave them the option of joining forces with Europe; and the French Government for its part was ready to drop its long-standing opposition, in which ill-humour had overruled reason and even self-interest. Among nations, as among men, misunderstandings pay no heed to facts: they succumb only to weariness. The British had persisted in the illusion of their power long after the nations of continental Europe had realized that they themselves were no longer a match for the modern world. When the British had ignored the European Community's appeals, and tried to set up rival groupings, they had hurt and discouraged many of their friends. So, when they had decided to join the Community they had once scorned and contested, they encountered incomprehension and mistrust. Then they in their turn had suffered humiliating rejection. What remained of their old insular pride had been galvanized anew, and the farsighted statesmen who had committed themselves to Europe had run into difficulties with public opinion. There had to be an end to these emotional minuets, and in this respect the Action Committee played an important role. It was perhaps its most striking contribution to the development of the European Community.

During my frequent trips to London, I saw that Wilson had made his mind up; and although he was embarrassed about the tactics to follow, he was strongly backed by Roy Jenkins, whose talent and European convictions – he later became President of the Commission – were a great support. I also saw Edward Heath, utterly committed and only awaiting his opportunity – which turned out to be Europe's opportunity too. When the British General Election of June 1970 brought Heath and the Conservative Party to power, I had no doubt that his sincerity would overcome the remaining obstacles. Pompidou still had to be persuaded of it; but a long talk in May 1971 established a personal understanding between them. From that moment on, the negotiations ceased to pile up difficulties, and it became clearer that the difficulties were in men's minds rather than in the things themselves. In London one day, a customs officer recognized me and said:

'I'd like to be sure about one thing, Sir: once we've gone into your Europe, shall we be able to get out again?'

It was the same atavistic fear of commitment that we had encountered in London in 1950. I said to Kohnstamm, who was with me: 'We'll have to talk to that man for a long time to change his point of view.'

Heath made a vigorous effort to explain matters to the British people, but the task was still incomplete when the Labour Party won the February 1970 election; and it was left to Harold Wilson to put the 'anti-Marketeers', as the British called them, on the defensive. The June 1975 referendum, in which two-thirds of the voters endorsed British membership of the European Community, set the seal on what was already obvious: Great Britain had no choice, now, except solitary decline or integration into a larger grouping. To tell the truth, that had been obvious for twenty-five years; but it takes a good quarter-century to efface the illusions that dead realities leave in the minds of nations and of men.

In this respect, public opinion in our countries had long outgrown the age of hesitation and achieved quiet maturity. There was a very broad consensus on the need to unite the peoples of the West, and in France more than 60% of those questioned said that they would be in favour of a European Government, even if it were headed by a non-French statesman. About the same number thought that it would be a good thing to elect the European Parliament by universal suffrage. In March 1972, 66% of the French people were in favour of Britain's joining the European Community. Pompidou decided that the time had come to exorcize the evil genius that for centuries had plagued relations between France and Britain, and at the same time to bring together the pro-European majority that was revealed by the polls. His April 1972 referendum on the Community's enlargement was positive, but the turnout was disappointing. People are interested in ideas only when they involve action; and what action in Europe then could have mobilized the crowds? What tangible signs of it had the French Government given when it asked its citizens to vote? It was clear that, if European feelings were to be expressed politically, discussion would have to give place to decision. And in Brussels there was a great deal of the former and very little of the latter.

The summit meetings of Heads of State and Government were a response to this need for decision-making; but they were too infrequent and spasmodic. What was more, they were as cumbersome as international conferences, weighed down with too many experts and made ineffective by too much formality. In October 1972, Pompidou invited his colleagues and their numerous retinue to Paris. Despite the solemnity of the conference, one could once more detect in it the European spirit that had lain dormant for so many years. Heath was there, and so were the Prime Ministers of Ireland and Denmark. An ancient quarrel seemed to be over, and the new proportions the Community

497

was assuming enabled it at last to cherish hopes that had too long been held in check.

Gradually there emerged the prospect of a more balanced and objective dialogue between the Community, which was in the process of being enlarged, and the United States, which was trying to end the war in Vietnam. Henry Kissinger's persistent efforts to negotiate a peace treaty with Hanoi were long frustrated by the blind forces of violence, which by its own increasing momentum began to spread far and wide, and even into our own societies. Everywhere, men's consciences were deeply troubled by the race between the desire for dialogue and the persistence of hate. Even when there was a chance of peaceful agreement, misunderstandings between men and nations continued in quarrels over ideas and words. And yet, in reality, once the fires of war were extinguished, nothing more stood in the way of constructive understanding, in particular between America and Europe, which together could help revive the world economy.

Meeting in Brussels in May 1973, the Action Committee proposed that two independent persons be appointed, one by the United States and the other by the Community, to draw up an inventory of the various trade and monetary problems. This would give leaders on both sides of the Atlantic an independent appreciation of the difficulties to be dealt with and the points on which they needed to concentrate their efforts. The idea began to take root; but in October the Arab-Israeli conflict once more threw men's minds into confusion. Between Paris and Washington there arose an unrealistic polemic which remained on the surface of things. Henry Kissinger seemed for a time to espouse it; but before long the statesman in him overruled the historian. In his vision of the past, Europe was a fascinating mosaic; but in his vision of the future it could only be united. In November 1975 in Paris, he gave me the Grenville Clark Prize, and in the course of the ceremony he declared:

'I want to tell you that the men of the present generation who are in charge of political affairs regard your vision as well-founded. They see that it is on the point of being fulfilled as you originally conceived it. The creation of a united Europe seems imminent. The United States gives it full support.'

Those words marked the end of ten years of pointless doubts and misunderstandings.

Europeans seemed to be the last to realize how great were these new proportions and prospects; but if their field of vision was too often limited by national horizons, at a distance the Community was revealed as an entity ever more present in the affairs of men and the calculations of States. The most striking testimony, for me, was that of the Chinese diplomats who came to see me to obtain information on the progress of European unity. I could well imagine why they were so interested in the strengthening of Western Europe on Russia's other flank; but while I disagreed with their political analysis, it seemed to me significant that they saw the Community as a factor in the stability of the world. World stability, in their eyes, was not adequately guaranteed by the balance of power between the United States and the USSR, and they were uneasy at the slowness with which our separate countries were catching up with a world on the move. After thousands of years of stability the Chinese were better equipped than anyone to understand change, and certainly better equipped than the Soviets. I was no more adept at reading their innermost thoughts than I had been forty years earlier; but I saw that they had recovered their pride, and I realized that they were seeking partners who like themselves were powerful and independent, and whose ancient civilization was presenting a new face to the world.

The new face of Europe was reassuring also to the less developed countries, some of whom were moving directly from having been colonies to becoming colleagues. For hundreds of millions of people in a number of continents, the Community was becoming a partner in freely negotiated agreements. Both at home and in Brussels, the representatives of those countries now met on equal terms with our own; and the institutionalized relationship between Europe and the African, Caribbean, and Pacific countries, established first by Jean-François Deniau and then by Claude Cheysson, is one of the Community's most imaginative and selfless achievements. While fifty-five countries were meeting in Lomé or Brussels to seek their common interests, our diplomats were holding pointless debates about a 'European identity'. Paradoxically, it already existed in the eyes of observers overseas.

What they seek from Europe is not, I think, primarily material aid. That aid is necessary; but it is only one aspect of the solidarity that needs to be established between the Community and all its partners. That means observing the same rules and seeking to achieve equality. This is the lesson our Community experience teaches; and it goes far beyond the confines of the Community itself. People sometimes forget that it applies to all human relationships. One day, Ollenhauer told me about a trip he had just paid to South-East Asia, and the tragic poverty he had seen there. My reaction was to ask him what form of aid our rich countries could together supply to those disinherited regions.

'No,' he said: 'they are not asking for aid. They are asking to be accepted.'

That dignified man had understood the dignity of all men. He had also understood, profoundly, what the Community was all about.

Chapter 21

THE EUROPEAN COUNCIL (1972-1975)

I
To the springs of power

The summit conference of October 1972 had been full of good intentions, and the objectives it had set for Europe had been both ambitious and precise. A specific timetable of economic, political, and institutional steps was to lead to a goal which the nine Heads of State and Government – the new recruits had been full members of the conference – announced as follows:

> The member States of the Community, which is the driving force in the construction of Europe, have set themselves the major objective of transforming, before the end of the present decade and with the fullest respect for the Treaties already signed, the whole complex of the relations of member States into a European Union.

The final form of that union was not further defined, but its content was described in a long communiqué listing a series of actions in which the members of our Committee could recognize a number of the proposals they had made under the heading of economic and monetary union, as in the fields of social and technological progress. A European Monetary Fund was proposed, as we had hoped, as well as a Regional Development Fund. These, however, had to be given guaranteed resources; and it was mainly for this reason that in May 1973 I called a meeting of the Action Committee, to urge on Governments the gradual pooling of exchange reserves and the floating of Community loans on the world market. Europe's ability to act would be proportional to the resources she could raise on the basis of her international credit, which was greater than was generally realized. In this respect, once again, the Heads of Government had neglected to delegate to the Community the means of achieving the political goals they had set it.

During the summer of 1973 I had a first balance-sheet drawn up to show how far the summit's programme had been fulfilled. It was clear that nothing was moving. In the monetary field, the disturbances created by the devaluation of the dollar and the repeated revaluation of the German mark had sapped the foundations of the future monetary union. When Italy faced a serious balance-of-payments crisis, it was America that came to her aid. Many other signs, too, showed that the Community institutions alone were powerless to perform the tasks assigned to them, although no one contested their rights. There was no ill-will anywhere, but a lack of will-power, suggesting that the institutions had run out of steam. The Brussels Commission was conscientiously continuing its task of making proposals; but the Council was not taking decisions on them, and individual countries were reacting to recession and inflation with purely national measures. What would remain of the Nine's new-found solidarity if a more serious crisis arose? Monetary ties were lacking; the common market in agriculture was becoming fragmented; the common energy policy, so obviously and urgently necessary, was still at the planning stage. And yet the Community was continuing to assert itself as a unit in the world: it was presenting a united front at the Helsinki Conference on Security and Co-operation in Europe, and replying with a single voice to the appeal of the US President, for whom 1973 was to be 'the year of Europe'. In other words, the Community's real internal strength no longer matched its external image and responsibilities. Its cohesion must be strengthened without delay.

Although this difficulty was not new, it in no way resembled those that we had faced for the past ten years, because now we were no longer involved in dogmatic jousting. The men in power were all European by conviction or persuasion, and this fact seemed to me exceptionally propitious for taking an initiative, provided that it was practical and did not involve any diminution of their authority. Authority, indeed, was at the heart of the problem, and there could be no question of doing anything but strengthen it. Experience in the Community's present phase showed that the decision-making machinery was blocked at the level of the Council of Ministers, where everyone acted as the defender of his own national administration. There would have been no point in reproaching them, or begging them to take a broader view of the interests they held in trust. Yielding to natural inertia, they came to Brussels to plead from dossiers prepared by their civil servants; and the Council, as an institution, was nothing more than a forum for fragmentary technical debates in which the continued rule of unanimity made decisions unattainable. It was as if the power to decide on European matters were exclusively national, but without any corresponding national centres for political decision-making. Europe was suffering less from the egoism of the States than from their irresponsibility. This was a situation which had to be put right before anything else.

President Pompidou's summit conference was indeed a response to that situation, but it had embraced too much too ineffectively. As had soon become clear, the long-term goals that it had set were binding on everyone in general and no one in particular. The Heads of State and Government had agreed to meet again in 1975 – as if the impetus they had given the Community in October 1972 would last for two whole years. And although the 1972 summit had been incomparably more realistic than some of its predecessors, which had produced only generalities, it had failed to follow through its own logic, which ought to have led it to establish a supreme body to steer Europe through the difficult transition from national to collective sovereignty. I was sure that matters could be set on a more solid basis if I appealed to the good sense of the statesmen who now led the major European countries. I knew that they would listen to me, because if I acted with total discretion I should be able to bring each of them the agreement of the others. To achieve that, my proposal would have to be as simple as my view of things, and it would have to enhance the power of Europe's leaders at the same time as that of Europe herself.

In the last few days of August 1973, I wrote the following draft:

1. International changes that are crucial for the future of Europe are taking place; and the future of every European country risks being compromised for generations to come, unless those countries face the changes with a clear view of the objectives they share. If Europe does not organize her own unity, decisions affecting her future will be taken by others without her.

That is why the President of the French Republic, the Chancellor of the Federal Republic of Germany, the Prime Minister of the United Kingdom, the President of the Council of the Italian Republic, the Prime Minister of Belgium, the Prime Minister of Denmark, the Prime Minister of Ireland, the President of Luxembourg, and the President of the Council of the Netherlands – the countries which form the European Community – have decided to set up a Provisional European Government.

2. The Provisional European Government will supervise the fulfilment of the programme which its members agreed on in Paris on October 19–21, 1972.

As required, and after consulting the Presidents of the Council and Commission of the European Communities, it will draw up instructions to the Ministers representing the member States in the Council of the European Communities. It will respect absolutely the Treaties already signed.

Within six months, it will set up a Committee to organize the European Union, giving it the necessary directives. It will draft a plan for the European Union which will be submitted for ratification by the member States.

The institutions of the Union will in particular include a European Government and a European Assembly elected by universal suffrage.

3. The Provisional European Government will meet at least once a quarter.

Its deliberations will be restricted to its members, who will keep them secret.

The Provisional European Government will have no administrative staff. It will appoint a Secretary, who will minute only its decisions.

I had no doubt that one of the Heads of State or Government would agree to take the initiative of proposing this text to his colleagues. But I wanted to make sure that it would not be the subject of negotiations, which might narrow its scope. So I had to prepare for its acceptance by the three men whose simultaneous presence at the head of their Governments was so fortunate for Europe: Georges Pompidou, elected President of France in June 1969, Willy Brandt, Chancellor of Germany since October 1969, and Edward Heath, Prime Minister of Britain since June 1970. They understood each other, and took great account of each other's positions. I also knew that they would listen to me. They were able to communicate with each other and with me through their very efficient assistants, all of whom I knew: Michel Jobert, first in Pompidou's *cabinet* and then his Minister of Foreign Affairs; Robert Armstrong, Heath's personal assistant; and at the German Chancellery, Katharina Focke, Minister for Health and the Family, and Wolf-Dietrich Schilling, both of whom were very close to Brandt. It was my task to activate this busy network of friends. From the start, I made it a rule to say the same thing to everyone and to keep everyone informed of everyone else's reactions. That way, there could be no misunderstandings.

Armstrong was very useful and influential with Heath. He was a most exceptional private adviser, and I liked him. We agreed to meet with Heath at Chequers on September 16, 1973; and when I told him in general terms what the meeting would be about, he reacted immediately. 'Yes,' he said, 'Europe does lack a focus of authority.'

On September 3 I wrote to Willy Brandt:

I should like very much to come and see you soon. I think that the Community institutions, as a whole, talk but don't act, and I think we risk letting ourselves drift into taking no decisions. The whole future of our countries – as we have often said – depends on the further organization of Europe. The Community's decisions, in so far as it takes any, are most often determined by the civil services. The supreme political authority of the Governments is not engaged in the search for joint solutions. I believe that it is possible to right matters, but I need a short talk with you.

We arranged to meet on September 19. Before then, I had to be sure that Pompidou would agree to the plan for a Provisional European Government, and I told Jobert about it.

'The point is,' I said, 'to place the responsibility for things with the Heads of Government, since it's they who have the last word. Today, every individual Minister in the Council negotiates on the basis of national instructions. In future, those instructions will have a common source. But it is quite clear that there will be no additional transfer of sovereignty, and that the European institutions will retain their full existing powers.'

'So far as I'm concerned,' said Jobert, 'I agree. It's a good proposal. All I ask is that you cut out the paragraph saying: "The institutions of the Union will in particular include a European Government and a European Assembly elected by universal suffrage." The Governments themselves will decide about that. I'll show the paper to M. Pompidou during our visit to China next week.'

On Sunday September 16, 1973, I had luncheon at Chequers. Heath was relaxed, in country clothes, and as friendly as ever. The weather was fine. Armstrong joined us. I said:

'We must give public opinion the feeling that European affairs are being decided: today, people have the impression that they're merely being discussed.'

'I very much agree with you,' said Heath. 'Something must be done, and right away: but what?'

I showed him my draft.

'Good,' he said; 'that's the way. But why make a public statement about what we're going to do? Let's just do it: that's enough, and it's better.'

'On the contrary,' I said, 'I think much of the point of this method is to get through to the public and convince people that the Community is now being governed – that decisions are being taken.'

'I'll accept that,' said Heath, 'but not the title "Provisional Government". That would get me into great difficulties. "Supreme Council" would be closer to the facts. On the other hand, a meeting every three months wouldn't be enough. Why not every month?'

Now it was my turn to express reservations. If meetings were too frequent, they would turn into technical debates: they had to be limited to general matters of policy. When I left, Heath confirmed that I could tell Brandt and Pompidou that he agreed with the plan.

On Wednesday September 19 I was in Bonn, in the Chancellor's office with Frau Focke and Schilling. Brandt is one of the most selfless statesmen I know, one of the few who are capable of giving something; he has proved that, and his courage has had its reward in the profound esteem of his contemporaries. His great, perhaps excessive humanity made politics harder for him than for other people. In my experience he had always been receptive to new ideas, and I felt sure that he would fall in with a plan which would set in motion fresh developments. He carefully read the text that I had put to Heath, and said:

'We must move fast. If M. Pompidou takes an initiative on these lines, I will give it my support.'

Two days later, I told Jobert the results of my talks.

'Here's what's happened on our side,' he said. 'I told M. Pompidou about your proposal, and I gave him the text while we were over Tibet. I told him: "This is a draft which I have had no hand in, but which seems to me very important. I have been waiting for a quiet moment to talk to you about it, and now we have the time." M. Pompidou read the text without saying anything – but an hour later he called me into his compartment to talk about it. He was obviously very interested. I can't tell you whether he has reached a conclusion or not, but personally I think he's hooked.'

I asked if the title 'Provisional European Government' caused any problem.

'The name doesn't bother him. On the other hand, he's less keen on the Committee that you suggest for organizing the European Union, and he doesn't think the meetings need be quite so frequent.'

I made no attempt to meet Pompidou, knowing his taste for behind-the-scenes activity, which his own people were better at handling than I was. If there was any chance of his taking the initiative and proposing something, it would have to be in his own time and his own way. A week later, in a press conference, he did so:

'There will be no genuine European Union until there is a European policy. And believe me: contrary to what is thought, France is not against it. Quite the reverse.

'Quite the reverse; and if, for instance, it were felt that for political co-operation to develop more rapidly, those in supreme authority ought to meet alone from time to time, at regular but not too frequent intervals, then I for my part should be in agreement; and I am prepared, not to take the initiative, but to talk about it with our partners. If we can now achieve a European policy *vis-à-vis* all the others, all third parties, then from that moment the way ahead will be clear.'

This was the clearest possible overture on his part; and I wrote to Heath and Brandt, who were due to meet in London on October 8. It was now Heath's turn to make a public statement, at the Conservative Party Congress in Blackpool, on October 13:

'I believe that already some of my colleagues as Heads of Government feel the need for us to get together regularly without large staffs so that we can jointly guide the Community along the path we have already set. I would like to see the Heads of Government of the member countries of the Community meeting together, perhaps twice a year, as I have said, alone and without large staffs, with the President of the Commission being present, as he was at the Summit, on matters which concern the Commission. I would hope that my partners would respond to an initiative of this kind.

'Our purpose in meeting together would be to lay down the broad direction of European policy, to keep up the momentum towards greater unity in foreign policy, to help forward the working out of common internal policies within the Community, and so to agree upon the strategic issues facing the Community as to avoid the damaging controversies which so often appear to the public to dog the deliberations in Brussels.'

The plan was well under way. Brandt had just written to Pompidou indicating his agreement; and Mariano Rumor, the Italian Prime Minister, had written to me in similar terms. It remained to convince the Benelux Governments, and then to settle on a convocation procedure and a date. This last point seemed to me decisive when I heard that Nixon was expected in Europe in the early weeks of 1974, and that on that account there was talk of postponing the meeting of the nine Heads of State and Government. I thought, on the contrary, that it was of the highest importance that they should meet beforehand, to reaffirm Europe's solidarity. Nixon was expecting to find European countries divided: it would change the atmosphere and meaning of his visit if Europe presented itself, united and strong. I said as much to my friends at the French Foreign Office and the Elysée palace, where the idea was welcomed.

'I agree,' said Jobert. 'In that case, we must hold the meeting before January.'

Events were spurred on by serious developments in the Middle East. Since October 6, the world had been rocked by the Yom Kippur war, which had put a strain on solidarity everywhere. On October 31, Pompidou told the French Cabinet that Europe's silence in this conflict, which left the United States and the USSR confronting each other alone, was a source of great danger:

'It seems to me essential,' he said, 'to put to the test the solidarity of united Europe, and its ability to contribute to the solution of world problems. The French Government therefore proposes to its partners in the political field that we should decide on the principle of regular meetings, under precise rules, of the Heads of State and Government, with the aim of comparing and harmonizing their attitude in the framework of political co-operation. *The first such meeting should be held before the end of 1973.*'

This initiative, which at once took practical shape in the form of a letter to the other eight Governments, was not only a surprise to the public. It also disconcerted civil-service and diplomatic circles, which were accustomed to European summits ruled by formality, submerged by large delegations, and master-minded from beginning to end by the administration. Their reservations made the French proposal seem venturesome. But a few days later Brandt declared:

'This body, a sort of regular conference of Presidents, without the burden of an administration, holding intensive discussions of the internal and external problems that face the union in the making, can become a well-established and essential step towards political union.'

The agreement was total and profound, because it had been arrived at among a small number of men who were able to take decisions. The method that had secured the establishment of the Supreme Council would also ensure that it worked.

Of course, there was some resistance, especially from certain Foreign Ministers, who were not accustomed to leaving the initiative to the Heads of their Governments. But the Heads of Government realized that their own authority would be enhanced by this new procedure for collective decision-making over the whole range of their responsibilities. I found this when I saw Joop den Uyl, the Dutch Prime Minister, on November 15. It was only a matter of saving the face of his Foreign Minister and a few others. I also assured François-Xavier Ortoli, the President of the Commission, that the Community institutions – which would be present at all discussions which concerned subjects in their domain – had much to gain from the establishment of a decision-making authority at the highest level, operating in conformity with the Treaties. He was a clear-headed and conscientious President, and he was concerned to preserve the authority of the Commission. I told him:

'You will be freer if you can put forward bold proposals which will not be stifled at birth by the technical Ministers of nine countries, as so often happens now.'

I added that the plan for a Provisional Government had none of the disadvantages of the Fouchet Plan, which in some ways it appeared to resemble. It brought together the same men – the Heads of State and Government; but it did not involve an elaborate structure designed to preserve a particular degree of co-operation, a Europe of the States. All it involved was a method of decision-making; but it was the only one that could ensure effective progress towards European Union. No one, now, was challenging the sovereignty of the existing Community institutions: on the contrary, everything was now organized to strengthen their powers, make them work successfully, and develop their potential. The only people who might be disappointed were those who imagined that their potential was political, and that one day the Government of Europe would spring fully armed from the institutions of the Economic Community.

In fact, the aims of the Community were limited to those areas of European solidarity that were written into the Treaties; and while we had always believed that these would lead to others and gradually involve a very broad integration of human activities, I knew that this process would stop where the frontiers of political power began. There, something new would have to be invented. The European Economic Commission, the Council, the Assembly, and the Court were admittedly a pre-federal model; but they were not the institutions of a political federation of Europe. That would have to be established by a specific creative act which would require a further delegation of sovereignty. We should have to return again to the springs of power, first to complete the economic union which had too long been lacking in vigour, and then to seek the forms of a closer and deeper union – federal or confederal, I could not say which. That was the point of the Provisional European Government, the idea of which was becoming more substantial as time went on. I was not concerned at the fact that Pompidou, Heath, and Brandt had not proposed it under that name or in a more ambitious guise. Whatever the reasons for their caution, the essential point was that they had accepted the principle and embarked on the process. The rest would come later. Gradually, people would come to see how strong the machinery was. It would be vindicated by its success and eventually earn its title.

II

The beginnings of a European authority

When an idea answers to the needs of an epoch, it ceases to belong to those who invented it and becomes more powerful than those who serve it. If it naturally meets with resistance, and is sometimes delayed by circumstances, that by no means destroys its chances of success. In November 1973, everything favoured the idea of the European Council, and the international crisis itself promised to speed it on its way. The Community was anxious to present a united front to the Americans, so as to contribute to peace in the Middle East. In response to Pompidou's appeal, the Danish Government invited its European partners to Copenhagen. Practical decisions were prepared, confirming the solidarity of the Nine on energy and regional policy, and account was taken of my own advice. Then, suddenly, when all seemed well, everything was thrown into turmoil. Future historians will explore the reasons and see more clearly where the responsibilities lay. What happened was that, surprised by the oil producers' embargo and literally jostled by their diplomacy, the Heads of State and Government lost control of their meeting, which degenerated into a traditional international conference, swarming with experts. The illusory quest for particular advantages revealed more dramatically than ever how weak our European States were if each was left to its own devices. What remained of the sentiments expressed a few weeks earlier by the Community's supreme leaders? A vague resolution to meet more frequently. But the failure was too spectacular, and certain changes of attitude were too startling, for what had occurred to be regarded as more than a passing accident. In such cases, there is nothing to be done but wait until necessity restores order.

Waiting does not come naturally to me. I saw the Middle East conflict on the point of breaking out again; yet the hostility between Israel and the Arabs seemed to me no more insuperable than that between France and Germany had been for more than seventy years.

Franco-German enmity was now a thing of the past; and what had ended it was neither warfare nor diplomacy, but a method which changed men's attitudes by transforming the very reasons for their rivalry. What divided people could still bring them together, anywhere in the world. Who would one day convince the Arabs and the Israelis that they had great tasks to perform together in the territory and with the resources for which they were now fighting? Who would be able to begin that process of change? I did not know; but what we had achieved in Europe, against all expectations, ought equally to be possible wherever men were still thinking in terms of domination and hoping to settle their dispute by force. I was convinced that the union of Europe was not only important for the Europeans themselves: it was valuable as an example for others, and this was a further reason for bringing it about. Yet now, just as our goal was in sight, we had once again shown the world the sad spectacle of selfishness and disunion. We had to try to rebuild, with the help of the same men, what had just come to grief.

The Heads of State and Government were due to hold a further summit meeting at the end of May. In the meantime, the Action Committee planned to meet; and with that in mind I drafted a paper:

> Times have changed; now we must change our methods, or else stop proclaiming something which we fail to achieve. . . . On all important questions, whether internal or external, the same obstacle arises. Existing European practices have proved inadequate as a means of enabling our countries to organize themselves for collective action, whether on monetary affairs, on energy, or in relations with the United States.
>
> We must break out of this vicious circle, in which the common interests of the Community countries are inadequately served. The existing European institutions are not strong enough today to do it on their own. But with the support of those institutions, Heads of Government could do it.

The situation I described would continue, I knew, so long as the Heads of Government did not become an entity capable of acting collectively; and there would be no genuine improvement unless they agreed on procedures to ensure that their decisions were carried out. The paper which I circulated in March 1974 contained proposals which there was no time to discuss in depth. A series of sudden events intervened, affecting the Heads of Government themselves, and sowing the seeds of uncertainty once more. On March 5, Wilson replaced Heath; on May 14, Schmidt replaced Brandt. Meanwhile, Pompidou had died. By May 19, when Valéry Giscard d'Estaing was elected President of France, supreme power had changed hands in the three largest

European countries. Heath and Brandt were my friends. Both were men of generous convictions; both had committed themselves totally to the struggle for Europe. Pompidou had reached the same conclusion by the more circuitous paths of reason and necessity. Together, they had been on the point of reaching a common view of their interests and those of Europe; and their next meeting might well have made up for the failure of the last. But it would not do to draw profound conclusions from mere coincidence, or give way to my personal disappointment. I refused to see as a portent what was only a chain of circumstances. Fundamentally, nothing had changed, and the realists who had now taken over would come to the same conclusions in their turn.

On March 28, Wilson had received me at No 10 Downing Street. He had seemed uncertain, worried by his nationalistic Left wing, and ready to make many concessions to maintain the unity of his party – but without going so far as to leave the Common Market. I had confidence in his skill, and in nothing else.

'We shan't ask for changes in the Treaty of Rome,' he said, 'but only for some adjustments to the Treaty of Accession.'

'I should advise against even that,' I said. 'It would open the way to modifying all the Treaties.'

'I shall give Callaghan a free hand,' Wilson said. James Callaghan was his Foreign Minister.

'Be careful,' I said. 'In this great business the responsibility for success or failure will be yours.'

I realized that he would not throw his personal weight into the scale until the very last moment. I was uneasy, that March, to see the leadership of Europe resting solely on the not very close relations between Pompidou and Brandt. But within two months, everything had changed. Giscard and Schmidt, in their new positions, continued the friendly relationship they had established when they had both been Ministers of Finance. They had striking points in common: both belonged to a new generation that was less closely linked with Europe's unhappy past, and both had earned a reputation as very able administrators. Even their differences were complementary. Giscard had the more analytical mind, while Schmidt was the more decisive. Together, they could renew action by France and Germany which would bring the others in its train.

In this second half of 1974, France was to assume the chairmanship of the Community Council, and Giscard had pledged himself to taking some initiatives. On September 19, at my request, he received me at the

Elysée palace. There was no doubt that this buoyant man had no fear of the future, no narrowness of vision. His mind was receptive to change, and Europe seemed to him a natural part of that process. I could not judge whether his ability in action would be on a par with his remarkable intelligence and the strength of his feelings; but what I had come to propose to him was a method for collective decision-making.

'I think that what's lacking more than anything in European affairs,' I said, 'is authority. Discussion is organized: decision is not. By themselves, the existing Community institutions are not strong enough. With this in mind, just a year ago, I gave M. Pompidou, Mr Heath, and Herr Brandt a note. Here it is. It proposes the beginnings of a European authority. All three were in agreement with it. At M. Jobert's request, I removed the following sentence: "The institutions of the Union will in particular include a European Government and a European Assembly elected by universal suffrage." I should like to reintroduce it.'

'My intention is to pursue that line,' Giscard answered; 'and I am in favour of regular meetings of Heads of State and Government – a real European Council. I also believed that we must set a date for European elections by universal suffrage. And one day we must give up the rule of unanimity so that decisions can be taken by qualified majority vote.'

We agreed that I should telephone him again when I had seen Helmut Schmidt.

During an hour's conversation with the French President I had encountered no refusals and no evasions; and on coming out of the the Elysée palace I was able to say that he seemed to me to be on the right road. But I made no bones about how hard the going would be: 'Europe will be in difficulties for a very long time. Besides, it's a fundamental error to think that one can make progress without difficulties.'

'What has to be done?' the newspapermen asked.

'Continue, continue, continue ...' I answered; and they seemed satisfied with that reply because they knew very well that it had been my watchword for twenty-five years. Through all the crises and vicissitudes in its history, the unification of Europe had continued irresistibly along the path that we had taken. For my part, I continued my essential quest, which was for a common authority capable of turning into decisions the will to live together which the vast majority of Europeans were at that very moment expressing in the public opinion polls.

On October 16 I was in Bonn, in the Chancellor's office. I found

Schmidt remarkably determined; and although I was familiar with his vigorous spirit, I was surprised at how willing he was to keep in step with Giscard.

'I shall back his initiative with all my power,' he said.

'A joint Franco-German initiative,' I said, 'would be better than a French initiative backed by Germany.'

'You're right,' he answered. 'The essential thing is that there should be no more separate national actions, but only European action.'

An opportunity for this was energy policy, which was dividing the Nine and isolating France. But, as I found on returning to Paris, the defensive positions adopted at the beginning of the year were still blocking the Government's strategy. Regional policy would be a more hopeful area in which to show the practical solidarity that Europe so badly needed. On this point, Schmidt intimated that he was prepared to go ahead: he was anxious to persuade the British to stay in the Community.

'But they'll have to be willing to make it a reality,' he said. 'I'll talk to Wilson about it soon.'

They met in London; and after that it became clear that Wilson had made up his mind and committed himself to Europe.

With Schmidt's consent, I gave Giscard a full account of our conversation, just as I reported to him the reactions I had had in Brussels from the Belgian Prime Minister Leo Tindemans, a man of wisdom and great goodwill. So now everything was clear, and the threads that had seemed to be broken in the spring of 1974 were once more drawing tight. Once more, the Community had a driving-force which would lead it to the stage of a European Government and a Parliament elected by all its citizens. That driving-force was formally established on December 10, when Giscard brought the meeting of the Nine to a close with the words:

'The Summit is dead. Long live the European Council.'

I summed up the conclusions of that meeting in a letter to the members of the Action Committee:

The Heads of Government have demonstrated their ability to achieve agreement. They have decided to meet at regular intervals and at least three times a year.

When the Heads of Government debate Community affairs, they will sit as the Council and will apply the terms of the Treaties of Rome and Paris, particularly with regard to the role of the Commission. Our Committee proposed this in its resolutions of June 26, 1962, June 1, 1964, and December 15–16, 1969.

In accordance with the Treaties and with common sense, the Heads of Government also agreed:
- that unanimity need no longer be required for every Council decision;
- to move towards an Assembly elected by universal suffrage from 1978 onward. . . . Our Committee called for this in particular in its resolutions of June 1, 1964, May 8–9, 1965, December 15–16, 1969, and again on February 23–24, 1971.

The Belgian Premier, M. Tindemans, was given the task of submitting a progress report on European Union to the Heads of Government before the end of 1975.

These results could not but give satisfaction to the members of the Committee, who had so long used their political influence to induce Governments, Members of Parliament, and the European institutions to take the decisions that were essential to create, operate, and develop the Community. Now, the European institutions were in charge of immense sectors of activity, over which they exercised the share of sovereignty that had been delegated to them. But if they were to work effectively, the Governments had to have the same European will and be prepared, acting together as a collective authority, to transfer the additional sovereignty required to achieve a true European Union. The creation of the European Council supplied the means for reaching that essential decision. A major step had been taken. Should the Action Committee not adapt to this new situation? That was the question I now asked.

III.

The roots of the European Community

At the beginning of 1975 I made preparations to go and consult the members of the Action Committee. They had placed their trust in me for twenty years. Now I wanted to study with them in what way we could most usefully help in the building of Europe. At a time when Governments had been unable, or as yet unwilling, to establish a European authority, the Committee had become a sort of political authority itself. Was it still as appropriate? Would it be as effective, now that those who held the supreme power of decision in each State had decided to take the Community's future into their own hands, together? These men, meeting at regular intervals in a Supreme Council, had powerful means of information, and machinery for making proposals, in the shape of the European institutions. Our Committee, which had helped to establish and stimulate that machinery, now seemed to me less indispensable and less well-equipped for a task which the Treaties, after all, had entrusted to the Community's institutions and Governments. The Committee could certainly still perform some services, but its ambitions today would be limited by the very fact that its original aims had so largely been fulfilled.

When we speak of influence waning, this is very often because it has succeeded, and its original force has been transmitted to the object of its pressure. In this way, the Committee had transferred most of its original energy to the living organism of the Community. The main political or technical proposals that it had stubbornly championed in parliamentary and governmental circles were now, as has been seen, being put into practice. How effective would our patient initiatives be in future by comparison with the rapid and binding procedures which regular and frequent Councils of Heads of State and Government were likely to set in motion? And if those procedures were themselves to prove powerless to advance matters, what hope would there be for our indirect political pressure? Indeed, the European Council, by virtue of the fact that it was the supreme authority, involved risks on a par with its opportunities. We could not dictate what it should do. We should have to leave it to assume its full responsibilities, and meanwhile take it on trust.

These were the conclusions which I wanted to discuss with my friends on the Action Committee, and I made preparations to see each of them in his own capital city during the month of March 1975. The more I thought about it, the more obvious it seemed to me that the Committee could no longer continue as before; and I began to wonder whether it might not be better to dissolve it altogether, rather than put it into cold storage for a while. Everything has its own rhythm, and if we left too long an interval between the meetings that maintained the bonds between us, we might risk disintegrating a team held together by its own collective momentum. It could be a mistake, I thought, to maintain that momentum by sheer habit, without being permanently and profoundly convinced of its necessity. If we were to face fresh crises like those which had made the Committee necessary, there would still be time to form a new political force. In fact, no two things are ever exactly similar, and that was why I refused to speculate now about what new system might be needed to deal with future situations which were still no more than hypothetical. In March 1975, the real situation seemed to me to be this: that nothing could rival the power of decision of nine Heads of State and Government meeting regularly around the same table with the President of the European Commission to try to solve problems that were stated in terms of the common interest. If they failed once, or several times at a stretch, that would be no surprise: no venture as ambitious as this can avoid facing very great difficulties. But if they were unable to muster the strength to succeed – then, we should have to seek new ways of reaching collective decisions.

Personal circumstances removed my remaining doubts. At the end of February, I fell seriously ill; and when after some weeks I began to be convalescent, my doctors advised me against making my proposed trips for a long time to come. So I sent Kohnstamm and Van Helmont to see the oldest members of the Committee on my behalf, to tell them that I had decided to retire, and to consult them about the future of the body that we had together established and run. All of them, from Brandt to Heath and Rumor, from Pleven to Malagodi and Tindemans, agreed that one chapter of our work was closed, and that my retirement should mark the end of the Committee in which I had brought them together. None of them showed any bitterness about a decision which reason had dictated and which my health would not let me avoid. But they all expressed the hope that the much valued personal relations which they had established over so many years would be maintained. Kohnstamm naturally remained at the centre of this great network of friendship, and he has worked ever since to see that it endures.

On April 15, 1975, I wrote to the members of the Committee to confirm what we had agreed on. I published the letter, in which I explained:

> I would like to take some time for reflection and rest and I am in the pro-
> cess of writing a book, which I hope will help to explain what we have
> achieved – the philosophy behind the idea which has been ours all along –
> and the profound reasons which have persuaded our countries to unite. I
> intend to cease my activities as President of the Committee on May 9, the
> twenty-fifth anniversary of the proposals for setting up the High Authority
> and pooling our coal and steel resources.

That anniversary was celebrated with some solemnity by two Heads of State, Valéry Giscard d'Estaing and Walter Scheel, in the presence of the Heads of Government, in the Salon de l'Horloge at the Quai d'Orsay where Robert Schuman had made the Declaration calling for the reconciliation of France and Germany and the union of Europe. To find myself among those assembled in the same room where a venture had been launched to which I had devoted my energies for a quarter of a century, accompanied as on that first day by Silvia and the same colleagues, still as loyal as ever, seemed to me a natural end to one phase of my life. I am not superstitious about dates or commemorative ceremonies; but I saw in that twenty-five-year cycle a true measure of the effort involved, and a significant reminder that for Europe it was still Spring.

But I did not leave the Salon de l'Horloge to withdraw into contemplative retirement. Another form of action was awaiting me, if I was still there and strong enough: this book. It had been my intention for many years; but it would only be completed, I knew, if I devoted myself to it and nothing else. There are no limits, except those of physical endurance, to the attention which must be paid to the work in hand if it is to succeed. No one should be surprised, or complain, at having failed in ventures carried on concurrently, with only partial care devoted to any one of them. I have never done well at anything to which I have given divided attention; but I admit that it is not easy to tackle only one thing, or rather only one thing at a time. Politics, in particular, does not lend itself to such an approach; so I have not lent myself to politics. To write a book requires total concentration, and I knew that it would be quite a different matter from writing notes in the midst of action. To tell the truth, I only began thinking about it very recently, because chances to intervene in European affairs were not lacking, and I could not help reacting every day to critical situations or favourable opportunities. I had neither time nor inclination to keep a diary which would later have supplied material for these *Memoirs*. To live and at the same time watch myself living was something I could not do.

I have not changed, either; and when I made up my mind to describe the events in which I have played a part, it was not for the pleasure of reliving the past or to add to the history libraries. It was to try to explain to my future readers the profound necessity for the unification of Europe, which continues unceasingly, however difficult it is. When one has accumulated a certain experience of action, to try to hand it on to others is also a form of action; and one day the time comes when the best thing one can do is teach others what seems to be right. There is only one way of building Europe at any given time. We are still in the phase of the European Community, of the delegation of sovereignty to common institutions: this is the only way to ensure independence and progress for our peoples and peace in this part of the world. That was what I wanted to say, in a book for which I needed all my time and all my strength.

The members of the Action Committee understood that if I was retiring it was not out of discouragement: quite the reverse. In my letter to them I said:

> Ours has been the rare privilege of having directly participated in the realization of what at the outset was no more than an idea, but is now becoming a living reality – the union of the countries of Europe. After twenty years of effective action, alongside the Community institutions, to bring together the peoples of Europe in freedom, the Committee will be wound up on May 9, 1975.

It was as we had agreed. The members of the Committee all wrote me letters full of feeling, reaffirming with remarkable strength of conviction the ideas that had inspired our work. And although those ideas are bound up with memories of the past, they are still as relevant as ever. There is not one of them that cannot serve to guide us in the future.

When I returned to my country home at Houjarray on the evening of May 9, 1975, freed from all outside responsibilities for the first time for many years, there lying on my table was the first sketch-plan of this book, a new and exacting task for which I was very little prepared. Now that it is nearly ended, dare I say without causing amusement, after so many pages written in the first person, that I dislike talking about myself? If I have told of my experience, it is because that is what I know best, and because it may be useful to others. I might have written a series of practical maxims; but I distrust general ideas, and I never let them lead me far away from practical things. I have described the dramatic events I have lived through and the lessons I have learned from them, in the hope of preventing their happening again. My purpose is very practical. Some may call it a philosophy, if they prefer: but the essential point is to make it useful beyond the experience of one individual; and because the most effective way was to tell that individual's story, I have bowed to the rules, which were new to me, and told the story from my own point of view.

A very wise man whom I knew in the United States, Dwight Morrow, used to say: 'There are two kinds of people – those who want to *be someone*, and those who want to *do something*.' I have seen the truth of that saying verified over and over again. The main concern of many very remarkable people is to cut a figure and play a role. They are useful to society, where images are very important and the affirmation of character is essential to the administration of affairs. But, in general, it is the other kind of people who get things moving – those who spend their time looking for places and opportunities to influence the course of events. The places are not always the most obvious ones, nor do the opportunities occur when many people expect them. Anyone who wants to find them has to forsake the limelight.

My friend Dwight Morrow put me in this second category of people; and it is true that I never remember saying to myself: 'I'm going to be someone.' But nor do I remember thinking: 'I'm going to do something.' What I have done, or helped to do, and what I have described in this book, has always been the product of circumstances as they arose. There has been no lack of such opportunities, and I have always been ready to seize them. It is perhaps this faculty, or this availability, that is the most important for action. Life is prodigal of opportunities to act, but one has to be prepared, by long reflection, to recognize them and exploit them when they occur. Life is made up of nothing but events: what matters is to use them for a given purpose. Mine was collective action. And the aim of this book is to show the way and the means to younger people who want to make their own lives useful to others.

As I write these pages, Silvia is finishing a picture in the large living-room where she has put up her easel. She likes the light in this room, which looks out on the garden. But the flowers she paints are not from Houjarray, but from all the gardens we have had in various parts of the world. In this picture they are tall white flowers that recall China and our house in Shanghai. Tomorrow, I know, she is going to work on a landscape from the Ile de Ré, which I had thought was finished. In fact, there was something missing. What, I could not say, but now she sees it clearly. Nothing is ever really completed; it takes talent to know at what point further effort will spoil the result. Silvia asks me my opinion of her picture; then I read her a few pages of this book to see what she thinks. We each take account of what the other says; but in the last resort the choice of when to stop is a matter of instinct. How many times my colleagues, inured to ceaseless changes in a text, have heard me say suddenly: 'That's it: we're there. Don't let's go any further, or we'll spoil the whole thing.' To decide is difficult: one must seize the moment. Yesterday, I wanted Silvia to add a touch to her portrait of a young woman we had met in China forty years ago. I was wrong: incompleteness is part of nature, and it needs great art, or great wisdom, to know when to lay down the brush, or bring to an end any form of action. We should always avoid perfectionism.

A year has gone by now since I came back to this house, with its thatched roof and blue shutters, and its large garden stretching out toward the rolling countryside of the Ile de France. I seldom leave it: those who want to see me have to come here. They talk to me about their worries. I understand their concern; but they have to realize that the building of Europe is a great transformation, which will take a very long time. They are naturally impatient for the success of what they have to do; but nothing would be more dangerous than to regard difficulties as failures. Perhaps they think that in my country retreat I am losing touch with current events and becoming too detached. They remember my former calls for urgent action. True enough, action is always urgent, and I am glad that those responsible for it are aware of the fact. But they must also be aware of the essential virtue of perseverance, which is the only way to overcome obstacles.

The obstacles will undoubtedly grow in number as we draw closer to our goal. In the building of Europe, as in all great ventures, men push the obstacles before them, and leave them to their successors. I am not troubled by the fact that there are still so many obstacles on the road ahead. We have overcome many others that were just as great. In this respect, nothing has changed; nor will it. The only difference is that something has begun, something which can no longer be stopped. Twenty-five years ago, the urge to have done with our violent past left us no choice but to advance towards a common goal. What was decided on then is still just as vital; and now it is part of the everyday reality of our lives.

I walk in the garden with my visitors. I go down towards the cottage at the foot of the meadow, where Marianne and my son-in-law Gérard Lieberherr spend their weekends. Their children – Jean-Gabriel, Catherine, Jean-Marc, and Marie – run on ahead. Now I have time to be with them, and get to know them individually as they grow up. I press on into the paths round Bazoches, where I meet my neighbour Pierre Viansson-Ponté. 'Good morning, Monsieur Monnet,' he says; and under that title I find in Le Monde some echoes of our conversation, filtered by his delicate art. The seasons go by: I had never noticed their passing before – I was too much distracted by activities in town. Spring comes round once more. Someone says to me: 'There will be no Spring for Europe in this year of grace 1976.' Perhaps; but we should look beyond the calendar, for stages, not time-limits: we should keep on course, and not worry too much, now, about deadlines. There is nothing talismanic about this or that month in 1976 or 1978; about dates, I make no wagers. But I am certain that the passing seasons will lead us inevitably towards greater unity; and if we fail to organize it for ourselves, democratically, it will be thrust upon us by blind force. There is no place any more for separate action by our ancient sovereign nations. We have long since passed the crossroads where we had a choice of ways ahead. Since 1950, we have been engaged in the process of unification by our own free will, and no one has been willing or able to reverse it. If there are arguments, they are about means, not ends; and arguments are essential to progress.

I have known this garden for thirty years, and have come back to it almost every night – except when I was in Luxembourg, where I had another garden, at Bricherhof. For me, it has no bounds: the world belongs to walkers. In the morning, as I have said, I make for the nearby woods, where I know every faintest path. Some of them are endless. It is essential for the spirit to start the day in the open air. In London, I had St James's Park outside my door. In Washington, the houses on Foxhall Road were in the woods, and there were no fences between the yards. I can claim no specialized knowledge of trees or birds: they are simply the background to my thoughts, my form of poetry. André Horré used to explain the things of Nature to me. He had started life in the mines of the north, and had then become a butler to follow his wife Amélie, who was a fine cook. When we settled in our Houjarray house, which I bought in 1945, he became a gardener. In London and Washington he had worked only indoors; there had been neither room nor need to grow vegetables. In France, at the end of the war, it became a duty, and he accepted it. The spirit of his ancestors revived his love of the soil. While Amélie, with masterly intelligence, looked after the house, André let his imagination roam as he laboured in the kitchen garden or among the flowers. They were a noble and devoted couple. They went with us to Luxembourg, and helped us settle in; then, they retired to the north. Their only son, a gifted boy, joined the staff of the High Authority. When he died in an accident in 1953, his parents' silent and dignified grief was heartbreaking.

In the course of their lives with us in various countries, André and Amélie had met many well-known people, who paid close attention to their simple good sense. I can still see André in his kitchen garden, talking with Walter Lippmann in 1948, shortly before the US Presidential election.

'Who do you think will win, Dewey or Truman?' asked Lippmann. Like most observers, he was sure it would be Dewey. André went on digging, and said:

'Well, obviously, Truman.'

'Why?' asked Lippmann in surprise. André straightened up and said:
'Look – it's as simple as my trees. Roosevelt was elected three times. Three times the Democrats have won: that gives them deep roots. They won't be pulled up in one go.'

The roots of the Community are strong now, and deep in the soil of Europe. They have survived some hard seasons, and can survive more. On the surface, appearances change. In a quarter-century, naturally, new generations arise, with new ambitions; images of the past disappear; the balance of the world is altered. Yet amid this changing scenery the European idea goes on; and no one seeing it, and seeing how stable the Community institutions are, can doubt that this is a deep and powerful movement on an historic scale. Can it really be suggested that the wellsprings of that movement are exhausted, or that other rival forces are taking their place? I see no sign of any such rival forces. On the contrary, I see the same necessity acting on our countries – sometimes bringing them together for their mutual benefit, sometimes dividing them to the detriment of all. The moral is clear, and it cannot be gainsaid. It has taken root in our peoples' consciousness, but it is slow to act on their will: it has to overcome the inertia that hinders movement and the habits that resist change. We have to reckon with time.

Where this necessity will lead, and toward what kind of Europe, I cannot say. It is impossible to foresee today the decisions that could be taken in a new context tomorrow. The essential thing is to hold fast to the few fixed principles that have guided us since the beginning: gradually to create among Europeans the broadest common interest, served by common democratic institutions to which the necessary sovereignty has been delegated. This is the dynamic that has never ceased to operate, removing prejudice, doing away with frontiers, enlarging to continental scale, within a few years, the process that took centuries to form our ancient nations. I have never doubted that one day this process will lead us to the United States of Europe; but I see no point in trying to imagine today what political form it will take. The words about which people argue – federation or confederation – are inadequate and imprecise. What we are preparing, through the work of the Community, is probably without precedent. The Community itself is founded on institutions, and they need strengthening; but the true political authority which the democracies of Europe will one day establish still has to be conceived and built.

Some people refuse to undertake anything if they have no guarantee that things will work out as they planned. Such people condemn themselves to immobility. Today, no one can say what form Europe will assume tomorrow, for the changes born of change are unpredictable. 'Tomorrow is another day,' my father used to say, with a zest which my mother, in her wisdom, did her best to calm. 'Sufficient unto the day is the evil thereof,' she would reply. They were both right. Day-to-day effort is needed to make one's way forward: but what matters is to have an objective clear enough always to be kept in sight. People who came to see me in Luxembourg were intrigued to see on my desk the photograph of a strange raft. It was the *Kon-Tiki*, whose adventure had thrilled the whole world, and which for me was a symbol of our own.

'Those young men,' I explained to my visitors, 'chose their course, and then they set out. They knew that they could not turn back. Whatever the difficulties, they had only one option – to go on. We too are heading for our objective, the United States of Europe; and for us too there is no going back.'

But time is passing, and Europe is moving only slowly on the course to which she is so deeply committed. . . . We cannot stop, when the whole world around us is on the move. Have I said clearly enough that the Community we have created is not an end in itself? It is a process of change, continuing that same process which in an earlier period of history produced our national forms of life. Like our provinces in the past, our nations today must learn to live together under common rules and institutions freely arrived at. The sovereign nations of the past can no longer solve the problems of the present: they cannot ensure their own progress or control their own future. And the Community itself is only a stage on the way to the organized world of tomorrow.

APPENDIX

RESOLUTION BY THE HEADS OF STATE AND GOVERNMENT IN LUXEMBOURG, APRIL 1 AND 2, 1976, MEETING AS THE EUROPEAN COUNCIL

Community Europe, which has been in existence for more than twenty-five years, is already, despite its imperfections and *lacunae*, a remarkable achievement. Meanwhile, hopes of a deeper European Union are beginning to take shape.

The positive balance-sheet that can be drawn up at the end of this first stage, and on the eve of progress towards political unification, is something we owe in large measure to the boldness and breadth of vision of a handful of men. Among them, Jean Monnet has played a leading role, whether as inspirer of the Schuman Plan, first President of the High Authority, or founder of the Action Committee for the United States of Europe. In these various capacities, Jean Monnet has resolutely attacked the forces of inertia in Europe's political and economic structure, with the aim of establishing a new type of relationship between States, making apparent their *de facto* solidarity and giving it institutional form.

As a realist, Monnet took economic interests as his starting-point, but without abandoning his vision of achieving a broader understanding among the men and nations of Europe which would extend into all fields. Sometimes, this objective may have been lost to view amid the vicissitudes of the unification of Europe. Nevertheless, that objective has never been disavowed. Now, more than ever, it should serve as a guide, enabling us to rise above our task of daily administration and give it its true and substantial meaning.

Jean Monnet recently retired from public life. He has devoted the best of his ability to the European cause. It is only fitting that Europe should pay him a particular tribute of gratitude and admiration.

That is why the Heads of State and Government of the Community, meeting in Luxembourg as the European Council, have decided to confer on him the title of Honorary Citizen of Europe.

INDEX

Prepared by Arthur Windsor

Monnet, Jean [*contd.*]
Wilson, 491; Grenville Clark Prize, 498; draft proposals on European government, 503–4; at Chequers, 504–5; in Bonn, 506; in London, 512; Paris, 513; Bonn, 513–14; and ACUSE members, 515–17; falls ill and decides to retire and write *Memoirs*, 517 *et seq.*; receives title of Honorary Citizen of Europe, 525
Monnet, Marianne, younger daughter of J.M.: birth, 175; 224; Mme Lieberherr, 521
Monnet, Marie-Louise, sister of J.M.: 37, 99, 223
Monnet, Mme, mother of J.M.: 37, 38, 39, 223
Monnet, Silvia, wife of J.M.: 24, 27; marriage, 109–10; 142; to Washington, 150; 171; help for, 216; 224, 304; painting, 339, 402; 471; in Berlin, 480; 518, 520
Monnet family, of Cognac: 36, 37, 41, 99 *et seq.*; under Occupation, 223
Monnet family cognac firm: 39, 40; J.M. rejoins, 99–102; reorganization, 102
Monnet-Murnane and Co.: set up, 115
Monzie, Anatole de, Under-Secretary, Merchant Marine: 62, 63
Moreau, Emile: 104
Morgenthau, Henry, Secretary, US Treasury: 119–20, 121, 131, 134–5, 138, 184, 217
Morrow, Dwight: quoted, 13, 519, 520
Morton, Desmond: 22, 23, 27, 28, 141
Moselle, canalization of: 365
Moulin, Jean: 196
Multilateral Force, and ACUSE: 467–8
Munich Conference (1938): 117, 118
Munitions Assignment Board: 184
Murnane, George, partner of J.M.: 115, 116, 271
Murphy, Robert, US diplomat: 178–9; *Diplomat among Warriors*, quoted, 180; 203, 208; 194
Mutual Aid agreements (1945): 225–6
Mutual Aid Societies: 38

NATO: 337, 342, 358; Lisbon meeting, 362; Germany and, 398; 435, 468
Nassau, Bahamas, meeting (1962): 457–8
Nasser, Gamal Abdel: 420, 422
Nathan, Bob: 172
National Consultative Council, French: proposed (1943), 196; later, Consultative Assembly (*q.v.*)

National Defence Committee: of Senate 117; of Executive Committee, Algiers, 207
National Economic Council, China: 110
National Resistance Committee, France: 196
Nelson, Donald: 174, 208
Nenni, Pietro: 415, 488, 489
Netherlands Government: and Schuman Plan, 319; and ECSC, 363; and EEC, 425, 435
Neutrality Act, USA: 119, 122, 124, 125; modified, 130
New Deal: 109, 174
New York Times, The: 271, 304, 306
Nivelle, General Robert: 60, 63
Nixon, Richard, US President: 476; to Europe, 507
Noël, Emile, Secretary-General, European Commission: 417, 423
Noguès, General Charles: continues struggle, 142–3, 144, 145; ambiguous position, 179, 199; recalled, 200
Norman, Montagu, Governor, Bank of England: 95, 104; on J.M., 330
Normandy landings: and de Gaulle, 219
North Africa *see* Africa, North
North Atlantic Treaty: 337; *see also* Atlantic Alliance, NATO
Norway and EFTA: 434
nuclear technology and weapons: 400, 401, 403, 418; *see also* Euratom
Nuclear Test Ban Treaty (1963): 469–70; J.M. on, 470
No. 18, rue de Martignac, Planning Commission HQ: 241–2, 243, 248, 256, 257, 275, 277, 283, 294–5, 302, 305, 324–5, 329, 334, 352, 364, 417
No. 83, Avenue Foch, ACUSE Secretariat: 414

OECD (Organization for Economic Co-operation and Development): 434
OEEC (Organization for European Economic Co-operation): set up, 268; Convention, 271–2; work of, 273; 313; becomes OECD, 434; 448
Occupation of France: and Resistance, 210; and Cognac, 223–4
Ollenhauer, Erich: 382; and ACUSE, 411–12, 419, 444; and S.E. Asia, 499–500
'one Parliament, one army': 21–30, 35
Oosterhuis, H.: 412
Operation Torch (1942): 175, 176–7, 178–80